AF644666

About Pearson

Pearson is the world's learning company, with presence across 70 countries worldwide. Our unique insights and world-class expertise comes from a long history of working closely with renowned teachers, authors and thought leaders, as a result of which, we have emerged as the preferred choice for millions of teachers and learners across the world.

We believe learning opens up opportunities, creates fulfilling careers and hence better lives. We hence collaborate with the best of minds to deliver you class-leading products, spread across the Higher Education and Test Preparation spectrum.

Superior learning experience and improved outcomes are at the heart of everything we do. This product is the result of one such effort.

Your feedback plays a critical role in the evolution of our products and you can contact us - reachus@pearson.com. *We look forward to it.*

CLASS

10

Trishna's

PEARSON IIT FOUNDATION

Chemistry

Thirteenth Edition

CLASS

10

Trishna's

PEARSON IIT FOUNDATION

Chemistry

Thirteenth Edition

2025

Pearson

Photo Credits

Chapter 1 Opener: Kim Christensen / Shutterstock
Chapter 2 Opener: Dr. Victor Wong / Shutterstock
Chapter 3 Opener: Caron Watson / Shutterstock
Chapter 4 Opener: isak55 / Shutterstock
Chapter 5 Opener: Andriy Popov / 123RF
Chapter 6 Opener: worradirek / Shutterstock
Chapter 7 Opener: Denis Belitsky / Shutterstock
Chapter 8 Opener: ARTFULLY PHOTOGRAPHER / Shutterstock
Chapter 9 Opener: anyaivanova / Shutterstock
Chapter 10 Opener: Sergey Tarasov / Shutterstock

The aim of this publication is to supply information taken from sources believed to be valid and reliable. This is not an attempt to render any type of professional advice or analysis, nor is it to be treated as such. While much care has been taken to ensure the veracity and currency of the information presented within, neither the publisher nor its authors bear any responsibility for any damage arising from inadvertent omissions, negligence or inaccuracies (typographical or factual) that may have found their way into this book.

Copyright © 2025 Trishna Knowledge Systems
Copyright © 2018, 2019, 2020, 2021, 2022, 2023, 2024 Trishna Knowledge Systems

This book is sold subject to the condition that it shall not, by way of trade or otherwise, be lent, resold, hired out, or otherwise circulated without the publisher's prior written consent in any form of binding or cover other than that in which it is published and without a similar condition including this condition being imposed on the subsequent purchaser and without limiting the rights under copyright reserved above, no part of this publication may be reproduced, stored in or introduced into a retrieval system, or transmitted in any form or by any means (electronic, mechanical, photocopying, recording or otherwise), without the prior written permission of both the copyright owner and the publisher of this book.

ISBN 978-93-6159-642-1

First Impression

Published by Pearson India Education Services Pvt. Ltd, CIN: U72200TN2005PTC057128.

Head Office: 1st Floor, Berger Tower, Plot No. C-001A/2, Sector 16B, Noida - 201 301, Uttar Pradesh, India.

Registered Office: Featherlite, 'The Address' 5th Floor, Survey No 203/10B, 200 Ft MMRD Road, Zamin Pallavaram, Chennai - 600044

Phone: 044-66540100

Website: in.pearson.com, Email: companysecretary.india@pearson.com

Compositor: Saksham Printographics, Delhi
Printed in India: Rahul Print O Pack

Brief Contents

Contents

Preface

"If you have a great ambition, take as big a step as possible in the direction of fulfilling it. The step may only be a tiny one, but trust that it may be the largest one possible for now.".

Mildred McAfee

The *Pearson IIT Foundation* Series has been created keeping in mind the learner's ambition to excel in a competitive examination like IIT-JEE. The series can be used in addition to the books being studied in school to attain that extra edge required to strengthen the concepts and prepare well for future endeavours.

Why Start Early with Pearson IIT Foundation

Classes VI to X are the base years of a learner's academic life. In these years learner explore their interests and determine the goals they wish to attain. *Pearson IIT Foundation* series is filled with interactive learning that not only nurtures a learner's interest in science and mathematics but also strengthens their concepts.

The series uses real-life examples and application-based problems to teach theoretical concepts. The objective of this series is to help learners cultivate an analytical mind.

Most of the lessons to be learnt are introduced to the learners in the books for class VI. As they get promoted to higher classes, new topics are added to these lessons. This additive method helps the learners' span their learning over four standards, from VI-X. Thus, learners are not overwhelmed by the introduction of completely new lessons every time they are promoted to a new class.

While their learning is being spanned across five years, so is their ability to resolve doubts for further conceptual clarity. For instance, they can use concepts learnt in class VI to solve questions in class VII. If, in case, they get stuck while answering a question, the learners can infer for themselves that they might be lacking in conceptual clarity. They can then approach their teachers, requesting them to explain the concept once again. This helps the learner to clarify their concepts while revising the lessons previously learnt.

Since classes VI-X are deemed to be a student's formative years, we, at Pearson, aim to provide a foundation level course which serves more than just a standard curriculum.

Here is how it makes a difference to a learner's overall learning...

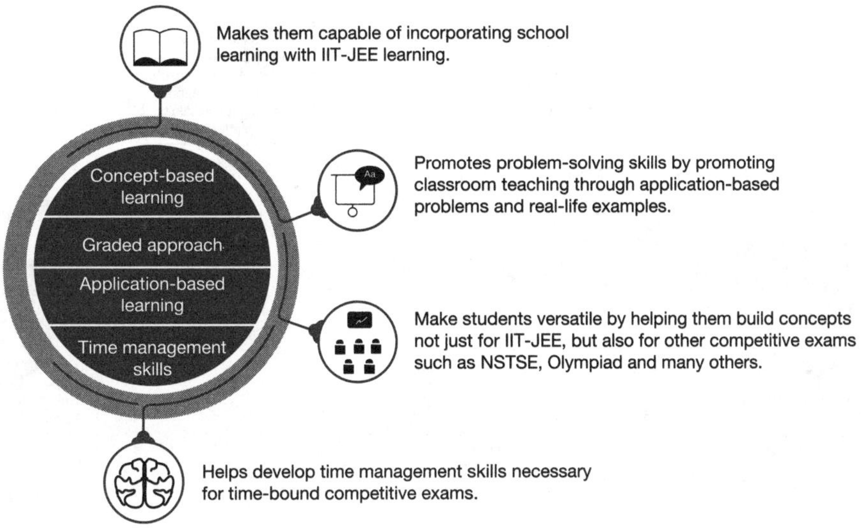

Other Uses of the Series

Instead of limiting themselves to IIT-JEE, a learner can also use this series to prepare for several other competitive examinations such as NSTSE, National and International Olympiads, NEET, BITSAT, etc. This series offers a level of concept learning that empowers learners to handle the challenging nature of questions posed in these examinations. Moreover, this will also allow the learners to have an early insight into their key strengths as well as improvement areas and help them work on themselves.

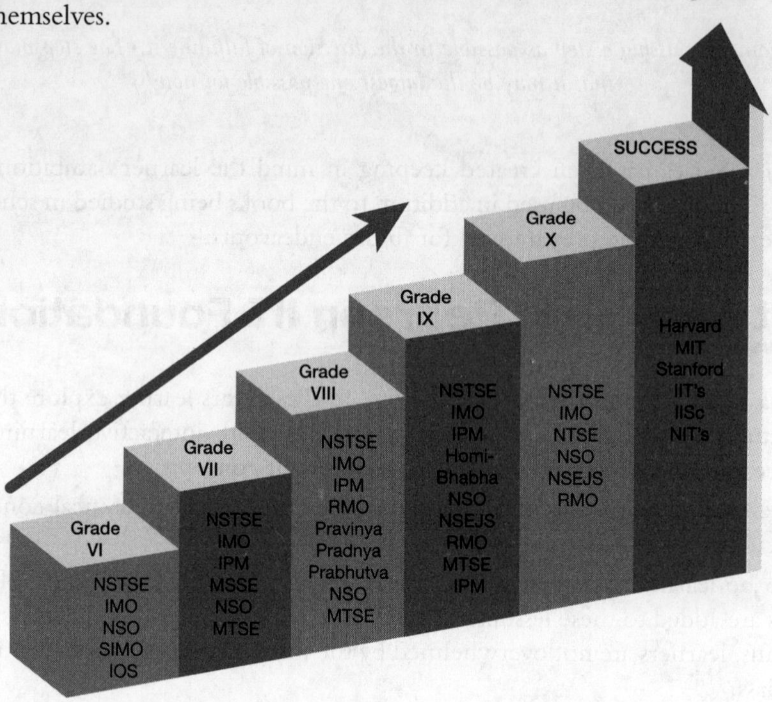

[IMO: International Mathematics Olympiad; NSO: National Science Olympiad, IOS: International Olympiad of Science, NSTSE: National Level Science Talent Search Examination, MTSE: Maharashtra Talent Search Examination, RMO: Regional Mathematical Olympiad, PPP: Pravinya Pradnya Prabhutva, NSEJS: National Standard Examination in Junior Science, IIT: Indian Institute of Technology, IISc: Indian Institute of Science, NIT: National Institute of Technology.]

Highlights of the Series

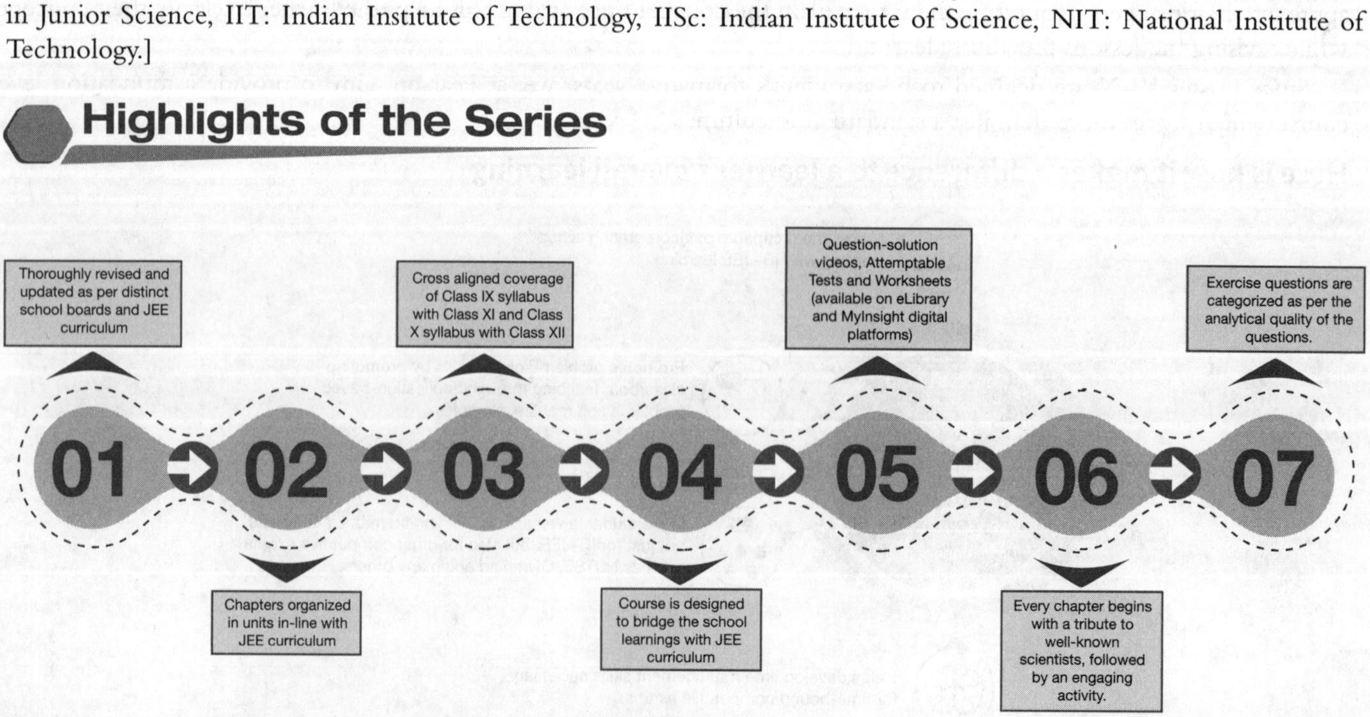

Pearson IIT Foundation series provides a perfect blend of learning through theory and practice questions with a fusion of school and JEE curriculum. It is imperative to note that this series would be as profound as you want it to be. Therefore, to get maximum benefit from this book, we recommend following the given study plan.

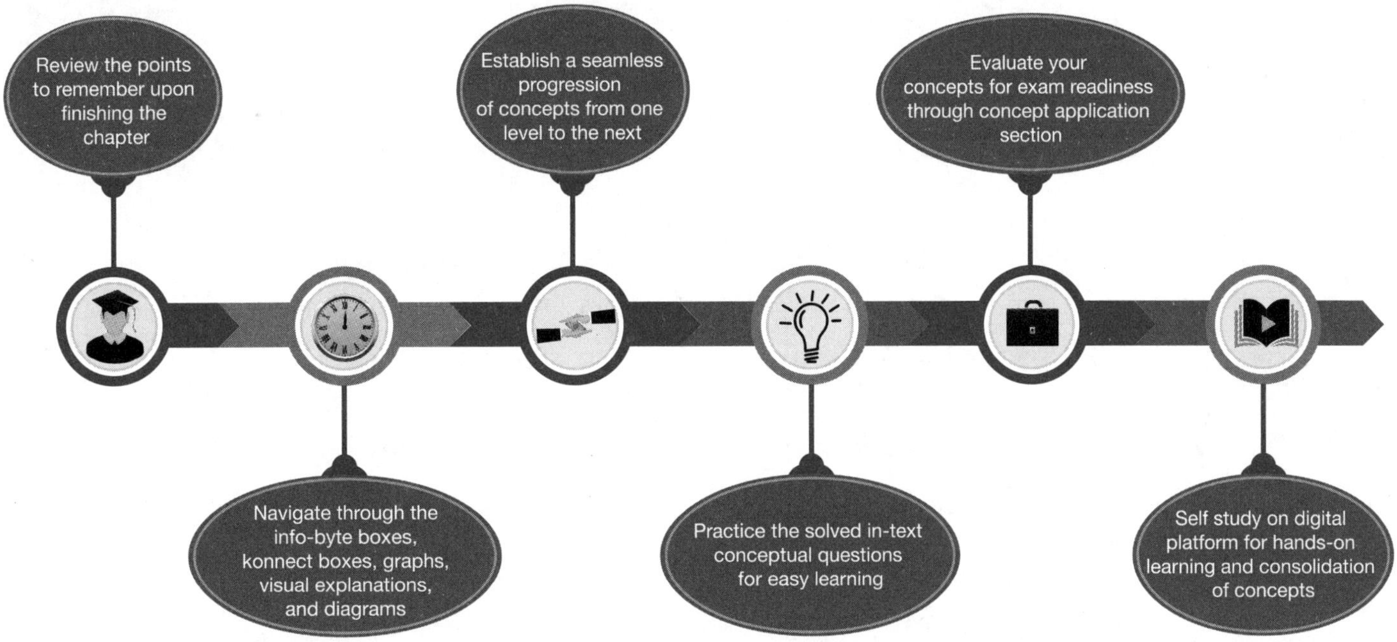

To provide a graded learning approach, the exercise part of each chapter is categorized by using four icons for question tagging. The question categorization helps the learners assess their own problem-solving and analytical skills and motivates them to improve to reach their objectives.

The following icons are used to categorize the questions with specific meanings:

Real-life Situations Questions: 

Analytical Questions: 

Conceptual Questions: 

Value-based Questions: 

With this refined and well-tuned course from Pearson, students will become more confident when they enter the competitive world for actual IIT-JEE preparation. The effort put in today will transform into a valuable asset, contributing to success in future competitive examinations.

Chapter Insights

Remember

Before beginning this chapter, you should be able to:

- understand the concept of matter and atoms.
- review the classification of matter and their

Remember section will help them to memorize and review the previous learning on a particular topic

Key points will help the students to identify the essential points in a chapter

Key Ideas

After completing this chapter, you should be able to:

- understand the kinetic molecular theory and inter-relationship among various measurable properties of gases.
- understand mole as the chemical counting

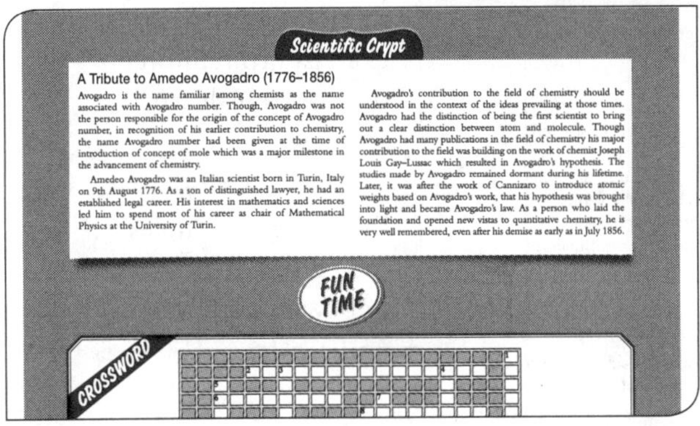

Scientific Crypt

A Tribute to Amedeo Avogadro (1776–1856)

Avogadro is the name familiar among chemists as the name associated with Avogadro number. Though, Avogadro was not the person responsible for the origin of the concept of Avogadro number, in recognition of his earlier contribution to chemistry, the name Avogadro number had been given at the time of introduction of concept of mole which was a major milestone in the advancement of chemistry.

Amedeo Avogadro was an Italian scientist born in Turin, Italy on 9th August 1776. As a son of distinguished lawyer, he had an established legal career. His interest in mathematics and sciences led him to spend most of his career as chair of Mathematical Physics at the University of Turin.

Avogadro's contribution to the field of chemistry should be understood in the context of the ideas prevailing at those times. Avogadro had the distinction of being the first scientist to bring out a clear distinction between atom and molecule. Though Avogadro had many publications in the field of chemistry his major contribution to the field was building on the work of chemist Joseph Louis Gay–Lussac which resulted in Avogadro's hypothesis. The studies made by Avogadro remained dormant during his lifetime. Later, it was after the work of Cannizaro to introduce atomic weights based on Avogadro's work, that his hypothesis was brought into light and became Avogadro's law. As a person who laid the foundation and opened new vistas to quantitative chemistry, he is very well remembered, even after his demise as early as in July 1856.

Scientific Crypt provides information about well-known scientists related to the chapter. The engaging activity is also given in the form of a crossword to keep the learners interested.

INTRODUCTION

The study of matter in different perceptions is dealt by a branch of science named Chemistry. Matter can be classified on the basis of molecular composition as elements, compounds, and mixtures. Various elements are given names and symbols, and the names and formulae of various compounds have been derived based on certain rules. The study of naming these compounds and derivation of formulae for these are the prerequisites for representing chemical reactions in the form of chemical equations. Therefore, the language of chemistry,

Introduction section helps to lay the foundation of the following chapter and leads the way for further learning

Concepts are explained in a well-structured and lucid manner

Symbols and Formulae

All elements are represented by means of their symbols. A symbol represents the atom of an element, which may consist of a single letter or a combination of letters derived either from its English name or its Latin name.

A **symbol** is the shorthand notation that represents a single atom of an element.

Examples:

Element	Symbol
Hydrogen	H
Mercury (formerly known as hydrargyrum)	Hg

Konnect boxes are some add-on information of related topic

Konnect

A common example of neutralization is our body's response to heartburn. Antacids are bases that neutralize the excess stomach acid.

Info Bytes!

The kinetic theory of gases is based on the assumption that gases are composed of a large number of tiny particles (atoms or molecules) that are in constant, random motion. This movement is what gives rise to pressure and temperature.

Info bytes are interesting trivia and facts that engage young minds and keep the grey cells ticking!

EXAMPLE 1.5 Gas laws are universally applicable for all gases whereas such universal laws could established for solids and liquids. Comment on this statement.

SOLUTION

Gases differ from solids and liquids in the extent of intermolecular forces of attraction. Since gases are characteriz negligible forces of attraction, the molecules behave independent of the neighboring molecules. Due to large intermo spaces, the coefficient of volume expansion is same for all gases. Moreover, in case of gases, the molecules are cons as point masses and hence, the volume occupied by the molecules is negligible in comparison to the total volume. The the physical behavior of all gases being similar, certain laws could be established which are universally applicable. In c liquids and solids, the molecules are considered as rigid spheres and the coefficient of volume expansion is not uniform substances, such universal laws cannot be established.

EXAMPLE 1.6 Boyle's law says that pressure and volume are inversely proportional to each other. Ho when a balloon is blown, both volume and pressure increase continuously. Justify.

SOLUTION

When a balloon is blown continuously, more and more air is forced into the balloon that increases the volume as we

Examples are given in the form of in-text exercises to reinforce the concepts learnt

Illustrative examples solved in a logical and step-wise manner

POINTS TO REMEMBER

- ✔ A symbol is the shorthand notation that represents a single atom of an element.
- ✔ A formula is the shorthand notation which represents a single molecule of an element or compound.
- ✔ The properties of solids and liquids differ widely from substance to substance, but the gases generally obey some common rules known as the gas laws.
- ✔ Boyle's Law states that the volume of a given mass of a gas is inversely proportional to
- ✔ Vapor density (VD) of a gas or vapor is the ratio of the mass of a certain volume of gas or vapor to the mass of the same volume of hydrogen gas when their volumes are measured under similar conditions of temperature and pressure.
- ✔ A mole is defined as the quantity of substance that contains the same number of elementary particles or chemical units as the number of atoms present in 12 g of C-12 isotope.
- ✔ Dalton's law states that 'the total pressure exerted by a mixture of non-reacting gases

Points to remember summarises the concepts and topics presented in each chapter

PRACTICE QUESTIONS CLASSROOM WING

Very Short Answer Type Questions

Directions for questions from 1 to 5:
Fill in the blanks.

1. The percentage of sulphur in SO_2 is ________ and ________ in SO_3.
2. The vapor density of SO_2 gas is ________ the vapor density of O_2 gas.
3. The molecular formula of a gas with vapor density 15

(A) Reaction between an acid and a base from salt and water
(B) Reaction between zinc and dil. H_2SO_4
(C) Preparation of oxygen from potassium nitrate
(D) Preparation of CO_2 from its constituents

9. What is the molarity of HCl solution containing 0.4 moles in 200 mL of the solution?
10. Calculate the volume occupied by 11 g of CO_2 gas at

Short Answer Type Questions

26. A spherical balloon of volume 253 mL is to be with helium gas at STP from a cylinder containi at 20 atm and 127°C. If the cylinder can hold water, then calculate the number of balloons th be filled up.
27. The composition of a gaseous mixture is N_2 =

Essay Answer Type Questions

41. The density of a mixture of He and O_2 at STP is 1.25 g/L. What is the partial pressure of O_2?
42. A bottle is heated from 27°C to 127°C at constant pressure. What fraction of air gets expelled?
43. An oxide of Cr contains 68.5% of Cr by weight. Find

Different typologies of questions have been included in the *Classroom Wing* which help students to develop the problem-solving skill

Competition Wing has been integrated chapter-wise in the exercise part to prepare students for various competitive examinations.

PRACTICE QUESTIONS COMPETITION WING

Level 1: Apply your Concepts

Direction for questions from 1 to 8:
State whether the following statements are true or false.

1. Doubling the pressure of a gas at constant temperature, doubles the volume occupied by the gas.
2.

16. 'ous' acid of a non-metal 'X' has 2 'O' atoms. Per acid of the same non-metal has the formula ________.
17. The ratio of the gram atomic weight of nitrogen and oxygen is ________.
18. Pressure exerted by water vapor in moist gas is called

Graded as per complexity: Level 1; Level 2; and Level 3

Level 2: Review Your Concepts

51. Out of oxygen, carbon dioxide, sulphur dioxide an nitrogen, which among these gases possesses maximu density at a given temperature and pressure?
52. If the Avogadro number is 9×10^{23}, calculate th weight of 1 mole of CO_2 gas.
53. A gas cylinder is filled with helium at 2000 mm. Du

Level 3: Assess Your Concepts

74. At constant temperature and at 4 atm pressure, the given amount of gas occupies 6 L. If the pressure is increased by 6 atm, calculate the percentage change in the volume of the gas.
75. A gaseous mixture contains 48 g of SO_2 and 33 g of CO_2 at constant temperature and pressure. Calculate the average molecular mass of the gaseous mixture.
76. Calculate the ratio of rates of diffusion of three isotopes of hydrogen protium, deuterium and tritium, respectively, at the same temperature and pressure.

Short Answer Type Questions

26. A spherical balloon of volume 253 mL is to be filled with helium gas at STP from a cylinder containing gas at 20 atm and 127°C. If the cylinder can hold 2 L of water, then calculate the number of balloons that can be filled up.
27. The composition of a gaseous mixture is N_2 = 56%, O_2 = 32%, Ar = 12% by mass. What is the partial pressure of nitrogen at 1 atm pressure?
28. A gold manufacturing company manufactures gold coins with absolutely pure gold. If the mass of each gold coin is 9.85 g and 1000 gold coins are manufactured per day, calculate the number of moles of gold consumed per day. (At. wt. of gold is 197 amu)
29. A closed cylinder is first evacuated and then connected to another cylinder of 75-L volume containing an ideal gas 'X'. The pressure of the gas in the second cylinder falls from 22 atm to 10 atm. Calculate the volume of the first cylinder.
33. What is the volume of 50% (w/v) H_2SO_4 required for the liberation of 5.6 L of hydrogen gas at STP on its reaction with magnesium?
34. Calculate the percentage composition of glucose.
35. Empirical formula of a compound is CH_3N. If the empirical formula weight is equal to one-fourth of its vapor density, find out the molecular formula of the compou
36. Calculat
(a) 4.5
(b) 0.2
(c) 1.2
37. A bulb connect through the pres tempera
38. Find ou

45. A vessel contains equal number of moles of helium and methane. Due to a hole in the vessel, half of the gaseous mixture effused out. What is the ratio of the number of moles of helium and methane remaining in the vessel?
46. A vessel contains double the number of moles of hydrogen than oxygen. Due to a hole in the vessel, one-fourth of the gaseous mixture is effused out. What is the ratio of the number of moles of hydrogen and oxygen remaining in the vessel?
47. A salt is formed between a bivalent metal cation and an oxyacid of a non-metal. The -ous acid of the non-metal

The icons are used for categorisation of the questions in Classroom Wing and Competition Wing

PRACTICE QUESTIONS JEE-NEET SPECIAL WING

Multiple-Answer Type Questions

Directions for Questions number 1 to 5:
Select one or more correct alternative(s) from the given choices.

1. Study the following reaction and answer the question that follows.
   Metal bisulphide + Hydrochloric acid → Salt + X↑.
   Which of the following statements are correct with respect to the given reaction.

3. Identify the statements that are true with respect to Kw, the ionic product of water.
   (a) The value of K_w changes with the addition of HCl or NaOH
   (b) Addition of an acid to water increases the H^+ ion concentration of the solution, but K_w remains unchanged.
   (c) The value of K_w is 10.1×10^{-13} at 25°C.
   K_w at 75°C > K_w at 50°C
   tify the incorrect match.

Comprehension-Based Questions

Directions for Questions 6 to 10:
Read the following passage and answer the que given below

Titration is a common laboratory method for quant chemical analysis used to determine the unk concentration of a known reactant. This method in

Match the Column

16. Two formula types describe a compound: the empirical formula, showcasing the simplest ratio of elements within a molecule, and the molecular formula, detailing the exact count of each element within a molecule of the compound. Sarita first rinsed the tomatoes(P) in a vinegar(Q) solution and prepared a tomato soup on an LPG(R) stove

JEE-NEET Special Wing is curated specifically for targeted preparation of JEE and NEET examinations.

Hints and Explanations

Classroom Wing

Very Short Answer Type Questions

1. 50%, 40%
2. higher than
3. Relation between vapor density and molecular weight. C_2H_6
4. 16/N
5. 40.043%
6. Since the molecular weight of hydrogen is less than

11. $\frac{P_1V_1}{T_1} = \frac{P_2V_2}{T_2}$
    = 5/9
12. Mole fraction = $\frac{\text{No. of moles of a Substance}}{\text{Total number of moles of all substances in the mixture}}$
    Sum of mole fraction in a mixture = 1
    = 0.7
13. $\frac{r_1}{r_2} = \sqrt{\frac{M_2}{M_1}}$

Hints and Explanation for key questions of classroom wing, competition wing and JEE-NEET special wing along with highlights on the common mistakes that students usually make in the examinations

Competition Wing

Level 1: Apply your Concepts

20. Calcium bisulphate → $Ca(HSO_4)_2$
    Ferric sulphate → $Fe_2(SO_4)_3$
    Calcium bisulphite → $Ca(HSO_3)_2$
    Ferrous sulphate → $FeSO_4$
    (i) → (C); (ii) → (D); (iii) → (B); (iv) → (A)
21. 80 g of SO is equal to 1 mole. 1 mole of any gas at STP occupies 22.4 L.
    Hence, the correct option is (a).
22. At low pressure and high temperature, inter-molecular forces of attraction among the gas molecules are negligible. Hence, the gases behave ideally.
    Hence, the correct option is (a).
23. (4) HCl + NaOH → NaCl + H_2O → Double displacement
    (3) $Cl_2 + H_2 \rightarrow HCl$ → Combination
    (2) $Mg + H_2SO_4 \rightarrow MgSO_4 + H_2$ → Displacement
    (1) NaCl Na + Cl → Decomposition

(C) potassium bicarbonate → $KHCO_3$
$\%\text{ of potassium} = \frac{39}{100} \times 100 = 39\%$
(D) potassium sulphide → K_2S
$\%\text{ of potassium} = \frac{39 \times 2}{110} \times 100 = 70.90\%$
∴ increasing order is (D) > (A) > (B) > (C)
Hence, the correct answer is (d).

38. Let the vapor density of compound be x
    Empirical formula weight = $x/2$
    Molecular formula weight = $2x$
    $n = \frac{\text{Molecular formula weight}}{\text{Empirical formula weight}} \times \frac{2x}{\left(\frac{x}{2}\right)} = 4$
    Molecular formula = $4 \times A_2B_4 = A_8B_{16}$
    Hence, the correct answer is (b).
39. Let the bivalent metal ion be M^{2+}, then the formula of the compound formed will be $M(ClO_4)_2$.
    1 mole of compound contains 8 N oxygen atoms.

JEE-NEET Special wing

Multiple-Answer Type Questions

1. Metal bisulphide + Hydrochloric acid → Salt + $H_2S\uparrow$
   Metal bisulphide can be formed with a representative element of valency 1.
   X is hydrogen sulphide gas with a characteristic pungent odour. It dissolves sparingly in water to form hydro sulphuric acid which is a hydracid.
   Hence, correct options are (c) and (d).
2. X is a dibasic acid. ⇒ its basicity is 2 and every one mole of X produces 2 moles of H^+ ions
   One mole of H+ ions will be obtained from every 0.5 mol of X
   0.7 moles of H+ ions will be obtained from 0.7 × 0.5 = 0.35 mol of X
   ⇒ only 0.35 moles of X is ionised while 0.15 moles of X is left behind unionised, i.e. it is in its molecular state
   At T, for every 0.5 moles of X 0.35 mol ionised.

Salt	Nature of its aqueous solution-Reason
(c) KNO_3	Neutral- Due to the presence of equal number of free H^+ and OH^- ions
(d) $(NH_4)_2CO_3$	Neutral- Due to the absence of free H^+ or OH^- ions

Hence, correct options are (a) and (b).

5. Conjugate Acid: It is the substance formed when a base gains a proton. It has one more proton (H^+) compared to its corresponding base.
   Conjugate Base: It is the substance formed when an acid loses a proton. It has one proton (H^+) less compared to its corresponding acid.
   (a) H_2CO_3 , HCO_3^- and
   (b) H_2O, H_3O^+ are conjugate acid base pairs.
   Hence, correct options are (a) and (b).

WORKSHEET

CHAPTER 1: MOLE CONCEPT, STOICHIOMETRY AND BEHAVIOR OF GASES

DW

DW: Downloadable worksheets supplementing textual exercises for hand-on learning

Direction for questions from 1 to 5:
Select the correct alternative from the following option.

1. A rubber balloon which is permeable to all the isotopes of hydrogen is filled with pure tritium. It is placed in a closed box containing pure hydrogen under similar conditions of temperature and pressure. Identify the correct observation regarding the balloon.
   (a) The balloon first expands and then contracts.
   (b) The balloon first contracts first and then expand.
   (c) The balloon expands.

Directions of questions from 6 to 10:
State whether the following statements are true or false.

6. 80 g of SO_3 corresponds to 1 mole.
7. Real gases behave ideally at high pressure and low temperature.
8. Reaction between an acid and a base form salt and water.
9. Equal volumes of all gases possess unequal number of moles at constant temperature and pressure.

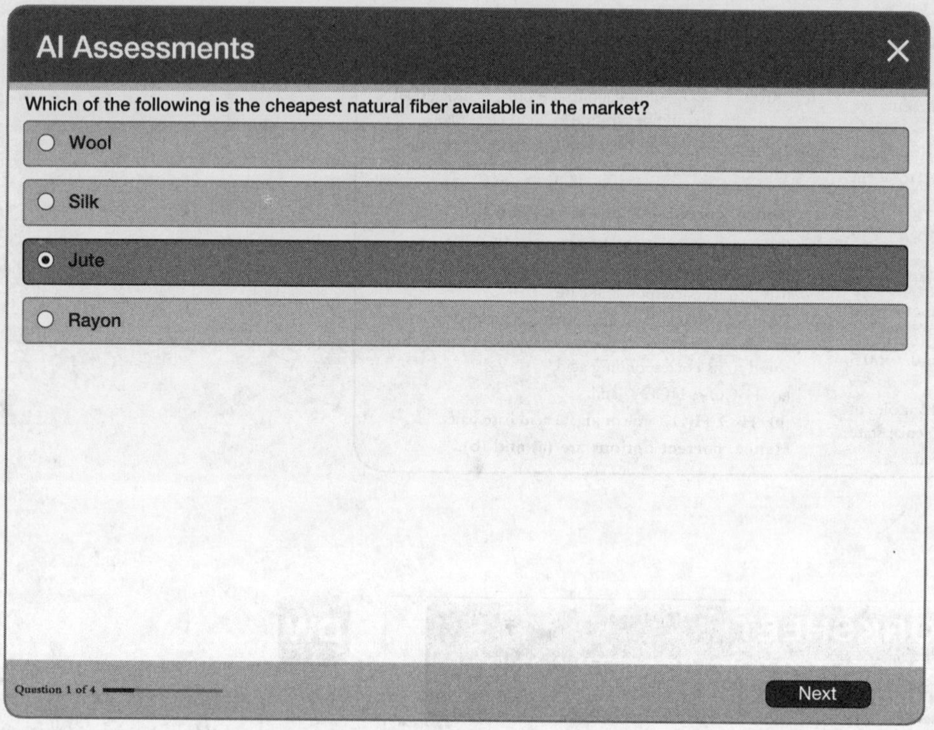

AT

AT: Attemptable Tests for assessing understanding of concepts and getting a clear picture of your exam readiness

51. Na_2CO_3 is dissolved in water at 25°C. Which of the following is/are correct regarding the given statement?

(a) In this solution anionic hydrolysis take place.

(b) The concentration of H^+ ion in the given solution is less than 10^{-7} mole/L

Video icon: Audio and visual learning to difficult questions for effective learning and retention

Unit I

Physical Chemistry

In this Unit

- ✶ **Chapter 1** Mole Concept, Stoichiometry and Behavior of Gases
- ✶ **Chapter 2** Acids, Bases and Salts
- ✶ **Chapter 3** Electrochemistry
- ✶ **Chapter 4** Periodic Table
- ✶ **Chapter 5** Chemical Bonding
- ✶ **Chapter 6** Metallurgy
- ✶ **Chapter 7** Industrial Chemistry

CHAPTER

1

Mole Concept, Stoichiometry, and Behavior of Gases

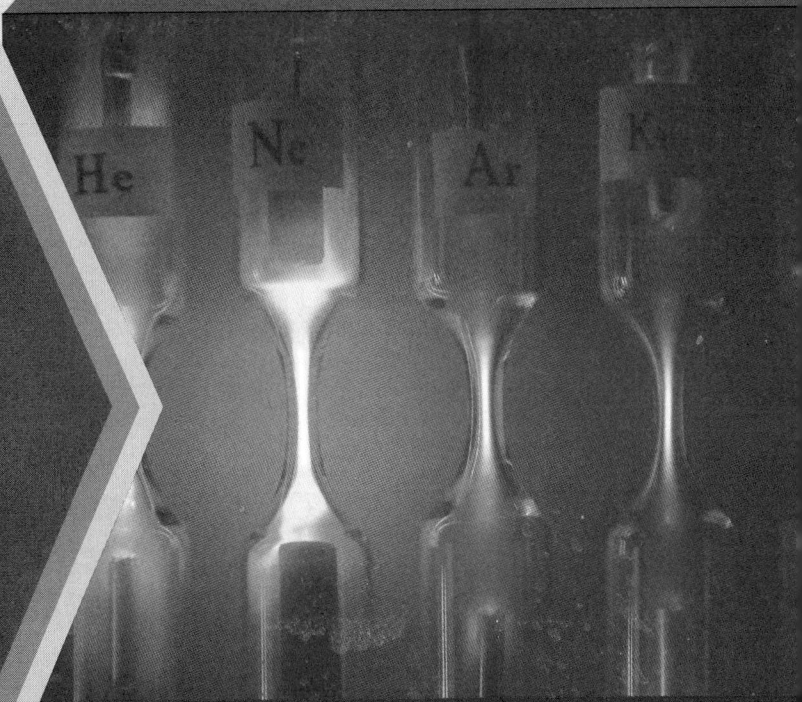

Remember

Before beginning this chapter, you should be able to:

- understand the concept of matter and atoms.
- review the classification of matter and their atomic structure.
- identify the types of chemical reactions.

Key Ideas

After completing this chapter, you should be able to:

- understand the kinetic molecular theory and inter-relationship among various measurable properties of gases.
- understand mole as the chemical counting unit.
- derive ideal gas equation from gas laws and draw a comparison between ideal and real gases.
- explain the behavior of gases in a mixture and their relative tendency to diffuse.
- understand and establish quantitative relationship between reactants and products, and develop numerical skills with regard to calculations based on chemical equations.

A Tribute to Amedeo Avogadro (1776–1856)

Avogadro is the name familiar among chemists as the name associated with Avogadro number. Though, Avogadro was not the person responsible for the origin of the concept of Avogadro number, in recognition of his earlier contribution to chemistry, the name Avogadro number had been given at the time of introduction of concept of mole which was a major milestone in the advancement of chemistry.

Amedeo Avogadro was an Italian scientist born in Turin, Italy on 9th August 1776. As a son of distinguished lawyer, he had an established legal career. His interest in mathematics and sciences led him to spend most of his career as chair of Mathematical Physics at the University of Turin.

Avogadro's contribution to the field of chemistry should be understood in the context of the ideas prevailing at those times. Avogadro had the distinction of being the first scientist to bring out a clear distinction between atom and molecule. Though Avogadro had many publications in the field of chemistry his major contribution to the field was building on the work of chemist Joseph Louis Gay–Lussac which resulted in Avogadro's hypothesis. The studies made by Avogadro remained dormant during his lifetime. Later, it was after the work of Cannizaro to introduce atomic weights based on Avogadro's work, that his hypothesis was brought into light and became Avogadro's law. As a person who laid the foundation and opened new vistas to quantitative chemistry, he is very well remembered, even after his demise as early as in July 1856.

FUN TIME

CROSSWORD

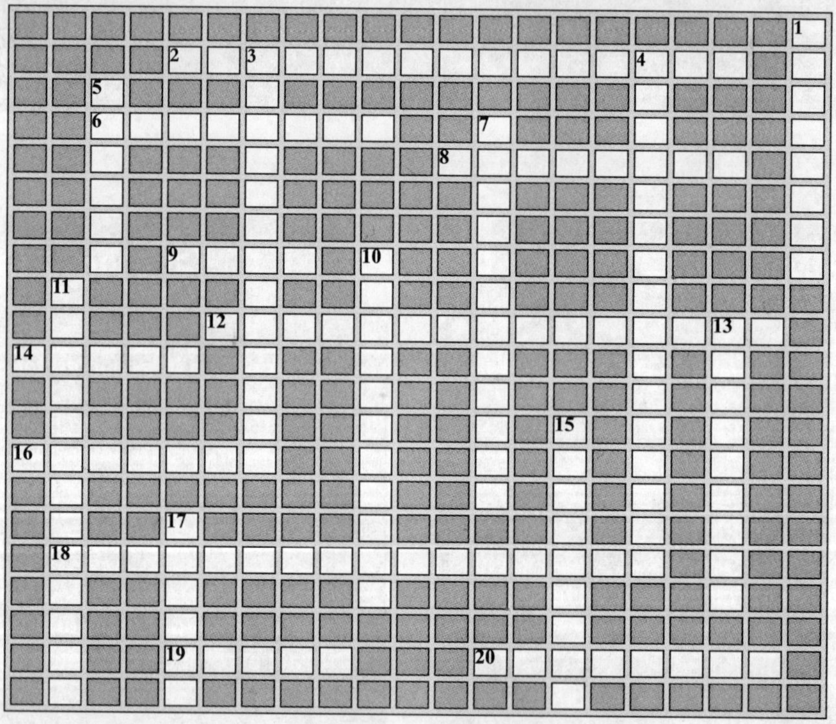

Across

2. The name given to the reagent which is taken in a lesser proportion in the reaction
6. The temperature used in the study of gases
8. Number of moles present in one litre of solution
9. Avogadro number of particles
12. Volume occupied by one mole of gas at STP
14. The law which gives the interrelationship between pressure and volume at constant temperature
16. The gas law which gives the relation between volume and temperature at constant pressure
18. The formula which gives exact number of atoms of different elements present in a compound
19. The gases which obey gas laws under all conditions
20. The law which gives the interrelationship between number of molecules and volumes of a gas

Down

1. The process of spreading of gas molecules through a small hole
3. The mass of Avogadro number of molecules
4. Formula which gives ratio of atoms of different elements present in a compound
5. The motion responsible for collisions between gas molecules
7. The ratio of number of moles of solute to that of solution
10. The parameter which results in change in pressure for a given mass of gas at constant volume
11. Quantitative relationship between reactants and products
13. Tiny particles present in all gases
15. Spontaneous process of spreading of gas molecules
17. The name of scientist associated with absolute temperature scale

INTRODUCTION

The study of matter in different perceptions is dealt by a branch of science named Chemistry. Matter can be classified on the basis of molecular composition as elements, compounds, and mixtures. Various elements are given names and symbols, and the names and formulae of various compounds have been derived based on certain rules. The study of naming these compounds and derivation of formulae for these are the prerequisites for representing chemical reactions in the form of chemical equations. Therefore, the language of chemistry, which involves the study of symbols, formulae, and chemical equations with respect to the above aspects, is of utmost significance.

Symbols and Formulae

All elements are represented by means of their symbols. A symbol represents the atom of an element, which may consist of a single letter or a combination of letters derived either from its English name or its Latin name.

A **symbol** is the shorthand notation that represents a single atom of an element.

Examples:

Element	**Symbol**
Hydrogen	H
Mercury (formerly known as hydrargyrum)	Hg
Helium	He

A molecule of an element or a compound is represented by means of a formula. Formula is written with the help of symbols of the respective constituent element(s) along with the actual number of atoms of the respective elements.

A **formula** is the shorthand notation which represents a single molecule of an element or compound.

Examples:

1. $Cl_2 \Rightarrow$ one molecule of chlorine consists of two atoms
2. $CaCO_3 \Rightarrow$ one molecule of calcium carbonate consists of one calcium atom, one carbon atom and three oxygen atoms.

Derivation of Formulae of Compounds

A **molecule** is formed by the combination of a positive radical and a negative radical, but by itself is electrically neutral. Hence, the number of positive and negative radicals, which form a molecule of the compound depends on the charge(s) on the respective radicals.

Table 1.1 Radicals present in compounds

Positive Radicals	Negative Radicals	Formulas	Explanation
Na^+	Cl^-	NaCl	One Na^+ neutralizes one Cl^- since both of them are unipositive
H^+	SO_4^{2-}	H_2SO_4	Two H^+ are required to neutralize one SO_4^{2-}
Al^{3+}	CO_3^{2-}	$Al_2(CO_3)_3$	Two Al^{3+} are required to neutralize three CO_3^{2-}
Ca^{2+}	PO_4^{3-}	$Ca_3(PO_4)_2$	Three Ca^{2+} are required to neutralize two PO_4^{3-}

Naming of Inorganic Compounds

Inorganic compounds are classified into three categories, namely, acids, bases, and salts. Naming of the respective categories follows certain rules, which have been discussed below.

Naming of Acids

Acids usually contain hydrogen ion (H^+) as the positive radical. Hence, the name of the acid depends on the constituent(s) of its negative radical.

Table 1.2 Naming of acids

Types of Acids	Types of Negative Radicals	Suffixes
Binary acids	Negative radical consists of a single non-metal. E.g., HCl, HBr, etc.	'ic' (prefix hydro) Hydrochloric acid, hydrobromic acid
Oxyacid	Negative radical consists of a non-metal and oxygen. The name of the oxyacid depends on the percentage of the oxygen associated with a specific non-metal.	
	Acids with comparatively less percentage of oxygen. E.g., H_2SO_3, HNO_2, H_3PO_3, etc.	'ous' Sulphurous acid, nitrous acid, phosphorous acid, etc.
	Acids with comparatively higher percentage of oxygen. E.g., H_2SO_4, HNO_3, H_3PO_4, etc.	'ic' Sulphuric acid, nitric acid, phosphoric acid, etc.

If an acid contains lesser number of oxygen atoms than the corresponding 'ous' acid, then 'hypo' prefix is given to the negative radical, whereas 'per' prefix is given to the negative radical when the acid contains greater number of oxygen atoms than the corresponding 'ic' acid.

Examples:

Hypochlorous acid	$HClO$
Chlorous acid	$HClO_2$
Chloric acid	$HClO_3$
Perchloric acid	$HClO_4$

Naming of Bases

Bases generally contain hydroxyl radical (OH^-) as the negative radical and a metal ion as its positive radical. While writing the name of the base, the name of the metal is written first followed by hydroxide.

Examples:

$Ca(OH)_2$	Calcium hydroxide
$Mg(OH)_2$	Magnesium hydroxide
NaOH	Sodium hydroxide
$Al(OH)_3$	Aluminium hydroxide

Info Bytes!

Bases are typically named by identifying the metal cation first, followed by the word 'hydroxide'. For instance, KOH is named Potassium Hydroxide.

Naming of Salts

The positive radical present in the salt comes from the corresponding base and the negative radical comes from the corresponding acid.

Name of the salt starts with the name of the metal present as a positive radical, which is followed by the name of a negative radical. Name of the negative radical depends on the name of the acid from which the salt is produced.

Table 1.3 Naming of salts

Acids from which the salt is produced	Suffixes and names of the salts
'ous' acid *E.g.*: Sulphurous acid (H_2SO_3) Nitrous acid (HNO_2) Phosphorous acid (H_3PO_3)	'ite' Calcium sulphite ($CaSO_3$) Zinc nitrite ($Zn(NO_2)_2$) Magnesium phosphite ($Mg_3(PO_3)_2$)
'ic' acid *E.g.*: Sulphuric acid (H_2SO_4) Nitric acid (HNO_3) Phosphoric acid (H_3PO_4)	'ate' Zinc sulphate ($ZnSO_4$) Sodium nitrate ($NaNO_3$) Aluminium phosphate ($AlPO_4$)

If NH_4^+ is present as the positive radical in the base or in the salt, ammonium is written in place of the name of the metal. For example, Ammonium hydroxide (base, NH_4PO_4) and Ammonium phosphate (salt, NH_4PO_4).

EXAMPLE 1.1 The formula of a metal phosphide is M_3P_2. Identify formulae of the **(i)** metal oxide **(ii)** metal nitrite **(iii)** metal bicarbonate

SOLUTION

Since the formula of metal phosphide is M_3P_2, metal ion is M^{2+}

(i) Formula of metal oxide is $M^{2+}O^{2-} \Rightarrow MO$

(ii) Formula of metal nitrite is $M^{2+}NO_2^- \Rightarrow M(NO_2)_2$

(iii) Formula of metal bicarbonate is $M^{2+}HCO_3^- \Rightarrow M(HCO_3)_2$

EXAMPLE 1.2 Metal M forms two oxides A and B in which the ratio of the number of oxygen atoms to the total number of atoms present in the molecule is 3 : 5 and 1 : 2, respectively. Determine the formulae of A and B.

SOLUTION

Metal ions present in A and B are M^{a+} and M^{b+}, respectively.

$\therefore$ Formula of A is $M^{a+}O^{2-} \Rightarrow M_2O_a$

$$\therefore \text{Ratio} = \frac{a}{2+a} = \frac{3}{5}$$

$\Rightarrow 5a = 6 + 3a \Rightarrow 2a = 6 \Rightarrow a = 3$

$\therefore$ Metal oxide A is $M^{3+}O^{2-} \Rightarrow M_2O_3$

Formula of B is $M^{b+}, O^{2-} \Rightarrow M_2O_b$

$$\therefore \text{Ratio} = \frac{b}{2+b} = \frac{1}{2}$$

$\Rightarrow 2b = 2 + b \Rightarrow b = 2$

$\therefore$ Metal oxide B is $M^{2+}, O^{2-} \Rightarrow MO$

Another aspect of the study of matter involves the different physical states of matter, i.e., solids, liquids, and gases. Existence of matter in three distinct states entirely depends on the arrangement of molecules.

Molecules are closely packed in solids, comparatively loosely packed in liquids, but very loosely packed in gases. This type of molecular arrangement gives the gas molecules maximum freedom of movement, which results in the various unique properties that gases exhibit. The gases neither have a definite shape nor a definite volume due to the random movement of gas molecules. The unique characteristics of gases can be explained with the help of **kinetic molecular theory**.

Kinetic Theory of Gases

The main postulates of kinetic theory of gases are:

1. All gases are made up of tiny particles known as molecules.
2. The huge intermolecular spaces make the forces of attraction between the gas molecules negligible.
3. The molecules are in constant random motion. During motion, the molecules collide with each other and also with the walls of the container. These collisions are perfectly elastic. The pressure exerted by a gas is due to the collisions of the molecules with the walls of the container.
4. The average kinetic energy of gas molecules is proportional to the absolute temperature of the gas.

Info Bytes!

The kinetic theory of gases is based on the assumption that gases are composed of a large number of tiny particles (atoms or molecules) that are in constant, random motion. This movement is what gives rise to pressure and temperature.

Characteristics of Gases

Gases are highly compressible and diffusible. They neither have a definite shape nor have definite volume. The gases occupy the entire volume available to them. Therefore, the volume of a gas is taken as the volume of the container.

The study of gases is much simpler than that of the solids and liquids because the physical properties of all the gases are found to be identical, for example, the compressibility or thermal expansion of all the gases is the same, but this is not so in case of solids and liquids. The properties of solids and liquids differ widely from substance to substance, but the gases generally obey some common rules known as the **gas laws**.

Gas Laws

Gas laws give the inter-relationships among the measurable properties of a gas that have been experimentally established.

Boyle's Law

The volume of a given mass of a gas is inversely proportional to the pressure exerted by the gas at constant temperature.

$$V \propto \frac{1}{P} \text{ (T = constant)}$$

$$V = \frac{K}{P}$$

$$PV = K \text{ (constant)}$$

The product of pressure and volume of a given mass of a gas is constant at constant temperature.

Konnect

The gas laws aren't just theoretical. Scuba divers have to be well aware of Boyle's Law when they dive. As they descend, pressure increases, causing the volume of the air in their lungs to decrease. If they hold their breath while ascending, the reduced pressure can cause the air to expand rapidly, possibly leading to lung injury. So, it's crucial to exhale while rising to the surface.

If at constant temperature, a gas occupies a volume V_1 at a pressure P_1 and a volume V_2 at a pressure P_2, then

$$P_1V_1 = P_2V_2 \text{ (T = constant).}$$

Graphical Representation of Boyle's Law

1. **Volume (V) vs Pressure (P)**

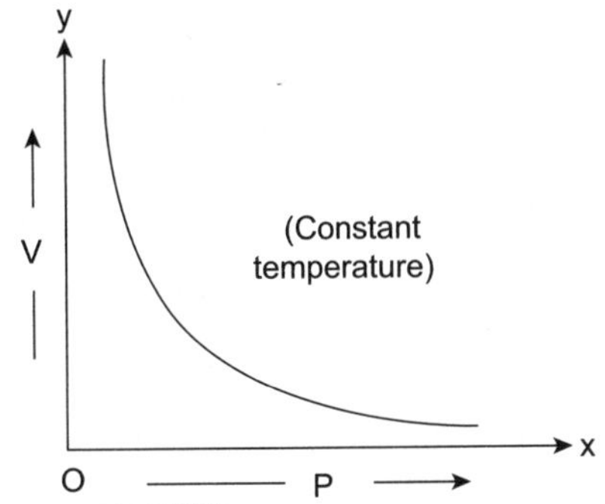

Figure 1.1 Boyle's law graph I

2. **Volume (V) vs $\frac{1}{\text{Pressure (P)}}$**

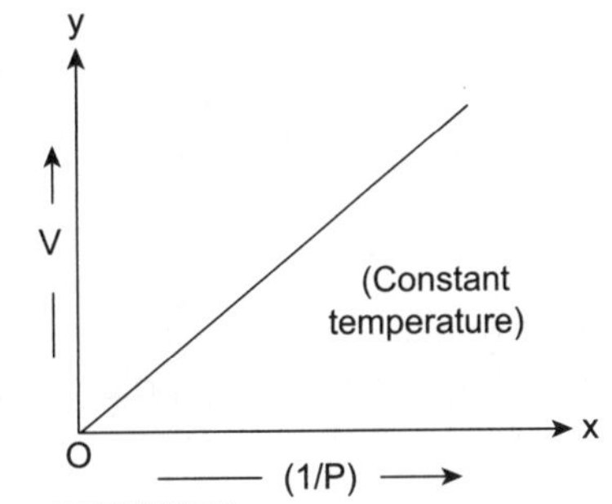

Figure 1.2 Boyle's law graph II

3. **The product of pressure and volume (PV) vs pressure (P)**

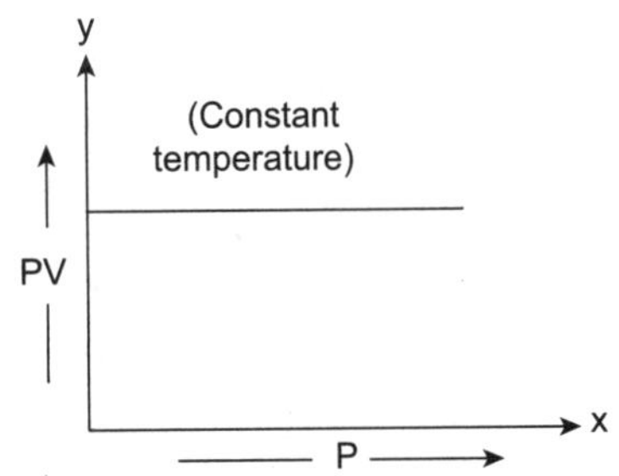

Figure 1.3 Boyle's law graph III

EXAMPLE 1.3

(i) 5 L of methane gas at 2 atm pressure is compressed to 1.6 L at constant temperature. Calculate the final pressure.

(ii) The pressure of a certain volume of a gas is reduced to half of its initial pressure at constant temperature. Calculate its new volume.

SOLUTION

(i) **Initial condition**	**Final condition**
$V_1 = 5$ L	$V_2 = 1.6$ L
$P_1 = 2$ atm	$P_2 = ?$

According to Boyle's law,

$$P_1V_1 = P_2V_2$$

$$P_2 = \frac{P_1V_1}{V_2} = \frac{5 \times 2}{1.6} = 6.25 \text{ atm}$$

Final pressure = 6.25 atm

(ii) Initial condition	**Final condition**
$V_1 = V$	$V_2 = ?$
$P_1 = P$	$P_2 = ½ P$

According to Boyle's law,

$$P_1V_1 = P_2V_2$$

$$\Rightarrow V_2 = \frac{V \times P}{\frac{1}{2}P} 2V$$

Final volume = 2V

Charles' Law

At constant pressure, the volume of a given mass of a gas increases or decreases by 1/273 of its original volume at 0°C for every 1°C increase or decrease in temperature, respectively. If V_0 is the volume of gas at 0°C and V_t is the volume of gas at t°C, (P = constant), then:

$$V_t = V_0\left[1 + \frac{t}{273}\right]$$

$$V_t = V_0\left[1 + \frac{273 + t}{273}\right]$$

$$V_t = V_0\left[\frac{T}{273}\right]; \text{ T = absolute temperature}$$

$$\frac{V_0}{273} = \text{Constant}$$

$$\therefore V \propto T$$

If V_1 and V_2 are the volumes occupied by a given mass of gas at temperatures T_1 and T_2, then

$$\frac{V_1}{T_1} = \frac{V_2}{T_2} \text{ (P = Constant)}$$

Charles' law can otherwise be stated as the volume occupied by a given mass of a gas is directly proportional to the absolute temperature of the gas at constant pressure.

Graphical Representation of Charles' Law

1. **Volume (V) vs absolute temperature (T)**

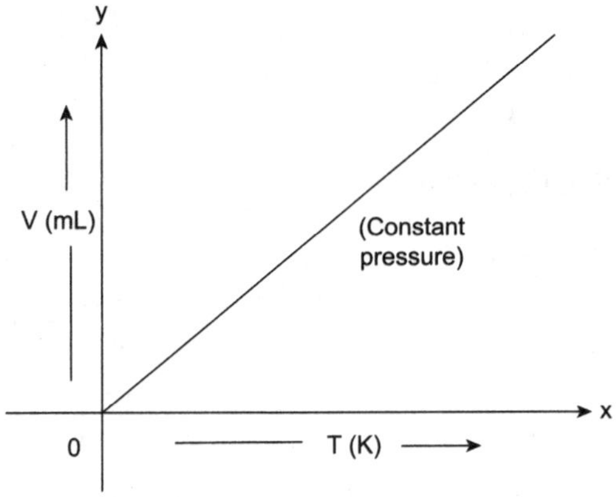

Figure 1.4 Charles's law graph-I

2. **Volume (V) vs temperature (t)**

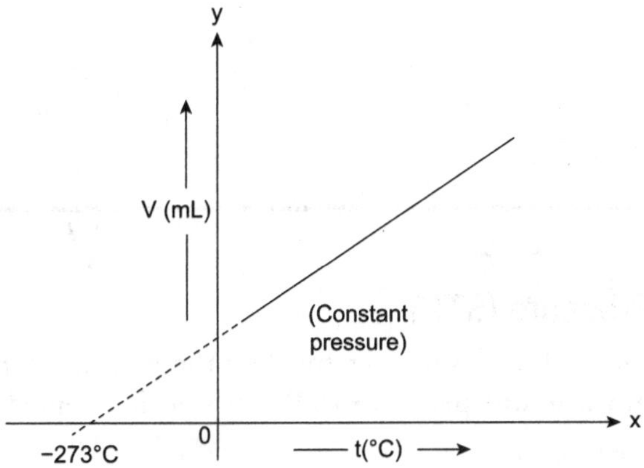

Figure 1.5 Charles's law graph-II

A straight line, which intersects the x-axis at −273°C, is obtained as V = 0, when t = −273°C.

Mathematically, volume at −273°C, $V_t = V_0 + \frac{V_0}{273}(-273)$,

$$\therefore\ V_t = V_0 + \left[\frac{273 - 273}{273}\right] = 0$$

Absolute Zero

From the Figure 1.5, V vs t, the straight line intersects the temperature axis at −273°C showing that the gas occupies zero volume at this temperature. That means it is the lowest temperature that can be attained theoretically. Therefore, it is called **absolute zero**.

EXAMPLE 1.4

(i) At a certain pressure, the volume occupied by a given mass of a gas is 10 L at 0°C, calculate the volume occupied by the gas at 91°C at the same pressure.

(ii) Calculate the temperature at which the volume of a given mass of gas gets reduced to 3/5th of original volume at 10°C without any change in pressure.

SOLUTION

(i) **Initial condition**	**Final condition**
$V_1 = 10$ L	$V_2 = ?$
$T_1 = 276$ K	$T_2 = (273 + 91)\text{K} = 364$ K

According to Charles' law,

$$\frac{V_1}{T_1} = \frac{V_2}{T_2}$$

$$\Rightarrow \frac{10}{273} = \frac{V_2}{364} \Rightarrow V_2 = \frac{10 \times 364}{273} = 13.33 \text{ L}$$

(ii) Initial condition **Final condition**

$V_1 = V$ $V_2 = \frac{3}{5} V$

$T_1 = (273 + 91)\text{K} = 364 \text{ K}$ $T_2 = ?$

According to Charles' law,

$$\frac{V_1}{T_1} = \frac{V_2}{T_2}$$

$$T_2 = V_2 \times \frac{T_1}{V_1}$$

$$\Rightarrow T_2 = \frac{3V}{5} \times \frac{283}{V}$$

$$\Rightarrow T_2 = 169.8 \text{ K} \Rightarrow T_2 = -103.2°\text{C}$$

Standard Temperature and Pressure (STP)

The volume of a given mass of gas depends on its temperature and the pressure imposed. Hence, in order to define the volume of a gas, a **standard temperature and pressure (STP)** has been accepted all over the world.

The conditions of STP are given below.

Standard temperature = 0°C = 273 K

Standard pressure = 760 mm of Hg (mercury)

= 76 cm of Hg = 1 atm

Gay-Lussac's Law of Combining Volumes of Gases

Gay-Lussac proposed a law pertaining to gaseous reactions that ultimately led to another gas law, the Avogadro's law.

Gay-Lussac's law states that when gases chemically react, they do so in volumes that bear a simple whole number ratio to each other and to the volumes of the products, provided the products are also in gaseous state under similar conditions of temperature and pressure.

Explanation:

In the reaction of carbon monoxide with oxygen, two volumes of carbon monoxide react with one volume of oxygen to give two volumes of carbon dioxide under similar conditions of temperature and pressure.

$$CO + O_2 \rightarrow CO_2 + CO_2$$

2 vol → 2 vol

The volume ratio of carbon monoxide, oxygen and carbon dioxide is 2 : 1 : 2.

Info Bytes!

Amedeo Avogadro, in 1811, gave his hypothesis to explain Gay-Lussac's law. It was experimentally confirmed later and was established as Avogadro's law.

Avogadro's Law

Avogadro's law states that equal volumes of all gases contain equal number of molecules under similar conditions of temperature and pressure.

If n is the number of molecules present in volume V of any gas at temperature T and pressure P, then $V \propto n$ when T and P are constant.

Example: 1 L of hydrogen, helium and hydrogen chloride contain equal number of molecules in them provided their volumes are measured at the same temperature and pressure.

In chemistry, the mass of any substance, irrespective of its state, is measured in terms of gram molecular weight or gram molecule and gram atomic weight or gram atom. Atomic weight of a substance expressed in grams is called its **gram atomic weight (GAW)** or **gram atom**. Molecular weight of a substance expressed in grams is called its **gram molecular weight (GMW)** or **gram molecule**.

Gram Molecular Volume

One gram molecule of any dry gas at STP occupies the same volume, i.e., 22.4 L or 22.4 dm^3. This is called gram molar volume (GMV).

Example: 1 gram molecule of dry chlorine gas occupies 22.4 L of volume at STP.

Since GMW of chlorine is 71 g, 71 g of chlorine gas occupies 22.4 L of volume at STP.

Vapor Density

Vapor density (VD) of a gas or vapor is the ratio of the mass of a certain volume of gas or vapor to the mass of the same volume of hydrogen gas when their volumes are measured under similar conditions of temperature and pressure.

Relation Between Molecular Weight and Vapor Density

VD of a gas or vapor at a certain temperature and pressure

$$= \frac{\text{Mass of the certain volume of gas or vapor}}{\text{Mass of the same volume of } H_2 \text{ gas}}$$ (Volumes of both the gases are measured at that particular temperature and pressure)

$$= \frac{\text{Mass of n molecules of the gas or vapor}}{\text{Mass of n molecules of } H_2 \text{ gas}}$$ (By applying Avogadro's law)

$$= \frac{\text{Mass of 1 molecule of the gas or vapor}}{\text{Mass of n molecules of } H_2 \text{ gas}}$$

$$= \frac{1}{2} \times \frac{\text{Mass of 1 molecule of the gas or vapor}}{\text{Mass of 1 atom of hydrogen gas}}$$

$$= \frac{1}{2} \times \text{relative molecular mass (Molecular weight)}$$

$\therefore$ Molecular weight or relative molecular mass = 2 × VD

i.e., relative molecular mass is twice the vapor density of the gas or vapor.

Konnect

Avogadro's number is a massive one. It's approximately 6.022×10^{23}. To give you an idea of how large this number is: if you were to count that many grains of sand at a rate of one grain per second, it would take you over 19 trillion years to finish – longer than the age of the universe itself. This number represents the amount of atoms or molecules in one mole of a substance, an essential concept in understanding the gas laws and chemistry in general.

EXAMPLE 1.5 Gas laws are universally applicable for all gases whereas such universal laws could not be established for solids and liquids. Comment on this statement.

SOLUTION

Gases differ from solids and liquids in the extent of intermolecular forces of attraction. Since gases are characterized by negligible forces of attraction, the molecules behave independent of the neighboring molecules. Due to large intermolecular spaces, the coefficient of volume expansion is same for all gases. Moreover, in case of gases, the molecules are considered as point masses and hence, the volume occupied by the molecules is negligible in comparison to the total volume. Therefore, the physical behavior of all gases being similar, certain laws could be established which are universally applicable. In case of liquids and solids, the molecules are considered as rigid spheres and the coefficient of volume expansion is not uniform for all substances, such universal laws cannot be established.

EXAMPLE 1.6 Boyle's law says that pressure and volume are inversely proportional to each other. However, when a balloon is blown, both volume and pressure increase continuously. Justify.

SOLUTION

When a balloon is blown continuously, more and more air is forced into the balloon that increases the volume as well as the number of collisions of air molecules on the walls of the balloon, that is, pressure. Boyle's law is applicable for a given mass of a gas. Hence, it is not valid in the above case.

EXAMPLE 1.7 Why is Kelvin temperature always positive?

SOLUTION

Absolute zero which is equal to −273°C is the minimum possible temperature for a gas. Any centigrade temperature greater than −273°C will become positive when converted to absolute scale. Since centigrade temperature less than −273°C is not possible, Kelvin temperature cannot have a negative value.

EXAMPLE 1.8 A certain mass of a gas taken in 1L cylinder exerts a pressure of 500 mm Hg at a certain temperature. If the gas is transferred to another cylinder where it exerts 20 per cent more pressure, calculate the volume of the cylinder at the same temperature.

SOLUTION

$V_1 = 1000$ cc, $P_1 = 500$ mm of Hg,

$$P_2 = P_1 + \frac{20P_1}{100} = 500 + \left(\frac{20 \times 500}{100}\right) = 600 \text{ mm of Hg}$$

$$P_2V_2 = P_1V_1,$$

$$V_2 = \frac{P_1V_1}{P_2} = \frac{1000 \times 500}{600} = 833 \text{ cc}$$

EXAMPLE 1.9 The slope of a given straight line graph with constant temperature is found to be 0.2 L atm at 5 atm pressure. Calculate the volume of gas at that pressure.

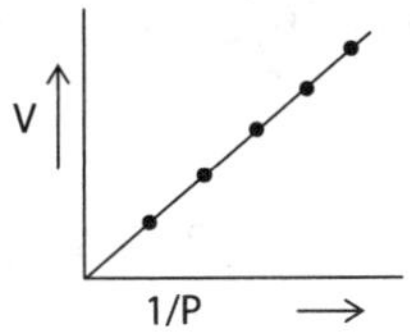

SOLUTION

Slope = 0.2 L atm, P = 5 atm.

According to Boyle's law, $P \propto \frac{1}{V}$,

$P = \text{constant} \times \frac{1}{V} = \text{slope} \times \frac{1}{V}$;

$0.2 \times \frac{1}{V} = 5$

$\Rightarrow V = \frac{0.2}{5} = 0.04$ L

EXAMPLE 1.10 J-shaped tube closed at one end was used by Boyle to study the relationship between the pressure of the trapped gas and its volume. Such a set up is given here. Initially, some amount of gas is taken in the tube and mercury is poured in it. The volume of the gas is 0.2 L and the difference in the height of the mercury column is 760 mm of Hg. Now, some more amount of mercury is poured and the difference in the height of the mercury column is found to be 1140 mm of Hg. Calculate the new volume of the gas considering the temperature constant.

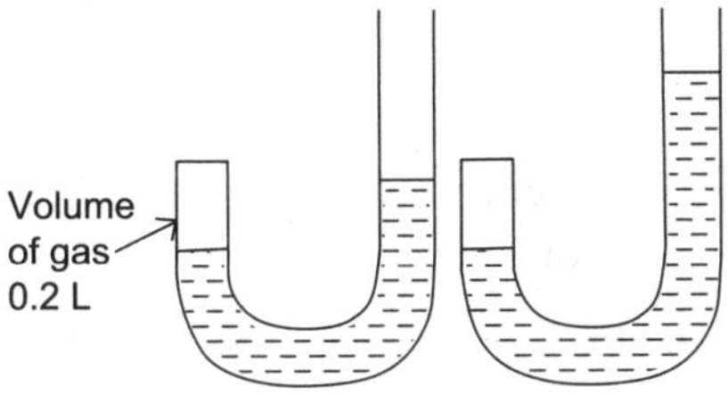

SOLUTION

$V_1 = 0.2$ L $\qquad V_2 = ?$

$P_1 = 760$ mm + 760 mm $\qquad P_2 = 1140$ mm + 760 mm

According to Boyle's law, $P_1 V_1 = P_2 V_2$

$1520 \times 0.2 = 1900 \times V_2 \Rightarrow V_2 = \frac{1520 \times 0.2}{1900} = 0.16$ L

EXAMPLE 1.11 A cylinder was filled with a gas at 2 atm pressure at 27°C and can withstand a pressure of 12 atm. At what temperature the cyliner bursts when the building catches fire?

SOLUTION

$P_1 = 2$ atm, $P_2 = 12$ atm

$T_1 = 27 + 273 = 300$ K, $T_2 = ?$

$\frac{P_1}{T_1} = \frac{P_2}{T_2} \Rightarrow T_2 = \frac{T_1 P_2}{P_1} \Rightarrow T_2 = \frac{12 \times 300}{2} = 1800 \text{ K} = 1527°\text{C}$

∴ Cylinder bursts at or above 1527°C

EXAMPLE 1.12 After usage for a certain period, a cooking gas cylinder was considered to be empty, as no gas was coming out of it. Is the cylinder empty in its true sense? Explain what happens if the cylinder is kept in hot water or shaken vigorously. Explain by applying kinetic molecular theory.

SOLUTION

No, it is not empty in its true sense. In a cooking gas cylinder, the gas was initially at a high pressure. As the gas was drawn out from the cylinder, the amount of gas in the cylinder decreases, thereby reducing the pressure inside the cylinder. The gas will come out of the cylinder as long as the pressure of the gas inside the cylinder is more than the atmospheric pressure. When it is kept in hot water or shaken vigorously, kinetic energy of gas molecules increases and the number of collisions increases. Thus, pressure increases and gas comes out of the cylinder.

Avogadro Number and Mole Concept

Avogadro Number

Scientists experimentally determined that the number of atoms present in 12 g of carbon, i.e., 1 g atom of carbon 12 isotope is 6.023×10^{23}.

Different experiments showed that 1 g atom or 1 g molecule of any substance contains the same number (6.023×10^{23}) of elementary particles or chemical units (atoms, molecules, or ions). This constant number is called the **Avogadro number** that is denoted by N_A or L. It also represents the number of molecules present in 1 g molar volume.

The Avogadro number, i.e., 6.023×10^{23} is taken as the unit to measure the amount of substances and is called **mole**.

Mole

A **mole** is defined as the quantity of substance that contains the same number of elementary particles or chemical units as the number of atoms present in 12 g of C-12 isotope.

Hence, 1 mole of any substance contains the Avogadro number of elementary particles or units. The elementary particles can be atoms, molecules, ions, etc.

Therefore, it can be concluded that:

1. 1 g atom of any substance is equivalent to one mole of atoms of that substance and contains the Avogadro number of atoms.
2. 1 g molecule of any substance is equivalent to one mole of molecules of that substance and contains the Avogadro number of molecules.

Examples:

One mole of hydrogen atoms	6.023×10^{23} hydrogen atoms
	1 g atom of hydrogen or 1 g hydrogen
One mole of carbon atoms	6.023×10^{23} carbon atoms
	1 g atom of carbon or 12 g of carbon
One mole of NaCl	6.023×10^{23} Na^+ ions and 6.023×10^{23} Cl^- ions. E.g., 1 g molecule of sodium chloride or 58.5 g of NaCl
One mole of ammonia gas	6.023×10^{23} NH_3 molecules
	1 g molecule of ammonia or 17 g of NH_3

EXAMPLE 1.13

(i) Calculate the number of atoms present in 112 g of N_2 and also find its volume at STP.

(ii) Determine the mass of water containing the same number of molecules as 667.5 g of aluminium chloride.

SOLUTION (I)

Gram molecular mass of N_2 = 28 g

$\therefore$ 112 g of N_2 is equivalent to $\frac{112}{28}$ = 4 moles of nitrogen

$\therefore$ 112 g of N_2 contains $4 \times 6.023 \times 10^{23}$ molecules = 24×10^{23} molecules = $2 \times 24 \times 10^{23}$ = 48×10^{23} atoms

The volume of the given mass of N_2 = (4×22.4) L = 89.6 L at STP.

SOLUTION (II)

Molecular mass of aluminium chloride ($AlCl_3$) = 133.5 g

$\therefore$ 667.5 g of aluminium chloride is equivalent to $\frac{667.5}{133.5}$ = 5 moles of aluminium chloride.

Number of molecules present in 667.5 g of aluminium chloride is equivalent to that present in 5 moles of water.

The mass of 5 moles of water = 18×5 = 90 g.

Relation Between GMV, Mole and Avogadro Number

1 g mole of any dry gas occupies 22.4 L volume at STP. Hence, 22.4 L of a dry gas at STP contains 6.023×10^{23} molecules, i.e., Avogadro number of molecules.

Example: 32 g or 1 mole of dry oxygen gas occupies 22.4 L volume at STP and contains 6.023×10^{23} molecules of oxygen.

Example: 4 g or 1 mole of dry helium gas occupies 22.4 L at STP and contains 6.023×10^{23} atoms because helium is a monoatomic gas.

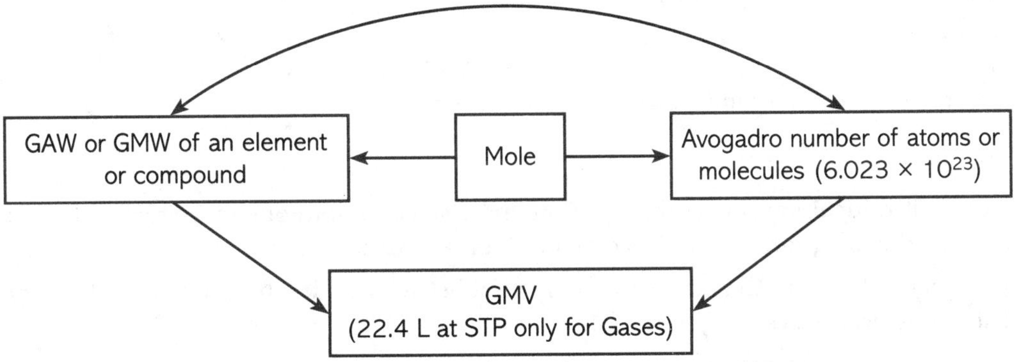

Figure 1.6 Schematic Representation of Different Relationships for Mole

EXAMPLE 1.14

(i) Calculate the number of molecules present in 16.8 L of gas 'X' at STP. Also determine its gram molecular weight if the above sample weighs 26.625 g.

(ii) Calculate the volume occupied by 200 g of SO_3 gas at STP and the number of molecules present in it.

(iii) What is the volume occupied by 30.1×10^{23} molecules of carbon dioxide gas at STP? Calculate the mass of this gas.

SOLUTION

(i) Volume of the given gas = 16.8 L at STP

Number of moles present in that volume = 16.8/22.4 = 0.75 mol

Number of molecules in 0.75 moles = $0.75 \times 6.023 \times 10^{23} = 4.52 \times 10^{23}$

Weight of 0.75 moles of the gas X = 26.625 g

Gram molecular weight of 'X' = Weight/No. of moles = 26.625/0.75 = 35.5 g

(ii) Weight of SO_3 taken = 200 g

Number of moles of $SO_3 = \frac{200}{\text{GMW of } SO_3} = \frac{200}{80} = 2.5$ mol

Volume occupied by 1 mole of gas is 22.4 L, at STP

Volume occupied by the given amount of gas = 2.5 × 22.4 = 56 L

Number of molecules present in 1 mole of gas = 6.023×10^{23}

Number of molecules present in the given amount of gas = $2.5 \times 6.023 \times 10^{23} = 15.05 \times 10^{23}$ molecules

(iii) Number of molecules = 30.1×10^{23}

Number of moles of gas = $\frac{30.1 \times 10^{23}}{6.023 \times 10^{23}} = 5$ mol

Volume occupied by 5 moles of gas = 22.4 × 5 = 112 L

Mass of the given gas = Number of moles × GMW = 5 × 44 = 220 g

Ideal Gas Equation

The behavior of gases can be described by three laws.

According to Boyle's law, for a given mass of gas, $V \propto \frac{1}{P}$ (T is constant)

According to Charles' law, for a given mass of gas, $V \propto T$ (P is constant)

According to Avogadro's law, $V \propto n$ (P and T are constant)

Combining the three gas laws,

$V \propto \frac{nT}{P}$ (when all the functions vary independently) or $PV \propto nT$

or $PV = nRT$ (R is a constant)

A hypothetical gas, called **ideal gas**, obeys the equation under all conditions of temperature and pressure. Hence, this equation is called an **ideal gas equation** and R is called **universal gas constant**.

However, no gas is perfectly ideal. All gases show nearly ideal behavior under the conditions of low pressure and high temperature, and are called **real gases**.

When one mole of a gas is considered, the equation becomes:

$PV = RT$ ($\because n = 1$ mole). The value of 'R' depends upon the units in which pressure and volume are taken.

EXAMPLE 1.15 Given that under similar conditions of temperature and pressure, 28 g of nitrogen occupies the same volume as 4 g of helium. Can you explain why?

SOLUTION

Both 28 g of nitrogen and 4 g of helium correspond to 1 mole of molecules and hence occupy the same volume under similar conditions of temperature and pressure.

EXAMPLE 1.16 'X' grams each of nitrogen and carbon monoxide are considered. Draw a comparison with respect to number of moles.

SOLUTION

Nitrogen and carbon monoxide possess equal gram molecular mass. Therefore, equal masses of these two gases possess equal number of moles.

EXAMPLE 1.17 **(i)** A gas at a pressure of 2.0 atm is heated from 0 to 273°C and the volume compressed to 1/4th of its original volume. Find the final pressure.

(ii) If a gas occupies 30 L at 27°C and 1 atm, what volume would it occupy at 227°C and 5 atm?

(iii) What is the volume occupied by 30 g of neon gas at 67°C and 750 mm of Hg?

SOLUTION

(i)

Initial condition	**Final condition**
$V_1 = V$	$V_2 = \frac{1}{4}V$
$T_1 = 0°C$ or 273 K	$T_2 = 273°C$ (or) 546 K
$P_1 = 2$ atm	$P_2 = ?$

According to gas equation, $\frac{P_1V_1}{T_1} = \frac{P_2V_2}{T_2}$

$$P_2 = \frac{P_1V_1}{T_1} \times \frac{T_2}{P_2} = \frac{2 \times V}{273} \times \frac{546}{V} \times 4,\ P_2 = 16 \text{ atm}$$

(ii)

Initial condition	**Final condition**
$V_1 = 30$ L	$V_2 = ?$
$P_1 = 1$ atm	$P_2 = 5$ atm
$T_1 = 27°C = 300$ K	$T_2 = 227°C = 500$ K

According to gas equation, $\frac{P_1V_1}{T_1} = \frac{P_2V_2}{T_2}$

$$V_2 = \frac{P_1V_1}{T_1} \times \frac{T_2}{P_2} = \frac{30 \times 1}{300} \times \frac{500}{5} = 10 \text{ L}$$

(iii) According to the ideal gas equation: $PV = nRT$ (1)

n = number of moles = weight/molecular weight = 30/20

Pressure = $\left(\frac{750}{760}\right)$ atm [1 atm = 760 mm of Hg]

$T = (273 + 67)$ K = 340 K

From equation (1),

$$V = \frac{nRT}{P}$$

$$V = \frac{30}{20} \times \frac{0.0821 \times 340}{750 / 760}\left(\frac{g \times L\ atm/kmol \times K}{g / mol \times atm}\right) = 42.43 \text{ L}$$

Dalton's Law of Partial Pressures

The ideal gas equation establishes the relationship among the pressure exerted by a certain number of moles of a gas, its temperature and the volume occupied by it. But, the pressure exerted by a mixture of gases present in a container was studied by Dalton. Dalton's law states that 'the total pressure exerted by a mixture of non-reacting gases taken in a container at a given temperature is the sum of the practical pressures of the individual gases that each gas would exert if it were taken alone in that container.' This statement is known as **Dalton's law of partial pressures.**

Partial pressure is the pressure exerted by each constituent of the gaseous mixture when they are kept individually in the same container.

If the partial pressures of the constituents of the gaseous mixture are p_1, p_2, p_3...... and so on, then according to Dalton's law of partial pressures, the total pressure P = p_1, p_2, p_3 ....

If n_1 is the number of moles of a constituent of the gaseous mixture, taken in a container of volume V and p_1 is the pressure exerted by it at temperature T, then:

$$p_1 = n_1 \times \frac{RT}{V} \quad \text{(1) (from the ideal gas equation)}$$

Similarly, if P is the total pressure exerted by the gaseous mixture at temperature T and n is the total number of moles taken in the container of volume V, then:

$$P = n\frac{RT}{V} \quad (2)$$

Dividing equation (1) by equation (2), we obtain,

$$\frac{p_1}{P} = \frac{n_1}{n}$$

$$\therefore p_1 = \frac{n_1}{n} \times P$$

$\therefore$ Partial pressure (p_1) = Mole fraction (n_1/n) $\times$ total pressure of the gas (P)

Mole fraction is the ratio of the number of moles of an individual gas to the total number of moles of all gases in a mixture.

Example: It is not applicable to a mixture of carbon monoxide and oxygen which react with each other to form carbon dioxide at ordinary temperature:

$$2CO + O_2 \rightarrow 2CO_2$$

Info Bytes!

Dalton's atomic theory is a milestone in the history of science, influencing not just chemistry but also the atomic models in physics.

EXAMPLE 1.18 A 2-L flask contains 22 g of carbon dioxide and 1 g of helium at 20°C. Calculate the partial pressure exerted by CO_2 and He if the total pressure is 3 atm.

SOLUTION

Number of moles of $CO_2 = \frac{\text{Weight of } CO_2}{\text{Molecular Weight of } CO_2} = \frac{22}{44} = 0.5.$

Number of moles of He $= \frac{1}{4} = 0.25.$

Partial pressure = Mole fraction × total pressure

$$p_{CO_2} = \frac{0.5}{0.5 + 0.25} \times 3 = 2$$

$$p_{He} = \frac{0.25}{0.75} \times 3 = 1 \text{ atm}$$

Graham's Law of Diffusion

Diffusion is one of the significant properties of gases. The process of spreading out of gas molecules spontaneously is called diffusion. As a result of this, gas molecules uniformly occupy the space available.

The number of gas molecules that pass through a unit area in unit time at a given temperature and pressure is called its **rate of diffusion**. In other words, the volume of the gas that diffuses in unit time at specific temperature and pressure is called its **rate of diffusion**. Rate of diffusion of a gas increases with the increase of temperature, while it decreases with the increase in pressure.

Thomas Graham observed that the rate of diffusion of different gases depends on their respective densities, provided they are under similar conditions of temperature and pressure. He established a quantitative relationship between the rate of diffusion of gases and their densities.

Under similar conditions of temperature and pressure, the rates of diffusion of different gases are inversely proportional to the square root of their densities.

i.e., $r_a \propto \frac{1}{\sqrt{d}}$ (T and P are constant)

or $\frac{r_1}{r_2} = \sqrt{\frac{d_2}{d_1}}$ (where r_1 and r_2 are the rates of diffusion of two gases having densities d_1 and d_2, respectively).

Rates of diffusion of gases are also inversely proportional to their molecular weights because equal volume of all gases contains equal number of molecules, if the temperature and pressure are kept constant.

$\therefore \frac{r_1}{r_2} = \sqrt{\frac{M_2}{M_1}}$ where r_1 and r_2 are the rates of diffusion of two gases and their molecular weights are M_1 and M_2, respectively.

Info Bytes!

Graham's investigations on diffusion were so pioneering that they laid the groundwork for many of the laws governing gaseous behaviour.

EXAMPLE 1.19

(i) What is the ratio of the rate of diffusion of helium gas to that of oxygen under identical conditions?

(ii) Rate of diffusion of a saturated hydrocarbon is about 1/6th of that of hydrogen under similar conditions of temperature and pressure. What is the molecular formula of that hydrocarbon?

SOLUTION

(i) According to Graham's law of diffusion,

$$\frac{r_{He}}{r_{O_2}} = \sqrt{\frac{M_{O_2}}{M_{He}}} = \sqrt{\frac{32}{4}}$$

$$\left(\frac{r_{He}}{r_{O_2}}\right) = 2\sqrt{2} : 1$$

(ii) Let the molecular weight of the hydrocarbon be M_x and its rate of diffusion be r_x

$$\frac{r_{H_2}}{r_x} = \sqrt{\frac{M_x}{M_{H_2}}}, = r_x = \frac{1}{6} r_{H_2}$$

$$\frac{r_{H_2}}{r_x} = 6 = \sqrt{\frac{M_x}{2}}$$

$\Rightarrow 36 \times 2 = M_x$

$\Rightarrow M_x = 72$

Molecular weight of the hydrocarbon is 72.

Let the number of carbon atoms present in one molecule of the hydrocarbon be m.

$\because$ the hydrocarbon is saturated, the number of hydrogen atoms present in that hydrocarbon molecule is 2 m + 2

$\therefore (12 \times m) + 2m + 2 = 72$

$\Rightarrow 14m + 2 = 72 \Rightarrow m = 5$

$\therefore$ Molecular formula of the hydrocarbon is C_5H_{12}

EXAMPLE 1.20 A certain amount of hydrogen gas is produced through the electrolysis of water and is collected by upward displacement of water. When the pressure of this collected hydrogen gas is measured, it is found to be different from the pressure recorded for the same volume of hydrogen from a standard cylinder, even when both are under the same conditions. Why is there a discrepancy in the measured pressures, and how would you explain it?

SOLUTION

When hydrogen gas is produced through electrolysis and collected over water, it's exposed to water vapour. This means the collected hydrogen is not pure, but rather it's moist with water vapour. The total pressure of this moist hydrogen gas is the cumulative result of the partial pressures of both hydrogen and water vapour. On the other hand, the hydrogen from a standard cylinder is dry and pure, leading to its pressure being different from that of the moist hydrogen. The contribution to the total pressure from the water vapour in the collected hydrogen gas is known as the aqueous tension.

Concentrations of Solutions

A solution is a homogeneous mixture of two or more components. The solution that contains only two components is called a **binary solution**. The component, which is present in minor proportions, is called the solute and the component, which is present in major proportions, is called the solvent.

The concentration of a solution refers to the relative proportions of solute and solvent present in the solution. The concentration of a solution can be expressed in various ways by applying the concept of mole.

Molarity

Molarity is the most convenient and commonly used unit for expressing the concentration of a solution.

Molarity can be defined as the number of moles of a solute present in 1 L of a solution. It is denoted by 'M.'

If n = number of moles of the solute present in the solution

W = Weight of the solute in grams

GMW = Gram molecular weight (mass) of the solute

V = Volume of the solution, then

$$M = \frac{n}{V} = \frac{W}{GMW} \times \frac{1}{V \text{ in L}} \text{ or } M = \frac{W}{GMW} \times \frac{1000}{V \text{ in mL}}$$

Example: 0.4 M sodium carbonate solutions means that 0.4 moles of sodium carbonate is present in 1000 mL of the solution.

Info Bytes!

The term 'molarity' was derived from the Latin word 'moles,' meaning 'a mass.' It's a measure of the number of moles of solute present in one litre of solution.

Mole Fraction

Mole fraction of a component in a solution can be defined as the ratio of the number of moles of that component to the total number of moles of all the components of the solution. If 'x' represents mole fraction, then

$$x_{solute} = \frac{n_{solute}}{n_{solute} + n_{solvent}},$$

where n represents number of moles

$$x_{solvent} = \frac{n_{solvent}}{n_{solute} + n_{solvent}}$$

The sum of mole fractions of all components in a solution is equal to unity.

$$x_{solute} + x_{solvent} = 1$$

The concentration of the solution can also be expressed in terms of weight percentage, volume percentage, and weight volume percentage.

Weight Percentage (w/w)

The mass of a solute expressed in grams, present in 100 g of a solution, is called the **weight percentage** of the solute in the solution.

$$\text{Weight percentage of the solute} = \frac{\text{Weight of the solute}}{\text{Weight of the solution}} \times 100$$

Example: 10% (w/w) sodium hydroxide solution

10 g of sodium hydroxide is present in 100 g of the solution.

Weight/volume percentage (w/v)

The mass of a solute, expressed in grams, present in 100 mL of a solution is called the **weight/volume percentage** of the solute in the solution.

$$\text{Weight/volume percentage of the solute} = \frac{\text{Mass of the solute (g)}}{\text{Total volume of the solution (mL)}} \times 100$$

Example: 10% (w/v) Na_2CO_3 solution

10 g of Na_2CO_3 present in 100 mL of the solution.

Volume Percentage (v/v)

The volume of the liquid in millilitre present in a 100-mL solution is called the **volume percentage** of the solute in the solution.

$$\text{Volume percentage of the solute} = \frac{\text{Volume of the solute}}{\text{Volume of the solution}} \times 100$$

Example: 70% (v/v) isopropyl alcohol solution

70 mL isopropyl alcohol is present in 100 mL of the solution.

Info Bytes!

While you may often see alcoholic beverages labelled with 'volume percentage (v/v)' to indicate alcohol content, juice concentrates might use 'weight/volume percentage (w/v)' to signify the amount of fruit content.

EXAMPLE 1.21

(i) What is the molarity of a solution containing 15 g of NaOH dissolved in 500 mL of solution?

(ii) A solution is prepared by dissolving 9.8 g of H_2SO_4 in 54 g of water. What is the mole fraction of H_2SO_4?

(iii) What is the percentage by weight of sulphuric acid, if 13 g of H_2SO_4 is dissolved to make 78 g of solution?

(iv) If 40 g of ethyl alcohol is dissolved in 50 mL of water, then calculate the weight/volume percentage of ethyl alcohol present in the solution. (density of ethyl alcohol = 0.8 g/mL)

(v) What is the molarity of 25% $\left(\frac{W}{V}\right)$ solution of HCl?

(vi) Specific gravity of 84% (w/w) pure HNO_3 is 1.54. What volume of HNO_3 is required to prepare one litre of 0.5M HNO_3 solution?

SOLUTION

(i) $\text{Molarity} = \frac{\text{Weight}}{\text{GMV}} \times \frac{1000}{V} = \frac{15}{40} \times \frac{1000}{500} = 0.75\text{M}$

(ii) Weight of $H_2SO_4 = 9.8$ g

GMW of $H_2SO_4 = 98$ u

Number of moles of H_2SO_4 present in the solution = 9.8/98 = 0.1 mol

Number of moles of H_2O = 54/18 = 3 mol

Mole fraction of H_2SO_4 = 0.1/(0.1+3) = 0.032

(iii) Weight of $H_2SO_4 = 13$ g

Weight of solution = 78 g

$$\left(\frac{W}{W}\right)\% \text{ of } H_2SO_4 = \frac{13}{78} \times 100 = 16.6\%.$$

(iv) Amount of ethyl alcohol = 40 g

$$\text{Volume of ethyl alcohol} = \frac{40}{0.8} = 50 \text{ mL}$$

Volume of water = 50 mL

Total volume of the solution is 100 mL

$$\left(\frac{W}{V}\right)\% \text{ ethyl alcohol is} = \frac{40}{100} \times 100 = 40\%$$

(v) $25\%\left(\frac{W}{V}\right)$ solution of HCl corresponds to 25 g of HCl present in 100 mL of solution.

Amount of HCl present in 1000 mL of solution = 250 g

$$\text{Molarity} = \frac{250}{36.5} \times \frac{1000}{1000} = 6.85 \text{ M (GMW of HCl 36.5).}$$

(vi) Specific gravity of $HNO_3 = 1.54$

$$M = \frac{w}{GMM} \times \frac{1000}{V} \Rightarrow 0.5 = \frac{x}{63} \times \frac{1000}{1000} \Rightarrow x = 31.5 \text{ g}$$

31.5 g of HNO_3 is present in 1 L of solution.

84 g is present in 100 g of solution

31.5 g is present in ? g of solution

$$= \frac{31.5 \times 100}{84} = 37.5 \text{ g}$$

Density = weight/volume ⇒ 1.54 = 37.5/volume ⇒ V = 37.5/1.54 = 24.35 mL

$V_1 M_1 = V_2 M_2$ 24.35 mL of given HNO_3 is required.

Stoichiometry

Stoichiometry is the area of study where we learn about the quantity of the reactants(s) required to get specific quantity of product(s).

In order to understand the quantitative relationship between the reactants and products, knowledge of the composition of the reactants and the products is required. This composition also helps us to determine the formulae of the molecules of the reactants and products.

Info Bytes!

The word stoichiometry is derived from the Greek word *'stoicheion'* meaning element and *'metron'* meaning measurement.

Percentage Composition of a Compound

Percentage composition is the mass of each constituent element present in 100 g of a compound.

$$\text{Percentage of an element present in a compound} = \frac{\text{Weight of the element in one mole of the compound}}{\text{GMW of the compound}} \times 100$$

Example:

Calculation of percentage composition of calcium carbonate.

$$\text{GMW of } CaCO_3 = 100 \text{ g}$$

$$\text{Percentage of calcium in calcium carbonate} = \frac{40}{100} \times 100 = 40\%$$

$$\text{Percentage of carbon in } CaCO_3 = \frac{12}{100} \times 100 = 12\%$$

$$\text{Percentage of oxygen in } CaCO_3 = \frac{48}{100} \times 100 = 48\%$$

Info Bytes!

In stoichiometry, the Law of Conservation of Mass is the governing principle. It dictates that matter cannot be created or destroyed in an isolated system, ensuring that the mass of reactants always equals the mass of products.

Molecular and Empirical Formula of a Compound

A compound can be represented by two types of formulae, i.e., empirical formula and molecular formula. Empirical formula gives the simplest integral ratio of the number of atoms of different constituent elements present in one molecule of the compound. Molecular formula represents the exact number of atoms of different elements present in one molecule of the compound.

Example:

Molecular formula of glucose → $C_6H_{12}O_6$

Empirical formula of glucose → CH_2O

The ratio of the number of atom of carbon, hydrogen and oxygen in glucose is 1 : 2 : 1.

EXAMPLE 1.22 Percentage compositions of various elements in a compound are as follows–carbon 20.04%, hydrogen 6.6%, nitrogen 46.03% and oxygen 26.67%. What is the empirical formula of the compound?

SOLUTION

Elements	Percentages of Element	Atomic Ratios	Simplest Ratios
C	20.04	$\frac{20.04}{12} = 1.67$	$\frac{1.67}{1.66} = 1$
H	6.66	$\frac{6.66}{1} = 6.66$	$\frac{6.66}{1.66} = 4$
O	26.67	$\frac{26.67}{16} = 1.66$	$\frac{6.66}{1.66} = 4$
N	46.03	$\frac{46.03}{14} = 3.28$	$\frac{3.28}{1.66} = 2$

Empirical formula of the compound = $CH_4O_4N_2$

EXAMPLE 1.23 The empirical formula of a compound is NO_2. If its vapour density is 46, what is the molecular formula of the compound?

SOLUTION

Empirical formula = NO_2

Nitrogen (N) = 14.01 g/mol

Oxygen (O) = 16.00 g/mol

Empirical formula weight = 14.01 + (2× 16.00) = 14.01 + 32.00 = 46.01 g/mol

Vapor density (VD) = 46

Molecular weight = VD × 2 = 92

Molecular formula = (empirical formula)n

$$n = \frac{\text{Molecular werigh}t}{\text{Empirical formula werigh}} = \frac{92}{46} = 2$$

This means that the molecular formula is twice as long as the empirical formula.

Thus, molecular formula = N(1 × 2)O_2 (2) or N_2O_4. (This compound is dinitrogen tetroxide)

EXAMPLE 1.24 What is meant by 18-carat gold in terms of percentage purity?

SOLUTION

24-carat gold is known to contain 999.99 per cent gold per 1000 g. As a result, one carat equals one part of 24. That is, 18-carat gold is divided into 24 parts. Parts of gold in 1000 g of 18-carat gold can thus be calculated. The percentage can be calculated from this.

The amount of gold contained in 1000 g of 22 carat gold = $\frac{18}{24}$ = 1000 = 750 *g*

Percentage of gold = 75%

Balanced Chemical Equation

A **balanced chemical equation** is the one in which the number of atoms of each element is equal in its reactants and products.

Examples:

$$2H_2 + O_2 \rightarrow 2H_2O$$

$$Zn + 2HCl \rightarrow ZnCl_2 + H_2$$

The information that can be obtained from a balanced chemical equation includes the following:

1. The nature and chemical composition of the reactants and the products in a chemical reaction.
2. The number of moles of various reactants and products involved in a chemical reaction.

The quantitative relationship between the various reactants and products can be established based on either the weight of the substances or the volume of the substances in case of gases.

Info Bytes!

The balanced chemical equation is called the stoichiometric equation.

Calculations Based on Chemical Equations

Three types of relationships can be established between the chemical substances involved in the chemical reaction.

1. Weight–weight relationship of the reactants and products.
2. Weight–volume relationship in reactions involving at least one gaseous substance.
3. Volume–volume relationship in case of reactions involving all gaseous substances.

We will study about these relationships in the following examples.

EXAMPLE 1.25 Calculate the weight of Aluminium required for the liberation of 9 g of hydrogen gas in reaction with HCl.

SOLUTION

Aluminium and hydrochloric acid react as follows:

$2Al + 6HCl \rightarrow 2AlCl_3 + 3H_2$

From this equation, we see those 2 moles of aluminium produce 3 moles of hydrogen gas.

Given that the molecular weight of hydrogen (H_2) is 2g/mole, 9g of hydrogen would be equivalent to $= \frac{9}{2} = 4.5$ moles.

From the balanced chemical equation, 2 moles of aluminium produce 3 moles of hydrogen. So, 4.5 moles of hydrogen would require $= \frac{2}{3} \times 4.5 = 3$ moles of aluminium

The atomic weight of aluminium (Al) is approximately 26.98g/mole.

Therefore, 3 moles of aluminium would weigh $= 3 \times 26.98 g/mol = 80.94 g$

Thus, 80.94g of aluminium is required to liberate 9g of hydrogen gas when reacted with hydrochloric acid.

EXAMPLE 1.26 Calculate the weight of calcium carbonate required to produce 1.12 L of CO_2 gas upon heating.

SOLUTION

Calcium oxide (CaO) and carbon dioxide (CO_2) is formed during the decomposition of calcium carbonate.

$CaCO_3 \rightarrow CaO + CO_2$

from the equation, 1 mole of ($CaCO_3$) produces 1 mole of (CO_2).

Given Information and Conversion:

Molar mass of ($CaCO_3$) = 100 g/mole (approximately)

1 mole of any gas at STP occupies 22.4 L.

Using the given information:

22.4L of CO_2 is produced from 100g of $CaCO_3$.

For 1.12 L of CO_2:

$$\text{Weight of } CaCO_3 = \frac{1.12 \times 100}{22.4} = 5 \text{ g}$$

Thus, you will need to heat 5 g of $CaCO_3$ to produce 1.12L of CO_2 gas.

EXAMPLE 1.27 Calculate the volume of hydrogen gas required to react with nitrogen gas to produce 6.72 L of ammonia gas NH_3 under similar conditions.

SOLUTION

The balanced chemical reaction for the formation of ammonia from nitrogen and hydrogen is:

$$N_2 + 3H_2 \rightarrow 2NH_3$$

From the balanced equation, 1 mole (or volume) of nitrogen gas (N_2) reacts with 3 moles (or volumes) of hydrogen gas (H_2) to produce 2 moles (or volumes) of ammonia (NH_3).

Given that 6.72 L of NH_3 is produced, let's determine the volume of H_2 required.

Using the stoichiometric coefficients from the equation:

2 volumes of NH_3 are produced from 3 volumes of H_2.

Given:

6.72 L of NH_3

Setting up a proportion, we can determine the volume of H_2:

$$\frac{3 \text{ volumes of } H_2}{2 \text{ volumes of } NH_3} = \frac{x \text{ volumes of } H_2}{6.72 \text{ L of } NH_3}$$

Solving for x, we get:

$$x = \frac{3 \times 6.72}{2} = 10.08 \ L \text{ of } H_2$$

Thus, 10.08 L of hydrogen gas is required to react with nitrogen gas to produce 6.72 L of ammonia gas under similar conditions.

Calculations Involving Percentage Purity of Compounds

Percentage purity of a chemical compound is the actual amount of pure substance present in a sample of compound, when it contains certain amount of impurities. For example, a sample of 90% pure limestone contains 90% calcium carbonate and 10 g of impurities for every 100 g of limestone.

EXAMPLE 1.28 Calculate the weight of 80% pure limestone required to produce 11 g of CO_2 gas.

SOLUTION

$$\underset{1 \text{ mole}}{CaCO_3} \rightarrow CaO + \underset{1 \text{ mole}}{CO_2}$$

44 g of CO_2 is produced from 100 g of $CaCO_3$

$\therefore$ 11 g of CO_2 is produced from $\frac{100}{44} \times 11 = 25$ g of $CaCO_3$

As the limestone is 80% pure, the weight of impure limestone required $= \frac{100}{80} \times 25 \text{ g} = 31.2 \text{ g}$

Calculations Involving Limiting Reagent

The reactant which decides the amount of products formed in a reaction is called the **limiting reagent**.

EXAMPLE 1.29 Calculate the amount of sodium oxide formed when 2.3 g of sodium reacts with 3.2 g of oxygen.

SOLUTION

$$\underset{4 \text{ mol}}{4Na} + \underset{1 \text{ mol}}{O_2} \rightarrow \underset{2 \text{ mol}}{2Na_2O}$$

4 × 23 g of sodium reacts with 32 g of O_2.

2.3 g of sodium reacts with $= \frac{2.3 \times 32}{4 \times 23} = 0.8$ g

As the amount of oxygen present is 3.2 g, all the oxygen is not utilized for formation of sodium oxide. The amount of sodium oxide formed is determined by sodium. 4 × 23 g of sodium produces 2 × 62 g of sodium oxide.

$$2.3 \text{ g of sodium produces} = \frac{2.3 \times 32 \times 62}{4 \times 23} = 3.1 \text{ g}$$

Amount of sodium oxide formed = 3.1 g

EXAMPLE 1.30 A mixture of sodium carbonate and sodium bicarbonate was subjected to heating. Some loss in weight was found. How does this information help us to find out the composition of mixture?

SOLUTION

Between sodium carbonate and sodium bicarbonate, only sodium bicarbonate decomposes to give sodium carbonate, CO_2 and H_2O. The gaseous products (CO_2 and H_2O) escape out into the atmosphere. Therefore, an apparent loss in weight occurs during the reaction.

This loss in weight corresponds to the amount of gaseous products formed. From the mass of gaseous products formed, amount of sodium bicarbonate in the mixture can be obtained, and thus composition of the mixture can be found out.

EXAMPLE 1.31 In an apparatus, 16.8 g of sodium bicarbonate was subjected to heating till it underwent complete decomposition, what is the expected loss in weight? When the same apparatus was fitted to a condenser, the loss in weight was different from the earlier loss in weight. Justify the difference.

SOLUTION

$2NaHCO_3 \rightarrow Na_2CO_3 + CO_2 + H_2O$

2 moles $NaHCO_3 \rightarrow$ 2 moles of gaseous product (CO_2 and H_2O)

Number of moles of $NaHCO_3 = \dfrac{16.8}{84 \times 2} = 0.1$

1 moles $NaHCO_3 \rightarrow$ 0.1 moles gaseous product $\rightarrow$ 0.05 moles CO_2 + 0.05 moles H_2O.

$\rightarrow$ 4.4 g CO_2 + 1.8 g H_2O

Expected loss in weight = 2.2 + 0.9 = 3.1

Actual loss in weight = Amount of CO_2 formed = 3.1 g.

The difference is due to the condensation of water vapor.

EXAMPLE 1.32 At STP, a certain amount of hydrogen is produced by the reaction of 550 g of impure zinc with excess amount of HCl. The same volume of hydrogen at STP reduces Fe_3O_4 and produces 336 g of iron. Find the percentage purity of zinc. (Atomic mass of Zn is 65)

SOLUTION

$Zn + 2HCl \rightarrow ZnCl_2 + H_2$; $4H_2 + Fe_3O_4 \rightarrow 4H_2O + 3Fe$

Amount of iron produced = 336 g $\Rightarrow$ number of moles of iron $= \dfrac{336}{56} = 6$ mol

To produce 6 moles of iron, it requires 8 moles of hydrogen which further requires 8 moles of Zn.

Weight of Zn = 8 × 65.5 = 524 g; % purity $= \dfrac{524}{550} \times 100 = 95.27\%$.

POINTS TO REMEMBER

- ✔ A symbol is the shorthand notation that represents a single atom of an element.
- ✔ A formula is the shorthand notation which represents a single molecule of an element or compound.
- ✔ The properties of solids and liquids differ widely from substance to substance, but the gases generally obey some common rules known as the gas laws.
- ✔ Boyle's Law states that the volume of a given mass of a gas is inversely proportional to the pressure exerted by the gas at constant temperature.
- ✔ Charles' law is stated as the volume occupied by a given mass of a gas is directly proportional to the absolute temperature of the gas at constant pressure.
- ✔ The lowest temperature that can be attained theoretically is called absolute zero.
- ✔ Gay-Lussac's law states that when gases chemically react, they do so in volumes that bear a simple whole number ratio to each other and to the volumes of the products, provided the products are also in gaseous state under similar conditions of temperature and pressure.
- ✔ Avogadro's law states that equal volumes of all gases contain equal number of molecules under similar conditions of temperature and pressure.
- ✔ Atomic weight of a substance expressed in grams is called its gram atomic weight (GAW) or gram atom.
- ✔ Molecular weight of a substance expressed in grams is called its gram molecular weight (GMW) or gram molecule.
- ✔ Vapor density (VD) of a gas or vapor is the ratio of the mass of a certain volume of gas or vapor to the mass of the same volume of hydrogen gas when their volumes are measured under similar conditions of temperature and pressure.
- ✔ A mole is defined as the quantity of substance that contains the same number of elementary particles or chemical units as the number of atoms present in 12 g of C-12 isotope.
- ✔ Dalton's law states that 'the total pressure exerted by a mixture of non-reacting gases taken in a container at a given temperature is the sum of the practical pressures of the individual gases that each gas would exert if it were taken alone in that container.'
- ✔ Mole fraction is the ratio of the number of moles of an individual gas to the total number of moles of all gases in a mixture.
- ✔ The process of spreading out of gas molecules spontaneously is called diffusion.
- ✔ The number of gas molecules that pass through a unit area in unit time at a given temperature and pressure is called its rate of diffusion.
- ✔ A solution is a homogeneous mixture of two or more components
- ✔ The concentration of a solution refers to the relative proportions of solute and solvent present in the solution.
- ✔ Molarity can be defined as the number of moles of a solute present in 1 L of a solution. It is denoted by 'M.'
- ✔ The mass of a solute expressed in grams, present in 100 g of a solution, is called the weight percentage of the solute in the solution.
- ✔ The mass of a solute, expressed in grams, present in 100 mL of a solution is called the

weight/volume percentage of the solute in the solution.

- ✔ The volume of the liquid in milli litre present in a 100 mL solution is called the volume percentage of the solute in the solution.
- ✔ Percentage composition is the mass of each constituent element present in 100 g of a compound.
- ✔ Empirical formula gives the simplest integral ratio of the number of atoms of different constituent elements present in one molecule of the compound.
- ✔ Molecular formula represents the exact number of atoms of different elements present in one molecule of the compound.
- ✔ A balanced chemical equation is the one in which the number of atoms of each element is equal in its reactants and products.
- ✔ Percentage purity of a chemical compound is the actual amount of pure substance present in a sample of compound, when it contains certain amount of impurities.
- ✔ The reactant which decides the amount of products formed in a reaction is called the limiting reagent.

DW

PRACTICE QUESTIONS CLASSROOM WING

Very Short Answer Type Questions

Directions for questions from 1 to 5:
Fill in the blanks.

1. The percentage of sulphur in SO_2 is __________ and __________ in SO_3.
2. The vapor density of SO_2 gas is __________ the vapor density of O_2 gas.
3. The molecular formula of a gas with vapor density 15 and empirical formula CH_3 is __________.
4. The mass of N molecules of helium is the same as the mass of __________ molecules of methane.
5. Percentage of calcium in calcium carbonate is ______.

Directions for questions from 6 to 25:
Answer the following questions.

6. A rubber balloon which is permeable to all the isotopes of hydrogen is filled with pure tritium. It is placed in a closed box containing pure hydrogen under similar conditions of temperature and pressure. What change will the balloon undergo?
7. 3 mol of ammonia undergoes decomposition to give two gases. One of the gases, on treatment with excess oxygen, gives a brown-coloured gas, 'X'. To calculate the volume occupied by X at STP, arrange the following steps in the correct sequence.
   (A) Identifying the number of moles of X formed.
   (B) Identifying the relation between the number of moles and volume occupied at STP.
   (C) Writing a balanced chemical equation for the decomposition of NH_3.
   (D) Identifying the number of moles of the gas that is used for the preparation of X.
   (E) Writing a balanced chemical equation for the formation of X.
8. Arrange the following reactions as a combination, decomposition, displacement and double displacement reactions.
   (A) Reaction between an acid and a base from salt and water
   (B) Reaction between zinc and dil. H_2SO_4
   (C) Preparation of oxygen from potassium nitrate
   (D) Preparation of CO_2 from its constituents
9. What is the molarity of HCl solution containing 0.4 moles in 200 mL of the solution?
10. Calculate the volume occupied by 11 g of CO_2 gas at STP.
11. If the pressure exerted on a gas is increased by 4 times and temperature is increased by 9 times, what will be the change in volume occupied by the gas?
12. If the mole fraction of a solute in a binary solution is 0.3, what could be the mole fraction of the solvent in the solution?
13. Calculate the ratio of the rate of diffusion of sulphur dioxide gas to helium gas.
14. Find out the number of moles constituted by 1.4 g of carbon monoxide.
    $\left(\text{Number of moles} = \dfrac{\text{Weight}}{\text{GMW}}\right)$
15. The empirical formula of a compound is CH_2O. If the vapor density is 60, what would be the molecular formula of the compound?
16. When 4 L of nitrogen completely reacts with hydrogen, what would be the volume of ammonia gas formed?
17. What is the amount of calcium oxide formed by the dissociation of 25 g of calcium carbonate?
18. State Avogadro's law.
19. Define amu.
20. The vapor density of a substance is 24. What is the gram molecular weight of the substance?
21. Calculate the weight of CO_2, which occupies a volume of 11.2 dm^3 at STP.

22. Calculate the percentage of chlorine present in calcium chloride.

23. Define molarity.

24. State Graham's law of diffusion.

25. How many litres of oxygen at STP are required for the combustion of 4 g of methane gas? Also calculate the volume of CO_2 gas produced at STP.

Short Answer Type Questions

26. A spherical balloon of volume 253 mL is to be filled with helium gas at STP from a cylinder containing gas at 20 atm and 127°C. If the cylinder can hold 2 L of water, then calculate the number of balloons that can be filled up.

27. The composition of a gaseous mixture is N_2 = 56%, O_2 = 32%, Ar = 12% by mass. What is the partial pressure of nitrogen at 1 atm pressure?

28. A gold manufacturing company manufactures gold coins with absolutely pure gold. If the mass of each gold coin is 9.85 g and 1000 gold coins are manufactured per day, calculate the number of moles of gold consumed per day. (At. wt. of gold is 197 amu)

29. A closed cylinder is first evacuated and then connected to another cylinder of 75-L volume containing an ideal gas 'X'. The pressure of the gas in the second cylinder falls from 22 atm to 10 atm. Calculate the volume of the first cylinder.

30. A cylinder can hold 7.2 g of ozone at 1 atm and 27°C. Calculate the weight of oxygen that can be filled in the same cylinder at 3 atm and −73°C.

31. A gaseous mixture contains 16 g of O_2 and 20 g of Ne at 3 atm pressure and 27°C. Calculate the partial pressure of O_2 gas.

32. What is meant by mole fraction? Find out the mole fraction of sodium hydroxide solution containing 4 g of solute in 90 g of water.

33. What is the volume of 50% (w/v) H_2SO_4 required for the liberation of 5.6 L of hydrogen gas at STP on its reaction with magnesium?

34. Calculate the percentage composition of glucose.

35. Empirical formula of a compound is CH_3N. If the empirical formula weight is equal to one-fourth of its vapor density, find out the molecular formula of the compound.

36. Calculate the number of atoms in:
    (a) 4.5 g atoms of potassium
    (b) 0.2 g atoms of chlorine
    (c) 1.2 g molecules of nitrogen

37. A bulb of volume V contains gas at 2 atm. This bulb is connected to another evacuated bulb of volume 1.5L through a stopcock. When the stopcock is opened, the pressure in each bulb becomes 600 mm at constant temperature. Find V.

38. Find out the relative rates of diffusion of methane and sulphur dioxide under similar conditions of temperature and pressure.

39. 1.8 g of oxalic acid ($H_2C_2O_4$) is dissolved in 200 mL of a solution. Find out the molarity of the resultant solution.

40. A gaseous hydrocarbon with a vapor density of 14 contains 85.2% carbon. Calculate its molecular formula.

Essay Answer Type Questions

41. The density of a mixture of He and O_2 at STP is 1.25 g/L. What is the partial pressure of O_2?

42. A bottle is heated from 27°C to 127°C at constant pressure. What fraction of air gets expelled?

43. An oxide of Cr contains 68.5% of Cr by weight. Find the empirical formula of the oxide. (Atomic weight of Cr = 52)

44. Two-gram atoms of Na are burnt in excess of oxygen and the oxide is dissolved in water to make up a 500 mL solution. Calculate the molarity of the solution.

45. Explain the relation between vapor density and molecular mass.

46. 2 g of an alloy of aluminium and magnesium when heated with excess of dilute HCl liberates hydrogen gas. The gas is collected over mercury at 127°C, has a volume of 1.6 l at 2 atm pressure. Calculate the composition of the alloy.

PRACTICE QUESTIONS COMPETITION WING

Level 1: Apply your Concepts

Direction for questions from 1 to 8:
State whether the following statements are true or false.

1. Doubling the pressure of a gas at constant temperature, doubles the volume occupied by the gas.
2. When a 200 mL gas, in a closed vessel, is heated to 50°C from 25°C, the volume becomes doubled.
3. The rate of diffusion of methane is double the rate of diffusion of sulphur dioxide gas.
4. 1 g atom of nitrogen contains 6.023×10^{23} atoms of nitrogen.
5. Gay-Lussac's law of combining volumes is applicable to the reaction, $2C + O_2 \rightarrow 2CO_2$.
6. Gases show deviations from ideal behavior at high temperature and high pressure.
7. The greater the critical temperature of a gas, the easier is the liquefaction of the gas.
8. Molecules of gases exert pressure when they collide with the walls of the container in which they are taken.

Direction for questions from 9 to 19:
Fill in the blanks.

9. The volume occupied by 7 g of nitrogen gas at STP is ______.
10. Temperature above which gases cannot be liquefied is called ______.
11. The number of molecules in 2.5 moles of water will be ______.
12. 2 moles of CO_2 gas contain the same number of atoms as ______ moles of CO.
13. The ratio of the volumes of 11 g of CO_2 and 28 g of CO at STP is ______.
14. The number of oxygen molecules required for the complete combustion of 5 moles of methane is ______.
15. The volume of CO_2 liberated at STP is ______, on thermal decomposition of 84 g of sodium bicarbonate.
16. 'ous' acid of a non-metal 'X' has 2 'O' atoms. Per acid of the same non-metal has the formula ______.
17. The ratio of the gram atomic weight of nitrogen and oxygen is ______.
18. Pressure exerted by water vapor in moist gas is called ______.
19. Mole fraction of NaOH in an aqueous solution is 0.3. Mole fraction of water is ______.

Direction for question 20:
Match the entries given in Column A with appropriate ones in Column B.

20. Match the entries of Column A with those of Column B.

Column A	Column B
(i) Calcium bisulphate	(A) $FeSO_4$
(ii) Calcium bisulphite	(B) $Fe_2(SO_4)_3$
(iii) Ferric sulphate	(C) $Ca(HSO_4)_2$
(iv) Ferrous sulphate	(D) $Ca(HSO_3)_2$

Direction for questions from 21 to 38:
Select the correct alternative from the given choices.

21. **Assertion (A):** 80 g of SO_3 occupies 22.4 L STP
Reason (R): 80 g of SO_3 corresponds to 1 mole.
(a) Both A and R are true and R is the correct explanation of A.
(b) Both A and R are true, but R is not the correct explanation of A.
(c) A is true and R is false.
(d) A is false and R is true.

22. **Assertion (A):** Real gases behave ideally at low pressure and high temperature.
Reason (R): At low pressure and high temperature, intermolecular forces of attraction among the gas molecules are negligible.
(a) Both A and R are true and R is the correct explanation of A.

(b) Both A and R are true, but R is not the correct explanation of A.

(c) A is true and R is false.

(d) A is false and R is true.

23. Arrange the following reactions in the order of double displacement, combination, displacement and decomposition reaction.

(1) Electrolysis of concentrated NaCl solution to form A and B (gas)

(2) Reaction between dil. H_2SO_4 and Mg to form C and D (gas)

(3) Reaction between B and D to form E

(4) Reaction between E and NaOH

(a) 1 2 3 4 (b) 4 3 2 1
(c) 2 3 4 1 (d) 4 2 3 1

24. **Assertion (A):** Gas laws are not applicable to the gases at all conditions of temperature and pressure.

Reason (R): Gas laws are derived based on the kinetic molecular theory of gases.

(a) Both A and R are true and R is the correct explanation of A.

(b) Both A and R are true, but R is not the correct explanation of A.

(c) A is true and R is false.

(d) A is false and R is true.

25. Arrange the following compounds in the correct order of percentage of metallic element.

(A) potassium hydroxide
(B) potassium carbonate
(C) potassium bicarbonate
(D) potassium sulphide

(a) A > B > C > D (b) B > A > C> D
(c) C > B > A > D (d) D > A > B > C

26. Empirical formula of a compound is A_2B_4. If its empirical formula weight is half of its vapor density, determine the molecular formula of the compound.

(a) A_4B_8 (b) A_8B_{16}
(c) A_2B_4 (d) A_3B_6

27. The number of oxygen atoms present in 2 moles of a compound, which consists of a bivalent metal and a perchlorate ion is:

(a) 4 N (b) 6 N
(c) 8 N (d) 16 N

28. $KMnO_4 + H_2SO_4 + FeSO_4 \rightarrow K_2SO_4 + MnSO_4 + Fe_2(SO_4)_3 + H_2O$

Coefficients of sulphuric acid and ferric sulphate in the balanced equation of above reaction are ____ and ____, respectively.

(a) 8, 4 (b) 5, 8
(c) 4, 3 (d) 8, 5

29. A certain mass of a gas occupies a volume of 600 mL at a certain temperature and pressure. If the temperature is increased by 80% what will be the volume occupied by the same mass of gas at the same pressure?

(a) 1080 mL (b) 108 mL
(c) 120 mL (d) 102 mL

30. The weight of an empty china dish is 39 g and when a saturated solution of potassium nitrate is poured into it, its weight is 108 g at 50°C. After evaporating the solution to dryness, if the weight of the dish along with the crystals is 72 g then the solubility of potassium nitrate at 50°C is ______.

(a) 83.9 (b) 95.6
(c) 91.6 (d) 87.4

31. If 15 mg of N_2O_3 is added to 4.82×10^{20} molecules of N_2O_3, the total volume occupied by the gas at STP is:

(a) 0.044 L (b) 0.022 L
(c) 0.22 L (d) 0.44 L

32. In a 2.5 L flask at 27°C temperature, the pressure of a gas was found to be 8 atm. If 2.41×10^{23} molecules of the same gas are introduced into the container, the temperature changed to T_2. The pressure of gas is found to be 10 atm. Find out the value of T_2.

(a) 253 K (b) 347 K
(c) 230 K (d) 370 K

33. A certain mass of a gas occupies a volume of 600 mL at a certain temperature and pressure. If pressure is decreased by 40% what will be the volume occupied by the same mass of the gas at the same temperature?

(a) 240 mL (b) 1000 mL
(c) 300 mL (d) 120 mL

34. Calculate the molarity of a solution obtained by mixing 250 mL of 0.5 M HCl with 750 mL of 2 M HCl.
(a) 1.8 (b) 2.0
(c) 1.6 (d) 0.8

35. 40% w/W $Ca(OH)_2$ solution has a molarity of 7.8 M. Calculate the density of the solution.
(a) 1.03 g/cc (b) 1.04 g/cc
(c) 1.54 g/cc (d) 1.44 g/cc

36. Which one of the following is different from the others with respect to valency?
(a) potassium (b) ammonium
(c) barium (d) lithium

37. Plumbous ion is represented as:
(a) Pb^{2+} (b) Pb^{4+}
(c) Pb^{3+} (d) Pb^{+}

38. 0.5 moles of a salt contains '3N' oxygen atoms. Identify the formula of the salt.
(a) MXO_3 (b) MX_2O_3
(c) M_2XO_3 (d) $M(XO_3)_2$

Level 2: Review Your Concepts

39. Out of oxygen, carbon dioxide, sulphur dioxide and nitrogen, which among these gases possesses maximum density at a given temperature and pressure?

40. If the Avogadro number is 9×10^{23}, calculate the weight of 1 mole of CO_2 gas.

41. A gas cylinder is filled with helium at 2000 mm. Due to leakage, the pressure dropped to 1500 torr in 40 min. When the same cylinder is filled with another gas at the same pressure, the pressure dropped from 2000 mm to 1500 mm in 200 min. What is the molecular weight of the gas?

42. A cation A^{+4x} and an anion B^{-2x} combine to form a compound. Similarly, C^{+2x} and D^{-4x} also combine to form a compound. When the molten compounds are subjected to electrolysis, the gaseous products obtained are in equimolar amounts. What should be the mole ratio of the compounds taken, respectively?

43. A sample of a mixture of Na_2CO_3 and $NaHCO_3$ is subjected to heating till there is no further loss in weight. Assuming, that the loss in weight of the sample is 22% of the initial weight of the mixture due to the evolution of CO_2, find out the relative percentages of the two components in the mixture.

44. (a) Calculate the mass of aluminium oxide which contains double the number of oxygen atoms in 192 g of oxygen gas.
(b) A cylinder is filled with 160 g of oxygen gas. 400 g of gas X and 140 g of gas Y are taken in two other cylinders separately. The volumes of all the three cylinders are same under similar conditions of temperature and pressure separately. Calculate the molecular masses of X and Y.

45. A vessel contains equal number of moles of helium and methane. Due to a hole in the vessel, half of the gaseous mixture effused out. What is the ratio of the number of moles of helium and methane remaining in the vessel?

46. A vessel contains double the number of moles of hydrogen than oxygen. Due to a hole in the vessel, one-fourth of the gaseous mixture is effused out. What is the ratio of the number of moles of hydrogen and oxygen remaining in the vessel?

47. A salt is formed between a bivalent metal cation and an oxyacid of a non-metal. The -ous acid of the non-metal has two oxygen atoms per molecule. If the salt contains a radical of per acid of the same non-metal, calculate the number of atoms of various elements present in 0.5 moles of the salt.

48. The percentage of oxygen in a metallic oxide of a bivalent metal is 20.1%. The molecular weight of the compound is 79.5. Write the molecular formula of the compound, considering the symbol of the metal as M and find out the atomic weight of the metal.

49. A hydrocarbon on combustion gives CO_2 and H_2O in a volume ratio of 2 : 1, under similar conditions of temperature and pressure. What is the empirical formula of the hydrocarbon?

50. An aqueous solution is prepared by dissolving 90 g of acetic acid in water to make a 1000 mL solution. Density of solution is 0.99. Calculate the molarity of solution and mole fraction of solute in the solution.

51. (a) A vessel contains equal masses of hydrogen, helium and methane. Find out the fractions of the partial pressures in the mixture.

(b) The volume of a mixture of O_2 and another gas A diffuses in 240 seconds is equal to the volume of pure O_2 that diffuses in 160 seconds. If the molar percentage of A in the gaseous mixture is 40, calculate the molecular mass of A.

Directions for questions from 52 to 61:
Application-Based Questions

52. The molecular mass of a salt of oxyacid of chlorine of a divalent metal, which contains more number of oxygen atoms than its corresponding '-ic' acid is 239. What will be the molecular masses of its following salts?
    (a) phosphate (b) iodide
    (c) bisulphate

53. Represent the following chemical changes in the form of chemical equations and balance them.
    (a) A copper coin is placed in a solution of corrosive sublimate, mercuric chloride. The products obtained are cupric chloride and mercury.
    (b) A piece of (a) sulphur, (b) charcoal burns vigorously when dropped in molten potassium nitrate, because potassium nitrate decomposes to form potassium nitrite and oxygen, and this oxygen helps to burn charcoal and sulphur giving out carbon dioxide and sulphur dioxide, respectively.
    (c) Aqueous ammonium hydroxide solution is made to react with aqueous copper sulphate solution and a bluish white precipitate of cupric hydroxide, and ammonium sulphate are formed.

54. The percentage of metal in two metal oxides, A and B is 74.2% and 59%, respectively. Show that the law of multiple proportions is obeyed.

55. A sample of air contains nitrogen and oxygen saturated with water vapor. The total pressure is 640 mm. The vapor pressure of water vapor is 40 mm and molar ratio of nitrogen and oxygen is 4 : 1. Find out the partial pressures of N_2 and O_2.

56. Calculate the partial pressures of each gas present in a mixture of 8 g of oxygen and 6 g of hydrogen, present in 2 L container at 27°C.

57. A particular compound contains only nitrogen and hydrogen. The percentage of nitrogen in the compound is 87.5%. Further, 96 g of the compound contains 18×10^{23} molecules of the substance. Find out the molecular formula of the compound.

58. When a sample of KNO_3 is subjected to heating, the volume of oxygen liberated was sufficient for the combustion of one mole of ethylene. For giving same amount of oxygen, what is the amount of lead nitrate required to be decomposed? Also, find out the volume occupied by the gaseous products at STP during this decomposition.

59. Brass is an alloy of copper and zinc. A sample of brass weighing 5.793 g, when treated with excess of dil. H_2SO_4 gave 336 mL of hydrogen gas at 136.5 K and 785 mm pressure. If the hydrogen gas is collected over water and pressure of water vapor under the given conditions is 25 mm, find out the percentage weight of copper in the alloy.

60. 50 mL of a gaseous hydrocarbon is mixed with excess of oxygen and burnt and cooled to the laboratory temperature. The reduction in volume was found to be 150 mL. The gas is then passed into caustic potash, when there is a further reduction in the volume of 150 mL. Provided all the volumes are measured at the same conditions of temperature and pressure, find out the molecular formula of the hydrocarbon.

61. X g of CO_2 is prepared by the reaction of $CaCO_3$ and HCl. How many grams of oxygen will be liberated, if X grams of CO_2 completely take part in the process of photosynthesis? 144 g of water is produced in the first reaction.

    Equation for photosynthesis is:
    $CO_2 + H_2O \rightarrow C_6H_{12}O_6 + O_2$

Level 3: Assess Your Concepts

62. At constant temperature and at 4 atm pressure, the given amount of gas occupies 6 L. If the pressure is increased by 6 atm, calculate the percentage change in the volume of the gas.

63. A gaseous mixture contains 48 g of SO_2 and 33 g of CO_2 at constant temperature and pressure. Calculate the average molecular mass of the gaseous mixture.

64. Calculate the ratio of rates of diffusion of three isotopes of hydrogen protium, deuterium and tritium, respectively, at the same temperature and pressure.

65. 3×10^{23} molecules of nitrogen are taken in a 1-L vessel at 27°C and exert 3 atm pressure. If 9×10^{23} molecules are added to the vessel, calculate the pressure exerted by the gas at the same temperature.

66. 1.6 g of sulphur on treatment with a limited amount of oxygen forms a gas X which is dissolved in water and made up to 1500 mL. Calculate the molarity of the solution.

Directions for questions from 67 to 70:
Application-Based Questions

67. From the graph given below compare the intermolecular forces of attraction in A and B.

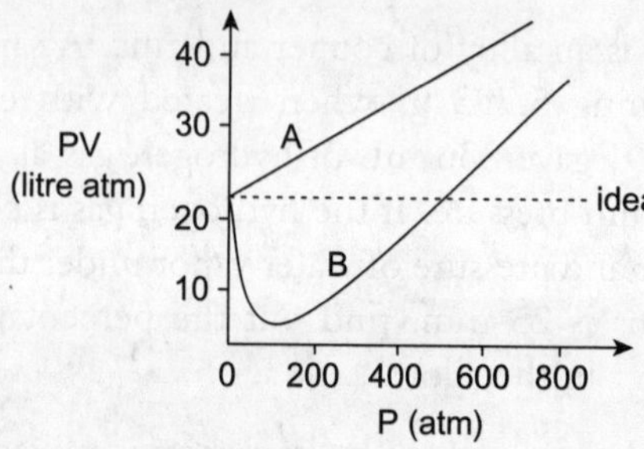

68. The various conditions required for the liquefaction of gases A, B, C, and D are given below:

Gas	Temperature	Pressure
A	−4°C	10 atm
B	−4°C	5 atm
C	25°C	5 atm
D	25°C	4 atm

Arrange these gases in the ascending order of their deviation from ideal behavior. Give reason in support of your answer.

69. The reduction of acidified solution of ferric ions by hydrogen gas takes place in the presence of zinc. Explain.

70. In the graph given below, identify the states of solution at the various points A, B, C, D, and E. If the solution is cooled from point 'A' at which temperature, precipitation normally starts? Also, find out the amount of solute precipitated at 40°C at A and the amount of solute in the solution at point 'E.' What would be the maximum amount of solute that can be precipitated in the process?

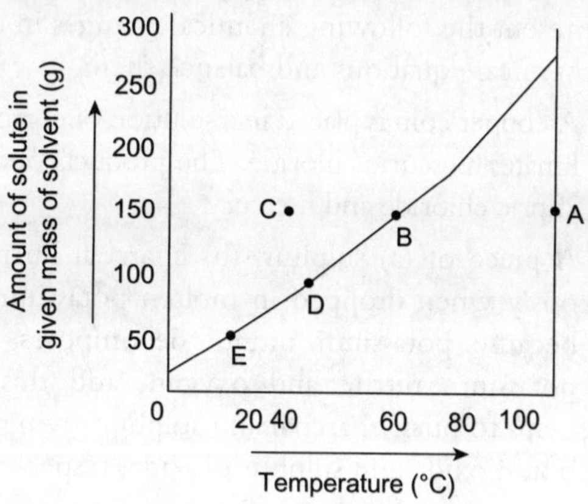

AT

PRACTICE QUESTIONS JEE-NEET SPECIAL WING

Multiple-Answer Type Questions

Directions for Questions number 1 to 5:

Select one or more correct alternative(s) from the given choices.

1. Which of the following is equal to one mole of substance?
   (a) 57.5g of sodium chloride
   (b) 12.046×10^{24} atoms of oxygen at STP
   (c) 4g of helium
   (d) 22.4L of CO at STP

2. Which of the following options correctly defines a one molar solution?
   (a) A solution containing the mass of the substance equivalent to the mass of Avogadro number of its molecules, present dissolved in 1000 mL of its solution.
   (b) A solution prepared by dissolving one-gram molecular mass of the substance in a given solvent and making the volume to one litre by adding solvent
   (c) A solution prepared by dissolving one mole of the substance to one litre of the solvent.
   (d) A solution that contains one mole of the substance dissolved in one litre of its solution.

3. Names of which of the following acids end with the suffix 'ous',
   (a) HCIO (b) $HCIO_2$
   (c) HNO_2 (d) H_3PO_3

4. Under similar conditions of temperature and pressure, the rate of diffusion of a saturated hydrocarbon 'Z' is approximately one-sixth of that of hydrogen. Identify the statement that is incorrect regarding the hydrocarbon 'Z'.
   (a) The molecular weight of hydrocarbon 'Z' is 70.
   (b) One mole of Z requires 8 moles of oxygen for combustion.
   (c) The weight ratio of carbon to hydrogen in one molecule of 'Z' is 5:1
   (d) The percentage of carbon in Z is approximately 62%.

5. Four moles of oxygen and 3 moles of sodium are taken in the reaction vessel to prepare sodium oxide. Choose the correct statements with respect to this reaction.
   (a) The quantity of product formed relies on the amount of metal reactant present in the reaction vessel.
   (b) The quantity of product formed depends on the amount of non-metal reactant taken in the reaction vessel.
   (c) The total mass of the resulting product upon reaction equals the combined initial mass of the reactants in the vessel.
   (d) The mass of metal in the resulting product is 69 g.

Comprehension-Based Questions

Directions for Questions 6 to 11:

Read the following passage and answer the questions given below.

The gases which obey the universal gas laws and comply with ideal gas equation, PV = nRT, under all conditions of temperature and pressure are said to be ideal gases. However, no gas universally confirms to this equation across all conditions, rendering this concept theoretical. Real gases comply with gas laws at low pressure and high temperature. All gases are inherently real gases.

The compressibility factor (Z), also known as the compression factor or the gas deviation factor, is calculated by the formula $Z=\frac{PV}{nRT}$. It describes the deviation of a real gas from ideal gas behaviour. It is defined as the ratio of the molar volume of a gas to the molar volume of an ideal gas at the same temperature and pressure. For an ideal gas the compressibility factor is Z = 1. The value of Z generally increases with pressure and decreases with temperature. At high pressures molecules are colliding more often. This allows repulsive forces between molecules to have a noticeable effect, making the molar volume of the real gas greater than the molar volume of the corresponding ideal gas which causes Z to exceed one(positive deviation). When pressures are lower, the molecules are free to move. In this case attractive forces dominate, making Z<1(negative deviation). The closer the gas is to its boiling point, the more Z deviates from the ideal case.

6. Answer the following questions.

(i) 'The pressure of the real gas(P_{real}) is less than the expected pressure (P_{ideal}) due to attractions between the molecules.' Identify the given statement as true or false. Justify your answer.

(ii) A real gas of one mole, when compressed, its volume is 1/3rd to that of an ideal gas at STP. Comment on its compressibility and deviation from ideal behaviour.

7. Calculate n_X and n_Y from the information given in the table and choose the correct option.

Gas	Temperature-T	Pressure P	Compressibility factor at the given T and P	Capacity of each balloon	No. of moles of gas required to fill a balloon
X	-23°C	800 atm	2	250 mL	n_X
Y	-33°C	101 KPa	0.1	480 mL	n_Y

(a) $n_X = 5$; $n_Y = 0.75$ (b) $n_X = 0.25$; $n_Y = 5$ (c) $n_X = 5$; $n_Y = 0.25$ (d) $n_X = 0.5$; $n_Y = 0.25$

8. Fill in the blanks.

(i) Oxygen gas is more compressible than Hydrogen gas at a certain given temperature and pressure conditions. This means that Z_{O2} is ________ Z_{H2}. **(greater than/lesser than)** at these temperature and pressure conditions.

(ii) At 0°C and 76 cm of Hg, the compressibility factor of one mole of a gas 'A' is greater than 1. The molar volume of 'A' at STP is ______ **22.4 l (greater than/less than/equal to)**

9. The isotherms plotted for one mole of different gases, A, B, C, D and E against the Z value and pressure, P at 0°C are shown below:

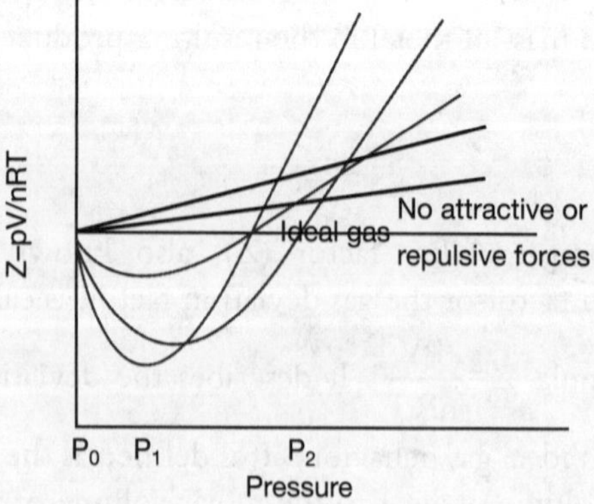

Observe the above figure and answer the following questions.

(i) Arrange A,B,C, D and E in the increasing order of

(p) compressibility at P_1.

(q) Real molar volume compared to its ideal molar volume at P_1.

(ii) If the same graph is plotted for hydrogen and helium gases under the same conditions, predict to which curves do they look similar. Justify

(iii) Compare forces of attraction and forces of repulsion among the molecules of these gases at:

(p) Pressure P_1

(q) Pressure P_2

(iv) Draw a general inference about the ability of these gases to get compressed at pressures greater than P_2.

10. Graph of Z vs P for a hypothetical gas 'M' is plotted at different temperatures as shown below. Observe the graph and answer the following question.

Arrange T_1, T_2, T_3 in decreasing order, and provide an explanation to support your arrangement.

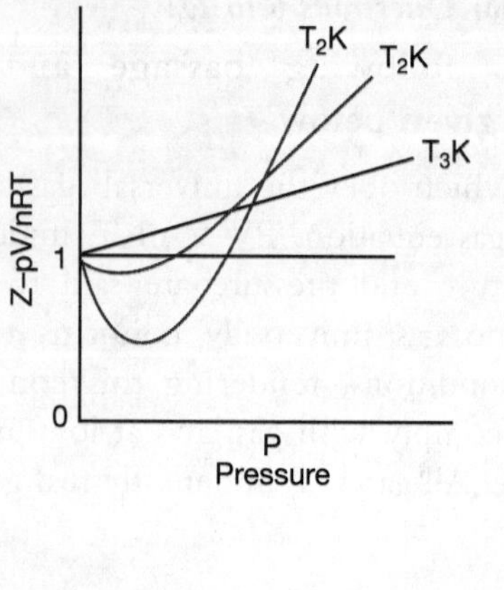

11. Compressibility factor (Z) of a gas at a given temperature and pressure, depends on the size of the gas molecules and intermolecular forces of attraction among the gaseous molecules. The larger is the size of the molecules and stronger the intermolecular forces of attraction between them, the more will be the compressibility of the gas.

List – I Name of the gas	List – II Type of intermolecular attractions	List – III Compressibility factor(Z) of one mole of gas at a given temperature and pressure
(1) Methane	(i) van der Waals interactions	(p) Z_2
(2) Hydrogen chloride	(ii) Hydrogen bonding	(q) Z_1
(3) Ammonia	(iii) Dipole -Dipole interactions	(r) Z_5
(4) Hydrogen sulphide		(s) Z_4
(5) Hydrogen		(t) Z_3

If $Z_1 > Z_2 > Z_3 > Z_4 > Z_5$, identify the correct matching of the gas, type of intermolecular attractions prevailing in it and possible compressibility factor.

	1	2	3	4	5
(a)	(iii) (s)	(ii) (p)	(ii) (r)	(iii) (t)	(iv) (q)
(b)	(i) (s)	(ii) (t)	(iii) (r)	(ii) (p)	(ii) (q)
(c)	(i) (p)	(iii) (s)	(ii) (r)	(iii) (t)	(i) (q)
(d)	(i) (p)	(iii) (s)	(ii) (q)	(iii) (t)	(ii) (r)

Directions for Questions 12 to 16:

These questions are based on the following passage.

P, Q, R and S are the four binary solution of different compounds. Details of the solute and solvent present in the solution are provided in the following table. Study the details given in the table, also observe the solubility curves of the corresponding salts and answer the questions that follow. (Consider density of water as 1g/cc respectively)

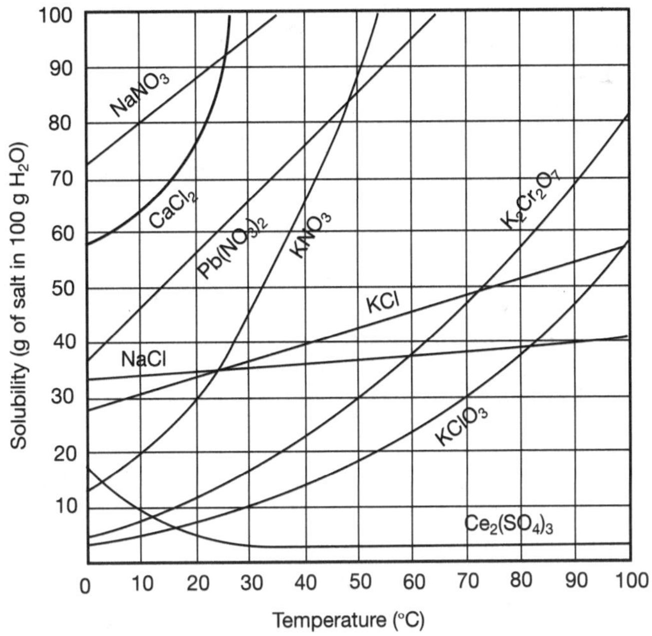

Solution	Compound	Amount of Solute	Amount of Solvent (water)
P	Sodium chloride	36	1000g
Q	Potassium chlorate	40	500g
R	Calcium chloride	750g	1000g
S	Potassium nitrate	20.2	250g

12. Choose the correct increasing order of the moles of the solute present in the following given solutions

Solution	Moles of the solute
P	m1
Q	m2
R	m3
S	m4

(a) m4 < m2 < m1 < m3.

(b) m4 < m1 < m2 < m3.

(c) m3 < m1 < m2 < m4.

(d) m3 < m2 < m1 < m4.

13. Among the options provided, the solution with highest percentage of solute by weight is.

(a) S (b) Q

(c) R (d) P

14. Which of the given solutions is super saturated?

(a) P (b) R

(c) S (d) Q

15. Molarity of the solution that is saturated is__________ (approximate value considering the density of solute as 2g/cc)

(a) 0.1M (b) 0.6M

(c) 0.8M (d) 0.4M

16. The density of a solution varies based on the quantity of matter within a specific volume. D1, D2, D3, and D4 represent changes in the densities of equal-volume aqueous solutions when their temperatures decrease from 20°C to 0°C. Given that D1 < D2 < D3 < D4, analyze the solubility curves of different salts and match the entries in List-I with those in List-II.

Match the following:

List – I Saturated aqueous solutions of salts at 20°C	List – II Change in the densities of the solutions when the temperature drops to 0°C
(a) Cerium sulphate	(i) D1
(b) Potassium nitrate	(ii) D2
(c) Calcium chloride	(iii) D3
(d) Potassium chloride	(iv) D4

ANSWER KEYS

Crossword

Across

2. Limiting reagent 6. Absolute 8. Molarity 9. Mole
12. Gram molar volume 14. Boyle 16. Charles 18. Molecular formula
19. Ideal 20. Avogadro

Down

1. Effusion 3. Molecular mass 4. Empirical formula 5. Random 7. Mole fraction
10. Temperature 11. Stoichiometry 13. Molecules 15. Diffusion 17. Kelvin

Classroom Wing

Very Short Answer Type Questions

1. 50%, 40% 2. higher than
3. Relation between vapor density and molecular weight.
C_2H_6
4. 16/N 5. 40.043% 9. 2 M 10. 5.6 L 11. 5/9
12. 0.7 13. 1 : 4 14. 0.05 16. 8 L 17. 14 g
21. 22 g 22. 36%

Competition Wing

Level 1: Apply your Concepts

1. False 2. False 3. True 4. True 5. False
6. False 7. True 8. True 9. 5.6 L
10. critical temperature 11. 15×10^{23} molecules. 12. 3 moles 13. 1 : 4
14. 6.023×10^{24} molecules 15. 11.2 L 16. HXO_4 17. 7 : 8
18. vapor pressure 19. 0.7 20. (i) → (C); (ii) → (D); (iii) → (B); (iv) → (A) 21. (a)
22. (a) 23. (b) 24. (a) 25. (d) 26. (b)
27. (d) 28. (d) 29. (a) 30. (c) 31. (b)
32. (a) 33. (b) 34. (c) 35. (d) 36. (c)
37. (a) 38. (d)

JEE-NEET Special Wing

Multiple-Answer Type Questions

1. (c, d) 2. (a, b, d) 3. (a, b, c, d) 4. (a, d) 5. (a, d)

Comprehension-Based Questions

6. (i) True 7. (c) 8. (i) lesser than (ii) greater than
9. (i) E < D < C < B < A. (ii) A < B < C < D < E 10. T3 > T2 > T1 11. (c)
12. (a) 13. (c) 14. (d) 15. (b)
16. (a)-(ii), (b)-(iv), (c)-(iii), (d)-(i)

Hints and Explanations

Classroom Wing

Very Short Answer Type Questions

1. 50%, 40%
2. higher than
3. Relation between vapor density and molecular weight. C_2H_6
4. 16/N
5. 40.043%
6. Since the molecular weight of hydrogen is less than that of tritium, it diffuses into the balloon more rapidly. Hence, the balloons will expand.
7. (C): Writing a balanced chemical equation for the decomposition of NH_3.

   (D): Identifying the number of moles of the gas that is used for the preparation of X.

   (E): Writing a balanced chemical equation for the formation of X.

   (A): Identifying the number of moles of X formed.

   (B): Identifying the relation between the number of moles and volume occupied at STP.

   The correct order is: CDEAB
8. (D): $C + O_2 \rightarrow CO_2 \rightarrow$ Combination reaction.

   (C): $2KNO_3 \rightarrow 2KNO_2 + 3O_2 \rightarrow$ Decomposition reaction

   (B): $Zn + H_2SO_4 \rightarrow ZnSO_4 + H_2 \rightarrow$ Displacement reaction

   (A): $NaOH + HCl \rightarrow NaCl + H_2O \rightarrow$ Double displacement reaction.

   The correct order is: DCAB
9. Molarity $= \frac{\text{No. of moles of solute}}{\text{Volume of solution}}$

   2 M
10. One mole of a gaseous substance occupies = 22.4 L

    5.6 L
11. $\frac{P_1V_1}{T_1} = \frac{P_2V_2}{T_2}$

    = 5/9
12. Mole fraction =

    $$\frac{\text{No. of moles of a Substance}}{\text{Total number of moles of all substances in the mixture}}$$

    Sum of mole fraction in a mixture = 1

    = 0.7
13. $\frac{r_1}{r_2} = \sqrt{\frac{M_2}{M_1}}$

    1 : 4
14. Number of moles $= \frac{\text{Given weight}}{\text{Gram molecular weight}}$

    = 0.05 mol
15. Molecular formula = Empirical formula × n

    Molecular weight = Vapor density × 2

    $$n = \frac{\text{Given weight}}{\text{Gram molecular weight}}$$

    $C_4H_8O_2$
16. $N_2 + 3H_2 \rightarrow 2NH_3$

    8 L
17. $CaCO_3 \rightarrow CaO + CO_2$

    14 g
18. Equal volumes of all gases contain equal number of molecules under similar conditions of temperature and pressure
19. Weight of 1/12th part of C – 12 isotope.
20. Molecular weight = Vapor density × 2 = 48
21. One mole of gaseous substance occupies 22.4 L (22.4 dm^3)

    22 g
22. % of element =

    $$\frac{\text{Weight of substance}}{\text{Molecular weight of compound}} \times 100$$

    = 36%

23. Molarity

$$= \frac{\text{Weight of solute in g}}{\text{Gram Molecular Weight of Solute}} \times \frac{1000}{\text{Volume of solution in (mL)}}$$

24. Graham's law of diffusion states that the rate of diffusion or of effusion of a gas is inversely proportional to the square root of its molecular weight.

25. (i) Calculation of the molar ratio of CO_2 and H_2O produced due to the combustion of hydrocarbon.

(ii) Derivation of the empirical formula of the compound.

Short Answer Type Questions

26. Volume of each balloon = 253 mL

According to the ideal gas equation $\frac{P_1 V_1}{T_1} = \frac{P_2 V_2}{T_2}$

$$\Rightarrow \frac{20 \times 2}{400} = \frac{I \times V_2}{273} \Rightarrow V_2 \frac{273}{10} L = 27.3 \text{ L}$$

∴ The volume of He gas available for filling balloons = Total volume − Volume of cylinder

= (27.3 − 2) = 25.3 L

∴ Number of balloons $\frac{25.3 \text{ L}}{0.253 \text{ L}} = 100$

27. $n_{N_2} = \frac{56}{28} = 2; n_{O_2} = \frac{32}{32} = 1; n_{Ar} = \frac{12}{40} = 0.3$

$nT = 2 + 1 + 0.3 = 3.3$

$$X_{N_2} = \frac{n_{N_2}}{n_T} = \frac{2}{3.3} = 0.6$$

∴ Partial pressure of $N_2 = X_{N_2}$; $P = 0.6 \times 1 = 0.6$ atm

28. Number of moles of gold present in 1 gold coin

$$= \frac{9.85\text{g}}{197\text{g}} = \frac{1}{20}$$

∴ Number of moles of gold consumed per day

$$= \frac{1000}{20} = 50 \text{ mol}$$

29. According to Boyle's law, $P_1 V_1 = P_2 V_2$

$\Rightarrow 22 \times 75 = 10\ [75 + V]$

$$\Rightarrow \frac{1650}{10} = 75 + V \Rightarrow V = 90 \text{ L}$$

∴ Volume of first cylinder = 90 L

30. According to the ideal gas equation,

$$\frac{P_{O_3}.V_{O_3}}{T_{O_3}.n_{O_3}} = \frac{P_{O_2}.V_{O_2}}{T_{O_2}.n_{O_2}}$$

$$\Rightarrow \frac{1 \times V_{O_3} \times 48}{300 \times 7.2} = \frac{3 \times V_{O_2} \times 32}{200 \times x}$$

$$\Rightarrow \frac{48}{300 \times 7.2} = \frac{3 \times 32}{200 \times x} (\because V_{O_3} = V_{O_2})$$

$$\Rightarrow x = \frac{300 \times 7.2 \times 96}{200 \times 48}$$

⇒ Weight of oxygen (x) = 21.6 g

31. According to Dalton's law, ⇒

$$P_{O_2} = \frac{\frac{16}{32}}{\frac{16}{32} + \frac{20}{20}} \times 3 = \frac{0.5}{1.5} \times 3 = 1 \text{ atm}$$

32. (i) Number of moles of a component, total number of moles of the solution

(ii) Number of moles = $\frac{\text{Weight of the component}}{\text{GMW}}$

(iii) Mole fraction of a component =

$$\frac{\text{Number of moles of that components}}{\text{Total number of moles of the solution}}$$

Mole fraction of NaOH = 0.1/0.1+5 = 0.02

33. (i) Balanced chemical equation,
$H_2SO_4 + Mg \rightarrow MgSO_4 + H_2$

(ii) Relation between the number of moles and volume of the gas at STP

(iii) 1 mole of H_2 is liberated from 1 mole of H_2SO_4

(iv) Relation between number of moles and mass of the solute

(v) Weight/Volume percentage = mass of the solute in grams present in 100 mL solution

Ans: 49 mL

34. (i) Molecular formula of glucose

(ii) Molecular weight of glucose

(iii) Percentage by weight of each component =

$$\frac{\text{number of atoms of each component present in one molecule of the compound} \times \text{atomic weight of the element} \times 100}{\text{(Molecular weight of the compound)}}$$

Ans: C → 40%, H → 6.6%, O → 53.3%

35. (i) Calculation of empirical formula weight

(ii) 2 × Vapor density = molecular weight

(iii) Molecular formula = (Empirical formula) × n

(iv) $n = \dfrac{\text{Molecular weight}}{\text{Empirical formulae weight}}$

Ans: $C_8H_{24}N_8$

36. (i) Gram atom or gram molecule represents number of moles

(ii) Number of atoms/molecules = moles × Avogadro number

37. On opening the stop cock the same number of moles of the gas occupy a volume of (V + 1.5) L at the same temperature.

According to Boyle's law, $P_1V_1 = P_2V_2$

$\Rightarrow 2 \times V = \dfrac{600}{760}(V + 1.5)$

$\Rightarrow 2V = 0.79\ (V + 1.5)$

$\Rightarrow 2.53V = V + 1.5$

$\Rightarrow V\ (2.53–1) = 1.5$

$\Rightarrow V = \dfrac{1.5}{1.53} \Rightarrow V \approx 1L$

38. $r \propto \dfrac{1}{\sqrt{M}}$

Ans: 2 : 1

39. (i) Molarity =

$\dfrac{\text{Weight of solute}}{\text{Molecular weight}} \times \dfrac{1000}{\text{Volume of solution in (mL)}}$

Ans: 0.1 M

40. (i) Molecular weight of hydrocarbon = 2 × vapor density

(ii) Percentage of carbon and hydrogen in the hydrocarbon

(iii) Determination of empirical formula of the hydrocarbon

(iv) Molecular formula = (Empirical formulae) × n

where $n = \dfrac{\text{Molecular weight}}{\text{Empirical formulae weight}}$

Ans: C_2H_4

Essay Answer Type Questions

41. Mass of 1 mole of gaseous mixture = (1.25 × 22.4) g = 28 g

Let the number of moles of $O_2 = a$

∴ No. of moles of helium = $(1 - a)$

∴ $32a + 4(1 - a) = 28$

∴ $28a + 4 = 28$

∴ $a = \dfrac{24}{28}$

∴ Partial pressure of $O_2 = \left(\dfrac{a}{1} \times 1\right)$ atm $= \dfrac{24}{28}$

42. According ideal gas equation $PV = nRT$ At const. P and for a given volume V, $n_1\ T_1 = n_2\ T_2$

Let n_1 be 1; T_1 = 27°C = 300 K, and T_2 = 127°C = 400 K

$\therefore 1 \times 300 = n_2 \times 400$

$\Rightarrow n_2 = 0.75$

∴% of air expelled = 25%

43.

Element	% Weight	Atomic Ratio	Simplest Ratio
Cr	68.5	$\dfrac{68.3}{52} = 1.32$	$\dfrac{1.32}{1.32} = 1 = 2$
O	31.5	$\dfrac{315}{16} = 1.96$	$\dfrac{1.96}{1.32} = 1.5$

∴ Empirical formula is Cr_2O_3.

44. $4Na + O_2 \xrightarrow{2H_2O} 2Na_2O \rightarrow 4NaOH$

4 g atoms of Na give 2 g atoms of Na_2O.

∴ 2 g atoms of Na gives.

= = 1 g atom of Na_2O

2 g atoms of Na_2O give 4 g atoms of NaOH.

1 g atom of Na_2O gives 2 g atom of NaOH

Molarity of the solution = n/V(L) = 2/0.5 = 4 M

45. (i) $VD = \dfrac{\text{Mass of certain volume of gas at a particular temperature and pressure}}{\text{Mass of the same volume of hydrogen at that temperature and pressure}}$

(ii) Applying Avogadro's law, V ∝ n

(iii) Molecular mass of the gas

$= \dfrac{\text{Mass of 1 molecule of the gas}}{\text{Mass of the 1 atom of hydrogen gas}}$

(iv) 1 molecule of H_2 gas contain 2 atoms of hydrogen gas.

(v) Relation between VD and molecular mass.

46. T = 127°C = 400 K, V = 1.6L P = 2 atm

$PV = nRT \Rightarrow n = \frac{PV}{RT} = \frac{2 \times 1.6}{0.08 \times 400}$

No. of moles of H_2 = 0.1

$Mg + 2HCl \rightarrow H_2 + MgCl_2$

$2Al + 6HCl \rightarrow 2AlCl_3 + 3H_2$

Let weight of Mg be x g

24 g of Mg gives 1 mole of H_2

x g of Mg gives $\frac{x}{24}$ moles of H_2

54 g of Al gives 3 moles of H_2

(2 – x) g of Al gives $\frac{3(2-x)}{54}$ moles of H_2

Total moles of H_2= 0.1

$\Rightarrow \frac{x}{24} + \frac{3(2-x)}{54} = 0.1$

$\Rightarrow \frac{x}{24} + \frac{2-x}{54} = 0.1$

$\Rightarrow 18x + 48 - 24x = 43.2 \Rightarrow 6x = 4.8$

$\Rightarrow x = 0.8$ g of Mg

% of Mg $= \frac{0.8}{2} \times 100 = 40\%$

% of Al = 60%

Competition Wing

Level 1: Apply your Concepts

20. Calcium bisulphate → $Ca(HSO_4)_2$

Ferric sulphate → $Fe_2(SO_4)_3$

Calcium bisulphite → $Ca(HSO_3)_2$

Ferrous sulphate → $FeSO_4$

(i) → (C); (ii) → (D); (iii) → (B); (iv) → (A)

21. 80 g of SO is equal to 1 mole. 1 mole of any gas at STP occupies 22.4 L.

Hence, the correct option is (a).

22. At low pressure and high temperature, inter-molecular forces of attraction among the gas molecules are negligible. Hence, the gases behave ideally.

Hence, the correct option is (a).

23. (4) HCl + NaOH → NaCl + H_2O → Double displacement

(3) $Cl_2 + H_2 \rightarrow HCl$ → Combination

(2) $Mg + H_2SO_4 \rightarrow MgSO_4 + H_2$ → Displacement

(1) NaCl Na + Cl_2 → Decomposition

The correct order is: 4 3 2 1

Hence, the correct option is (b).

24. According to the kinetic molecular theory of gases, intermolecular forces of attraction among the gas molecules are negligible. The statement holds goods at low pressure and high temperature.

Hence, the correct option is (a).

25. (A) potassium hydroxide → KOH

$$\% \text{ of potassium} = \frac{39}{56} \times 100 = 69.64\%$$

(B) potassium carbonate → K_2CO_3

$$\% \text{ of potassium} = \frac{78}{138} \times 100 = 56.52\%$$

(C) potassium bicarbonate → $KHCO_3$

$$\% \text{ of potassium} = \frac{39}{100} \times 100 = 39\%$$

(D) potassium sulphide → K_2S

$$\% \text{ of potassium} = \frac{39 \times 2}{110} \times 100 = 70.90\%$$

∴ increasing order is (D) > (A) > (B) > (C)

Hence, the correct answer is (d).

26. Let the vapor density of compound be x

Empirical formula weight = $x/2$

Molecular formula weight = $2x$

$$n = \frac{\text{Molecular formula weight}}{\text{Empirical formula weight}} \times \frac{2x}{\left(\frac{x}{2}\right)} = 4$$

Molecular formula = 4 × A_2B_4 = A_8B_{16}

Hence, the correct answer is (b).

27. Let the bivalent metal ion be M^{2+}, then the formula of the compound formed will be $M(ClO_4)_2$.

1 mole of compound contains 8 N oxygen atoms.

∴ 2 moles of compound contain 16 N oxygen atoms.

Hence, the correct answer is (d).

28. $2KMnO_4 + 8H_2SO_4 + 10FeSO_4$
$\rightarrow 5Fe_2(SO_4)_3 + K_2SO_4 + 2MnSO_4 + 8H_2O$

Hence, the correct answer is (d).

29. Initial volume, V_1 = 600 mL

Initial temperature, $T_1 = x$

Final temperature, $T_2 = \frac{180x}{100}$

Final volume, V_2 = ?

$$\frac{V_1}{T_1} = \frac{V_2}{T_2} \text{ as per Charles' law}$$

$$\frac{600}{x} = \frac{V_2 \times 100}{180x} = V_2 = 1080 \text{ mL}$$

Hence, the correct answer is (a).

30. The weight of saturated solution = 108 – 39 = 69 g

The weight of KNO_3 crystals = 72 – 39 = 33 g

The weight of water in saturated solution = 69 – 33 = 36 g

$$\therefore \text{Solubility of } KNO_3 = \frac{\text{Weight of } KNO_3}{\text{Weight of water}} \times 100$$

$= \frac{33}{36} \times 100 = 91.6 \text{ at } 50°C$

Hence, the correct answer is (c).

31. Gram molecular weight of N_2O_3 is 76 g and 76 g of N_2O_3 contains 6.023×10^{23} molecules.

$\therefore$ Weight of 4.82×10^{20} molecules

$$= \frac{76 \times 4.82 \times 10^{20}}{6.023 \times 10^{23}} g = 0.061 g$$

15 mg of N_2O_3 = 0.015 g

$\therefore$ Total weight of N_2O_3 = 0.061 + 0.015

= 0.076 g

76 g occupies 22.4 L at STP.

0.076 g occupies ? L at STP.

$$= \frac{0.076 \times 22.4}{76} = 0.022 \text{ L}$$

Hence, the correct answer is (b).

32. 6.023×10^{23} molecules correspond to 1 mole

2.41×10^{23} molecules correspond to?

$$= \frac{2.41 \times 10^{23}}{6.023 \times 10^{23}} = 0.4 \text{ moles}$$

Case (i)

$P_1V_1 = n_1.R_1.T_1$

$8(2.5) = n_1 (0.08).(300)$

$$n_1 = \frac{8(2.5)}{(0.08)(300)}$$

n_1 = 0.833 moles

Total moles, n_2 = 0.833 + 0.4

n_2 = 1.233

Case (ii)

$P_2V_2 = n_2R\ T_2$

$10\ (2.5) = 1.233\ (0.08).T_2$

T_2 = 253.4 K

Hence, the correct answer is (a).

33. Initial volume, V_1 = 600 mL

Let initial pressure be $P_1 = x$

Final pressure, $P_2 = \frac{60x}{100}$

Final volume, V_2

As per Boyle's law, $P_1V_1 = P_2V_2 \Rightarrow V_2 = \frac{P_1V_1}{P_2}$

$$V_2 = \frac{x \times 600 \times 100}{60x}$$

$$V_2 = 1000 \text{ mL}$$

Hence, the correct answer is (b).

34. $N_{Mixture} = \frac{N_1V_1 + N_2V_2}{V_1 + V_2}$

$$= \frac{(0.5)250 + (2 \times 750)}{250 + 750} = 1.625 N$$

$\therefore$ Molarity = 1.625 N (as HCl is monobasic acid)

Hence, the correct answer is (c).

35. Let the density of solution be = x g/cc

Molarity = 7.8 M

Molecular mass of $Ca(OH)_2$ = 40 + 34 = 74

Mass of solute = 40 g

$$\text{Molarity} = \frac{\text{mass of solute}}{\text{molecular mass of solute}} \times \frac{1000}{\left(\frac{100}{x}\right)}$$

$$\left(\because v = \frac{m}{d}\right)$$

$$7.8 = \frac{40}{74} \times \frac{1000}{100} \times x \quad \Rightarrow x = 1.44$$

Hence, the correct answer is (d).

36. Barium's valency is 2, whereas the valency of rest of the elements is 1.

Hence, the correct answer is (c).

37. Suffix 'ous' denotes lower valency exhibited by the metal, when compared with suffix 'ic', which denotes higher valency of the metal. Hence, plumbous is Pb^{2+}.

Hence, the correct answer is (a).

38. 0.5 moles of salt contains 3N oxygen atoms.

$\therefore$ 1mole of salt contains $= \frac{1 \times 3N}{0.5}$

= 6 N oxygen atoms

∴ The salt is $M(XO_3)_2$.

Hence, the correct answer is (d).

Level 2: Review Your Concepts

39. According to the ideal gas equation,

$PV = nRT$

$PV = \frac{W}{M}RT$

$\Rightarrow P = \frac{W}{V}\frac{RT}{M}$

$\Rightarrow P = \frac{dRT}{M}$

$\Rightarrow d = \frac{PM}{RT}$

At constant temperature pressure $P \propto M$.

∴ SO_2 gas possesses maximum density.

40. 1 mole of CO_2 = 44 g

44 g weight corresponds to 6×10^{23} molecules.

weight corresponds to 9×10^{23} molecules.

$= \frac{44 \times 9 \times 10^{23}}{6 \times 10^{23}} = 66$ g

41. (i) relation between drop in pressure and rate of diffusion
(ii) relation between the rate of diffusion and molecular weight of gases
(iii) 100

42. (i) application of criss-cross method
(ii) derivation of the formulae of both the compounds
(iii) determination of the ratio of the number of atoms of B and D, present in the respective molecule
(iv) determination of molar ratio of the compounds taken
(v) 1 : 2

43. (i) action of heating on the compounds Na_2CO_3 and $NaHCO_3$.
(ii) determination of the mass of Na_2CO_3 and $NaHCO_3$ from the mass of CO_2 produced
(iii) 84% $NaHCO_3$
16% Na_2CO_3

44. (a) (i) atomicity of oxygen
(ii) chemical composition of Al_2O_3
(iii) determination of mass of Al_2O_3
(iv) 408 g

(b) Since the volumes of cylinders are same they contain same number of molecules.

32 g of $O_2 \rightarrow 1$ mole

160 g of $O_2 \rightarrow 5$ moles

400 g of gas X also contains 5 moles

Molecular mass of X $= \frac{400}{5} = 80$

140 g of Y also contains 5 moles

Molecular mass of Y $= \frac{140}{5} = 28$.

45. (i) relation between molecular weight and rate of effusion
(ii) determination of the ratio of the number of molecules of helium and methane which are effused out
(iii) calculation of the ratio of the remaining molecules
(iv) $\frac{2x}{3}$ moles

46. (i) relation between number of moles of gases
(ii) relation between number of moles of gases effused and molecular weight
(iii) comparison of number of moles of H_2 and O_2 effused
(iv) calculation of number of moles of H_2 and O_2 left over
(v) 28 : 17

47. (i) identification of acidic radical and formula of salt
(ii) determination of the formula of the 'per' acid radical
(iii) determination of the formula of the salt
(iv) determination of the number of atoms of each constituent element, present in one molecule of the salt
(v) determination of the number of atoms of each constituent element, present in 5 moles of the salt
(vi) 4 N oxygen atoms
N chlorine atoms

48. (i) calculate the number of atoms of oxygen present in the compound
(ii) calculation of the number of atoms of oxygen present in one molecule of the metallic oxide from the percentage of oxygen given
(iii) determination of the formula of the compound
(iv) calculation of atomic weight of the metal
(v) 63.5

49. (i) relation between the ratio of the volumes and ratio of the number of moles

(ii) determination of the empirical formula based on the molar ratio of the product

(iii) CH

50. (i) number of moles of solute

(ii) calculation of weight of solution, solvent

(iii) calculation of number of moles of solvent

(iv) calculation of mole fraction and molarity

(v) 1.5 M, 0.03

51. (a) (i) fraction of number of moles of CH_4, H_2, and He in the mixture

(ii) relation between mole fraction and total pressure

(iii) $\frac{8P}{13}, \frac{4P}{13}, \frac{P}{13}$

(b) According to Graham's law, $\frac{r_{mix}}{r_{O_2}} = \frac{V_{mix}}{t_{mix}} \times \frac{t_{O_2}}{t_{mix}}$

$$= \sqrt{\frac{M_{O_2}}{M_{mix}}}$$

$$\Rightarrow \frac{160}{240} = \sqrt{\frac{32}{M_{mix}}}$$

$$\Rightarrow M_{mix} = \frac{240 \times 240 \times 32}{160 \times 160}$$

$$\Rightarrow M_{mix} = \frac{24 \times 24 \times 32}{16 \times 16}$$

$M_{mix} = 72$

As the mixture contains 40% of A, the molar ratio of O_2 and A = $0.6x : 0.4x$

$$M_{mix} = \frac{(32 \times 0.6x) + (0.4x)M_A}{0.6x + 0.4x}$$

$$\Rightarrow 72 = \frac{19.2x + 0.4xM_A}{x} \Rightarrow 72 = 19.2 + 0.4M_A$$

$\Rightarrow M_A = 132$

molecular mass of A = 132.

52. The formula of perchlorate of a divalent metal M is $M(ClO_4)_2$.

Molecular mass of $M(ClO_4)_2$ is 239.

Let x be the atomic mass of bivalent metal.

$\therefore x + 2[35.5 + 64] = 239 \Rightarrow x = 40$

$\therefore$ The element is calcium.

(a) The formula of its phosphate is $Ca_3(PO_4)_2$.

$\therefore$ Its molecular mass is $(3 \times 40) + 2[31 + 64]$ = 310

(b) The formula of its iodide is CaI_2.

$\therefore$ Its molecular mass is $40 + (2 \times 127) = 294$

(c) The formula of bisulphate is $Ca(HSO_4)_2$

$\therefore$ Its molecular mass is $40 + 2[1 + 32 + 64]$ = 234

53. (a) The copper displaces the mercury from mercuric chloride and forms cupric chloride and mercury.

($Cu + HgCl_2 \rightarrow CuCl_2 + Hg$)

(b) $2\ KNO_3 \rightarrow 2\ KNO_2 + O_2$

$S + O_2 \rightarrow SO_2$

$C + O_2 \rightarrow CO_2$

(c) $2NH_4OH + CuSO_4 \rightarrow Cu(OH)_2 + (NH_4)_2SO_4$

54.

Metal Oxides	Percentage of Metal	Percentage of Oxygen
A	74.2	25.8
B	59	41

In A, 74.2 g of metal combines with 25.8 g of oxygen

? g of metal A will combine with 1 g of oxygen

$$= \frac{74.2\,g}{25.8\,g} = 2.87\,g$$

In B, 59 g of metal combines with 41 g of oxygen

? g of metal B will combine with 1 g of oxygen

$$= \frac{59}{41} g = 1.43\,g$$

$\therefore$ The ratio by weight of metal combining with fixed mass of oxygen in A and B

= 2.87 : 1.43 = 2 : 1

Hence, law of multiple proportions is obeyed.

55. Total pressure, $P_{N_2} + P_{O_2} + P_{H_2O} = 640$ mm

Vapor pressure of water vapor = 40 mm

$$\therefore P_{N_2} + P_{O_2} = 640 - 40 = 600 \text{ mm}$$

Mole fraction of nitrogen = 4/5

Mole fraction of oxygen $= \frac{1}{5}$

Partial pressure of N_2 = total pressure $\times X_{N_2}$

$= 600 \times \frac{4}{5} = 480$ mm

Partial pressure of $O_2 = 600 \times \frac{1}{5} = 120$ mm

56. Number of moles of oxygen, $n_{O_2} = \frac{8}{32} = 0.25$

Number of moles of hydrogen, $n_{H_2} = \frac{6}{3} = 2$

Total number of moles, n = 0.25 + 2 = 2.25

PV = nRT

2P = 2.25 × 0.08 × 300

P = 27 atm

Partial pressure of oxygen, p_{O_2} = (mole fraction of O_2).

$= \left(\frac{0.25}{0.25 + 2}\right) = 27 = 3$ atm

$P_{total} = P_{O_2} + P_{H_2}$

Partial pressure of H_2 = 27 – 3 = 24 atm

57. Number of moles of the given substance

$= \frac{18 \times 10^{23}}{6 \times 10^{23}} = 3$

Weight of compound = 96

Gram molecular mass of the compound

$= \frac{96}{3} = 32\,g$

% of N_2 = 87.5%

Number of nitrogen atoms in 1 molecule of the compound $= \frac{87.5 \times 32}{100 \times 14} = 2$

Similarly number of hydrogen atom in 1 molecule of the compound $= \frac{12.5 \times 32}{100 \times 2} = 4$

Molecular formula is N_2H_4.

58. $2KNO_3 \rightarrow 2KNO_2 + O_2$

$C_2H_4 + 3O_2 \rightarrow 2CO_2 + 2H_2O$

1 mole of ethylene requires 3 moles of oxygen

$2Pb(NO_3)_2 \rightarrow 2PbO + 4NO_2 + O_2$

6 moles of $Pb(NO_3)_2$ is required to give 3 moles of oxygen

∴ Weight of $Pb(NO_3)_2$ = 6 × 330 = 1980 g

Volume occupied by gaseous (NO_2 and O_2) products:

= 15 × 22.4 L at STP = 336 L

59. Among Cu and Zn, only Zn displaces H_2 from H_2SO_4

$Zn + H_2SO_4 \rightarrow ZnSO_4 + H_2$

Pressure = 785 – 25 = 760 mm

Temperature = 136.5 K, volume = 336 mL

$\frac{P_1V_1}{T_1} = \frac{P_2V_2}{T_2}$

$\frac{760 \times 336}{136.5} = \frac{760 \times V_2}{273}$

V_2 = 672 mL

(V_2) Vol. of H_2 liberated at STP = 672 mL

Weight of zinc required $= \frac{65.5 \times 672}{22400} = 1.965\,g$

Weight of copper in brass = 5.793 – 1.965 = 3.828 g

% of Cu in the alloy $= \frac{3.828}{5.793} \times 100 = 66\%$

60. Chemical reaction equation to combustion reaction is

$C_xH_y + O_2 \rightarrow CO_2 + H_2O$

50 moles 150 moles 150 moles

We know volume of gas has same number of moles, at same temperature and pressure:

$C_xH_y + \left(x + \frac{y}{4}\right)O_2 \rightarrow xCO_2 + \frac{y}{2}H_2O$

50 mole 150 mole 150 mole

Given that reduction in volume, when the gases mixture is cooled to the laboratory temperature = 150 mL

$\therefore \frac{y}{2}(50) = 150 \Rightarrow y = 6.$

and $x(50) = 150 \Rightarrow x = 3$

∴ Hydrocarbon is C_3H_6.

61. $CaCO_3 + 2HCl \rightarrow CaCl_2 + CO_2 + H_2O$

$6CO_2 + 6H_2O \rightarrow C_6H_{12}O_6 + 6O_2$

Number of moles of water formed in the first reaction

$= \frac{144}{18} = 8$

Number of moles of CO_2 produced = 8

Number of moles of oxygen produced by using 8 moles CO_2 is 8.

Weight of oxygen liberated = 32 × 8 = 256 g

Level 3: Assess Your Concepts

62. Given that P_1 = 4 atm; V_1 = 6 L

$P_2 = 10$ atm; $V_2 = ?$

$P_1V_1 = P_2V_2$

$\Rightarrow 4 \times 6 = 10 \times V_2 \Rightarrow V_2 = 2.4$ L

% decrease in volume

$$= \left(\frac{6-2.4}{6}\right) \times 100 = 60\%$$

% change in volume = −60%

63. $n_{N_2} = \frac{23}{84} = 0.33$

$$n_{CO_2} = \frac{28}{84} = 0.33$$

Average molecular mass =

$$\frac{n_{CO_2} \times (\text{GMM})_{SO_2} + n_{CO_2} \times (\text{GMM})_{CO_2}}{n_{SO_2} + n_{CO_2}}$$

$$= \frac{(0.75 \times 64) + (0.75 \times 44)}{0.75 + 0.75} = 54$$

64. Let the rates of diffusion of protium, deuterium, and tritium be r_1, r_2, and r_3, respectively.

According to Graham's law of diffusion,

$$\frac{r_1}{r_2} = \sqrt{\frac{M_2}{M_1}}; \frac{r_1}{r_2} = \sqrt{\frac{M_3}{M_1}}$$

$$\Rightarrow \frac{r_1}{r_2} = \sqrt{\frac{2}{1}} = \sqrt{2}; \frac{r_1}{r_3} = \sqrt{\frac{3}{1}}$$

$$\Rightarrow r_1 = \sqrt{2} \cdot r_2$$

$$\Rightarrow r_1 = \sqrt{3} \cdot r_3$$

From Eq. (1) and (2), $\sqrt{2} \cdot r_2 = \sqrt{3} \cdot r_3$

$$\Rightarrow r_3 = \frac{\sqrt{2}}{\sqrt{3}} \cdot r_2$$

$$\therefore r_1 : r_2 : r_3 = \sqrt{2} \cdot r_2 : r_2 : \frac{\sqrt{2}}{\sqrt{3}} \cdot r_2$$

$$= \sqrt{2} : 1 : \frac{\sqrt{2}}{\sqrt{3}}$$

$$= 1 : \frac{1}{\sqrt{2}} : \frac{1}{\sqrt{3}}$$

65. Initial moles n_1 $n_1 = \frac{3 \times 10^{23}}{6 \times 10^{23}} = 0.5$

No. of moles added, $n = \frac{9 \times 10^{23}}{6 \times 10^{23}} = 1.5$

Final moles $n_2 = 0.5 + 1.5 = 2$

Initial pressure $P = 3$ atm

Final pressure $P_2 = ?$

At constant volume and temperature

$$\frac{P_1}{P_2} = \frac{n_1}{n_2}$$

$$\Rightarrow P_2 = \frac{P_1 . n_2}{n_1} = \frac{3.2}{0.5} = 12 \text{ atm}$$

66. $S + O_2 \rightarrow SO_2$

32 g of S gives 64 g of SO_2.

1.6 g of S gives ? of SO_2.

$$= \frac{1.6 \times 64}{32} = 3.2 \text{ g of } SO_2$$

$SO_2 + H_2O \rightarrow H_2SO_3$

64 g of SO_2 gives 82 g of H_2SO_3.

3.2 g of SO_2 gives ? of H_2SO_3.

$$= \frac{3.2 \times 82}{64} = 4.1 \text{ g of } H_2SO_3$$

$\Rightarrow$ Molarity of H_2SO_3 solution

$$= \frac{4.1}{82} \times \frac{100}{1500} = 0.03 \text{ M}$$

67. At extremely low pressure, all the gases behave almost ideally. From the graph, it is known that as pressure increases, PV decreases showing that with increase in pressure the intermolecular spaces between molecules of B can be decreased to a great extent. This is possible when the intermolecular forces between the molecules are more. At a certain stage PV reaches minimum and then increases showing that further increase in pressure cannot decrease the volume to that extent. While in A though the intermolecular spaces are more, the decrease in volume of 'A' with the increase of pressure is lesser than ideal gas. This shows that intermolecular forces of attraction of A are less.

68. Among A, B, C, and D gases, D is the most easily liquefiable gas since the temperature required is the highest and pressure required is the lowest. The easier liquefaction indicates greater intermolecular forces of attraction and hence larger deviation from ideal behavior. The order of ease of liquefaction is D > C > B > A, thus the ascending order of extent of deviation from ideal behavior could be A < B < C < D.

69. Reduction of acidified solution of ferric ions by hydrogen gas does not take place. If a small amount of Zn is added to reaction mixture, the hydrogen gas is converted into nascent hydrogen by Zn. The nascent hydrogen is highly reactive and it reduces ferric ions to ferrous ions.

70. The curve indicates that the solubility of the solute at 100°C is 250 g. However, the given solution contains only 150 g of solute. The solution at point 'A' is an unsaturated solution. Therefore, no precipitation takes place up to point 'B' at 60°C, where the solution becomes saturated, with just 150 gas solubility. Point 'B' indicates saturated solution and hence, precipitation normally starts at 60°C. With the fall in temperature, solubility decreases and the extra amount should get precipitated. Point 'C' at 40°C indicates that the solution still contained 150 g of solute, which is a supersaturated solution. That means, it is possible to cool a solution from 60°C to 40°C without any crystallisation by creating conditions such as absence of dust particles. At 40°C, when crystallisation starts, the solution ultimately becomes saturated, and this is represented by point D. At point D (40°C), the solubility is 100 g. That means, 50 g of solute would have been precipitated. At 'E' also the solution remains saturated by precipitating 25 g more of solute leaving behind 75 g of solute in the solution. At 0°C, when water starts to solidify, the solution still contains 5 g of solute without precipitation. That means, 125 g of solute can be precipitated.

JEE-NEET Special Wing

Multiple-Answer Type Questions

1. Mole = GMM of the substance = One Avogadro number of particles/species = 22.4L at STP

   For NaCl, GMM = 23 + 35.5 = 58.5g

   For Oxygen,

   One Avogadro number of molecules of O_2 or 2 × Avogadro number of oxygen atoms.

   $\Rightarrow 2 \times 6.023 \times 10^{23}$ oxygen atoms

   $\Rightarrow 12.046 \times 10^{23}$ oxygen atoms.

2. $$\text{Molarity} = \frac{\text{No of moles of the solute}}{\text{Volume of the solution in litres}}$$

   $$= \frac{\text{One GMW of the solute}}{\text{Volume of the solution in litres}}$$

   A solution prepared by completely dissolving one-gram molecular mass of the substance/one mole/ mass of the substance equivalent to the mass of one Avogadro number of its molecules in a given solvent and subsequently adjusting the volume to one litre by adding more solvent.

3. (a) HClO-Hypochlorous acid

   (b) $HClO_2$-Chlorous acid

   (c) HNO_2-Nitrous acid.

   (d) H_3PO_3-Phosphorous acid

4. Given, the rate of diffusion of a saturated hydrocarbon 'Z' is approximately one-sixth of that of hydrogen.

   Let the molecular mass of Z be M_x and its rate of diffusion is r_x

   According to Graham's law of diffusion,

   $r \, a \, 1/\sqrt{d}$ (T and P are constant)

   Rates of diffusion of gases are also inversely proportional to the square root of their molecular weights because equal volume of all gases contains equal number of molecules, if the temperature and pressure are kept constant.

   $rH2/rx = \sqrt{Mx/MH2} = rx = 1/6\, rH2$

   $rH2/rx = 6 = \sqrt{Mx/2}$

   $\Rightarrow 36 \times 2 = Mx$

   $\Rightarrow Mx = 72$. Therefore, Molecular weight of the hydrocarbon is 72.

   Given Z is a saturated hydrocarbon.

   $\Rightarrow$ General formula is C_nH_{2n+2}

   $\Rightarrow (12 \times n) + (2n + 2) \times 1 = 72$

   $\Rightarrow 14n + 2 = 72$

   $\Rightarrow n = 5$

   Therefore, Molecular formula of the hydrocarbon is C_5H_{12}.

   No of moles of oxygen required for the combustion of hydrocarbon with formula C_xH_y

   $= x + (y/4)$. Substituting $x = 5$ and $y = 12$,

   $=5 + 3 = 8$ moles of oxygen

5. $4Na + O_2 \rightarrow 2Na_2O$

   4 mol 1 mol 2 mol

   ⇒ 3 moles of sodium react with 0.75 moles of oxygen to form 1.5 moles of sodium oxide.

   ⇒ Sodium is completely utilised in the reaction and 3.25 moles of oxygen is left unused in the reaction. Hence, sodium determines the amount of product formed in the reaction and is the limiting agent.

   ⇒ As total amount of oxygen taken in the reaction vessel is not utilized in the reaction, the total initial mass of the reactants taken in the reaction vessel for the reaction is greater than the actual mass of the reactants consumed in the reaction. Hence, the mass of product formed after completion of the reaction is less than the total initial mass of the reactants taken in the reaction vessel.

   ⇒ (3×23) 69g of sodium react with (0.75×32) 24g of oxygen to form (1.5×62) 93g of sodium oxide.

   ⇒ 1.5 moles of sodium oxide contain $(1.5 \times 2 \times 23)$ = 69g of sodium.

Comprehension-Based Questions

6. (i) True.

   Explanation: Molecular attractions slow down the motion of gas molecules and result in:

   Decrease in the number of collisions or frequency of collisions on to the walls of the container and decrease in the force with which the molecules collide with the walls of the container.

   Hence, $P_{real} < P_{ideal}$

   (ii) **Compressibility:**

   $$Z = \frac{\textit{Molar volume of real gas}(V\ real)}{\textit{Molar volume of ideal gas}(V\ ideal)} = \frac{V/3}{V} = 0.33$$

   $\Rightarrow Z < 1$

⇒ Gas can be compressed more than its corresponding ideal gas at STP.

Deviation:

Z value for an ideal gas will be 1. As Z value of the given real gas is less than one, it shows negative deviation from ideal behaviour.

7.

Gas	Temperature-T	Pressure P	Compressibility factor at the given T and P	Capacity of each balloon	No. of moles of gas required to fill a balloon
X	-23°C	800 atm	2	250 mL	**5**
Y	-33°C	101 KPa	0.1	480 mL	**0.25**

Explanation:

$$Z = \frac{PV}{nRT}$$

Where P is the pressure of the gas in atom, V in litres, R = 0.0821 L- atm/(mol K), n is the no. of. moles of the gas. T is absolute temperature, Z is the compressibility factor

For gas X:

Given Z = 2, P = 800 atm, V = 250mL = (250/1000 L), T = –23°C = 250 K (–23 + 273), n = ?

$$N = \frac{PV}{ZRT} = \frac{800 \times 250/1000}{2 \times 0.08 \times 250} = 5 \text{ mol}$$

For gas Y:

Given Z = 0.1, P = 101Kpa = 1 atm, V = 480 mL = (480/1000 L), T = –33°C = 240 K (–33 + 273), n = ?

$$n = \frac{PV}{ZRT} = \frac{1 \times 480/1000}{0.1 \times 0.08 \times 240} = \mathbf{0.25 \text{ mol}}$$

8. (i) Oxygen gas is more compressible than Hydrogen gas at a certain given temperature and pressure conditions. This means that Z_{O2} is lesser than $Z_{H2.}$ at these temperature and pressure conditions.

Explanation: Oxygen gas being more compressible than hydrogen gas at certain given temperature and pressure conditions suggests that, unlike hydrogen, the attractive forces in oxygen gas dominate its repulsive forces. In such scenarios, the compressibility factor (Z), which is the ratio of the molar volume of a gas to the molar volume of its ideal gas at the same temperature and pressure, will obviously be lesser than that of hydrogen gas.

(ii) At 0°C and 76cm of Hg, the compressibility factor of one mole of a gas 'A' is greater than 1.

The molar volume of 'A' at STP is greater than 22.4 L.

Explanation: At 0°C and 76cm of Hg, ⇒ at STP, $Z > 1 \Rightarrow V_{real} > V_{ideal}$

Therefore, the volume occupied by gas A at STP will be greater than that of 22.4 L.

9. (i) (p) compressibility at P_1: E < D < C < B < A.

(q) Real molar volume compared to their respective ideal molar volume at P_1: A < B < C < D < E.

(ii) If the same graph is plotted for hydrogen and helium gases under the same conditions, they resemble to the curves of gases D and E. As helium is an inert gas, it will be less compressible compared to hydrogen under same conditions of T and P. The curve representing gas D indicates higher Z values compared to those of gas E at the same temperature and pressure conditions. Hence graphs if plotted for He and H_2 should look similar to curves D and E respectively.

(iii) (p) **Pressure P_1:**

For gases A, B, C, Z < 1 at P_1.

⇒ forces of attraction among the molecules are greater compared to their forces of repulsion at P_1.

For gases D and E, Z is >1 at P_1.

⇒ forces of repulsion among the gaseous molecules are greater compared to their forces of attraction at P_1.

(q) **Pressure P_2:**

Z > 1 at P_2 for all the given gases.

⇒ forces of repulsion among the gaseous molecules for all the given gases are greater compared to their forces of attraction at P_2.

(iv) Z > 1 for all gases at pressures greater than P_2.

⇒ For all the given gases, the forces of attraction among their gaseous molecules are greater than their repulsions. Hence, it can be inferred that none of the given gases be compressed under pressures greater than P_2.

10. $T_3 > T_2 > T_1$. At more temperatures (and less pressure), behaviour of the gases will be close to their ideal behaviour. As the curve corresponding to the temperature T_3K is closer in its behaviour to the ideal gas curve at Z = 1 compared to that of T_2 and T_1, the correct decreasing order of temperature of the gas should be $T_3 > T_2 > T_1$.

11.

	1	2	3	4	5
(c)	(i) (p)	(iii) (s)	(ii) (r)	(iii) (t)	(i)(q)

Option (c) is the correct match for the given gases in list-I.

Explanation:

The correct order of the strength of intermolecular attractions is: Hydrogen bonding > dipole-dipole interactions > van der Waals forces. Greater is the strength of intermolecular attractions and larger is the size of the molecule, the greater will be the forces of attractions among the molecules compared to their forces of repulsion and thus increasing the compressibility of the gas. Gases with more compressibility possess lesser compressibility factor.

Type of intermolecular interactions	Name of the given gas that contain these type of interactions	Explanation	Possible Z value among the given Z values at a given T and P conditions
Hydrogen bonding	Ammonia	These types of interactions being strong among the other given types, this gas is more compressible among the given one and hence its Z value should be the least possible one	Z_5
Dipole-Dipole	Hydrogen chloride Hydrogen sulphide	Chlorine being more electronegative than sulphur, the electronegativity difference between Cl and H will be greater compared to that of S and H. So, Intermolecular interactions are stronger in HCl compared to that in H_2S. Therefore, Z value of HCl should be less compared to that of H_2S as it is more compressible than the later one	Z_4 Z_3
Vander Waals forces	Methane Hydrogen	Both Methane and hydrogen are non-polar molecules. But the size of methane is far greater than that of hydrogen. So, the intermolecular forces of attraction will be more among the methane molecules compared to that in hydrogen making it comparatively more compressible than the later one. Hence Z value of methane will be less compared to that of hydrogen	Z_2 Z_1

12.

Solution	Mass of the solute in the solution	Molecular weight of the solute	Moles of the solute= $\frac{\text{Mass of the solute}}{\text{Gram molecular mass}}$ (approximate values)
P	36	58.5	$m1 = \frac{36}{58.5} = 0.6$
Q	40	122.5	$m2 = \frac{40}{122.5} = 0.3$

R	750g	111	$m3 = \frac{750}{111} = 7.5$
S	20.2	101	$m4 = \frac{20.2}{101} = 0.2$

So the correct increasing order of the moles solute in the given solutions is m4 < m2 < m1 < m3.

13. Weight percentage of the solute $= \frac{\text{Weight of the solute}}{\text{Weight of solution}} \times 100$

Solution	Compound	Amount of		Weight percentage of the solute $= \frac{\text{Weight of the solute}}{\text{Weight of [solute + solvent]}} \times 100$
		Solute	Solvent (water)	
P	Sodium chloride	36	1000g	$\frac{36}{36+1000} \times 100 = 3.45$
Q	Potassium chlorate	40	500g	$\frac{40}{40+500} \times 100 = 7.4$
R	Calcium chloride	750g	1000g	$\frac{750}{750+1000} \times 100 = 43$
S	Potassium nitrate	20.2	250g	$\frac{20.2}{20.2+250} \times 100 = 7.5$

Solution R contains highest % weight of the solute.

14. A Solution holding a greater amount of solute than its holding capacity (solubility) at that temperature is known as a super saturated solution.

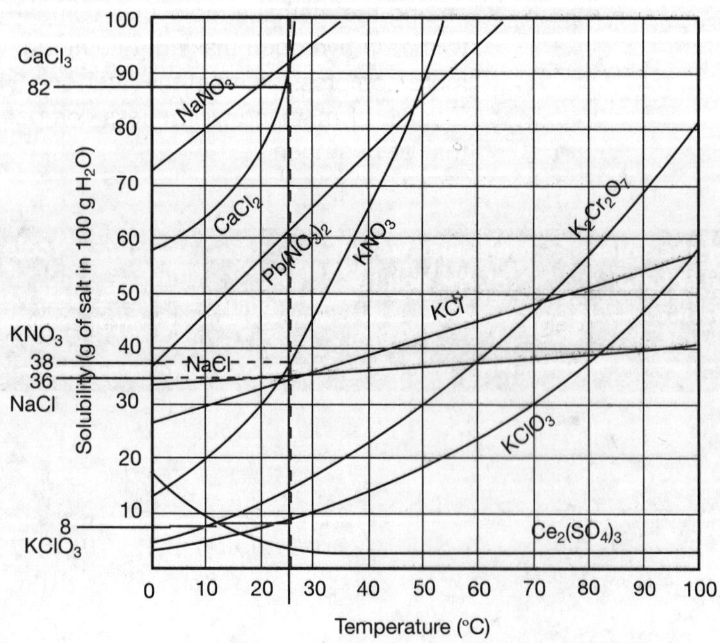

Solution	Compound	Amount of Solute	Amount of Solvent (water)	Amount of solute in 100g of the solvent	Solubility at 25°C from the graph	Type of solution
P	Sodium chloride	36	100g	36g	36	= its solubility. Hence Saturated
Q	Potassium chlorate	40	250g	16 g	8	> its solubility. Hence Supersaturated
R	Calcium chloride	750g	1000g	75 g	82	< its solubility. Hence Unsaturated
S	Potassium nitrate	20.2	250g	8.08 g	38	< its solubility. Hence Unsaturated

Solution Q contains solute more than the dissolution capacity of the solvent at 25°C. Hence it is supersaturated.

15. Among the given four solutions, only solution P is saturated.

In P, 36g of NaCl is present in 1000g + 36g = 1036g of the solution. To determine the volume of the solution, we convert the mass to volume using the densities of both the solute and the solvent.

$$\text{Density of NaCl} = \frac{\text{Mass of NaCl}}{\text{Volume of NaCl}} = 2$$

$$= \frac{36}{V} \Rightarrow V = 18 \text{ mL},$$

Density of water = 1g/cc, so, 1000g of solvent = 1000mL

Therefore, 36g of NaCl is present in 1000 + 18 = 1018 mL of the solution.

1018 mL of the solution contains 36g of the solute

$$\text{1000 mL of the solution contains } \frac{36 \times 1000}{1018}$$

= approximately 36g

$$\text{Formula: Molarity} = \frac{\text{No of moles of the soulte}}{\text{Volume of solution in litres}}$$

$$= \frac{0.6}{1} = 0.6\text{M}$$

Analyzing, solubility curves, it is clear that,

16. Change in mass of KCl < $Ce_2(SO_4)_3$ < $CaCl_2$ < KNO_3. As Change in density of a specified volumes changes with the change in the mass of the solute, change in density of the solutions will be KCl < $Ce_2(SO_4)_3$ < $CaCl_2$ < KNO_3.

CHAPTER

2

Acids, Bases, and Salts

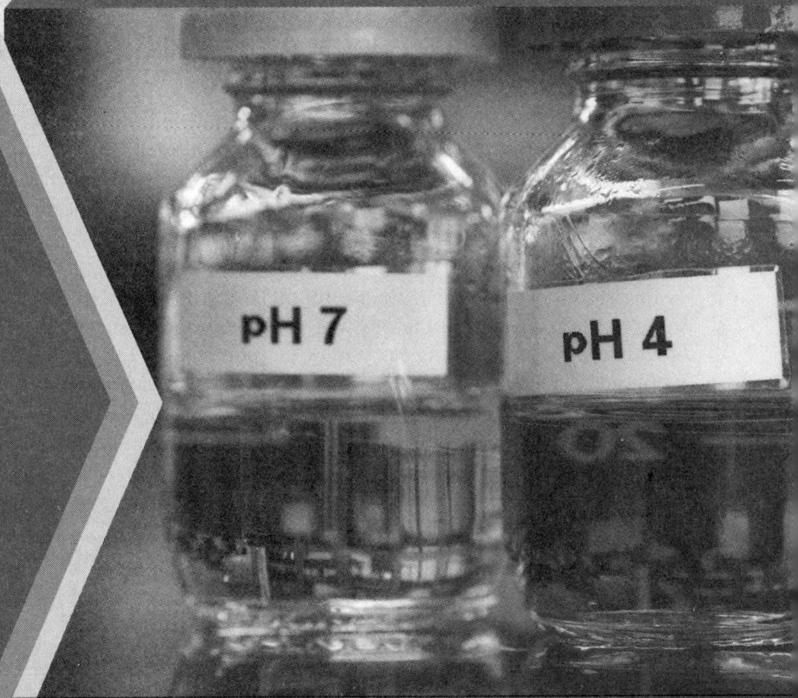

Remember

Before beginning this chapter, you should be able to:

- recall the methods of preparation, properties, and uses of acids and bases.
- remember the types of salts, their methods of preparation, properties, and uses.
- describe neutralization reaction.

Key Ideas

After completing this chapter, you should be able to:

- classify the acids and bases based on different properties and calculate the equivalent masses of acids and bases.
- describe the preparation of standard solution and estimation of volumes of solutions (volumetric analysis).
- explain self-ionization of water and the ionic product of water.
- define and calculate pH values.
- classify salts based on their characteristics.
- describe laboratory preparation of specific soluble and insoluble salts.
- understand the application of the concepts of acids and bases in qualitative analysis of simple salts.

Scientific Crypt

A Tribute to Svante August Arrhenius (1859–1927)

Svante Arrhenius was a Swedish scientist who was originally a physicist but often regarded as a chemist. He was born in Vik at Uppsala in Sweden. His father had been a land supervisor. During early childhood, at the age of 3, he taught himself to read without the help of his parents. At the age of 8, he was admitted in a local cathedral school in 5th grade.

He emerged as the youngest graduate and a distinguished student in Physics, Chemistry and Mathematics in 1876. Later, he left for study at the physical institute of Swedish academy of Sciences in Stockholm. While pursuing his studies, he published a 150 page work on the conductivities of electrolytes. According to Arrhenius, even in the absence of electric current, solutions of salts contain ions and chemical reactions in solutions are the reactions between the ions.

Based on the extension of his works, Arrhenius gave definition for acids and bases. He was made a member of Royal Swedish academy of sciences in 1901. He was also the member of Nobel committee on Physics and Chemistry. For his works on electrolytic theory of dissociation, in 1903 he became the first Swedish scientist to be awarded the Nobel prize in Chemistry. He was made a fellow of Royal society in 1990. He was the first person to report about the changes in the percentage of CO_2 in the atmosphere which alter the surface temperature of earth, a process called green house effect. Arrhenius also is known for his equation which establishes the dependence of the rate constant of a chemical reaction on the temperature and activation energy. He was also awarded Faraday medal of Chemical Society. He married twice and took his last breath on 2nd October in 1927 and was buried at Uppsala.

FUN TIME

CROSSWORD

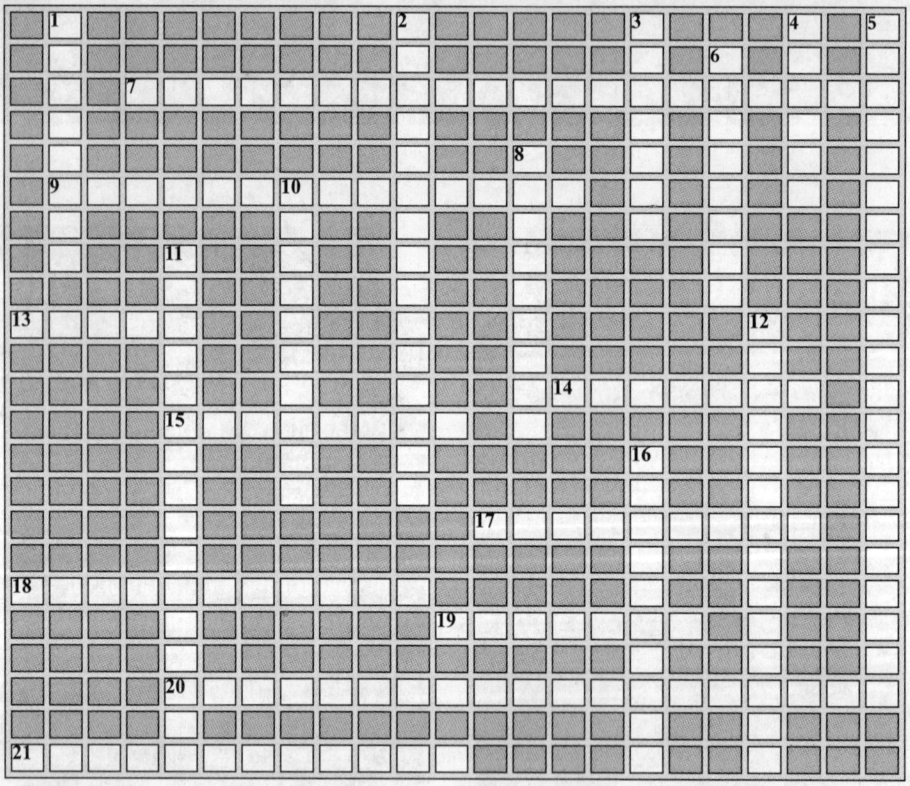

Across

7. Heat released by the reaction of one equivalent of acid by one equivalent of base
9. Opposite process of acid-base neutralization
13. Neutral pH at 25°C temperature
14. The Latin word from which the term acid is derived
15. The bases that are soluble in water
17. A salt made up of one type of cation and two types of anions.
18. A salt which gives reactions only for the simple ions present in it
19. Nature of solution of potassium sulphate
20. The product of molar concentrations of H^+ and OH^- ions in solution
21. Acids derived from plant sources

Down

1. The scientist who introduced pH scale
2. An acidic indicator
3. The number of OH^- ions given by one molecule of based on ionisation
4. Nature of solution of ammonium sulphate
5. Acid and base formed by transfer of single proton
6. The number of replaceable H^+ ions in a molecule of acid
8. The process of addition of acid from burette to base present in flask
10. Salt which is mixture of two or more simple salts
11. Solution of known concentration
12. Number of parts by weight of acid that replaces 1 part by weight of hydrogen
16. The organic compounds that give different colours in acidic or basic solutions

INTRODUCTION

Among the various classes of compounds in chemistry, acids and bases are very important. Initially, the substances that are sour to taste were termed as acids. In fact, the name acid was derived from a Latin word '*acidum*' meaning 'sour.' Similarly, bases or alkalies were characterized by their bitter taste and their slippery touch.

The earliest idea regarding acids was that all acids necessarily contain oxygen as one of the elements. Later, researches proved that the acids are of two categories. The first category of acids called **hydracids** contains only hydrogen and a non-metal, for example, HCl. The second category of acids that contain oxygen in addition to hydrogen and a non-metal is called **oxyacids**, for example, H_2SO_4. These two types of acids are together called **mineral acids** as they originate from mineral sources in contrast to the **organic acids** that have their origin from plant and animal sources.

Acids and bases were basically distinguished by their response to litmus test. Acids turn blue litmus red and bases turn red litmus blue. 'Salts' is another important category of chemical compounds. The term salt is generally used in our daily life for common salt, which is an important component of our diet. In the language of chemistry, however, the term 'salts', covers all electrovalent compounds having positive and negative radicals formed by the reactions of corresponding acids and bases. Therefore, the study of salts is invariably associated with the study of acids and bases.

Theories of Acids and Bases

Several theories were proposed by various chemists and scientist out of which few are discussed below.

Arrhenius Theory of Acids and Bases

Svante Arrhenius, for the first time in 1884, proposed a systematic theory to explain the nature of acids and bases.

Postulates

1. An acid is a substance that contains hydrogen and produces H^+ ions in an aqueous solution.

   Examples:

   $HCl \rightarrow H^+ + Cl^-$

   $H_2SO_4 \rightarrow H^+ + HSO_4^-$

   $HSO_4^- \rightarrow H^+ + SO_4^{2-}$

2. A base is a substance that produces OH^- ions in the aqueous solution.

   Examples:

   $NaOH \rightarrow Na^+ + OH^-$

   $KOH \rightarrow K^+ + OH^-$

   $Mg(OH)_2 \rightarrow Mg^{2+} + 2OH^-$

Info Bytes!

Svante Arrhenius, the brain behind the Arrhenius theory, wasn't just known for his work on acids and bases. He also developed the concept that increasing carbon dioxide concentrations could lead to global warming, way back in 1896.

3. All acids that ionize completely and hence, produce more concentration of H^+ ions are called **strong acids**. All acids that ionize partially and hence, produce less concentration of H^+ ions are called **weak acids**.

   Examples:

   $HNO_3 \rightarrow H^+ + NO_3^-$ (100% ionization, strong acid)

   $CH_3COOH \rightleftharpoons H^+ + CH_3COO^-$ (partial ionization, weak acid)

4. All bases that ionize completely and hence, produce more concentration of OH^- ions in their aqueous solutions are called **strong bases**. All bases that ionize partially and produce less concentration of OH^- ions are called **weak bases**.

Examples:

$KOH \rightarrow K^+ + OH^-$ (100% ionization, strong base)

$NH_4OH \rightleftharpoons NH_4^+ + OH^-$ (partial ionization, weak base)

5. **Neutralization** is defined as the reaction between an acid and a base to give salt and water.

Example:

$HCl + NaOH \rightarrow NaCl + H_2O$

Acid Base Salt

Since the strong acid and the strong base are completely ionized in aqueous solutions, they will be present in the form of ions. During the reaction, the anion of acid and cation of the base do not undergo any net change. Therefore, the net reaction would be formation of water by the combination of H^+ and OH^- ions. The other ions that remain unchanged during the reaction are called **spectator ions**.

Examples:

$HCl + NaOH \rightarrow NaCl + H_2O$

$H^+ Cl^- + Na^+ OH^- \rightarrow Na^+ + Cl^- + H_2O$

The net reaction of neutralization becomes $H^+ + OH^- \rightarrow H_2O$

After proposing his theory of electrolytic dissociation, Arrhenius himself gave a modified version of his theory.

According to this version, the **acid** is defined as a substance that increases the concentration of H^+ ions or hydronium ions in aqueous solutions. The **base** is defined as a substance that increases the concentrations of OH^- ions in their aqueous solutions.

Examples:

$CO_2 + 3H_2O \rightarrow SO_4^{2-} + 2H_3O^+$

$NH_3 + H_2O \rightarrow SO_4^{2-} + OH^-$

Limitations of Arrhenius Theory

1. Arrhenius theory could not explain the acidic nature of substances, which do not contain hydrogen. For example, non-metal oxides are generally acidic, but they do not contain hydrogen.

   Examples: CO_2, SO_3, etc.

2. Bases, which do not contain OH^- ions also could not be explained by Arrhenius concept. For example, metal oxides are generally basic, but they do not contain OH^- ions.

   Examples: CaO, MgO, etc.

3. Arrhenius theory was confined only to aqueous solutions. It could not explain the nature of acidic and basic substances in gas phase or in non-aqueous solutions.

4. Arrhenius theory failed to explain the neutralization reactions that do not involve formation of water.

   Example: $CaO + CO_2 \rightarrow CaCO_3$

5. Later studies on solutions have revealed that H^+ ions have no independent existence in aqueous solutions. They exist as hydronium ions (H_3O^+). This is in contradiction to Arrhenius theory.

In order to account for these drawbacks, a more advanced theory was proposed, which introduced the protonic concept of acids and bases.

Brønsted-Lowry Theory of Acids and Bases

In 1923, J. N. Brønsted and J. M. Lowry independently proposed a broader concept of acids and bases in order to overcome some of the drawbacks of Arrhenius theory.

Postulates

1. The **acid** is a substance that donates protons to any other substance(s).

   Example:

   HCl acts as a proton donor and hence, is called an acid.

   $HCl \rightarrow H^+ + Cl^-$

2. The **base** is a substance that accepts protons from any other proton donors.

   Example:

   NH_3 acts as a base as it is a proton acceptor.

   $NH_3 + H^+ \rightarrow NH_4^+$

3. An acid on losing a proton produces a species that has proton-accepting tendency that means the tendency of a base. The base so formed is called **conjugate base** of the acid.

   Example:

   $HCl \rightarrow H^+ + Cl^-$

   Acid　　Conjugate base

4. The base on accepting a proton produces a species that has proton-donating tendency that means the tendency of an acid. The acid so formed is called **conjugate acid** of the base.

   Example:

   $NH_3 + H^+ \rightarrow NH_4^+$

   Base　　Conjugate acid

5. Neutralization is defined as the transfer of a proton from the acid to the base to form a conjugate acid–base pair.

   Example:

   $HCl + NH_3 \rightarrow NH_4^+ + Cl^-$

   Acid　Base　Conjugate acid　Conjugate base

Info Bytes!

As this theory mainly focuses on proton transfer, this is also known as **protonic concept of acids and bases.**

Merits of Brønsted-Lowry Theory

1. The acidic and basic nature of substances in gas phase could be convincingly explained by this theory, which could overcome the major limitations of Arrhenius theory.
2. It involves a broader coverage of acids and bases in comparison to Arrhenius theory. This is because it is not confined to aqueous solutions alone.
3. The basic nature of substances that do not contain OH^- ions could also be explained on the basis of protonic concept.

Limitations of Brønsted-Lowry Theory

1. The acidic nature of substances that do not contain hydrogen cannot be explained.

   Examples: CO_2, SO_2, etc.

2. This theory mainly involves proton transfer. Proton donation or acceptance being a relative tendency of substances, cannot give the absolute acidity or basicity of substances.

In order to explain the nature of acids and bases in cases where there is no role for protons, a more advanced theory was proposed that introduced the electronic concept of acids and bases.

Lewis Theory of Acids and Bases

In 1930, G. N. Lewis introduced another theory of acids and bases that could successfully explain the cases where there is no role for protons.

Postulates

1. The **acid** is a substance that can act as an electron pair acceptor. The molecule or ion should be associated with shortage of electrons to act as the acid.

   Examples: BF_3, H^+, etc.

2. The **base** is a substance that can act as an electron pair donor. The molecule or ion should be associated with one or more lone pairs of electrons to act as the base.

   Examples: NH_3, OH^-, etc.

3. **Acid–base neutralization** can be defined as the transfer of an electron pair from the base to the acid.

   Examples:

   $H^+ + NH_3 \rightarrow [H^+ \leftarrow NH_3]^+$

   Formation of a hydronium ion and an ammonium ion can be explained by means of Lewis theory of acids.

   Formation of hydronium ions (H_3O^+):

   $H^+ + H_2O \rightarrow H_3O^+$

   Formation of ammonium ion:

   $NH_3 + H^+ \rightarrow NH_4^+$

Info Bytes!

Lewis theory, proposed by Gilbert N. Lewis in 1923, provides the broadest definition of acids and bases. It doesn't just consider proton transfer but focuses on electron pairs. This theory brought a revolution in the way chemists understand acid-base reactions, especially in non-aqueous solvents.

Merits of Lewis Theory

1. This theory could explain the acidic nature of those substances that do not contain hydrogen molecules.
2. It could explain the neutralization reactions that do not involve any transfer of protons.

Limitations of Lewis Theory

1. This theory failed to explain the acidic and basic nature of general acids and bases.
2. This theory could not explain the general neutralization reactions involving the formation of salt and water.
3. Generally, the acid–base reactions are fast reactions. However, the formation of a co-ordinate bond is a slow process.
4. This theory cannot explain the relative strengths of acids and bases.

The three different theories of acids and bases explain the nature of various acids and bases in different perceptions. However, none of the theories could convincingly explain all the properties of acids and bases and hence, cannot be universally applicable. Depending on the nature and conditions of a reaction, an appropriate theory is made applicable. Thus, all the three theories put together can cover the entire range of acids and bases. Acids and bases can be further classified on the basis of certain properties as discussed below.

Classification of Acids

1. **On the basis of strength**

   (a) Strong Acids: The acids that undergo nearly 100% ionization in aqueous solutions are called strong acids. These produce a high concentration of H^+ ions in the solution.

Info Bytes!

Lewis acids are a broader category than the traditional Brønsted-Lowry acids. While the latter donate protons, Lewis acids accept electron pairs.

Example:

HCl (aq) $\rightarrow H^+ + Cl^-$ (~100% ionized)

(b) Weak Acids: Acids that undergo partial ionization in aqueous solutions are called weak acids. These produce low concentration of H^+ ions in the solution.

Example:

$CH_3COOH \rightleftharpoons CH_3COO^- + H^+$

2. On the basis of basicity

Number of H^+ or H_3O^+ ions produced by ionization of one molecule of an acid in aqueous solution is called its **basicity**.

(a) Monobasic Acids: The acids that dissociate in aqueous solutions to produce one hydronium ion per molecule of the acid are called monobasic acids.

Examples: HCl, HBr, HNO_3, HI, CH_3COOH

$CH_3COOH \rightleftharpoons CH_3COO^- + H^+$

(b) Dibasic Acids: The acids that dissociate in aqueous solutions to produce two hydronium ions per molecule of the acid are called dibasic acids.

Examples:

H_2SO_4, $H_2C_2O_4$, H_2SO_3, H_2CO_3

$H_2SO_4 + H_2O \rightleftharpoons H_3O + + HSO_4^-$

$HSO_4^- + H_2O \rightleftharpoons H_3O^+ + SO_4^{2-}$

(c) Tribasic Acids: The acids that dissociate in aqueous solution to produce three hydronium ions per molecule of the acid are called tribasic acids.

Examples:

$H_3PO_4 + H_2O \rightleftharpoons H_3O^+ + H_2PO_4^-$

$H_2PO_4^- + H_2O \rightleftharpoons H_3O^+ + HPO_4^{2-}$

$HPO_4^{2-} + H_2O \rightleftharpoons H_3O^+ + PO_4^{3-}$

3. On the basis of concentration

(a) Concentrated Acid: An aqueous solution that has high percentage of acid and low percentage of water is said to be a concentrated acid.

(b) Dilute Acid: An aqueous solution that has low percentage of acid and high percentage of water is said to be a dilute acid.

4. On the basis of volatility

(a) Acids that vaporize easily below 100°C are volatile acids.

Examples: HCl, HNO_3, H_2SO_3, H_2CO_3 etc.

(b) Acids that do not vaporize even on strong heating are non-volatile acids.

Examples: H_2SO_4, H_3PO_4, etc.

Classification of Bases

1. **On the basis of strength**

   (a) Strong Bases: Bases that undergo nearly 100% (complete) ionization in aqueous solutions. These produce high concentration of OH^- ions in the solution.

   Examples:

   $Ba(OH)_2(aq) \rightarrow Ba^{2+}(aq) + 2OH^-(aq)$ (~100% ionized)

   $NaOH \rightarrow Na^+ + OH^-$

   (b) Weak Bases: Bases that undergo partial ionization in aqueous solutions. It produces low concentration of OH^- ions in the solution.

   Example:

   $NH_4OH \rightleftharpoons NH_4^+ + OH^-$

Info Bytes!

Soap is basic. The process of making soap, called saponification, uses a base to react with fats.

2. **On the basis of acidity**

   Number of OH^- ions produced by the ionization of one molecule of the base in the aqueous solution is called its **acidity**.

   (a) Monoacidic Bases: The bases that dissociate in the aqueous solution to produce one hydroxyl ion per molecule of the base are called monoacidic bases.

   Examples: NaOH, KOH, NH_4OH, etc.

   $NaOH \rightleftharpoons Na^+ + OH^-$

   (b) Diacidic Bases: The bases that dissociate in aqueous solutions to produce two hydroxyl ions per molecule of the base are called diacidic bases.

   Examples: $Ca(OH)_2$, $Cu(OH)_2$, $Mg(OH)_2$, etc.

   $Ca(OH)_2 \rightleftharpoons Ca^{2+} + 2OH^-$

   (c) Triacidic Bases: Triacidic bases are those that dissociate in the aqueous solutions to produce three hydroxyl ions per molecule of the base.

   Examples: $Al(OH)_3$, $Fe(OH)_3$, etc.

   $Fe(OH)_3 \rightleftharpoons Fe^{3+} + 3OH^-$

General Preparation Methods of Acids

1. **By synthesis/direct combination (for hydracids and binary acids).**

   Hydrogen + Non-metal → Acid

   $H_2 + Cl_2 \xrightarrow{\text{sunlight}} 2HCl$

   $H_2 + Br_2 \xrightarrow[\text{dischrarge}]{\text{electic}} 2HBr$

   $H_2 + I_2 \longrightarrow 2HI$

Info Bytes!

The production of acids, especially sulfuric acid, is a major global industry. Over 200 million tons of sulfuric acid are produced annually worldwide.

2. **By the reaction of non-metallic (acidic) oxides with water.**

Non-metallic oxide + Water → Acid

$SO_3 + H_2O \rightarrow H_2SO_4$

$P_2O_5 + 3H_2O \rightarrow 2H_3PO_4$

$N_2O_5 + H_2O \rightarrow 2HNO_3$

3. **By the oxidation of non-metals with oxyacids.**

Non-metal + Acid → Acid + Water + Oxide

$S + 6HNO_3 \xrightarrow{\Delta} H_2SO_4 + 2H_2O + 6NO_2$

$2P + 5H_2SO_4 \xrightarrow{\Delta} 2H_3PO_4 + 5SO_2 + 2H_2O$

4. **By the displacement of salts of more volatile acids with less volatile acid.**

Salt + Less volatile acid → Salt + More volatile acid

$NaCl + H_2SO_4 \xrightarrow{\Delta} NaHSO_4 + HCl$

$NaNO_3 + H_2SO_4 \xrightarrow{\Delta} NaHSO_4 + HNO_3$

General Preparation Methods of Bases

1. **By the action of water on metals.**

Water + Metal → Base/Alkali + Hydrogen↑

(cold)

$2H_2O + 2Na \rightarrow 2NaOH + H_2\uparrow$

$H_2O + Mg \rightarrow MgO + H_2\uparrow$
(steam)

$4H_2O + 3Fe \rightleftharpoons Fe_3O_4 + 4H_2\uparrow$
(steam)

2. **By the action of metallic oxides on water.**

Metallic oxide + Water → Base

$K_2O + H_2O \rightarrow 2KOH$

$MgO + H_2O \rightarrow Mg(OH)_2$

3. **By the action of oxygen on metals.**

Metal + Oxygen → Metallic oxides

$2Mg + O_2 \rightarrow 2MgO$

$4Fe + 3O_2 \rightarrow 2Fe_2O_3$

4. **By the decomposition of metal carbonates.**

Metal carbonate $\xrightarrow{\Delta}$ Basic oxide + Carbon dioxide

$ZnCO_3 \xrightarrow{\Delta} ZnO + CO_2\uparrow$

$CuCO_3 \xrightarrow{\Delta} CuO + CO_2\uparrow$

Info Bytes!

The Solvay process, named after Belgian industrialist Ernest Solvay, revolutionized the production of sodium carbonate, a basic compound, in the 19th century.

5. **Using soluble metal salts and NaOH/KOH.**

Soluble metal salt + NaOH/KOH → Salt + Insoluble metal hydroxide

$AlCl_3 + 3NaOH \rightarrow 3NaCl + Al(OH)_3\uparrow$

$Zn(NO_3)_2 + 2KOH \rightarrow 2KNO_3 + Zn(OH)_2\downarrow$

6. **Strong heating of metal nitrates.**

Metal nitrate $\xrightarrow{\Delta}$ Metal oxide + NO_2 + $O_2\uparrow$

$2Ca(NO_3)_2 \xrightarrow{\Delta} 2CaO + 4NO_2\uparrow + O_2\uparrow$

$2Zn(NO_3)_2 \xrightarrow{\Delta} 2ZnO + 4NO_2\uparrow + O_2\uparrow$

7. **By the action of oxygen on metal sulphides.**

Metal sulphide + Oxygen → Metal oxide + Sulphur dioxide

$2ZnS + 3O_2 \rightarrow 2ZnO + 2SO_2$

$2Cu_2S + 3O_2 \rightarrow 2Cu_2O + 2SO_2$

8. **Dissolution of NH_3 in H_2O.**

$NH_3 + H_2O \rightarrow NH_4OH$
(weak alkali)

Chemical Properties of Acids

1. **Action with metallic oxides.**

Metal oxide + dilute acid → Salt + Water

$CuO + H_2SO_4 \rightarrow CuSO_4 + H_2O$

$ZnO + 2HNO_3 \rightarrow Zn(NO_3)_2 + H_2O$

2. **Action with metallic carbonates and bicarbonates.**

Carbonate or bicarbonate + Acid → Salt + H_2O + $CO_2\uparrow$

$CaCO_3 + 2HCl \rightarrow CaCl_2 + H_2O + CO_2\uparrow$

$NaHCO_3 + HCl \rightarrow NaCl + H_2O + CO_2\uparrow$

3. **Action with metallic sulphite and bisulphite.**

Metal sulphite/bisulphite + Acid → Salt + H_2O + $SO_2\uparrow$

$CaSO_3 + 2HCl \rightarrow CaCl_2 + H_2O + SO_2\uparrow$

$NaHSO_3 + HCl \rightarrow NaCl + H_2O + SO_2\uparrow$

4. **Action with metallic sulphide and bisulphide.**

Metal sulphide/bisulphide + acid → Salt + H_2S

$FeS + 2HCl \rightarrow FeCl_2 + H_2S$

$NaHS + HCl \rightarrow NaCl + H_2S$

5. **Action of active metals with dilute acids.**

Active metal + dilute acid → Salt + $H_2\uparrow$

$Zn + H_2SO_4 \rightarrow ZnSO_4 + H_2\uparrow$

$Mg + 2HCl \rightarrow MgCl_2 + H_2\uparrow$

6. **Reaction with chlorides.**

   Metal chloride + acid → Salt + acid

   $NaCl + H_2SO_4 \rightarrow NaHSO_4 + HCl\uparrow$

   $NaCl + NaHSO_4 \rightarrow Na_2SO_4 + HCl\uparrow$

7. **Reaction with nitrates.**

   $KNO_3 + H_2SO_4 \xrightarrow[\text{dischrarge}]{\text{electic}} KHSO_4 + HNO_3$

   $KHSO_4 + KNO_3 \xrightarrow[\text{dischrarge}]{\text{electic}} K_2SO_4 + HNO_3$

Chemical Properties of Bases

1. **Action with non-metallic oxides.**

   Alkali + CO_2 → Metal carbonate + H_2O

   $2NaOH + CO_2 \rightarrow Na_2CO_3 + H_2O$

   $Mg(OH)_2 + SO_2 \rightarrow MgSO_3 + H_2O$

2. **Action with ammonium salt.**

   Ammonium salt + Alkali → Metal salt + H_2O + $NH_3\uparrow$

   $2NH_4Cl + Ca(OH)_2 \rightarrow CaCl_2 + 2H_2O + 2NH_3\uparrow$

   $(NH_4)_2SO_4 + 2NaOH \rightarrow Na_2SO_4 + 2H_2O + 2NH_3\uparrow$

3. **Action with soluble salts of metals other than that of Na, K, and Ca.**

   Soluble metallic salt + Base → Soluble salt + Insoluble hydroxide

   $CuSO_4 + 2NH_4OH \rightarrow (NH_4)_2SO_4 + Cu(OH)_2\uparrow$

Table 2.1 Uses of acids

Some important acids	Uses
Sulphuric acid	Manufacture of fertilizers, dyes, drugs, explosives, paints, chemicals, artificial fabrics, etc.
Hydrochloric acid	Printing, tanning and tinning industries
Nitric acid	Manufacture of dyes, explosives, drugs, fertilizers and chemicals
Acetic acid	Preservation of food and as a flavoring agent
Citric acid	Curdling of milk, flavoring of soft drinks and as a (source of vitamin C) medicine
Carbonic acid	Used in soft drink
Oxalic acid	Used as an ink stain remover
Boric acid	Preservation of grains, to wash eyes
Benzoic acid	As a food preservative
Tartaric acid	Constituent of baking powder

Table 2.2 Uses of bases

Some important bases	Uses
NaOH	Manufacture of soap
KOH	Manufacture of soft soap and in alkaline batteries
NH_4OH	Used to remove grease stains from woollen clothes
$Ca(OH)_2$	Manufacture of mortar, softening temporary hard water, neutralizing acidity of soil and as a general germicide
$Mg(OH)_2$	Used as an antacid for neutralizing gastric acidity
$Al(OH)_3$	Used as a foaming agent in fire extinguishers

Neutralization

Neutralization is the reaction of acid and base to form salt and water and is associated with the liberation of heat. The relative quantities of acid and base undergoing neutralization reaction and hence, the heat liberated depends upon the concentration of H^+ and OH^- produced by the dissociation of the acid or the base in a given reaction. Since the acids and bases differ in their basicities and acidities, the concentration of H^+ and OH^- ions furnished by them also differs. Therefore, the quantities of acids and bases are expressed in terms of equivalents that represent quantities of substances that have same combining capacities in chemical reactions.

In a neutralization reaction, one equivalent of the acid is the quantity of the acid that furnished one mole of H^+ ions and for the base one mole of OH^- ions.

Konnect

A common example of neutralization is our body's response to heartburn. Antacids are bases that neutralize the excess stomach acid.

Example:

$H_2SO_4 \rightarrow 2H^+ + SO_4^{2-}$

1 mole $H_2SO_4 \rightarrow$ 2 moles of H^+ ions

1 mole of H^+ ions $\rightarrow \frac{1}{2}$ mole H_2SO_4

= 1 equivalent H_2SO_4

Example:

Molecular weight of HCl = Equivalent weight = 36.5

For the acids and bases that have their basicity or acidity greater than one, the equivalent weight must be calculated by taking the reaction into consideration.

$$\text{Equivalent weight of the acid} = \frac{\text{Molecular weight}}{\text{Number of replaceable hydrogen ions in the given reaction}}$$

$$\text{Equivalent weight of the base} = \frac{\text{Molecular weight}}{\text{Number of replaceable } OH^- \text{ ions in the given reaction}}$$

$$\mathbf{H_2SO_4 + NaOH \rightarrow NaHSO_4 + H_2O}$$

$$\text{Equivalent weight} = \frac{\text{Molecular weight}}{1} = 98$$

$$\mathbf{H_2SO_4 + 2NaOH \rightarrow Na_2SO_4 + 2H_2O}$$

$$\text{Equivalent weight} = \frac{\text{Molecular weight}}{2} = 49$$

$$Ca(OH)_2 + 2HCl \rightarrow CaCl_2 + 2H_2O$$

$$\text{Equivalent weight} = \frac{\text{Molecular weight}}{2} = \frac{74}{2} = 37$$

$$\text{Equivalent weight of salt} = \frac{\text{Molecular weight}}{\text{Net charge on ion}}$$

Na_2SO_4

$$\text{Equivalent weight} = \frac{\text{Molecular weight}}{2} = \frac{142}{2} = 71$$

Neutralization Reaction

Reaction between acid and base to form salt and water liberating heat in the process.

$$\text{Acid} + \text{Base} \longrightarrow \text{Salt} + \text{Water} + \text{Heat}$$

$$HCl + NaOH \longrightarrow NaCl + H_2O + \text{Heat}$$

$$HNO_3 + KOH \longrightarrow KNO_3 + 2H_2O + \text{Heat}$$

$$H_2SO_4 + Ca(OH)_2 \longrightarrow CaSO_4 + 2H_2O + \text{Heat}$$

Heat of Neutralization

Heat of Neutralization is the amount of heat liberated when one equivalent of the acid reacts with one equivalent of the base. For any strong acid–strong base reaction, the heat of neutralization has the same value, that is, 13.7 kcal/mol since the acid and base involved are completely ionized.

Example: $HCl + NaOH \rightarrow NaCl + H_2O + 13.7$ kcal/mol

When the weak acid or the weak base is involved in the reaction, some amount of heat is utilized to ionize the acid or base to furnish ions. This is called **heat of ionization**. Therefore, the net heat released is less than the heat of neutralization for strong acid–strong base reaction.

Example:

Weak acid + strong base $\rightarrow$ salt + H_2O + 13.4 kcal/mol

$$\begin{aligned}\text{Heat of ionization} &= 13.7 - \text{net heat liberated}\\ &= 13.7 - 13.4 = 0.3 \text{ kcal/mol}\end{aligned}$$

$NaOH \rightarrow Na^+ + OH^-$

$CH_3COOH \rightarrow CH_3COO^- + H^+$ (consume 0.3 kcal)

$H^+ + OH^- \rightarrow H_2O$ (liberates 13.7 kcal)

$CH_3COOH + NaOH \rightarrow Na^+ + CH_3COO^- + H_2O + 13.4$ kcal/mol

Konnect

The concept of equivalent masses helps in determining the number of moles of the acid needed to neutralize the base and vice versa. This also plays a major role in determining the concentration of a solution in terms of normality.

Uses of Neutralization

1. Slaked lime ($Ca(OH)_2$) is added to reduce the acidity of soil.
2. Antacid tablets with $Mg(OH)_2$ or cold milk are used to treat acidity by neutralizing HCl in stomach.
3. Sting of ants/bees containing HCOOH (formic acid) can be neutralized by rubbing soap (NaOH).
4. Sting of wasps that contains an alkali can be treated by neutralizing it with CH_3COOH.
5. Lithium hydroxide is used to neutralize CO_2 exhaled by astronauts in spaceships or submariners in submarines.

Normality

The number of equivalents of a solute present in one litre of the solution is called **normality**. It is denoted by 'N.'

$$\text{Normality} = \frac{\text{Number of equivalents}}{\text{Volume of solution in litres}}$$

$$= \text{Number of equivalents} \times \frac{1000}{\text{V in mL}}$$

$$= \frac{\text{weight}}{\text{Equivalent weight}} \times \frac{1}{\text{V in L}} = \frac{\text{weight}}{\text{Equivalent weight}} \times \frac{1000}{\text{V in mL}}$$

Info Bytes!

Normality depends on the type of reaction under consideration, while molarity is based solely on the number of moles of solute.

The normality of the solution is helpful in expressing the concentration of the solution. However, in case of the acids and bases, the concentration can also be expressed in terms of pH. The pH of the solution represents the hydrogen ion concentration in it. This is a single factor that represents not only the concentration but also helps in determining whether a solution is acidic or basic. To calculate the pH of a solution, the concept of ionic product of water should be well understood.

Ionic Product of Water

Water molecules ionize partially to give H^+ and OH^- ions. Equilibrium exists between the ionized and unionized molecules:

$$H_2O \rightleftharpoons H^+ + OH^-$$

Applying the law of mass action to the above equilibrium, $K = \frac{[H^+][OH^-]}{[H_2O]}$

Since $[H_2O]$ is constant (Molar concentration of water in its pure sample is $= \frac{1000}{18} = 55.55$ M)

$K[H_2O] = K_w = [H^+]\,[OH^-]$,

where K_w is called the **ionic product of water.**

At normal temperature (25°C), the concentration of H^+ and OH^- ions remains equal, that is, 10^{-7} M

$\therefore [H^+] = [OH^-] = 10^{-7}$ mol/L

$K_w = [H^+]\,[OH^-] = 10^{-7} \times 10^{-7}$

$= 10^{-14}$ mol^2/L^2

Info Bytes!

The ionic product of water helps us understand that if the concentration of H^+ ions increase, the concentration of OH^- ions will decrease to keep the product constant.

On adding a base, $[OH^-]$ increases and $[H^+]$ decreases but K_w remains constant at constant temperature.

Examples:

$[H^+]$ mol ion/L	$[OH^-]$ mol ion/L	K_w (mol ion)^2/L^2
1×10^{0}	1×10^{-14}	1×10^{-14}
1×10^{-3}	1×10^{-11}	1×10^{-14}

At 25°C,

Neutral solution $\rightarrow [H^+] = [OH^-] = 10^{-7}$ mol ion/L

Acidic solution $\rightarrow [H^+] > [OH^-] < 10^{-7}$ mol ion/L

Basic solution $\rightarrow [H^+] < [OH^-] > 10^{-7}$ mol ion/L

In all the cases, the product of $[H^+]$ and $[OH^-]$ remains constant and is equal to 10^{-14} at 25°C.

Thus, at a given temperature the value of ionic product of water remains constant. Addition of the acid or the base does not change the value of K_w. On the addition of acid, when $[H^+]$ increases, a corresponding decrease in $[OH^-]$ keeps the K_w value constant.

pH

The concept of pH was introduced by Sørensen in order to avoid the use of negative exponents in expressing the concentration of acids and bases.

pH is defined as the negative logarithm to base 10 of H^+ ion concentration (or) logarithmic reciprocal of H^+ ion concentration.

$$pH = -\log_{10}[H^+] \text{ or } \log_{10}\frac{1}{[H^+]}$$

Info Bytes!

In pH, p means *potentz* and 'H' stands for hydrogen.

Similarly,

$$pOH = -\log_{10}[OH^-] \text{ or } \log_{10}\frac{1}{[OH^-]}$$

At 25°C, for a neutral solution, $[H^+] = [OH^-] = 10^{-7}$ mol ion/L

$$\text{The pH} = -\log_{10}\frac{1}{[H^+]} = -\log_{10}\frac{1}{10^{-7}} = -\log_{10} 10^7 = 7$$

Konnect

Human blood has a pH level between 7.35 and 7.45, making it slightly basic.

For the acidic solution: $[H^+] > [OH^-] < 10^{-7}$ mol ion/L

$$pH = -\log_{10}\frac{1}{> 10^{-7}} = < 7$$

Lower the pH value, the greater will be the acidic strength of the solution.

For the basic solution: $[H^+] < [OH^-] > 10^{7-}$ mol ion/L

$$pH = -\log_{10}\frac{1}{> 10^{-7}} = > 7$$

Greater the pH value, greater will be the basic strength of the solution.

Relation between pH and concentration of H⁺ ions

$[H^+]$	10^0	10^{-1}	10^{-2}	10^{-3}	10^{-4}	10^{-5}	10^{-6}	10^{-7}	10^{-8}	10^{-9}	10^{-10}	10^{-11}	10^{-12}	10^{-13}	10^{-14}
pH	0	1	2	3	4	5	6	7	8	9	10	11	12	13	14

Acid
← Acidity increases

Base
Basicity increases →

Table 2.3 pH of some common substances

Substances	pH values
HCl (gastric juice in stomach)	1.0
H_2SO_4	1.2
Citric acid	2.3
Lime juice	2.4
Acetic acid	2.9
Carbonic acid	3.0
Orange	3.5
Boric acid	5.2
Milk (lactic acid)	6.6
Pure water	7.0
Human blood	7.3
Albumin (egg)	7.9
$NaHCO_3$ solution	8.4
Sea water	8.5
Milk of magnesia	10.5
Ammonium hydroxide	11.1
Na_2CO_3 solution	11.6
NaOH	13

Uses of pH Value

1. In brewing, pH values are strictly controlled for wines of desired flavor.
2. pH value of soils is tested to enhance growth of crops in acidic/alkaline soils.
3. pH value of milk is controlled in dairies.
4. Depending on pH values of skin secretion, different soaps for oily/dry skin are prepared.
5. In medicine, for diagnosis of certain diseases, pH values of blood and urine are determined.

By mathematically calculating the pH, nature of a solution can be determined. In laboratory, however, certain chemicals are used as indicators to determine whether a solution is acidic or basic.

Indicators

Indicators are organic dyes that have one color in acidic solutions and another color in basic solutions. There are two types of indicators as discussed below.

Common Indicators

These are specific and work only in a specified pH range. Using these, it is possible to identify the acidic, basic and neutral solutions and the pH range of the solution. However, it is not possible to know the exact pH value of the solution.

Table 2.4 Common color indicators

Indicators	Colors in acidic solution	Colors in basic solution
Litmus	Red	Blue
Methyl orange	Red	Yellow
Phenolphthalein	Colorless	Pink

Table 2.5 Determination of pH using indicators

Name of the indicators	Acid colors	pH range of color change	Base colors
Methyl violet	Yellow	0.0–1.6	Blue
Thymol blue	Red	1.2–2.8	Yellow
Methyl orange	Red	3.2–4.4	Yellow
Bromocresol green	Yellow	3.8–5.4	Blue
Methyl red	Red	4.8–6.0	Yellow
Litmus	Red	5.0–8.0	Blue
Bromothymol blue	Yellow	6.0–7.6	Blue
Thymol blue	Yellow	8.0–9.6	Blue
Phenolphthalein	Colorless	8.2–10.0	Pink
Thymolphthalein	Colorless	9.4–10.6	Blue
Alizarin yellow R	Yellow	10.1–12.0	Red

Universal Indicator

Universal Indicator is a mixture of organic dyes that gives different colors with solutions of different pH values. This is more sensitive than other common indicators.

Determination of pH using universal indicators

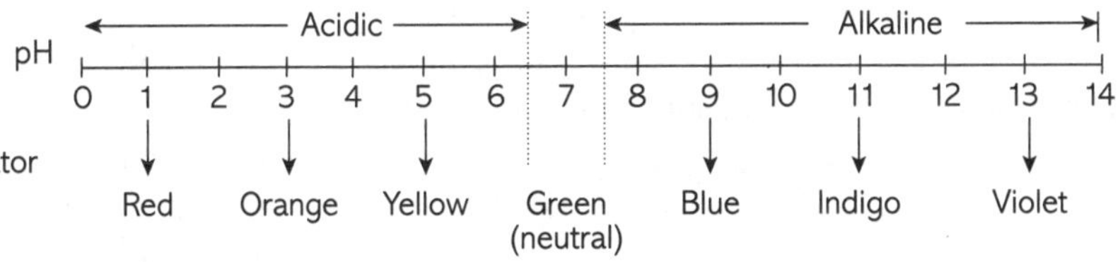

EXAMPLE 2.1 Is it correct that when a base undergoes dilution, the concentration of hydroxide ions per unit volume drops?

SOLUTION

When a base is diluted, the total volume of the solution increases due to the addition of more solvent (usually water). The total number of hydroxide ions (OH^-) in the solution does not change with dilution, as no base is removed or added, only more solvent is introduced. However, since concentration is a measure of the amount of solute (hydroxide ions in this case) per unit volume, the concentration of hydroxide ions decreases as the volume of the solution increases.

EXAMPLE 2.2 Give reasons for the following:

(i) Metals like sodium and potassium are stored under kerosene.

(ii) Dry hydrogen chloride gas does not change the colour of dry blue litmus paper.

(iii) Diluting a concentrated acid with water is an exothermic process.

SOLUTION

(i) Sodium and potassium are highly reactive with atmospheric oxygen and moisture; storing them under kerosene prevents these reactions.

(ii) For the colour change to occur, ionization of HCl is needed, which requires the presence of moisture.

(iii) The process of dilution releases heat due to the formation of solvent-solute interactions.

EXAMPLE 2.3 Explain the action of bromothymol blue indicator in the titration of hydrochloric acid (HCl) and ammonia (NH_3).

SOLUTION

Hydrochloric acid (HCl) is a strong acid and has a low pH value. Ammonia (NH_3) is a weak base and, when added, neutralizes the H^+ ions from HCl. As NH_3 is added, the pH of the solution increases gradually from acidic towards neutral. The titration range for this reaction lies between pH 6.0 and 7.6. Bromothymol blue has a pH range from about 6.0 (yellow) to 7.6 (blue), making it change from yellow to green and then to blue as the solution becomes more basic. Therefore, bromothymol blue acts as a suitable indicator for this titration, turning green at the equivalence point.

EXAMPLE 2.4 Is a solution with pH 8 acidic, basic, or neutral? Justify.

SOLUTION

A solution with pH 8 is basic. Under standard conditions (25°C), a solution with pH 7 is considered neutral. pH values less than 7 indicate acidic solutions, while values greater than 7 indicate basic solutions. Hence, a solution with pH 8 is basic in nature.

Salts

All salts are basically ionic compounds and are electrically neutral as the total positive charge on positive radicals is equal to the total negative charge on negative radicals. These oppositely charged ions are held together by strong electrostatic forces of attraction when the salts are in the solid state. In fused state or in aqueous solutions, these forces of attraction are broken and the salts are dissociated into ions. This accounts for the electrical conductivity of their solutions. Thus, all salts are electrolytes in their molten states as well as in their aqueous solutions.

Formation of Salts

Salts are the compounds formed during the neutralization reaction between the acid and the base. Therefore, **salts** can also be defined as the compounds formed by either partial or complete replacement of ionizable hydrogen atoms of the acid by one or more metal ions or ammonium ions of a base.

$NaOH + H_2SO_4 \rightarrow NaHSO_4 + H_2O$ (partial neutralization)

$2NaOH + H_2SO_4 \rightarrow Na_2SO_4 + H_2O$ (complete neutralization)

Ionic definition of salt can be given as the ionic compound that on dissociation in water yields one or more positive ions other than H^+ ions and one or more negative ions other than OH^- ions.

> **Info Bytes!**
> Salts can be acidic, basic, or neutral depending on their parent acid and base.

Examples:

$MgCl_2 \rightarrow Mg^{2+} + 2Cl^-$

$(NH_4)_2SO_4 \rightarrow 2NH_4^+ + SO_4^{2-}$

There are a large number of salts present. To make the study of salts easier, they are classified into four different categories on the basis of their composition.

Classification of Salts

Salts can be classified as shown in the following flow chart.

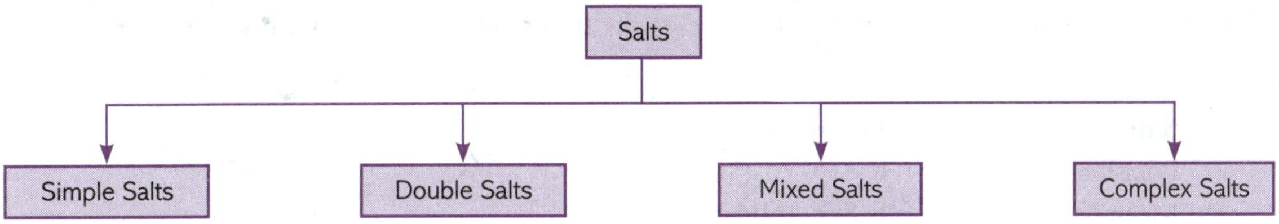

Simple Salts

The salts that contain only one type of positive ion and one type of negative ion are called **simple salts**. These are further classified into three types based on their chemical nature.

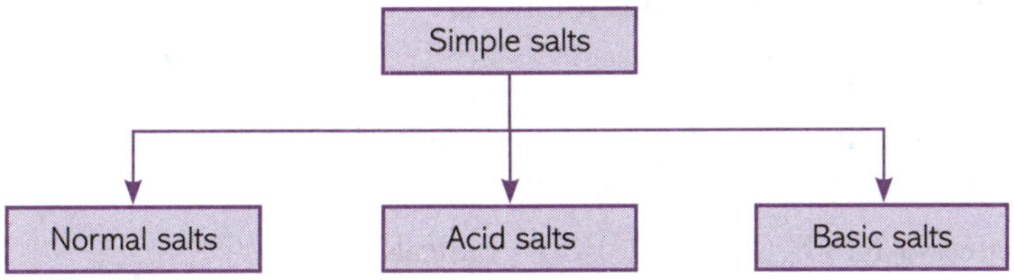

Table 2.6 Comparative study of normal, acid, and basic salts

Parameters	Normal salts	Acid salts	Basic salts
Definition	The salts that do not contain any replaceable hydrogen or 'OH' groups	The salts that contain one or more replaceable hydrogen groups	The salts that contain one or more replaceable 'OH' groups
Formation	By complete neutralization of acids and bases. E.g. $2NH_4OH + H_2SO_4$ $\downarrow$ $(NH_4)_2SO_4 + H_2O$	By incomplete neutralization of acids and bases E.g. $NaOH + H_2SO_4$ $\downarrow$ $NaHSO_4 + H_2O$	By incomplete neutralization of acids and bases. E.g. $Cu(OH)_2 + HNO_3$ $\downarrow$ $Cu(OH)NO_3 + H_2O$
Composition	All ionizable hydrogens are replaced by a metal or NH_4^+ ion	Partial replacement of ionizable hydrogen by a metal or NH_4^+ ion	Partial replacement of ionizable hydroxyl groups by non-metal ions or negative radicals
Thymolphthalein	Neutral in nature. Do not react with acids or bases	Acidic in nature. React with bases.	Basic in nature. React with acids.
Examples	NaCl, $(NH_4)_2SO_4$, $Al_2(SO_4)_3$	$NaHSO_4$, NH_4HSO_4	$Cu(OH)NO_3$, $Cu(OH)Cl$

Double Salts

The salts that contain more than one simple salt are called **double salts**. These salts are formed by the crystallization and union of two simple salts dissolved in water. Double salts undergo complete dissociation in aqueous solutions. They give reactions of all ions present in both the simple salts. These salts are usually associated with water of crystallization.

Examples:

Salt	**Formulae**
Potash alum	$K_2SO_4.Al_2(SO_4)_3.24H_2O$
Mohr's salt	$FeSO_4.(NH_4)_2SO_4.6H_2O$
Dolomite	$CaCO_3.MgCO_3$

Mixed Salts

The salts that contain more than one basic or acidic radicals are called **mixed salts**. These are formed by multi-step reactions involving corresponding acids and bases. Mixed salts undergo complete dissociation in aqueous solutions. They give the reactions of all the ions produced in aqueous solutions.

Examples:

Sodium potassium carbonate ($NaKCO_3$) (Na^+, K^+ and CO_3^{2-} radicals)
Bleaching powder ($CaOCl_2$) (Ca^{2+}, OCl^-, Cl^- radicals)
Disodium potassium phosphate Na_2KPO_4 (Na^+, K^+, PO_4^{3-} radicals)

Complex Salts

The salts that contain one complex ion and one or more simple ions are called **complex salts**. These salts are formed by mixing saturated solutions of simple salts followed by crystallization.

Examples:

Sodium argentocyanide $Na[Ag(CN)_2]$
Potassium ferrocyanide $K_4[Fe(CN)_6]$

A complex salt dissociates into complex ion and simple ions. Simple ions react individually, while the complex ions react as one unit.

Example:

$K_4[Fe(CN)_6] \rightleftharpoons 4K^+ + [Fe(CN)_6]^{4-}$

It gives reactions of potassium ions and ferrocyanide ions. However, it cannot give reactions of ferrous ions and cyanide ions separately.

Preparation of Salts

Preparation of Soluble Salts

(a) By Direct Combination (Synthesis): Heating a metal and a non-metal together. The non-metal is over the surface of the hot metal to get the salt.

Examples:

$2Al + 3Cl_2 \rightarrow 2AlCl_3$

$2Fe + 3Cl_2 \rightarrow 2FeCl_3$

(b) By the Action of Dilute Acids on Metals: Active metals like sodium and potassium are treated with acids like HCl, H_2SO_4 and HNO_3 to give their respective salts.

Examples:

$Zn + 2HCl \rightarrow ZnCl_2 + H_2\uparrow$

$Mg + H_2SO_4 \rightarrow MgSO_4 + H_2\uparrow$

(c) By the Action of Dilute Mineral Acids on Oxides: Metal oxides are generally insoluble and basic in nature. When these oxides are treated with dilute acids, displacement takes place. As, metal oxides are basic in nature, neutralization takes place.

Examples:

$FeO + H_2SO_4 \rightarrow FeSO_4 + H_2O$

$PbO + 2HNO_3 \rightarrow Pb(NO_3)_2 + 2H_2O$

(d) Action of Dilute Mineral Acids on Hydroxides: Soluble salts are obtained by the titration of an acid with a soluble hydroxide.

Example:

$2NH_4OH + H_2SO_4 \rightarrow (NH_4)_2SO_4 + 2H_2O$

(e) Action of Dilute Acids on Carbonates: Soluble salts are obtained by the titration of a carbonate salt solution with an acid.

Example:

$(NH_4)_2CO_3 + H_2SO_4 \rightarrow (NH_4)_2SO_4 + H_2O + CO_2$

(f) Action of Dilute Mineral Acid on Hydroxide: Soluble salts are obtained by the neutralization of an acid with its respective insoluble hydroxide.

Example: $Fe(OH)_2 + H_2SO_4 \rightarrow FeSO_4 + 2H_2O$

(g) Action of Dilute Acids on Carbonates: Soluble salts are obtained by the neutralization of the acid with an insoluble carbonate.

Example: $PbCO_3 + 2HNO_3 \rightarrow Pb(NO_3)_2 + H_2O + CO_2$

Preparation of Insoluble Salts

(a) By Direct Combination (Synthesis): Heating the powdered metal with sulphur.

Example: $Fe + S \rightarrow FeS$

(b) Precipitation from Soluble Salts: In this method, when two soluble salt solutions are mixed, double decomposition takes place and the insoluble salt is precipitated. This is the most common method for the preparation of insoluble salts.

Example: $BaCl_2 + H_2SO_4 \rightarrow BaSO_4 + 2HCl$

General Characteristics of Salts

1. **Physical State**: Salts are non-volatile crystalline solids.
2. **Electrical Conductivity**: Salts being electrovalent (ionic) compounds conduct current in molten as well as in aqueous state due to their dissociation into ions.
3. **Solubility**: The salts are ionic compounds. However, all the salts are not soluble in water. Some salts remain insoluble.

Table 2.7 Table showing the solubility of salts

Solubility of salts in water	
Solubility of compounds	**Exceptions**
All NH_4^+, Na^+, K^+ compounds are soluble	–
All nitrates and nitrites are soluble	–
All chlorides are soluble in water	Hg_2Cl_2, AgCl, $PbCl_2$
	$PbCl_2$—Soluble in hot water
All sulphates are soluble	$CaSO_4$, $PbSO_4$, $BaSO_4$
All oxides and hydroxides are insoluble	Oxides of Na^+, K^+, Mg^{2+}
All carbonates are insoluble	K_2CO_3, Na_2CO_3, $(NH_4)_2CO_3$
All sulphides are insoluble	K_2S, Na_2S, $(NH_4)_2S$

Salt Hydrolysis

The phenomenon in which a simple salt on dissolution in water forms a parent acid and a parent alkali resulting in acidic, basic, or neutral solution is called **salt hydrolysis**. It is the most important property of salts.

Depending on the nature of the salts, it is classified into the following four types.

1. **Hydrolysis of Salts of Strong Acids and Weak Bases**: This type of hydrolysis produces a strong acid that ionizes and a weak base that does not ionize. This increases the concentration of H^+ ion making the solution acidic.

   Example: $(NH_4)_2SO_4$, $CuSO_4$, NH_4NO_3, $FeCl_3$, etc.

   $Cu^{2+} + SO_4^{2-} + 2H_2O \rightarrow Cu(OH)_2 + 2H^+ + SO_4^{2-}$

   As only the cation of the salt reacts with water, it is also called **cationic hydrolysis**.

2. **Hydrolysis of Salts of Weak Acids and Strong Bases**: This produces a weak acid that does not ionize and a strong base that ionizes and gives OH^- ions. This makes the solution basic and has a $pH > 7$.

   Example: Na_2CO_3, CH_3OOK, CH_3COONa

   $CH_3COO^- + Na^+ + H_2O \rightarrow CH_3COOH + Na^+ + OH^-$

   As the anion of the salt reacts with water, it is also called **anionic hydrolysis**.

3. **Hydrolysis of Salts of Strong Acids and Strong Bases**: This type of hydrolysis produces a strong acid and a strong base that are completely ionized giving equal number of H^+ and OH^- ions. Thus, this solution is neutral with a $pH = 7$.

   Example: NaCl, K_2SO_4, KNO_3

   $Na^+ + Cl^- + H_2O \rightarrow Na^+ + OH^- + H^+ + Cl^-$

4. **Hydrolysis of Salts of Weak Acids and Weak Bases**: This produces a weak acid and weak base which exist in the molecular form. Thus, there are no free H^+ or OH^- ions and the solution is neutral with $pH = 7$.

   Examples: $(NH_4)_2CO_3$, CH_3COONH_4

   $2NH_4^+ + CO_3^{2-} + 2H_2O \rightarrow 2NH_4OH + H_2CO_3$

Qualitative Analysis of Simple Salts

A simple salt contains an acidic (anion) and a basic radical (cation). The analysis of a simple salt involves identification of the constituent acidic and basic radicals of the salt.

Table 2.8 Identification of some important anions

Anions	Tests	Reactions involved	Observations and inference
Carbonate	Action of dilute HCl	$CaCO_3 + 2HCl$ ↓ $CaCl_2 + H_2O + CO_2$	Colorless gas with brisk effervescence that puts off burning splinter and turns lime water milky. CO_2 gas is evolved.
Chloride	Action of conc. H_2SO_4	$BaCl_2 + H_2SO_4$ ↓ $BaSO_4 + 2HCl$ $HCl + NH_4OH$ ↓ $NH_4Cl + H_2O$	A colorless and pungent smelling gas is evolved (HCl). The gas when exposed to a glass rod dipped in NH_4OH forms white dense fumes.
Nitrate	Action of conc. H_2SO_4 + in the presence of copper turnings	$4NaNO_3 + 2H_2SO_4 + Cu$ ↓ $2Na_2SO_4 + 2NO_2 + Cu(NO_3)_2 + 2H_2O$	A reddish brown pungent gas is evolved (NO_2) and the solution turns blue $Cu(NO_3)_2$.

Table 2.9 Confirmatory tests for anions

Anions	Tests	Reactions involved	Observations
Carbonate	Reaction with $BaCl_2$ solution	$CaCO_3 + BaCl_2$ ↓ $BaCO_3 + CaCl_2$	A white precipitate that is insoluble in conc. HCl ($BaCO_3$)
Chloride	Reaction with $AgNO_3$ solution	$2BaCl_2 + 2AgNO_3$ ↓ $2AgCl + Ba(NO_3)_2$	White curdy precipitate (AgCl)
Nitrate	Brown ring test: Salt solution + Freshly prepared ferrous sulphate solution + conc. H_2SO_4		A reddish brown ring is formed at the junction of the two layers

Identification of Some Important Cations

For the identification of cations in the salts, NaOH and NH_4OH are the generally used reagents. They form insoluble precipitates with characteristic colors.

Table 2.10 Table showing different characteristic precipitations given by different metal ions

	Precipitates formed	
Cations of salts	**NaOH**	**NH_4OH**
Fe^{2+}	$Fe(OH)_2$ Dirty green Insoluble in excess NaOH	$Fe(OH)_2$ Dirty green Insoluble in excess NH_4OH
Fe^{3+}	$Fe(OH)_3$ Reddish Brown Insoluble in excess NaOH	$Fe(OH)_3$ Reddish Brown Insoluble in excess NH_4OH
Ca^{2+}	$Ca(OH)_2$ Milky white Insoluble in excess NaOH	No reaction – –
Zn^{2+}	$Zn(OH)_2$ White Soluble in excess NaOH (colorless solution)	$Zn(OH)_2$ White Soluble in excess NH_4OH (colorless solution)
Pb^{2+}	$Pb(OH)_2$ Chalky white Soluble in excess NaOH	$Pb(OH)_2$ Chalky white Insoluble in excess NH_4OH
Cu^{2+}	$Cu(OH)_2$ Pale blue Insoluble in excess NaOH	$Cu(OH)_2$ Pale blue Soluble in excess NH_4OH (deep blue solution)
Al^{3+}	$Al(OH)_3$ White gelatinous Soluble in excess NaOH	$Al(OH)_3$ White gelatinous Soluble in excess NH_4OH

EXAMPLE 2.5 Define salt hydrolysis. Explain the nature of aqueous solution of $CuSO_4$ on the basis of the above phenomenon.

SOLUTION

The phenomenon in which a simple salt on dissolution in water forms a parent acid and a parent alkali resulting in acidic, basic, or neutral solution is called salt hydrolysis. It is the most important property of salts.

$CuSO_4$ on hydrolysis produces a strong acid that ionizes and a weak base that does not ionize. This increases the concentration of H^+ ions making the solution acidic with pH < 7 (at 25 °C)

$$Cu^{2+} + SO_4^{2-} + 2H_2O \rightarrow Cu(OH)_2 + 2H^+ + SO_4^{2-}$$

As cation of the salt reacts with water, it is called cationic hydrolysis.

EXAMPLE 2.6 Explain the amphoteric nature of zinc oxide and aluminium oxide.

SOLUTION

On warming zinc oxide with dilute sulphuric acid, the zinc oxide dissolves rapidly and forms clear solution of zinc sulphate. Similarly, when aluminium oxide is warmed with dilute sulphuric acid forms aluminium sulphate.

On warming zinc oxide with dilute sulphuric acid, the zinc oxide dissolves rapidly and forms clear solution of zinc sulphate. Similarly, when aluminium oxide is warmed with dilute sulphuric acid forms aluminium sulphate.

$$ZnO + H_2SO_4(\text{dil.}) \rightarrow ZnSO_4 + H_2O$$

$$Al_2O_3 + 3H_2SO_4(\text{dil.}) \rightarrow Al_2(SO_4)_3 + 3H_2O$$

On warming zinc oxide with concentrated sodium hydroxide or potassium hydroxide, the zinc oxide rapidly dissolves to form clear solution of sodium zincate or potassium zincate.

Similarly, aluminium oxide reacts with concentrated sodium hydroxide to form sodium metaluminate.

$$ZnO + 2NaOH \rightarrow Na_2ZnO_2 + H_2O$$

$$Al_2O_3 + 2NaOH \rightarrow 2NaAlO_2 + H_2O$$

As the oxides of zinc and aluminium react with acids as well as alkali to form salt and water, they are amphoteric in nature.

EXAMPLE 2.7 How do you identify the following cations in their aqueous solutions by using a caustic soda solution?

(i) Cu^{2+} (ii) Pb^{2+} (iii) Ca^{2+}

SOLUTION

(i) Cu^{2+} gives a light blue precipitate of copper (II) hydroxide ($Cu(OH)_2$).
(ii) Pb^{2+} gives a white precipitate of lead(II) hydroxide ($Pb(OH)_2$).
(iii) Ca^{2+} generally, gives a white precipitate of calcium hydroxide ($Ca(OH)_2$) although this precipitate is sparingly soluble and might not be as evident as the others.

EXAMPLE 2.8 Why is it essential to choose the correct indicator in a titration? Name the indicator used when acetic acid is titrated against sodium hydroxide.

SOLUTION

The correct indicator ensures the accurate detection of the endpoint of a titration. When acetic acid is titrated against sodium hydroxide, the appropriate indicator is phenolphthalein.

POINTS TO REMEMBER

- ✔ According to Arrhenius Theory of Acids and Bases, an acid is a substance that contains hydrogen and produces H^+ ions in an aqueous solution and A base is a substance that produces OH^- ions in the aqueous solution.
- ✔ All acids that ionize completely and hence, produce more concentration of H^+ ions are called strong acids. All acids that ionize partially and hence, produce less concentration of H^+ ions are called weak acids.
- ✔ All bases that ionize completely and hence, produce more concentration of OH^- ions in their aqueous solutions are called strong bases. All bases that ionize partially and produce less concentration of OH^- ions are called weak bases.
- ✔ Neutralization is defined as the reaction between an acid and a base to give salt and water.
- ✔ According to Brønsted-Lowry Theory of Acids and Bases, the acid is a substance that donates protons to any other substance(s) and the base is a substance that accepts protons from any other proton donors.
- ✔ An acid on losing a proton produces a species that has proton-accepting tendency that means the tendency of a base. The base so formed is called conjugate base of the acid.
- ✔ The base on accepting a proton produces a species that has proton-donating tendency that means the tendency of an acid. The acid so formed is called conjugate acid of the base.
- ✔ According to Lewis Theory of Acids and Bases, the acid is a substance that can act as an electron pair acceptor and the base is a substance that can act as an electron pair donor.
- ✔ Number of H^+ or H_3O^+ ions produced by ionization of one molecule of an acid in aqueous solution is called its basicity.
- ✔ An aqueous solution that has high percentage of acid and low percentage of water is said to be a concentrated acid.
- ✔ An aqueous solution that has low percentage of acid and high percentage of water is said to be a dilute acid.
- ✔ Number of OH^- ions produced by the ionization of one molecule of the base in the aqueous solution is called its acidity.
- ✔ Heat of Neutralization is the amount of heat liberated when one equivalent of the acid reacts with one equivalent of the base.
- ✔ When the weak acid or the weak base is involved in the reaction, some amount of heat is utilized to ionize the acid or base to furnish ions. This is called heat of ionization.
- ✔ The number of equivalents of a solute present in one litre of the solution is called normality.
- ✔ pH is defined as the negative logarithm to base 10 of H^+ ion concentration (or) logarithmic reciprocal of H^+ ion concentration.
- ✔ Salts can also be defined as the compounds formed by either partial or complete replacement of ionizable hydrogen atoms of the acid by one or more metal ions or ammonium ions of a base.
- ✔ The salts that contain only one type of positive ion and one type of negative ion are called simple salts.
- ✔ The salts that contain more than one simple salt are called double salts.
- ✔ The salts that contain more than one basic or acidic radicals are called mixed salts.
- ✔ The salts that contain one complex ion and one or more simple ions are called complex salts.
- ✔ The phenomenon in which a simple salt on dissolution in water forms a parent acid and a parent alkali resulting in acidic, basic or neutral solution is called salt hydrolysis.

PRACTICE QUESTIONS CLASSROOM WING

Very Short Answer Type Questions

Directions for questions from 1 to 5:
Fill in the blanks.

1. The formula of the basic salt formed by treating calcium hydroxide with HCl is _____.
2. Normality of 0.01M aluminium hydroxide is ________ (assuming complete ionization).
3. The hydroxyl ion concentration of sodium hydroxide having a pH value of 12, at 25°C is ________.
4. Non-metallic oxides are either _____ or _____ in nature.
5. The number of ions produced by one mole of $[Co(NH_3)_6]Cl_3$ in its aqueous solution is ___________.

Directions for questions from 6 to 25:
Answer the following questions.

6. Arrange the colours of solutions on the addition of a universal indicator in the order of the given pH values of solutions.

   (i) 11 (ii) 7
   (iii) 3 (iv) 9
   (v) 5
   (A) Orange (B) Yellow
   (C) Blue (D) Indigo
   (E) Green

7. Is the reaction feasible?

   Potassium ferricyanide + NaOH → Reddish brown precipitate

8. Does pH value change during the usage of aluminium hydroxide as a foaming agent in fire extinguishers?
9. Is this reaction possible?

   Sodium argentocyanide → Na^+, Ag^+, CN^-

10. How does a complex salt dissociate in its aqueous solution?
11. What is the principle involved in the preparation of $FeCl_3$?
12. In the equation $X + HCl \rightarrow NaCl + H_2S$, what is X?
13. Mention any two methods of preparation of acids. Illustrate with equations.
14. How are basic salts formed?
15. How are soluble salts prepared by direct combination? Give an example.
16. Illustrate any one method of preparation of bases with equations.
17. What is the pH range in which phenolphthalein is colorless?
18. Name the insoluble salts that can be prepared by direct combination?
19. What are the pH values of the following solutions at 25°C?

    (i) 0.001 M of HCl
    (ii) 0.05 M of H_2SO_4
    (iii) 0.01 M of NaOH

20. Which method is employed for the preparation of sulphate of Ba, Ca, and Pb?
21. Define pH and give its mathematical representation.
22. What would be the nature of aqueous solutions of the following salts?

    (i) KNO_3
    (ii) Na_2CO_3
    (iii) CH_3COONa

23. Define basicity of an acid. Give an example each for monobasic, dibasic and tribasic acids.
24. Write the equation for the action of a dilute acid on a metal oxide.
25. Mention the steps involved in ionization of phosphoric acid.

Short Answer Type Questions

26. The ion product of water is 10^{-12} mole^2 L^{-2} at a certain temperature. Identify the wrong statements regarding the solutions under the same conditions.
   (i) The water should have been at a temperature of less than 25°C.
   (ii) 10^{-7} M solution in the abovementioned sample of water is basic in nature.
   (iii) 10^{-5} M solution in the abovementioned sample of water is acidic in nature.
   (iv) Addition of 0.01 M HCl to the abovementioned water changes the K_w value to 10^{-14} mole^2 L^{-2}.
27. Calculate the pH of 0.01 M nitric acid solution.
28. Write conjugate acid and conjugate base of $H_2PO_4^-$ and H_2O.
29. Write the reactions of anionic hydrolysis of Potassium carbonate and sodium acetate.
30. What will be the effect on pH of soil on addition of fertilizer to the field?
31. Arrange the following H^+ ion concentrations of the solutions in the order of the colours obtained by the addition of a universal indicator.
   (A) 10^{-13} (B) 10^{-5} (C) 10^{-7}
   (D) 10^{-9} (E) 10^{-1}
   (i) Green (ii) Red (iii) Yellow
   (iv) Violet (v) Blue
32. How do bases react with the following? Write the equations.
   (i) non-metallic oxide (ii) ammonium salt
   (iii) soluble metallic salt
33. What is meant by neutralization? Give some examples identifying spectator ions in the reactions.
34. What is the value of ionic product of water at 25°C? How does it change with temperature?
35. (a) Give pH range for various solutions at 25°C.
   (b) 0.25 moles of an acid is added to water and one litre acidic solution is prepared. The degree of the dissociation of the acid is 60%. The number of moles of H^+ furnished by the acid is found to be 0.45 moles in one litre solution. Calculate the basicity of the acid.
36. Distinguish between acidic and basic salts giving examples.
37. Mention any four applications of pH.
38. Define basicity of an acid. Give an example each for monobasic, dibasic, and tribasic acids.
39. What is the difference between mixed and complex salts with respect to chemical reactions? Explain with an example.

Essay Answer Type Questions

40. Barium chloride is soluble in water, whereas silver chloride is insoluble in water. What conclusion can be made from the above statement?
41. When H_2S gas is passed through a solution containing ammonium ions and zinc ions, zinc sulphide is precipitated but not ammonium sulphide. Why?
42. Explain the formation of hydronium ion and ammonium ion.
43. Define salt hydrolysis. Explain the nature of aqueous solution of the following salts on the basis of salt hydrolysis.
   (i) $(NH_4)_2CO_3$ (ii) $CuSO_4$
   (iii) $NaNO_3$ (iv) $CaCl_2$
44. Explain with examples the use of NaOH and NH_4OH as reagents for the identification of cations in salts.
45. Draw the structures and names of different oxyacids of chlorine and explain the influence of different number of oxygen atoms attached to the chlorine atom in each acid on their acidic strength.

PRACTICE QUESTIONS COMPETITION WING

Level 1: Apply your Concepts

Direction for questions from 1 to 10:
State whether the following statements are true or false.

1. Formation of co-ordinate covalent bond between NH_3 and BF_3 is an example of neutralization reaction according to Bronsted theory.
2. A di-acidic base has one replaceable hydroxide ion.
3. For a dibasic acid, normality is twice the molarity for a given solution.
4. S^{2-} is the conjugate base of HS^-.
5. Methyl orange exhibits yellow color in basic medium.
6. Curd is sour in taste due to the presence of an acidic substance.
7. $K_2SO_4 \cdot Al_2(SO_4)_3 \cdot 24H_2O$ gives reactions of both K^+ and Al^{3+} ions, respectively.
8. The product of concentrations of H^+ and OH^- ions is called ionic product of water.
9. BF_3 is basic in nature.
10. Acid which contains oxygen, hydrogen and a non-metal like N, S, P are called oxyacids.

Direction for questions from 11 to 19:
Fill in the blanks.

11. According to Bronsted–Lowry theory neutralization reaction is the formation of ______.
12. $X + H_2O \rightarrow Y$. Y is used to remove grease stains from woolen clothes. X is ______ and Y is ________.
13. Phenolphthalein is a/an_______ indicator.
14. The salt obtained by partial neutralization of sodium hydroxide and sulphuric acid is ________ in nature.
15. Metallic oxides are either ______ or ______ in nature.
16. $[H^+]$ of nitric acid having a pH value of 6 is ____
17. The pH of aqueous solution of salt obtained by the reaction between NaOH and CH_3COOH is ________ at 25°C.
18. A salt, X is prepared by the complete neutralization of $Cu(OH)_2$ with H_2SO_4. The nature of X is ________
19. The units of K_w are __________.

Direction for question 20:
Match the entries given in Column A with appropriate ones from Column B.

20. Match the entries of Column A with those of Column B.

Column A (Type of salts)	Column B (Example)
(i) Normal salt	(A) $NaHCO_3$
(ii) Acidic salt	(B) $CaOCl_2$
(iii) Basic salt	(C) $CaCO_3MgCO_3$
(iv) Double salt	(D) $Cu(OH)NO_3$
(v) Mixed salt	(E) KNO_3

Direction for questions from 21 to 42:
For each of the questions, four choices have been provided. Select the correct alternative.

21. **Assertion (A):** Generally, the colour of indicators changes in a particular pH range.

    Reason (R): Indicators are weak acids or weak bases and exhibit different colours in molecular form and ionic form.

    (a) Both A and R are true and R is the correct explanation of A.
    (b) Both A and R are true, but R is not the correct explanation of A.
    (c) A is true and R is false.
    (d) A is false and R is true.

22. **Assertion (A):** All indicators are not suitable for all sorts of titrations.

    Reason (R): The colour of the indicator keeps changing continuously with the change in pH values.

    (a) Both A and R are true and R is the correct explanation of A.
    (b) Both A and R are true, but R is not the correct explanation of A.

(c) A is true and R is false.
(d) A is false and R is true.

23. **Assertion (A):** Acetic acid is a monobasic acid.

Reason (R): Acetic acid is a weak acid and produces less concentration of H^+ ions.

(a) Both A and R are true and R is the correct explanation of A.
(b) Both A and R are true, but R is not the correct explanation of A.
(c) A is true and R is false.
(d) A is false and R is true.

24. Which of the following indicators is the best indicator for the detection of end point in the titration of CH_3COOH and KOH?

(a) methyl orange (b) phenolphthalein
(c) methyl red (d) none of these

25. According to Lewis theory, neutralization is the:

(a) transfer of proton from acid to base.
(b) transfer of proton from base to acid.
(c) transfer of electron pair from acid to base.
(d) transfer of electron pair from base to acid.

26. The indicator that shows color changes in the entire pH range is:

(a) phenolphthalein
(b) methyl orange
(c) universal indicator
(d) thymol blue

27. Which of the following has the highest value of pH?

(a) HCl (b) NaOH
(c) $Ca(OH)_2$ (d) CH_3COOH

28. Heat of neutralization is less than 13.7 kcal/mol for the reaction:

(a) $HCl + NaOH \rightarrow NaCl + H_2O$
(b) $H_2SO_4 + 2NaOH \rightarrow Na_2SO_4 + 2H_2O$
(c) $HNO_3 + NaOH \rightarrow NaNO_3 + H_2O$
(d) $CH_3COOH + NaOH \rightarrow CH_3COONa + H_2O$

29. Which among the following does not undergo hydrolysis?

(a) Na_2CO_3 (b) CH_3COOH
(c) CH_3COONH_4 (d) K_2SO_4

30. Which of the following acts as both Bronsted acid and Lewis acid?

(a) Cu^{2+} (b) SO_2
(c) Fe^{3+} (d) NH_4^+

31. Which among the following factors changes the value of ionic product of water?

(a) change in temperature
(b) addition of acid
(c) addition of base
(d) addition of either acid and base

32. Which of the following solutions has the same concentration of H^+ ions as 0.1 N HCl?

(a) 0.1N H_2SO_4
(b) 0.3 N H_3PO_4
(c) 0.2 N HNO_3
(d) All of these

33. Which of the following cannot show acidic nature?

(a) H_2CO_3 (b) $CaCO_3$
(c) HCl (d) HSO_4^-

34. The spectator ions in the hydrolysis of $(NH_4)_2CO_3$ are:

(a) NH_4^+, H^+, OH^-
(b) NH^+_4, CO_3^{2-}, H^+, OH^-
(c) CO_3^{2-}, H^+, OH^-
(d) no spectator ions

35. Disodium potassium phosphate is a/an _____ salt.

(a) acid (b) mixed
(c) complex (d) double

36. V_1 mL of x molar hydrochloric acid is mixed with V_2 mL of y molar sodium hydroxide. Arrange the following steps in correct sequence for calculation of pH of the mixture. ($y > x$ and $V_1 > V_2$)

(1) Calculation of the number of equivalents of acid and base.
(2) Calculation of the total volume of mixture.
(3) Calculation of the normality of acid and base.
(4) Calculation of the net OH^- ion concentration.
(5) Taking the negative logarithm of H^+ ion concentration.
(6) Dividing K_w by OH^- ion concentration.

(a) 1 3 2 6 4 5 (b) 3 1 2 4 5 6
(c) 3 1 2 6 4 5 (d) 1 2 3 4 5 6

37. A strongly acidic solution is taken and a base is slowly added to it drop by drop. Arrange the colors observed during the process of addition in proper sequence.

(1) green (2) indigo
(3) orange (4) red
(5) blue (6) violet
(7) yellow

(a) 3 4 1 7 2 5 6 (b) 4 3 7 1 5 2 6
(c) 4 3 1 7 5 2 6 (d) 3 4 7 1 6 2 5

38. A red litmus paper when dipped in an aqueous solution of potassium acetate turned blue. Arrange the following steps in proper sequence to explain the above observation.

(1) identification of spectator ions.
(2) identification of free ions that caused the color change of the litmus paper.
(3) identification of positive and negative radicals.
(4) writing the net reaction taking place.
(5) writing ionic equation for the reaction of positive and negative radicals with water.

(a) 3 5 1 4 2 (b) 3 1 5 4 2
(c) 5 1 4 3 2 (d) 5 3 1 4 2

39. Identify the species that can give both conjugate acid and conjugate base.

(a) NH_4^+ (b) $H_2PO_4^-$
(c) PO_4^{3-} (d) H_3O^+

40. Barium chloride is soluble in water, whereas silver chloride is insoluble in water. Which of the following conclusions can be drawn on the basis of the above-mentioned facts?

(a) All barium salts are highly soluble in water.
(b) All silver salts are insoluble in water.
(c) Solubility product of barium chloride is much greater than that of silver chloride.
(d) Solubility product of silver chloride is much greater than that of barium chloride.

41. Which of the following salts can produce only two types of radicals?

(a) $NaKCO_3$ (b) $CaOCl_2$
(c) NH_4HSO_4 (d) $Na(NH_4)HPO_4$

42. Na_2CO_3 is dissolved in water at 25°C. Which of the following is/are correct regarding the given statement?

(a) In this solution anionic hydrolysis take place.
(b) The concentration of H^+ ion in the given solution is less than 10^{-7} mole/L
(c) The product of H^+ and OH^- in the solution is equal to 10^{-14} mole^2/L^2
(d) The solution contains CO_3^{-2} as spectator ion.

Level 2: Review Your Concepts

43. If the pH of a solution of a diacidic base is 12 at 25°C, calculate its molarity considering 100% ionization.

44. Species 'X' has only conjugate acid OH^-. Species 'Y' has only conjugate base NH_3. What are X and Y?

45. What could be the probable pH value of a neutral solution at 50°C?

46. Calculate the normality of resultant solution whose 500 mL of 0.01 N H_2SO_4 solution is diluted to 2 L.

47. Find out the pH of the resultant solution whose 500 mL of 0.01 N H_2SO_4 solution is mixed with 500 mL 0.005 N KOH solution (log 5 = 0.7).

48. Account for the variation of acidic character with increase in the oxidation state of central atom.

49. Two salts are dissolved in water separately. When phenolphthalein is added to the two solutions, one solution turned pink and the other solution was colorless. How do you justify this?

50. How many moles of NaOH must be added to 200 mL of 0.1 M solution of HNO_3 to get a solution having pH value 2.00?

51. Explain the nature of the following salts:

(a) NaH_2PO_2 (b) Na_2HPO_3
(c) Na_2HPO_4

52. An aqueous solution of Mohr's salt can give a precipitate with NaOH or NH_4OH. But the aqueous solution of potassium ferrocyanide cannot give a precipitate with both reagents. How do you account for this?

53. Two colored salt solutions of two metals A and B gave precipitates with NaOH and NH_4OH. On further addition of NH_4OH, the precipitate disappears, in the case of B. There is no such change in the case of

'A' either with NaOH or NH_4OH. Identify A and B. Give equations.

54. Compare and contrast the nature of aqueous solutions of ammonium acetate and sodium sulphate.

55. Find the pH of resultant solution when 100 mL of 0.005 M H_2SO_4 at 25°C is diluted to 1000 mL. What is the amount of NaOH required to be dissolved in 500 mL to exactly neutralize the above solution?

56. A strong alkali forms an acidic salt with a dibasic acid. From the aqueous solution of the salt formed on the addition of dilute acid evolves a gas that turns lime water milky. Identify the salt and predict the reactions involved in it.

57. Explain the variation in basic strengths of hydrides of VA group elements.

Direction for questions from 58 to 67:
Application-Based Questions

58. 14.3 g of $Na_2CO_3 \cdot xH_2O$ is dissolved in water and the volume is made up to 200 mL. 20 mL of this solution required 40 mL of $\frac{N}{4}$ HNO_3 for complete neutralization. Calculate x.

59. 10 mL of 1 N HCl, 25 mL of 2 N H_2SO_4 and 40 mL of X N HNO_3 are mixed and made up to 2000 mL. 100 mL of this solution required 30 mL of NaOH taken from a solution containing 4 g of NaOH in 250 mL of solution. What is the value of X?

60. 8 g of mixture of $NaNO_3$ and Na_2CO_3 are dissolved and made into 500 mL of solution. 50 mL of this solution neutralizes completely 25 mL of N/5 HNO_3. Calculate the percentage composition of the mixture.

61. Do equimolar solutions of NaOH and $Ca(OH)_2$ possess same pH value at the same temperature? Justify.

62. Explain why no indicator can be used for the titration between formic acid and ammonium hydroxide.

63. Sodium bicarbonate can be manufactured by Solvay process where addition of brine solution to ammonium bicarbonate solution gives precipitation of sodium bicarbonate. But, its analogue, potassium bicarbonate cannot be prepared by the above process. Explain with respect to the concept of solubility product.

64. Explain the acidic and basic nature of the following substances on the basis of protonic concept.

(a) H_2SO_4 (b) HPO_4^{2-}
(c) NH_3 (d) NH_4^+

65. (a) 'All Lewis bases are Bronsted bases. But all Lewis acids are not Bronsted acids.' Comment on the statement.

(b) In 500 mL of 0.01 M H_2SO_4 solution, 0.2 g $CaCO_3$ is added. Then 500 mL of 0.01 M KOH solution is added. Then you are asked to prepare a solution of pH 5, from 50 mL the resultant solution without adding any reagent other than water.

(i) Calculate the volume of gas at STP liberated during process.
(ii) Calculate the pH of the resultant solution.
(iii) How do you obtain the solution of the required pH from the resultant solution?

66. Find the pH of resultant solution when 100 mL of 0.005M H_2SO_4 at 25°C is diluted to 1000 mL. What is the amount of NaOH required to be dissolved in 500 mL to exactly neutralize the above solution?

67. Explain the strengths of conjugate acid-base pairs of the following species:

(a) HSO_4^- (b) NH_3
(c) HS^- (d) ClO_4^-

Level 3: Assess Your Concepts

68. The normality of a solution changes from 0.01 N to 0.005 N by adding some amount of water in 1 L of the solution. How much water was added?

69. Calculate the volume of 0.02 N NaOH solution required to be added to 500 mL 0.005 N HCl solution in order to obtain the resultant solution with pH value 12.

70. Though zinc and manganese get precipitated as their sulphides, they do not get precipitated along with lead or copper when H_2S is passed through acidified solutions of their salts. Justify and also explain how the precipitation of Zn^{2+} and Mn^{2+} ions takes place.

71. How does the acidic character vary among the trihalides of boron? Give a reason in support of your answer.

Direction for questions from 72 to 77:
Application-Based Questions

72. Among H_3PO_2, H_3PO_3 and H_3PO_4 which has the maximum acidic strength? Explain.

73. Calculate the pH value of the 10^{-6} M HCl solution when diluted by 100 times. Justify (log 1.1 = 0.041).

74. Why do both acidic indicator and basic indicator show different colors in acidic and basic solutions?

75. A complex, salt with formula $[Co(NH_3)_6]Cl_3$ can form a white curdy precipitate with silver nitrate solution. Another complex with same ligands cannot form precipitate with $AgNO_3$ solution. What would be the probable formula of that complex? Give reasons in support of your answer.

76. Explain why the strengths of strong acids and strong bases cannot be determined in water. How is it possible to compare the acidic strengths in acetic acid?

77. Assume that in 10 L of water, the number moles of water that remains in dissociated form is 10^{-n} at t°C temperature. Calculate the ionic product of water and pH of a neutral solution at t°C.

AT

PRACTICE QUESTIONS JEE-NEET SPECIAL WING

Multiple-Answer Type Questions

Directions for Questions number 1 to 5:

Select one or more correct alternative(s) from the given choices.

1. Study the following reaction and answer the question that follows.

Metal bisulphide + Hydrochloric acid → Salt + X↑.

Which of the following statements are correct with respect to the given reaction.

(a) Metal can be a representative element with valency 1 or 2.

(b) X is a lower oxide of sulphur

(c) X dissolves sparingly in water to form the hydracid

(d) X is a characteristic gas which turns acidified potassium dichromate green

2. 0.5 moles of a dibasic acid 'X' is added to water to prepare one litre solution. The solution of X at a given temperature 'T' contains 0.7 mol of H^+ ions. Identify the incorrect statements with respect to X.

(a) The percentage degree of dissociation of X at temperature T could be 70%.

(b) X could be predicted as Sulphuric acid.

(c) 0.15 moles of X remain in a molecular state at T.

(d) pH of the solution of X increases with dilution.

3. Identify the statements that are true with respect to Kw, the ionic product of water.

(a) The value of K_w changes with the addition of HCl or NaOH

(b) Addition of an acid to water increases the H^+ ion concentration of the solution, but K_w remains unchanged.

(c) The value of K_w is 10.1×10^{-13} at 25°C.

(d) K_w at 75°C > K_w at 50°C

4. Identify the incorrect match.

Salt	Nature of its aqueous solution-Reason
(a) $FeCl_3$	Basic-Due to the formation of $Fe(OH)_3$
(b) Na_2CO_3	Basic- Due to the presence of NaOH molecules
(c) KNO_3	Neutral- Due to the presence of equal number of free H^+ and OH^- ions
(d) $(NH_4)_2CO_3$	Neutral- Due to the absence of free H^+ or OH^- ions

5. Choose the correct set of conjugate acid base pairs.

(a) H_2CO_3, HCO_3^- (b) H_2CO_3, CO_3^{-2}

(c) H_2O, H_3O^+ (d) H_3O^+, OH^-

Comprehension-Based Questions

Directions for Questions 6 to 10:

Read the following passage and answer the questions given below

Titration is a common laboratory method for quantitative chemical analysis used to determine the unknown concentration of a known reactant. This method involves using a reagent of known concentration (standard solution) and volume to react with an analyte solution of unknown concentration.

In the standard practice of titrations, the analyte is taken in the conical flask while the standard solution (titrant) is taken in the burette.

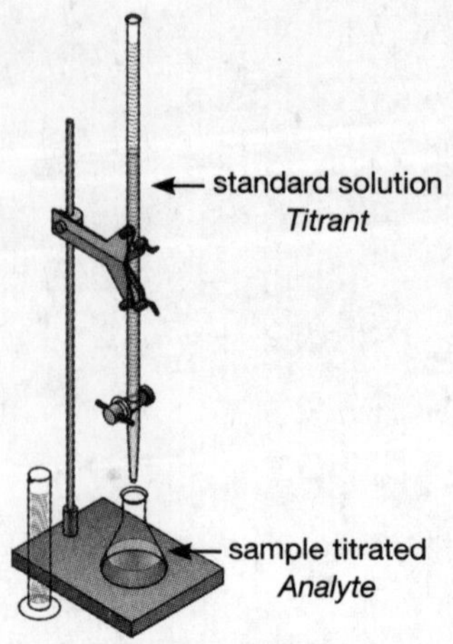

The titrant is slowly run down from the burette into the conical flask, and changes in pH, conductivity values, or the colour of an indicator (if added) are recorded after regular intervals of 0.5mL or 1mL volume additions of the solution. The completion of the reaction is determined by identifying the equivalence point or the end point of the titration. At the end point, a sudden change in pH or conductivity values, the formation of a precipitate, or a sharp colour change in the indicator indicates the stoichiometric delivery of the reagent (titrant) into the analyte. At this point, the number of equivalents of the reagent equals the number of equivalents of the analyte.

When pH values are used to determine the end point, a graph of pH against the volume of the titrant is plotted. The volume of the titrant at the end point is then determined from the graph. Typically, the end point is indicated by a sudden change in pH value without a significant change in the titrant volume or by a sharp bend in the curve. It's important to note that the pH value of an acid-base titration at the equivalence point is not necessarily equal to 7.

A sample acid-base titration is performed, and the following graph of pH versus volume of the titrant is plotted. Study the graph and answer the questions that follow.

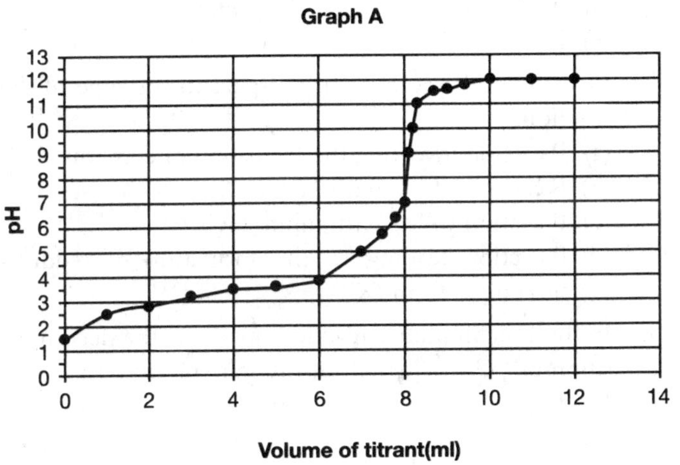

6. Predict which of the following is correct with respect to graph A.
It is a graph that would have plotted for the titration between.
(a) Sulphuric acid Vs Potassium hydroxide
(b) Sodium hydroxide Vs Acetic acid
(c) Ammonium hydroxide Vs Acetic acid
(d) Hydrochloric acid Vs Ammonium hydroxide

7. Choose the correct interpretation related to graph A.
(a) OH^- ion concentration of the analyte solution is decreasing with the addition of the titrant
(b) H^+ ion concentration of the analyte solution is decreasing with the addition of the titrant
(c) H^+ ion concentration of the analyte solution is increasing with the addition of the titrant
(d) H^+ ion concentration of the analyte solution remains unchanged but more and more OH^- ions are getting added to the analyte due to the addition of the titrant.

8. What is the approximate volume of the titrant at which the reaction is complete?
(a) 11 mL (b) 6 mL
(c) 7 mL (d) 8mL

9. A 20 mL of sulphuric acid of unknown concentration is titrated with 0.2N NaOH. Volume of NaOH at the end point from the pH graph was identified as 10 mL. Find the concentration of sulphuric acid.
(a) 0.2 M (b) 0.1 M
(c) 0.05 M (d) 0.5M

10. In the process of using an acid-base indicator to pinpoint the endpoint of a titration involving an acid and a base, the selection of the indicator is determined by its pH working range. This range corresponds to the pH values at which the indicator undergoes a colour change. Typically, an indicator with a pH working range that closely matches the pH range expected at the end point of the titration is chosen for the procedure.

Acid base indicator	Working pH range of the indicator	Colour change in acidic/basic medium
(1) Methyl orange	3.2-4.4	Orange-yellow
(2) Phenolphthalein	8.2-10	Colourless-blue
(3) Methyl violet	0.0-1.6	Yellow-bluish violet
(4) Bromothymol blue	6.0-7.6	Yellow- blue

Match the following:

List – I Acid -base titration	List – II Approximate value of pH at the end of the titration	List – III Indicator best suitable for the titration
(1) Sulphuric acid Vs Sodium hydroxide	(i) pH ≈ 7	(p) Methyl orange
(2) Acetic acid vs Ammonium hydroxide	(ii) pH< 6.5	(q) Methyl violet
(3) Hydrochloric acid Vs Ammonium hydroxide	(iii) pH>7.5	(r) Phenolphthalein
(4) Oxalic acid vs Sodium hydroxide		(s) Bromothymol blue
		(t) No indicator is best suitable for this titration

★ The extent of dissociation of acetic acid and ammonium hydroxide is almost same

Identify the correct match.

	1	2	3	4
(a)	(i) (r) (s)	(i) (s)	(ii) (p)	(iii) (r)
(b)	(i) (r) (p)	(i) (t)	(ii) (p)	(iii) (r)
(c)	(iii) (r) (s)	(ii) (q)	(i) (s)	(ii) (p)
(d)	(ii) (r) (s)	(iii) (t)	(iii) (s)	(ii) (s)

Directions for Questions 11 to 15:

Read the following passage and answer the questions given below.

Study the given figure and answer the questions that follow:

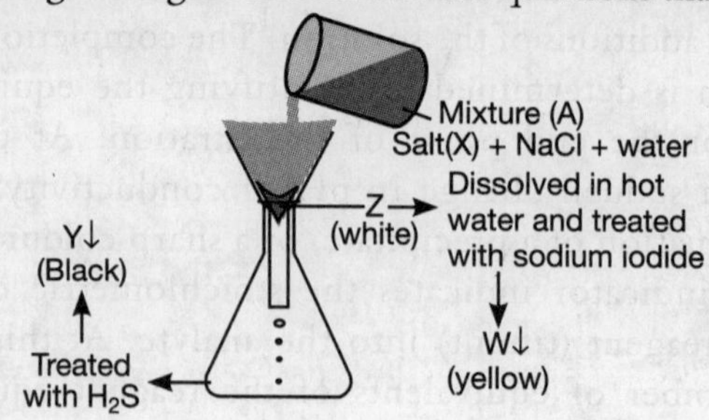

Compound (X) emits a reddish-brown gas upon heating but does not liberate any gas on heating with dil. HCl. Its chloride salt is sparingly soluble in water.

11. 'Compound (X) emits a reddish-brown gas upon heating'. Choose your correct inference about 'X' from this statement.
X would be a,
(a) Nitrate salt (b) Sulphate salt
(c) Carbonate salt (d) Sulphide salt

12. Salt 'X' consists of which of the following cations?
(a) Silver(I) (b) Mercuric (II)
(c) Lead(IV) (d) None of the above

13. Compound 'Y' is
(a) Ag_2S (b) HgS
(c) PbS (d) Na_2S

14. Pick the odd one out with respect to the type of the reaction.
(a) Reaction involving the formation of compound W
(b) Reaction of 'X' with NaCl
(c) Reaction of 'X' with dilute HCl
(d) Reaction leading to the formation of reddish-brown gas from 'X'

15. In the stoichiometric reaction involving the decomposition of 'X', coefficient of the solid product is.
(a) 1 (b) 2
(c) 4 (d) 6

Match the Column

16. Two formula types describe a compound: the empirical formula, showcasing the simplest ratio of elements within a molecule, and the molecular formula, detailing the exact count of each element within a molecule of the compound. Sarita first rinsed the tomatoes(P) in a vinegar(Q) solution and prepared a tomato soup on an LPG(R) stove. She served the prepared soup to her guest in a bowl and took a sugar cane (S) juice for herself.
Read the given passage and based on the description about the compound present in the underlined substance in the passage, match the entries in list-I with that given in list-II

List-I Compound	List-II Empirical formula of the compound
(a) Acid present in P	(i) CH_2O
(b) Solute in the solution of Q	(ii) Same as its molecular formula
(c) Hydrocarbon present in major component in 'R'	(iii) HCO_2
(d) Complex carbohydrate present in 'S'	(iv) C_2H_5

ANSWER KEYS

Crossword

Across

7. Heat of neutralization
9. Salt hydrolysis
13. Seven
14. Acidum
15. Alkalies
17. Mixed salt
18. Complex salt
19. Neutral
20. Ionic product of water
21. Organic acids

Down

1. Sorenson
2. Phenolphthalein
3. Acidity
4. Acidic
5. Conjugate acid base pair
6. Basicity
8. Titration
10. Double salt
11. Standard solution
12. Equivalent mass
16. Indicators

Classroom Wing

Very Short Answer Type Questions

1. Ca(OH)Cl
2. 0.03 N
3. 0.01
4. neutral, acidic
5. 4 N (N indicates Avogadro number)

Competition Wing

Level 1: Apply your Concepts

1. False
2. False
3. True
4. True
5. False
6. True
7. True
8. True
9. False
10. True
11. conjugate acid base pair
12. X = NH_3, Y = NH_4OH
13. Acidic
14. Acidic
15. Basic, amphoteric
16. 0.000001 mol ion/L
17. Greater than 7
18. Normal salt
19. $Mol^2\ lit^{-2}$
20. (i) - (E), (ii) - (A), (iii) - (D), (iv) - (C), (v) - (B)
21. (a)
22. (c)
23. (b)
24. (b)
25. (d)
26. (c)
27. (b)
28. (a)
29. (d)
30. (d)
31. (a)
32. (a)
33. (b)
34. (d)
35. (b)
36. (c)
37. (b)
38. (a)
39. (b)
40. (a)
41. (c)
42. (a), (b) and (c)

JEE-NEET Special Wing

Multiple-Answer Type Questions

1. (c, d)
2. (b, d)
3. (b, d)
4. (a, b)
5. (a, b)

Comprehension-Based Questions

6. (a)
7. (b)
8. (d)
9. (c)
10. (b)
11. (a)
12. (d)
13. (c)
14. (d)
15. (b)

Match the Columns

16. (a)-(iii), (b)-(i), (c)-(iv), (d)-(ii)

Hints and Explanations

Classroom Wing

Very Short Answer Type Questions

1. Ca(OH)Cl
2. 0.03 N
3. 0.01
4. neutral, acidic
5. 4 N (N indicates Avogadro number)
6. (D) pH = 11 → Indigo
   (E) pH = 7 → Green.
   (A) pH = 3 → Orange
   (C) pH = 9 → Blue
   (B) pH = 5 → Yellow
7. Potassium ferricyanide is a complex salt and it ionizes as K and $[Fe(CN)_6]^{-3}$ ions. The formation of a reddish-brown precipitate with NaOH is the characteristic reaction of Fe^{+3} ions. As the complex ferricyanide ion cannot be further ionized to give Fe^{+3} ions. This salt cannot give the above-mentioned reaction for Fe^{+3} ions.
8. Aluminium hydroxide is used in fire extinguishers as it can produce foam in which oil vapours can be trapped and hence can extinguish oil-fed fires. This does not involve any change in pH value.
9. The salt sodium argentocyanide has the formula $Na_2[Ag(CN)_2]$ produces Na^+ and $[Ag(CN)_2]^{-2}$ ions but not Ag^+ ions.
10. A complex salt dissociates into a complex ion and simple ions.
11. Direct combination (synthesis) of Fe with Cl_2
12. Na_2S
13. By the action of acidic oxides with water.
    $SO_3 + H_2O \rightarrow H_2SO_4$
    By the oxidation of non-metal with oxy acids.
    $S + 6HNO_3 \rightarrow H_2SO_4 + 2H_2O + 6\ NO_2$
14. By incomplete neutralization of acids and bases.
15. By heating a metal with a non-metal.
    Example: $2Al + 3Cl_2 \rightarrow 2AlCl_3$.
16. Reaction of water with metals
    Example: $2H_2O + 2Na \rightarrow 2NaOH + H_2\uparrow$
    $2H2O + Mg \rightarrow Mg(OH)_2 + H_2\uparrow$
17. 0 to 6
18. FeS (iron sulphide)
19. (i) $pH = -\log_{10}[H^+]$
    $HCl \rightleftharpoons H^+ + Cl^-$
    0.001 M 0.001 M
    $\therefore pH = -\log_{10}[0.001]$
    pH = 3
    (ii) $[H^+] = 0.05 \times 2$
    $= 0.1$
    pH = 1
    (iii) $[OH^-] = 0.01$
    pOH = 2
    pH = 12
20. Precipitation from soluble salts.
21. Negative logarithm to base 10 of H^+ ion concentration
    $pH = -\log_{10}[H^+]$
22. (i) Neutral
    (ii) Basic
    (iii) Basic
23. Numbers of H^+ or H_3O^+ ions produced by ionization of one molecule of an acid in aqueous solution.
    Monobasic → HCl, Dibasic → H_2SO_4,
    Tribasic → H_3PO_4.
24. Metal oxide + dilute acid → Metal salt + water
    $ZnO + 2HNO_3 \rightarrow Zn(NO_3)_2 + H_2O$
25. $H_2O + H_3PO_4 \rightleftharpoons H_3O^+ + H_2PO_4-$
    $H_2O + H_2PO_4^- \rightleftharpoons H_3O^+ + HPO_4^{2-}$
    $H_2O + HPO_4^{2-} \rightleftharpoons H_3O^+ + PO_4^{3-}$

Short Answer Type Questions

26. At 25°C, the ionic product of water is 10^{-14} mol^2 L^{-2}. K_w value increases with an increase in temperature due to the increase in the degree of dissociation. Value of K_w of 10^{-12} mole^2 l^{-2} corresponds to a higher temperature.

Addition of acid or base changes only H^+ or OH^- ion concentration keeping K_w value constant.

Hence, (i) and (iv) are the wrong options.

27. $V_1 = 100$ mL

$N_1 = 0.05 \times 2 = 0.1$ N

$V_2 = 1000$ mL

$N_1V_1 = N_2V_2$

$N_2 = N_1V_1/V_2$

$N_2 = 0.01N$

$pH = -\log 10^{-2} = 2$

$[H^+]$ of nitric acid $= 0.01 = 10^{-2}$

$\therefore$ pH = 2

28. Conjugate acid of $H_2P^-O_4$ is H_3PO_4.

Conjugate base of $H_2PO_4^-$ is HPO_4^{-2}.

Conjugate acid of H_2O is H_3O^+.

Conjugate base of H_2O is OH^-.

29. $K_2CO_3 \rightarrow 2K^+ + CO_3^{-2}$

$CO_3^{-2} + 2H_2O \rightarrow +2OH^-$

$CH_3COONa \rightarrow CH_3COO^- + Na^+$

$CH_3COO^- + H_2O \rightarrow CH_3COOH + OH^-$

Potassium carbonate and sodium acetate are salts of strong bases and weak acids. Therefore, the anions of these salts undergo hydrolysis producing free OH^- ions.

30. Addition of fertilizers to crops increases the acidity of the soils and hence, decreases the pH value of the soils.

31. (C) Green - pH = 7 $\rightarrow [H^+] = 10^{-7}$

(E) Red - pH = 1 $\rightarrow [H^+] = 10^{-1}$

(B) Yellow - pH = 5 $\rightarrow [H^+] = 10^{-5}$

(A) Violet - pH = 13 $\rightarrow [H^+] = 10^{-13}$

(D) Blue - pH = 9 $\rightarrow [H^+] = 10^{-9}$

32. (ii) $2NH_4Cl + Ca(OH)_2 \rightarrow CaCl_2 + 2H_2O + 2NH_3\uparrow$

(iii) $AlCl_3 + 3NaOH \rightarrow 3NaCl + Al(OH)_3\uparrow$

33. (i) Neutralization is defined as the reaction between an acid and a base to give salt and water.

Example: $HCl + NaOH \rightarrow NaCl + H_2O$

34. (i) Product of concentrations of H^+ and OH^- ions

(ii) 10^{-7} is concentration of each ions.

(iii) Temperature dependence

35. (a) (i) pH range of acidic solution

(ii) pH range of basic solution

(iii) Relate pH range to H^+ ion concentration

(b) 60% of 0.25 moles of $= 0.25 \times 0.6 = 0.150$ moles of acid molecules

0.15 moles of acid molecules produces 0.45 mole of H^+

1 moles produces 3 moles of H^+

Hence the basicity of the acid is 3

36. (i) Replaceable hydrogen ions, hydroxide ions.

(ii) Basic radicals

(iii) Incomplete neutralization of base

37. (i) pH and Plants

(ii) pH in our Digestive System

(iii) pH and Tooth Decay

(iv) pH of the Soil

38. Number of H^+ or H_3O^+ ions produced by ionization of one molecule of an acid in aqueous solution is called its basicity. Examples of monobasic acid - HCl,

dibasic acid - H_2SO_4

dibasic acid - H_3PO_4

39. Difference between mixed and complex salts on the basis of:

(i) Products on dissociation of salts.

(ii) Reactions of products formed on dissociation.

Essay Answer Type Questions

40. The condition for precipitation is that the ionic product of the solution should exceed the value of its solubility product. As the solubility product of barium chloride is much greater than that of silver chloride, the ionic product always remains lesser than the solubility product. It prevents precipitation of barium chloride. Silver chloride has a low ionic product of the solution. Therefore, it remains insoluble.

41. When H_2S gas is passed through a solution containing both NH_4^+ ions and Zn^{+2} ions, the addition of S^{-2} ions cause the precipitation of ZnS. This is because the ionic product exceeds the low value of the solubility product of ZnS. The solubility product of ammonium sulphide being much higher than ZnS, the addition of a few S^{-2} ions do not make the ionic product exceed the solubility product.

42. (i) Presence of lone electron pair on H_2O/NH_3 molecule

(ii) Donation of lone electron pair to H^+ ions

43. The phenomenon in which a simple salt on dissolution in water forms a parent acid and a parent alkali resulting in acidic, basic or neutral solution is called salt hydrolysis. It is the most important property of salts. Refer page no. 2.21 for detailed answer.

44. For the identification of cations in the salts, NaOH and NH_4OH are the generally used reagents. They form insoluble precipitates with characteristic colors.

    (i) Formation of hydroxide precipitates

    (ii) Different colors for different precipitates

    (iii) Solubility of different precipitate in excess of reagent. Refer table 2.10 on page 2.24

45. Structures of oxyacids of chlorine

Cl – OH Hypochlorous acid (HOCl)

O = Cl – OH Chlorous acid ($HClO_2$)

O = Cl – OH Chloric acid ($HClO_3$)
‖
O

O
‖
O = Cl – OH Perchloric acid ($HClO_4$)
‖
O

From the given structures we can observe that the number of non protonated (double bonded) oxygen atoms gradually increases from hypochloros acid to perchloric acid. With the increase in the number of non protonated (double bonded) oxygen atoms partial +ve charge developed on the chlorine atom increases. The higher the partial +ve charge on the chlorine atom, the easier the release of proton from the Protonated oxygen atom (OH) is. Since the number of protonated oxygen atom in all the oxy acids are same that is -1, The easier the release of proton, the stronger is the acid. Hence the order or acidic strength is

$$HClO < HClO_2 < HClO_3 < HClO_4$$

From the above explanation, it can be concluded that the acidic strength of oxyacids decreases with the decrease in oxidation state provided their basicities are same.

Competition Wing

Level 1: Apply your Concepts

20. Correct matching is

(i) → (E) (ii) → (A)

(iii) → (D) (iv) → (C)

(v) → (B)

21. Since indicators are weak acids or weak bases, their percentage of existence in the molecular state and in the ionized state depends on the strength of the acidic/basic/neutral solution to which they are added. Hence, their colours change at a particular pH range.

Hence, the correct option is (a).

22. All indicators are not suitable for all sorts of titrations since the colours of different indicators change at different pH ranges. The colours of indicators do not change continuously with the change in pH value.

Hence, the correct option is (c).

23. Acetic acid is a monobasic acid as only one hydrogen atom is attached to an oxygen atom and is replaceable. Acetic acid is a weak acid, but it has no relevance to the basicity of acid.

Hence, the correct option is (b).

36. (3) calculation of the normality of acid and base

(1) calculation of the number of equivalents of acid and base

(2) calculation of the total volume of the mixture

(6) calculation of the net OH^- ion concentration

(4) dividing K_w by OH^- ion concentration

(5) taking the negative logarithm of H^+ ion concentration

Hence, the correct answer is (c).

37. (4) red (3) orange (7) yellow

(1) green (5) blue (2) indigo

(6) violet

Hence, the correct answer is (b).

38. (3) identification of positive and negative radicals

(5) writing ionic equations for the reaction of positive and negative radicals with water

(1) identification of spectator ions

(4) writing the net reaction taking place

(2) identification of free ions that caused the color change of litmus paper

Hence, the correct answer is (a).

39. $H_2PO_4^-$ can form conjugate base HPO_4^{2-} and conjugate acid H_3PO_4

Hence, the correct answer is (b).

40. Basicity of acetic acid = 1 since it ionizes as $CH_3COOH \rightleftharpoons CH_3\ COO^- + H^+$ and gives only one H^+ ion. HNO_3 also possesses only one replaceable hydrogen and has basicity = 1.

Hence, the correct answer is (a).

41. $NaKCO_3 \rightarrow Na^+ + K^+ + CO_3^{2-}$

$CaOCl_2 \rightarrow Ca^{2+} + OCl^- + Cl^-$

$NH_4HSO_4 \rightarrow NH_4^+ + HSO_4^-$

(two types of radicals)

$Na(NH_4)\ HPO_4 \rightarrow Na^+ + NH_4^+ + HPO_4^-$

Hence, the correct answer is (c).

42. In Na_2CO_3 solution, Na^+ and CO_3^{2-} are formed

Na^+ is the cation generated from a strong base. It does not undergo hydrolysis it is spectator ion

CO_3^{2-} is generated from the weak acid, (H_2CO_3)

CO_3^{2-} undergoes hydrolysis

$CO_3^{2-} + H_2O \rightarrow H_2CO_3 + OH^-$

The solution is basic and pH is more than 7

∴ The concentration of H^+ ion in the given solution is less than 10^{-7} mole/L

Ionic product of water at 25°C is 10^{-14} mole^2/L^2

∴ (a), (b) and (c) are correct

(d) is wrong

Hence, the correct answer is (a,b,c).

Level 2: Review Your Concepts

43. pOH of the diacidic base = 14 – 12 = 2

∴ $[OH^-] = 10^{-2}$ mole/L

Since it is a diacidic base the molarity

$= \frac{10^{-2}}{2}$ mole/L = 0.5×10^{-2} = 0.005 mole/L.

44. Conjugate acid of O^{-2} is OH^-. It has no conjugate base. Conjugate base of NH_4^+ is NH_3. It has no conjugate acid. X and Y are O^{-2} and NH_4^+, respectively.

45. At 50°C, the ionic product of water is more than 10^{-14} mole^2/L^2. ∴ The probable ionic product can be 10^{-10} mole^2/L^2 and then the pH of the neutral solution is 5.

46. 500 mL 0.01 N H_2SO_4 solution contains 0.005 mole H^+ ions.

It is diluted to 2 L.

∴ The normality of the resultant solution

$= \frac{0.005}{2} = 0.0025$ N.

47. 500 mL 0.005 N KOH → 0.0025 [OH^-]

500 mL 0.01 N H SO → 0.005 [H^+]

∴ (0.005 – 0.0025) = 0.0025 moles of H^+ will be neutralized.

∴ 0.0025 moles of H^+ is present (500 + 500) mL.

= 1 L of the resultant solution

∴ pH of the solution = log (0.0025)

$= -\log(5^2 \times 10^{-4})$

$= -(2\log 5 - 4)$

$= -\{(2 \times 0.7) - 4\}$

$= -(1.4 - 4)$

$= 2.6$

48. (i) effect of electronegative atom on the O–H bond strength

(ii) effect of oxidation state of the central atom on the position of electron cloud present between oxygen atom and the central atom

(iii) relation between the position of the above electron cloud and the charge separation between hydrogen and oxygen atom of the hydroxyl radical attached to the central atom

(iv) relation between the above charge separation and ease of formation of hydrogen ion

(v) relation between ease of formation of hydrogen ion with the acidic character of the respective acids

49. (i) nature of solution where phenolphthalein is pink and colorless

(ii) nature of the components produced on hydrolysis of salts

(iii) relation between the components produced and the color change of indicator

50. Number of moles of H^+ ion in HNO_3

= 200 × 0.1 = 20 mmol

The concentration of H^+ ion in HNO_3 = 0.1 M

So, pH of the solution before introduction of NaOH

pH = –log [H^+]

= –log[0.1]

= 1

So, to make the solution of pH = 2, the NaOH is added to it.

At pH = 2 the H^+ ion concentration must be = 0.01 M

Or the number of moles of H^+ ion present at pH 2 in 200 mL = 0.01 × 200 = 2 mmol

So, as we can see that remaining H^+ ion i.e 18 mmol must be neutralized by NaOH.

Hence, the required moles of NaOH for making the solution of pH 2 will be 18 mmol or 0.018 mol.

51. (i) identification of parent acid from which the respective salts are formed

(ii) structures of the given salts

(iii) number of hydroxyl radical present in the respective acid

(iv) number of replaceable hydrogen in the respective acid

(v) identification of the negative radical(s) that can be formed from the given acids

(vi) determination of the number of replaceable hydrogen(s) present in the given salts based on the composition of the above negative radicals

(vii) relation between the number of replaceable hydrogen(s) present in the salt and its nature

52. Mohr's salt is a double salt containing two cations and one anion, and is obtained by combination of two different salts which gives precipitates when added with NaOH and NH_4OH, because it is a complex salt and do not form hydroxide with base.

53. (i) metals giving colored salts

(ii) colored salts that give precipitates with NaOH and NH_4OH

(iii) comparison between the reactions of the precipitates obtained with excess NaOH and NH_4OH

(iv) solubility of the product formed

54. $Na_2(SO_4)$ is a neutral salt because it is made from the strong acid and strong base. Whereas $NaCO_3$ is a basic salt because it is made from a strong base and a weak acid.

55. (i) calculation of H^+ ion concentration in the diluted solution

(ii) calculation of the number of moles of hydrogen ions present in 100 mL of 0.005 M H_2SO_4

(iii) calculation of the concentration of the hydrogen ions of H_2SO_4 solution after dilution
(iv) calculation of the number of moles of NaOH required to neutralize the above solution
(v) calculation of the amount of NaOH required
(vi) Ans: 4×10^{-2} g.

56. (i) CO_2 gas turns lime water milky
(ii) identification of gas
(iii) dibasic acid responsible to produce this gas
(iv) acidity of the alkali
(v) requisite for acidic salt

57. As the electron density of the lone pair is spread over a greater volume(as the atomic size of the central atom increases down the group) and is consequently more diffuse, the lone pair of electrons becomes less nucleophilic and hence, less basic.

58. $V_1N_1 = N_2V_2$

$20\ (N_1) = 40 \times 0.25$

$N_1 = 0.5$ N

Normality of $Na_2CO_3 \,.\, xH_2O$ solution is 0.5

$$0.5 = \frac{14.3}{\text{Eq.wt.}} \times \frac{1000}{200}$$

$$\text{Eq.Wt.} = \frac{14.3 \times 5}{0.5}$$

$$\text{Eq.Wt.} = 143$$

But equivalent weight $Na_2CO_3 \,.\, xH_2O$ is

$$\frac{106 + x(18)}{2} = 143.$$

$$\therefore x = \frac{286 - 106}{18}$$

$$x = 10$$

$$\therefore Na_2CO_3 \,.\, 10H_2O$$

59. Normality of NaOH

$$N_1 = \frac{4}{10} \times \frac{1000}{200}$$

$$N_1 = 0.4\text{N}$$

$$\therefore N_1V_1 = N_{mix}V_{mix}$$

$$0.4 \times 30 = N_{mix} \times 100$$

$$N_{mix} = 0.12\text{N}$$

$$\frac{(10 \times 1) + (25 \times 2) + (40 \times x)}{2000} = 0.12\text{N}$$

$$240 = 60 + 40x$$

$$180 = 40x$$

$$x = \frac{180}{40} = 4.5$$

$$N_{HNO_3} = 4.5\text{N}$$

60. $Na_2CO_3 + 2HNO_3 \rightarrow 2NaNO_3 + H_2CO_3$

Only sodium carbonate reacts with acid (HNO_3)

$N_1V_1 = N_2V_2$

Normality of Na_2CO_3 is $\frac{0.2 \times 25}{50} = 0.1$N

$$\therefore 0.1 = \frac{\text{wt of } Na_2CO_3}{53} \times \frac{1000}{500}$$

$$\therefore \text{wt of } Na_2CO_3 = \frac{0.1 \times 53 \times 500}{1000} = 2.65\text{g}$$

$$\therefore \text{wt of } NaNO_3 \text{ is } = 8 - 2.65 = 5.35\text{g}$$

$$\%\text{ of } NaNO_3 = \frac{5.35}{8} \times 100 = 66.8\%$$

$$\%\text{ of } Na_2CO_3 = \frac{2.65}{8} \times 100 = 33.2\%$$

61. Sodium hydroxide being a strong base than calcium hydroxide furnishes more number of OH^- as it undergoes complete dissociation. Greater the OH^- concentration greater will be the basic character. A stronger base will have pH value greater than a weak base. Hence, NaOH, which is a strong base has higher pH value than $Ca(OH)_2$.

62. In acid–base titrations, the end point is detected by the use of a substance called acid–base indicator. Acid–base indicator exhibits a sharp change in its color at the end point. The experimentally determined point of completion of an acid–base titration is called end point. For the titration between a weak acid and weak base, there is no sharp change in pH. Hence, no indicator can be used.

63. Sodium bicarbonate has low value of solubility product. Addition of sodium chloride solution to ammonium carbonate solution results in the double displacement reaction that results in the precipitation of sodium bicarbonate, as ionic product easily exceeds the low value of solubility product. Potassium bicarbonate has high value of solubility product and is highly soluble. In this case, though double displacement takes place, ionic product cannot exceed the high value of solubility product of $KHCO_3$. Therefore, precipitation cannot take place. Hence, this method cannot be employed for the preparation of potassium bicarbonate.

64. (a) H_2SO_4 is a proton donor and hence, can act as an acid according to protonic concept.
(b) HPO_4^{2-} can act as a proton donor and form PO_4^{3-} ion. Therefore, it acts as an acid. HPO_4^{2-} ion can also accept proton and form $H_2PO_4^-$ Therefore, it acts as a base.

(c) NH_3 can act as a proton donor to form NH_2^- and can act as an acid. NH_3 can act as a proton acceptor to form NH_4^+ ion and can act as a base.

(d) NH_4^+ can act as a proton donor to form NH_3 and it can act as an acid only.

65. (a) A Lewis base is an electron pair donor. A molecule that has excess electron pair can only act as an electron pair donor. As it has an excess electron pair, it invariably accepts a proton. Therefore, it can act as a proton acceptor that is a Bronsted base. However, this is not the case with Lewis acids. A Lewis acid is an electron pair acceptor and hence, should be deficient in electrons. It need not necessarily be a proton donor as it may or may not possess hydrogen.

(b) (i) 2 g $CaCO_3 = \frac{0.2}{100} = 0.002$ moles $CaCO_3$

500 ml of 0.01 M H_2SO_4 contain

0.005 moles of H_2SO_4

$CaCO_3 + H_2SO_4 \rightarrow CaSO_4 + CO_2 + H_2O$

0.002 moles $CaCO_3$ reacts with 0.002 moles H_2SO_4 which liberates 0.002 moles of CO_2 at STP

The volume of CO_2 liberated at STP

$= (0.002 \times 22.4)$ L

$= 44.8 \times 10^{-3}$ L

(ii) The number of moles of H_2SO_4 that is left over in 500 ml of solution = (0.005 – 0.002)

= 0.003 = 0.006 moles of H^+

500 ml of 0.01 M KOH solution is added to it

Now, the normality of H_2SO_4 solution

$= \frac{0.006}{500} \times 1000 = 0.012$ N

0.01 M KOH = 0.01 N KOH

$\therefore N_AV_A - N_BV_B = N_{new}V_{new}$

$\therefore 0.012 \times 0.5 - 0.01 \times 0.5 = N_{new} \times 1$

$\therefore 0.0060 - 0.005 = N_{new}$

$\therefore N_{new} = 0.001$

$\therefore$ pH of the resultant solution = – log [0.001]

= 3

(iii) 50 ml of this solution is taken for converting to pH = 5

$N_1V_1 = N_2V_2$

$0.001 \times 50 = 10^{-5} \times V_2$

$\therefore V_2 = \frac{0.05}{10^{-5}} = 5 \times 10^3$

= 5000 ml

Hence the solution has to be diluted to 100 times by adding (5000 – 50) ml = 4950 ml = 4.95 l water

66. Normality of H_2SO_4

= Molarity × 2 = 0.005 × 2 = 0.01

According to dilution law

$100 \times 0.01 = 1000 \times x$

$= \frac{100 \times 0.01}{1000} = 0.001 = 1 \times 10^{-3}$

$pH = -\log 1 \times 10^{-3} = 3$

If this solution neutralized by 500 mL of NaOH solution

$1000 \times 10^{-3} = 500 \times c$

$c = 2 \times 10^{-3}$

Amount of NaOH required

$2 \times 10^{-3} = \frac{x}{40} \times \frac{1000}{500}$

$x = 2 \times 10^{-3} \times \frac{40}{2} = 2 \times 10^{-2}$ g.

67. (a) $HSO_4^- \rightarrow SO_4^{2-}$

H_2SO_4 is a strong acid, HSO_4^- is a strong weak conjugate base. So, HSO_4^- is a strong acid; so, its conjugate base SO_4^{2-} is weak.

(b) $NH_3 + H^+ \rightarrow NH_4^+$

As ammonia is a weak base its conjugate acid is strong.

(c) $HS^- \rightarrow S^{2-}$

H_2S is a weak acid. HS^- is a strong conjugate base So, HS^- is weak acid so its conjugate base 5^{-2} is strong.

(d) $Cl_4^- \rightarrow HClO_4$

ClO_4^- is the conjugate base of strong acid $HClO_4$. As ClO_4^- is the conjugate base of strong acid it has to be weak.

Level 3: Assess Your Concepts

68. 0.01 N solution contains 0.01 mole H^+ in 1 L

The normality changes to 0.005 N

$\therefore$ 0.005 mole H^+ are present in 1 L of the resultant solution

$\therefore$ 0.01 mole H^+ ions are present in $\frac{0.01}{0.005}$ L resultant solution

$= \frac{1}{0.5} = 2$ L of the resultant solution

$\therefore$ 1 L water is added.

69. 500 mL 0.005 N HCl contains 0.0025 mole of H^+

pH = 12 $\therefore$ pOH = 14 - 12 = 2

$\therefore$ 10^{-2} moles of OH^- is present in 1 L of the resultant solution.

$\therefore$ 1 L of the given NaOH solution contains 0.02 moles of OH^-.

If x l of NaOH is added, then

$$\frac{0.02x - 0.0025}{x + 0.5} = 10^{-2} = 0.01$$

$\therefore 0.02x - 0.0025 = 0.01x + 0.005$

$\therefore 0.01x = 0.0075$

$$x = \frac{0.0075}{0.01} = 0.75 \text{ L}$$

= 750 mL

or

$N_1 \rightarrow 0.005$

$V_1 \rightarrow 0.5$ L

$N_2 \rightarrow 0.02$

$V_2 \rightarrow x$ L

Since the resultant solution is basic,

$\therefore (0.02 \times x) - (0.005 \times 0.5) = 0.01\ (0.5 + x)$

[pOH = 2 = 10^{-2} mole/L = 0.01 mole/L]

$\therefore 0.02x - 0.0025 = 0.005 + 0.01x$

$\therefore 0.01x = 0.0075$

$\therefore$ = 750 mL

$$x = \frac{0.0075}{0.01} = 0.75 \text{ L}$$

70. (i) requisite for precipitation of the respective sulphides

(ii) difference in the types of ions present in an acidified salt solution and normal salt solution

(iii) ions present in the solution when H_2S is passed through it

(iv) influence of extra ions present in the acidified solution on the degree of dissociation of H_2S

(v) relation between the degree of dissociation of H_2S and the availability of sulphide ions in the solution

(vi) relation between the number of sulphide ions and the precipitation of the selective salts

71. (i) comparison of electronegativities of halogens attached to boron in various trihalides

(ii) reason for the trihalides of boron to act as an acid

(iii) comparison of valence electronic configuration of fluorine, chlorine, bromine, iodine with that of boron

(iv) orbitals in which the lone pairs of electrons of halogens are present

(v) identification of vacant orbital of boron

(vi) comparison of energy of vacant orbital of boron with the orbitals containing lone pairs of electrons in halogens

(vii) comparison of tendency of donating the electron pair to the vacant orbital of boron among the halogens

(viii) relation between the tendency of formation of the above kind of bond and availability of vacant orbital of boron for accepting the lone pairs of electrons from other species

(ix) comparison of acidic characters of trihalides of boron according to Lewis concept

72. Generally, the acidic strength of oxyacids of an element with different oxidation states increases with the increase in oxidation state of central atom. So, the expected order of acidic strength should be

$H_3PO_4 > H_3PO_3 > H_3PO_2$.

But actual order is

$H_3PO_2 > H_3PO_3 > H_3PO_4$.

This can be explained based on the number of OH^- groups attached to central P-atom. With increasing number of OH groups on central P-atom the acidic strength decreases. Hence, H_3PO_4 is having minimum acidic strength and H_3PO_2 is having maximum acidic strength.

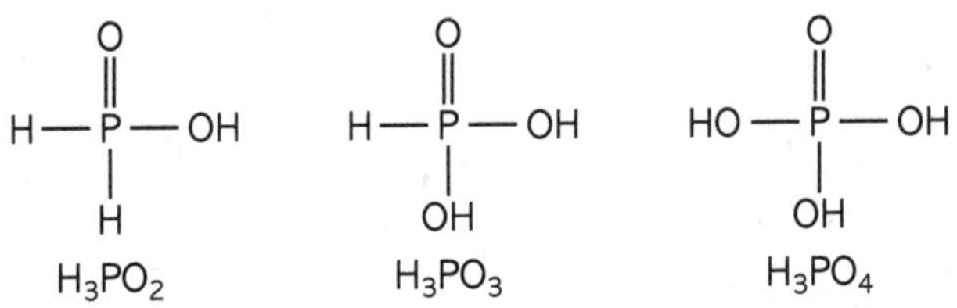

With the increases in number of $-OH$ groups, the strength of conjugate base formed increases due to

greater proton accepting tendency. Therefore, the strengths of corresponding acids decrease accordingly.

73. 10^{-6} M HCl solution when diluted by 100 times, should become 10^{-8} M solution. Then the pH value should increase from 6 to 8. However, a solution having pH value of 6 is acidic and the solution having pH value of 8 indicates basic nature. An acidic solution can never become neutral or basic howsoever dilute it is. The pH value of the solution is slightly less than 7. This is because in very low concentrated solution, the dissociation of water also should be taken into consideration. H^+ ion concentration should be equal to the sum of H^+ ion concentration from HCl and H_2O.

$[H^+]$ from HCl = 10^{-8}

$[H^+]$ from $H_2O = 10^{-7}$

$[H^+] = 10^{-8} + 10^{-7} = 10^{-7}(10^{-1} + 1) = 1.1 \times 10^{-7}$

$\text{pH} = -\log(1.1 \times 10^{-7})$

$= 7 - \log 1.1 = 7 - 0.041 = 6.96$

74. Acid–base indicators are either weak organic acids or weak organic bases. These indicators show one color in molecular form and another color in ionic form. Acidic indicator is represented by HIn.

$$HIn \rightleftharpoons H^+ + In^-$$

In acidic solution, the equilibrium shifts towards left. Hence, an acidic indicator has the color of HIn in acidic solutions. In basic solution, the equilibrium shifts towards right and shows color of In– in alkaline solutions.

Basic indicator is represented by InOH.

$$InOH \rightleftharpoons In^+ + OH^-$$

In acidic solution, the equilibrium shifts towards right. In basic solution, the equilibrium shifts towards left. Hence, basic indicator is having color of In^+ in acidic solutions, and shows color of InOH in basic solutions.

75. In a complex salt, there are two parts namely coordination sphere and ionization sphere. The part present in ionization sphere gives reactions of the respective ions. But the part present in coordination sphere gives the reactions of complex ions only and cannot give reactions of individual ions. In the complex of the formula $[Co(NH_3)_3]Cl_3$, chloride ions are present in the ionization sphere and give the reactions of Cl^- ions. The complex $[Co(NH_3)_3Cl_3]$ has no chloride ions in the ionization sphere and does not give the reactions of Cl^- ions because the components present within the sphere do not further undergo any hydrolysis and hence, do not behave independently.

76. In presence of any strong acid, water acts as a proton acceptor. In presence of any strong base, water acts as a proton donor. Therefore, the ability of a strong acid to donate protons is determined by the proton-accepting capacity of water and not on the acid. Hence, all strong acids show equal tendency to donate protons. Same thing happens with bases also. When the strong acids are taken in acetic acid, which is a very weak proton acceptor than water, the different acids donate protons to different extents. Therefore, the strengths of various strong acids can be compared in acetic acid.

77. $H_2O \rightleftharpoons H^+ + OH^-$

10 l of water contain 10^{-n} moles of H^+ and OH^- ions

∴ Ionic product of water at that temperature is

$$\left(\frac{10^{-n}}{10} \times \frac{10^{-n}}{10}\right) \text{mole}^2/\text{L}^2$$

$$= \frac{10^{-2n}}{10^2} \text{mole}^2/\text{L}^2$$

$$= 10^{-2n-2} = 10^{-2(n+1)} \text{ mole}^2/\text{L}^2$$

∴ pH of the neutral solution at t°C

$$= -\log\left[\frac{10^{-n}}{10}\right]$$

$$= -\log 10^{-(n+1)}$$

$$= n + 1$$

JEE-NEET Special wing

Multiple-Answer Type Questions

1. Metal bisulphide + Hydrochloric acid → Salt + $H_2S\uparrow$
Metal bisulphide can be formed with a representative element of valency 1.
X is hydrogen sulphide gas with a characteristic pungent odour. It dissolves sparingly in water to form hydro sulphuric acid which is a hydracid.

2. X is a dibasic acid. ⇒ its basicity is 2 and every one mole of X produces 2 moles of H^+ ions
One mole of H+ ions will be obtained from every 0.5 mol of X
0.7 moles of H+ ions will be obtained from 0.7 × 0.5 = 0.35 mol of X
⇒ only 0.35 moles of X is ionised while 0.15 moles of X is left behind unionised, i.e., it is in its molecular state
At T, for every 0.5 moles of X 0.35 mol ionised.
$$\Rightarrow \text{For 100 moles of X } \frac{(100 \times 0.35)}{0.5} = 70 \text{ moles ionised}$$
⇒ Degree of dissociation of X at temperature T is 70%.
Sulphuric acid is a strong acid. ⇒ its degree of dissociation will be near to 100% at any dilution.
⇒ X cannot be predicted as sulphuric acid.

3. Ionic product K_w of water increases with the increase with temperature due to the increase in the auto ionization of water.
Addition of an acid or base increases the concentration of H^+ and OH^- of the solution respectively thereby changing the pH value of the solution. But due to common ion effect, K_w at that temperature remains unchanged. Hence, the value of K_w does not change with the addition of an acid or base.
At 25°C, the value of K_w is 1.01×10^{-14}.

4.

Salt	Nature of its aqueous solution-Reason
(a) $FeCl_3$	Acidic-Due to the formation of a strong acid HCl that ionizes and increases the concentration of H^+ ions
(b) Na_2CO_3,	Basic- Due to the formation of a strong base NaOH that ionizes and increases the concentration of OH^- ions
(c) KNO_3	Neutral- Due to the presence of equal number of free H^+ and OH^- ions
(d) $(NH_4)_2CO_3$	Neutral- Due to the absence of free H^+ or OH^- ions

5. Conjugate Acid: It is the substance formed when a base gains a proton. It has one more proton (H^+) compared to its corresponding base.
Conjugate Base: It is the substance formed when an acid loses a proton. It has one proton (H^+) less compared to its corresponding acid.
(a) H_2CO_3 , HCO_3^- and
(b) H_2O, H_3O^+ are conjugate acid base pairs.

Comprehension-Based Questions

6. As pH value in the graph starts from 1 and goes up to 12, it should be of a strong acid vs strong base. Among the given options, option (a) should be correct as sulphuric acid is a strong acid while potassium hydroxide is a strong base.

7. pH = -log[H^+] ⇒ pH value increases with the decrease in [H^+], i.e., the concentration of H^+ ions and vice versa. In graph A, pH value of the analyte solution is increasing with the addition of titrant indicating the decrease in the concentration of H^+ ions with the continuous addition of OH ions by the titrant. H^+ ions get neutralised by OH^- ions forming water.

8. 8 mL

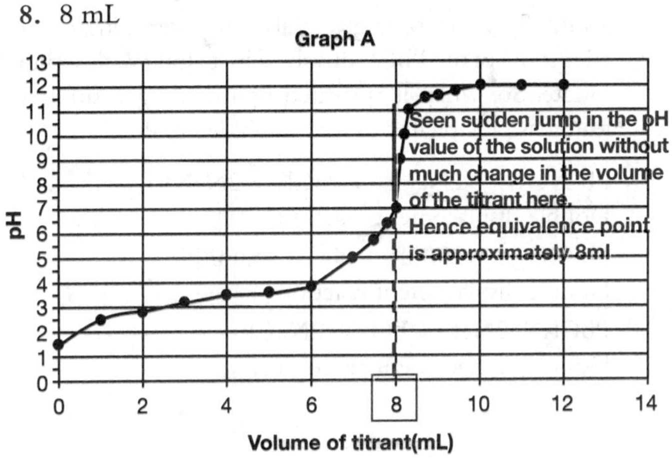

9. Given that 'At the equivalence or end point, the number of equivalents of an acid is indeed equal to the number of equivalents of the base'.
We know that: Normality,
$$\left(N = \frac{\text{Gram equivalent of the solute}}{\text{Volume of the solution in litres}}\right)$$
If V_1, V_2 and N_1, N_2 are the volume and normality of acid and base respectively. Then
⇒ At the end point,
No of equivalents of acid = No of equivalents of the base

$\Rightarrow V_1N_1 = V_2N_2$ (given $V_1 = 20mL$, $V_2 = 10mL$, $N_2 = 0.2N$ and $N_1=?$)

$\Rightarrow 20 \times N_1 = 10 \times 0.2$

$\Rightarrow N_1 = \frac{2}{20} = 0.1N$

So, normality of sulphuric acid is 0.1N.

For acids,

Normality = Molarity × Basicity

⇒ Molarity of Sulphuric acid = 0.1/2 =0.05M

10. The correct match is as follows:

	1	2	3	4
(b)	(i) (r) (p)	(i) (t)	(ii) (p)	(iii) (r)

11. Nitrate salts on decomposition gives reddish brown nitrogen dioxide gas.

12. Given 'Z is a white precipitate and dissolved in hot water'. Also mentioned that chloride of (X) is sparingly soluble in water. As like lead(II)chloride, Silver and mercuric chloride are also white precipitates, but silver and mercuric chloride are not water soluble. So, cation should be Lead(II) ion but not Lead(IV) as Lead(IV)chloride is a yellow colour liquid.

13. As $PbCl_2$ (Z) is sparingly soluble in water, filtrate contains some of the $PbCl_2$ dissolved in it along with sodium nitrate. So, when it is treated with hydrogen sulphide, lead gets precipitated as lead sulphide i.e. PbS.

14. $Pb(NO_3)_2 + 2NaCl \rightarrow PbCl_2 + 2NaNO_3$---
Double displacement reaction

$Pb(NO_3)_2 + 2HCl \rightarrow PbCl_2 + 2HNO_3$------
Double displacement reaction

$PbCl_2 + 2NaI \rightarrow PbI_2 + 2NaCl$ -------------
Double displacement reaction

$2Pb(NO_3)_2 \rightarrow 2PbO + 4NO_2 + O_2$-------
Decomposition reaction

15. $2Pb(NO_3)_2(s) \rightarrow 2PbO(s) + 4NO_2(g) + O_2(g)$

Lead oxide is the solid product formed in the decomposition of lead nitrate.

Match the Columns

16.

List-I Compound	List-II Empirical formula of the compound
(a) Acid present in P i.e. tomatoes is Oxalic acid and its molecular formula is $H_2C_2O_4$	(i) CH_2O
(b) Solute in the solution of Q	(ii) Same as its molecular formula
(c) Hydrocarbon present in major component in 'R'	(iii) HCO_2
(d) Complex carbohydrate present in 'S'	(iv) C_2H_5

(a) Acid present in P i.e. tomato is Oxalic acid, and its molecular formula is $H_2C_2O_4$-So its empirical formula is HCO_2

(b) Solute in the solution of Q, i.e., Vinegar (5% acetic acid) is acetic acid-CH_3COOH. So, its empirical formula is CH_2O.

(c) Hydrocarbon present in major component in 'R' i.e. LPG is butane- C_4H_{10}. So, its empirical formula is C_2H_5.

(d) Complex carbohydrate present in 'S' i.e. sugar cane juice is sucrose-$C_{12}H_{22}O_{11}$. So, its empirical formula is same as its molecular formula.

CHAPTER

3

Electrochemistry

Remember

Before beginning this chapter, you should be able to:

- describe the types of metals and non-metals along with the knowledge of oxidation and reduction.

Key Ideas

After completing this chapter, you should be able to:

- understand the process of electrolytic conduction and mechanism of electrolysis on the basis of Arrhenius theory.
- solve the numerical on relative amounts of electrolytic products in correlation with Faraday's laws.
- understand the concept of galvanic cells and the discharge of substances at the electrodes as part of electrochemical series.
- describe the technique of electroplating and its importance.
- explain the extraction and refining of metals with the concept of electrochemistry.

Scientific Crypt

A Tribute to Michael Faraday (1791–1867)

Michael Faraday was an English chemist and physicist who gained worldwide reputation for his commendable contributions to the fields of eletromagnetism and electrochemistry. It is largely due to his efforts that electricity became viable for use in day to day life and technology.

Faraday received only basic school education and at the tender age of 14, hebecameanapprentice to a local bookbinder and bookseller. During his apprenticeship, he read many books and developed a passion and interest in science particularly electricity. At the end of his apprenticeship, he attended lectures of eminent English chemists like Humphry Davy. This gave breakthrough for Faraday's career as he was later appointed as secretary and then became chemical assistant to Humphry Davy. Faraday's early chemical work was carried out under Humphry Davy, which resulted in Faraday'smentor relationship with Davy.

Michael Faraday's major and the most significant contribution to Chemistry was study of electrolysis and his laws of electrolysis. His other contributions to Chemistry include discovery of benzene, system of oxidation numbers, liquefaction of gases, alloys of steel, various kinds of optical glass etc. Invention of early form of Bunsen burner which is universally used in science laboratories is another feather in his cap. Throughout his career, Faraday secured very high positions. He was the first Fullerian professor of Chemistry at the Royal Institution of Great Britain, a position to which he was appointed for life. There Faraday gave a series of lectures entitled "Chemical History of a candle". Faraday rejected a knighthood and twice refused to become President of the Royal society. He was elected as foreign member of Royal Swedish Academy of Sciences and French Academy of Sciences.

FUN TIME

CROSSWORD

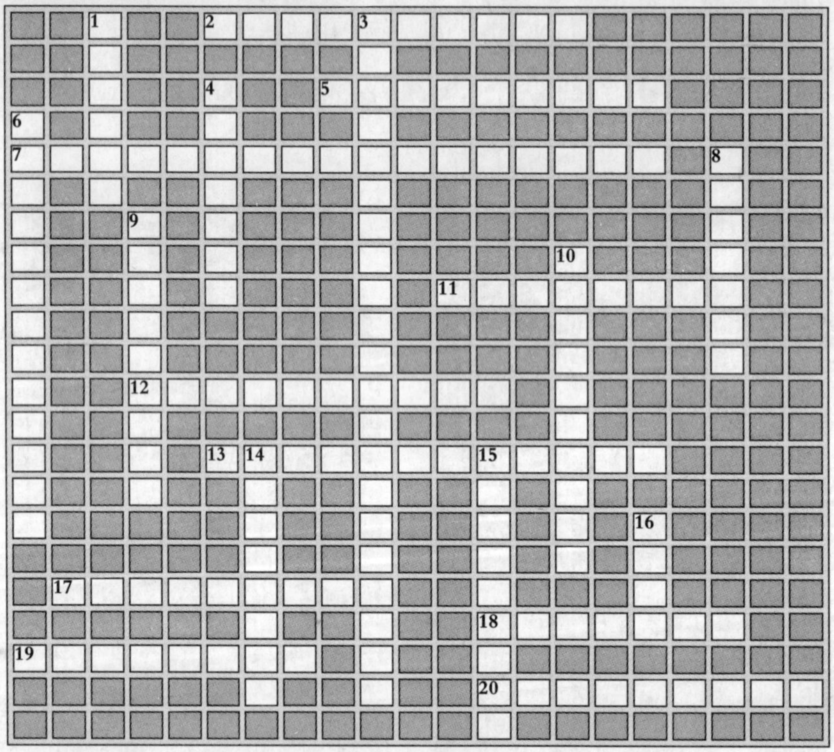

Across

2. Zn-Cu galvanic cell
5. process taking place at cathode
7. method of extraction employed for magnesium
11. element with the highest SRP value
12. the device which connects two half cells
13. a cell in which chemical energy is converted into electrical energy
17. instrument used to measure potential difference
18. equivalent of ampere per second
19. the metal used in SHE
20. process taking place at anode

Down

1. the gas that combines with the anode during anodising
3. arrangement of electrodes in the order of SRP
4. charge of one mole electricity which is scientist name
6. difference between SRP of cathode and anode
8. electrical device used in cars and automobiles
9. covering of aluminium metal with black thin film of aluminium oxide
10. a cell in which electrical energy is converted into chemical energy
14. name given to the collection of metals remaining after refining of another metal
15. the substance which allows the passage of electricity
16. the electrode potential of SHE

INTRODUCTION

Under the purview of electrochemistry, the interconversion of electrical energy and chemical energy by the means of oxidation–reduction reactions is widely studied. Electrochemistry finds application in various industries for the extraction, refinement, and protection of metals. A very common natural phenomenon like rusting of iron also comes under the study of electrochemistry. Starting from a small dry cell used in toys to microprocessors of computers, electrochemical processes are involved.

Electrochemical Reaction

Electrochemical reactions are basically of two types. First, the oxidation–reduction reactions that take place with the passage of electricity and is known as **electrolysis** and second, the oxidation–reduction reactions that result in the generation of electricity.

Since electric current is considered as flow of electrons or flow of electric charges, a conducting medium is required. The substances that allow the passage of electric current through them are called **electrical conductors**. They are of two types as stated below:

1. metallic conductors
2. electrolytic conductors

In metallic conductors, conduction takes place due to the flow of free electrons and hence these are called **electronic conductors**. Some compounds like HCl, NaOH, and KCl conduct electricity because of the movement of ions in their molten state or in aqueous solution. These types of conductors are called **electrolytic conductors**.

The electrochemical reactions involve the process of decomposition of an electrolyte either in fused state or in solution state by the passage of electricity.

Mostly, all the electrovalent compounds in their fused or molten state conduct electricity. The electrical conduction in these can be attributed to the presence of mobile ions.

> **Info Bytes!**
>
> Electrochemical reactions are at the heart of every battery-powered device you use. From your mobile phone to electric cars, they all rely on electrochemical processes to generate electricity.

Conduction in Electrovalent Compounds

The electrovalent compounds contain an aggregate of oppositely charged ions in the solid state. The ions in the solid state are held in their positions by strong electrostatic forces of attraction. Hence, they are immobile. When they are melted or dissolved in a suitable solvent, the force of attraction between their ions is weakened and the ions then move, thereby conducting electricity.

The process due to which an ionic solid dissociates into ions, in the fused state or in dissolved state is called **electrolytic dissociation**.

Example: Electrolytic dissociation of NaCl.

In fused state, the high temperature weakens the electrostatic force of attraction between Na^+ and Cl^- ions, whereas in dissolved state of NaCl, they get separated due to the dielectric effect of the solvent and hence conducts electricity.

The extent of electrolytic dissociation depends upon the nature of the solvent because the role of the solvent is to weaken the electrostatic forces of attraction between the ions.

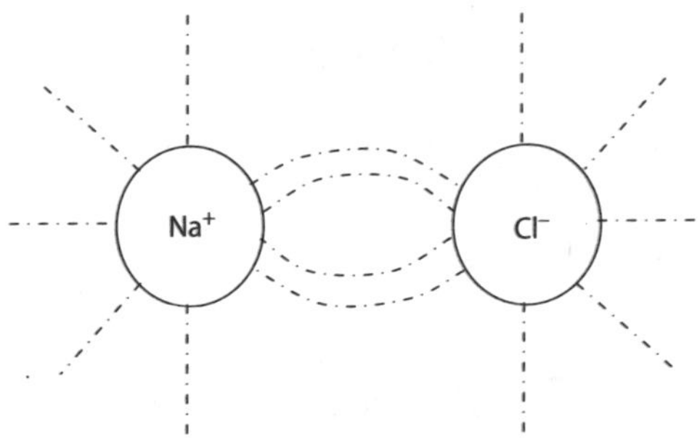

Figure 3.1 Dissociation of NaCl

Not only the ionic compounds but also the polar covalent compounds conduct electricity in solution state. Due to the polarity within the molecules of polar covalent compounds, charge separation takes place in solution state. The process of formation of oppositely charged ions from the molecules of polar covalent compound is called **ionization**.

Example: $HCl + H_2O \rightarrow H_3O^+ + Cl^-$

Arrhenius Theory of Electrolytic Dissociation

In order to explain the process of electrolysis, Arrhenius, in 1887, proposed a theory known as **theory of electrolytic dissociation** largely confined to aqueous solutions of the electrolytes.

Postulates of Arrhenius Theory of Electrolytic Dissociation

1. The molecules of the electrolyte when dissolved in water dissociate into two kinds of charged particles—positively charged particles and negatively charged particles or ions. This process is known as **ionization** or **electrolytic dissociation**.
2. When a voltage is applied, cations move towards the cathode and anions move towards the anode.
3. The number of positively charged ions and negatively charged ions may be different, but the total positive and total negative charges carried by anions and cations are same. Hence, the electrolytic solution at any instant remains electrically neutral.
4. There is equilibrium between the ions and undissociated molecules of the electrolyte.
$$AB \rightleftharpoons A^+ + B^-$$
5. The fraction of the total number of molecules that are present as ions in the solution is called **degree of dissociation** of the electrolyte.

On the basis of degree of dissociation, electrolytes can be classified into two types. They are strong electrolytes and weak electrolytes.

Table 3.1 Comparative study of strong and weak electrolytes

Strong electrolytes	Weak electrolytes
These electrolytes are highly ionized in the solution and have high degree of ionization	These electrolytes are feebly ionized and have low degree of ionization
They conduct a good amount of electricity	They conduct less amount of electricity
These contain only freely moving ions in the solution or molten state	These contain some ions and also molecules in the solution or molten state
For example, HCl, H_2SO_4, HNO_3, NaOH, KOH, KCl, NaCl, etc.	For example, CH_3COOH, H_2CO_3, $Al(OH)_3$, NH_4OH, $BaSO_4$, etc.

With an increase in temperature, the conductivity of the electrolyte increases while conductivity of the electrolyte decreases with an increase in concentration.

Process of Electrolysis

The process of electrolysis takes place in an electrochemical cell called **electrolytic cell** or **voltameter**.

The electrolytic cell consists of a glass vessel in which an electrolyte is taken in a molten state or in an aqueous solution. Two conductors (metal plates or graphite rods) are dipped in the electrolyte and are known as **electrodes**. The electrode, which is connected to the positive terminal of the battery (i.e., the source of electricity) is called **anode** and the one that is connected to the negative terminal of the battery is called **cathode**.

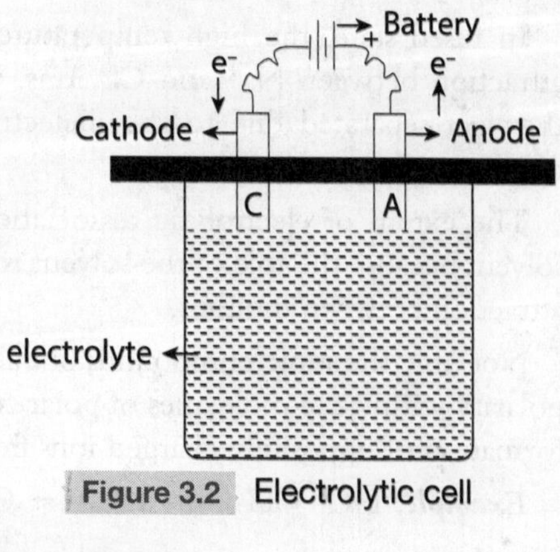

Figure 3.2 Electrolytic cell

When an electric current is passed through an electrolyte, cations move towards the cathode and anions move towards the anode. Cations accept the electrons from the cathode and get neutralized, whereas anions give up their negative charge by releasing electrons at the anode and become neutral.

Hence, oxidation takes place at the anode and reduction takes place at the cathode. The number of electrons gained by the anode is equal to the number of electrons lost at the cathode. Generally, metals and H_2 are deposited/liberated at the cathode and non-metals are liberated at the anode.

The process of electrolysis thus results in the decomposition of the electrolyte and subsequent deposition or liberation of the constituent products at the respective electrodes. However, the quantities of the electrolytic products at the respective electrodes are not same for all the electrolytes.

For the establishment of quantitative relationship between the electricity passed through the electrolyte and the products obtained at the electrodes, Michael Faraday conducted some experiments. The results were given out as Faraday's laws of electrolysis.

Faraday's Laws of Electrolysis

First Law

The amount of substance deposited or liberated or dissolved at an electrode is directly proportional to the quantity of electricity passing through the electrolyte.

Mathematical Representation

$m \propto Q$ (m = mass of substance deposited at the electrode; Q = quantity of electricity passing through the electrolyte)

$Q = c \times t$ (c = current strength in amperes; t = time of flow of current in seconds)

$m \propto ct$ or $m = ect$ (e = constant called electrochemical equivalent)

If $c = 1$ amp and $t = 1$ s (or Q = 1 coulomb), then $m = e$.

Electrochemical equivalent can be defined as the mass of substance that undergoes electrode reaction at an electrode by the passage of one coulomb of electricity through the electrolyte.

Since the charge of an electron is equal to 1.602×10^{-19} coulombs (C), passage of one mole of electrons through an electrolyte corresponds to passage of $(6.023 \times 10^{23} \times 1.602 \times 10^{-19})$ C of electricity.

Charge of 1 mole of electrons = $6.023 \times 10^{23} \times 1.602 \times 10^{-19}$ = 96,496 C ≈ 96,500 C, and is called **one faraday**.

The amount of substance that undergoes electrode reaction by the passage of one faraday (96,500 C) of electricity is equal to the **equivalent weight** of the substance.

Calculation of Equivalent Weight

The equivalent weight of an element or radical is calculated by dividing its atomic weight/formula weight by its valency. The unit of equivalent weight is **atomic mass unit.**

$$\text{Equivalent weight of an element} = \frac{\text{Atomic weight}}{\text{valency}}$$

$$\text{Equivalent weight of a radical} = \frac{\text{Formula weight of the radical}}{\text{valency}}$$

$$\text{Equivalent weight of aluminium} = \frac{\text{Atomic weight of the aluminium}}{\text{valency of aluminium}} = \frac{27}{3} = 9$$

$$\text{Equivalent weight of oxygen} = \frac{\text{Atomic weight of oxygen}}{\text{valency}} = \frac{16}{2} = 8$$

$$\text{Equivalent weight of sulphate radical} = \frac{\text{Formula weight of sulphate radical}}{\text{valency}} = \frac{96}{2} = 48.$$

Therefore, the number of equivalents of a substance deposited or liberated or dissolved at an electrode is equal to the number of faradays of electricity passed through the electrolyte.

Relation Between Equivalent Weight and Electrochemical Equivalent

$$\text{Electrochemical equivalent} = \frac{\text{Equivalent weight}}{96500} = \frac{\text{Atomic weight}}{z \times 96500} \text{ (where z = valency of the element)}$$

Second Law

For the passage of same quantity of electricity through different electrolytes, the amounts of respective substances deposited at the electrodes are in the ratio of the equivalent weights of the substances.

If m_1, m_2 and m_3 are mass of different substances and E_1, E_2, and E_3 are the equivalent weights of the substances, then $m_1 : m_2 : m_3 = E_1 : E_2 : E_3$ (when quantity of electricity is constant).

EXAMPLE 3.1 A current of 9.65 A is passed through three different electrolytes NaCl, $AgNO_3$, and $CuSO_4$ for 30 min separately. Calculate the ratio of the metals deposited at the respective electrodes. Also find out the weights of various metals deposited at the respective electrodes.

SOLUTION

Quantity of electricity passed through the electrolyte = current strength × time of flow
= 9.65 × 30 × 60 coulombs

$m_{Na} : m_{Ag} : m_{Cu} = E_{Na} : E_{Ag} : E_{Cu}$

$E_{Na} = \frac{23}{1} = 23$ $(Na^+ + e^- \rightarrow Na)$

$E_{Ag} = \frac{108}{1} = 108$ $(Ag^+ + e^- \rightarrow Ag)$

$E_{Cu} = \frac{63.5}{2} = 31.75$ $(Cu^{2+} + 2e^- \rightarrow Cu)$

$m_{Na} : m_{Ag} : m_{Cu} = 23 : 108 : 31.75$

$$\text{Weight of sodium deposited} = \frac{23 \times 9.65 \times 30 \times 60}{96500} = 4.14 \text{ g}$$

$$\text{Weight of silver deposited} = \frac{108 \times 9.65 \times 30 \times 60}{96500} = 19.44 \text{ g}$$

$$\text{Weight of copper deposited} = \frac{31.75 \times 9.65 \times 30 \times 60}{96500} = 5.715 \text{ g}$$

EXAMPLE 3.2 Molten lead bromide conducts electricity, but solid lead bromide does not. Give reason.

SOLUTION

In the molten state, lead bromide dissociates into Pb^{2+} and Br^- ions which move freely and conduct electricity. In the solid state, these ions are held together in a lattice structure, restricting their movement and preventing conduction.

EXAMPLE 3.3 Explain the mechanism of electrolysis of molten potassium bromide.

SOLUTION

Molten potassium bromide dissociates into its ions as:

$$KBr \rightarrow K^+ + Br^-$$

At the anode (where oxidation occurs): $2Br^- \rightarrow Br_2 + 2e^-$

At the cathode (where reduction occurs): $K^+ + e^+ \rightarrow K$

Therefore, the products of the electrolysis of molten potassium bromide are bromine gas at the anode and potassium metal at the cathode.

EXAMPLE 3.4 Distinguish between the role of valence in the electrochemical equivalent (Z) and equivalent mass (E) of a substance.

SOLUTION

Electrochemical Equivalent (Z): The valence (n) represents the number of electrons involved in the electrochemical reaction for the substance. The higher the valence, the smaller the value of Z, since more electrons are required to deposit or liberate a fixed amount of the substance.

Equivalent Mass (E): The valence (n) determines the amount of a substance that can replace or react with a fixed amount of another reference substance (e.g., 1 g of hydrogen). Higher valence will reduce the equivalent mass, as it increases the reactivity of the substance per mole.

EXAMPLE 3.5 Does the passage of the same quantity of electricity through different electrolytes yield the same volume of gases at the electrodes? Explain.

SOLUTION

No, the volume of gases produced at the electrodes does not necessarily remain the same. It depends on the number of electrons involved in the respective half-reactions at the electrodes. For instance, for the discharge of one mole of oxygen gas from water, four electrons are required, while only two electrons are needed for the discharge of one mole of hydrogen gas. The volume of gases produced is directly related to the number of moles of the gas and, hence, the number of electrons exchanged.

Galvanic Cells or Voltaic Cells

Based on the concept of electrolysis, it is obvious that chemical reactions can be carried out by making use of electrical energy. Similarly, it is possible to generate electrical energy by means of spontaneous redox reactions. The electrochemical cell used for this purpose of conversion of chemical energy into electrical energy is also known as a **galvanic cell** or **voltaic cell**.

The galvanic or voltaic cell consists of two half-cells, viz., anodic half-cell where oxidation takes place and cathodic half-cell where reduction takes place.

Principle and Working of the Galvanic Cell

When a metal strip (e.g., zinc) is dipped in a solution of its own ions, equilibrium exists between the metal atoms and the metal ions. This is because, the metal atoms may have a tendency to lose electrons and enter the solution as metal ions. The electrons so released remain on the rod. The region of solution, which is very close to the metal strip becomes rich in positive charge.

Other metals like copper behave in a different way. The metal ions from the solution have a tendency to take out electrons from the metal atoms on the strip and become neutralized. In this case, the metal rod is left with positive charge and the part of the solution, which is in contact with the metal rod becomes slightly negatively charged. These metal rods are called **electrodes**.

The equilibrium [$M^{n+}(aq) + ne^- \rightleftharpoons M(s)$] is set up in both the cases and an electrical double layer is formed.

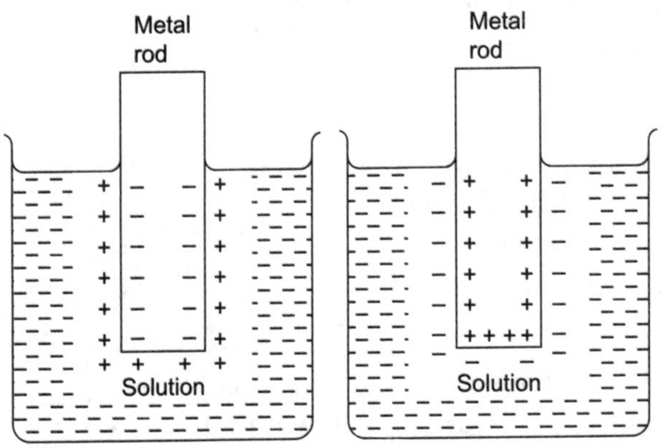

Figure 3.3 Schematic representation of zinc and copper electrodes

Single Electrode Potential

Since the metal rod and the solution surrounding it differ in charge, a potential is developed between the metal rod and the salt solution. This potential developed at the interface of metal rod and the solution of its own ions is called **single electrode potential**. It is denoted by E.

Each electrode system (the metal rod in contact with its salt solution) is called a half-cell. If oxidation takes place in the half-cell, it is called **oxidation half-cell** and if reduction takes place in the half-cell, it is called **reduction half-cell**. The electrode at which oxidation takes place is called anode and the electrode at which reduction takes place is called cathode. Since measurement of single electrode potentials for any electrode is not possible, it is absolutely necessary to combine it with an electrode whose potential is known. For this purpose, hydrogen electrode has been taken as a standard whose potential has been arbitrarily fixed as zero volts. This is known as standard hydrogen electrode.

Standard Hydrogen Electrode (SHE)

Hydrogen gas at 1 atm pressure is taken in contact with platinum surface and HCl solution of 1 M concentration at 25°C. This is called **standard hydrogen electrode**. The electrode potential has been assigned a value of zero volts.

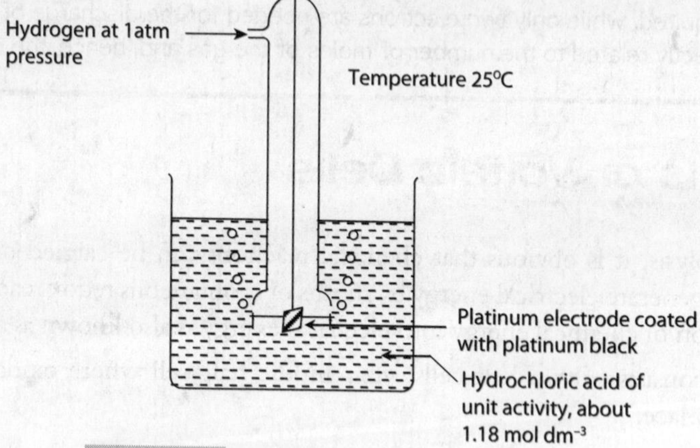

Figure 3.4 Standard hydrogen electrode

Standard Electrode Potential

Electrode potential depends upon the nature of electrode, concentration of the salt solution, and the temperature. Therefore, certain standard conditions are considered. The salt solution of 1M concentration is taken at 25°C temperature. The electrode potential measured under these standard conditions is called standard electrode potential. It is denoted by E°.

When any electrode is connected to the SHE, the potential difference between the two electrodes is called **standard electrode potential** of that electrode.

The hydrogen electrode constitutes one half-cell and the other electrode system constitutes another half-cell. These two half-cells are separated by a salt bridge. A salt bridge is a U-shaped tube containing KCl solution in agar agar. This salt bridge serves the purpose of providing an electrical contact between the two half-cells. The two half-cells are connected through a voltmeter. The reading of the voltmeter gives the electromotive force (emf) of the cell.

$$\textbf{EMF of the cell} = E^{\circ}_{RHE} - E^{\circ}_{LHE}$$

The half-cell in which oxidation takes place is taken on the left-hand side, whereas the half-cell in which reduction takes place is taken on the right-hand side.

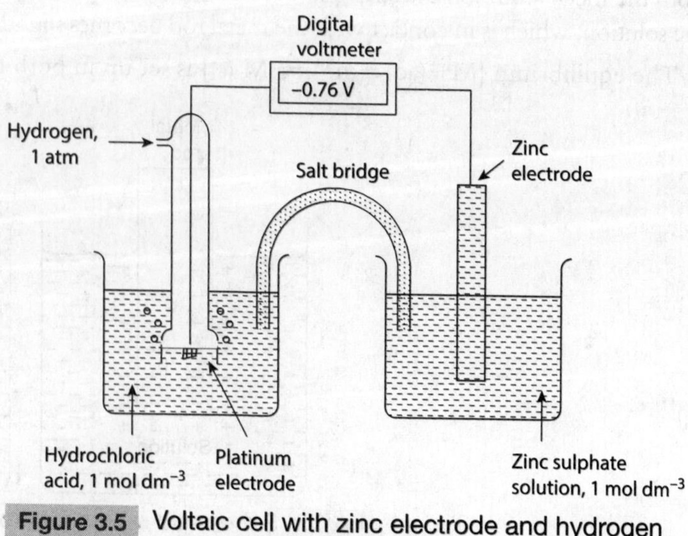

Figure 3.5 Voltaic cell with zinc electrode and hydrogen electrode

When zinc electrode is coupled with SHE, zinc electrode is taken as RHE and SHE is taken as LHE.

$$H^+ + e^- \rightarrow H_2 \text{ (RHE)}$$

$$Zn \rightarrow Zn^{2+} + 2e^- \text{ (LHE)}$$

$$E^0_{Zn^{2+}/Zn} = 0.76 \text{ V}$$

In the similar way, the standard electrode potentials of all the electrodes can be calculated by coupling with SHE.

Depending on whether the loss or gain of electrons takes place in the electrode system, the standard electrode potential may be oxidation or reduction potential. Oxidation and reduction potentials for an electrode are equal in magnitude but with opposite sign.

However, according to IUPAC convention, usually, reduction potentials are considered for the various electrodes. Therefore, standard electrode potentials correspond to standard reduction potentials only.

Electrochemical Series

The arrangement of the electrodes in the order of their standard electrode potentials is called **electrochemical series.** A greater negative value indicates the greater ease of reduction and greater positive value indicates greater ease of oxidation.

Table 3.2 Standard reduction potentials at 25°C

Half-reactions	E°, Volts
$F_2(g) + 2e^- \rightarrow 2F^-$	2.87
$Cl_2(g) + 2e^- \rightarrow 2Cl^-$	1.36
$O_2(g) + 4H+ + 4e^- \rightarrow 2H_2O(l)$	1.23
$Br_2(\ell) + 2e^- \rightarrow 2Br^-$	1.07
$Ag^+ + e^- \rightarrow Ag(s)$	0.80
$Fe^{3+} + e^- \rightarrow Fe^{2+}$	0.77
$I_2(s) + 2e^- \rightarrow 2I^-$	0.54
$Cu^+ + e^- \rightarrow Cu(s)$	0.52
$Cu^{2+} + 2e^- \rightarrow Cu(s)$	0.34
$Cu^{2+} + e^- \rightarrow Cu^+$	0.16
$2H^+ + 2e^- \rightarrow H_2(g)$	0.00
$Fe^{3+} + 3e^- \rightarrow Fe(s)$	–0.04
$Cr^{3+} + e^- \rightarrow Cr^{2+}$	–0.42
$Fe^{2+} + 2e^- \rightarrow Fe(s)$	–0.44
$Cr^{3+} + 3e^- \rightarrow Cr(s)$	–0.74
$Zn^{2+} + 2e^- \rightarrow Zn(s)$	–0.76
$Cr^{2+} + 2e^- \rightarrow Cr(s)$	–0.90
$Al^{3+} + 3e^- \rightarrow Al(s)$	–1.67

(Continued.)

Table 3.2 Continued

Half-reactions	E°, Volts
$Mg^{2+} + 2e^- \rightarrow Mg(s)$	–2.36
$Na^+ + e^- \rightarrow Na(s)$	–2.71
$Ca^{2+} + 2e^- \rightarrow Ca(s)$	–2.84
$Sr^{2+} + 2e^- \rightarrow Sr(s)$	–2.87
$Ba^{2+} + 2e^- \rightarrow Ba(s)$	–2.92
$Cs^+ + e^- \rightarrow Cs(s)$	–2.92
$Rb^+ + e^- \rightarrow Rb(s)$	–2.93
$K^+ + e^- \rightarrow K(s)$	–2.93
$Li^+ + e^- \rightarrow Li(s)$	–3.05

A voltaic or galvanic cell is constructed by combining two electrode systems wherein the potential difference between the two electrode systems can be measured by means of an voltmeter and this potential difference of the given cell is called **cell emf or cell potential**. An example of the voltaic cell is the Daniel cell.

Daniel Cell

Daniel cell can be constructed by connecting a Zn/Zn^{2+} half-cell with a Cu^{2+}/Cu half-cell with a wire. Zinc ions leave the surface of the electrode and move into the solution. Electrons from the zinc electrode move to the copper electrode through the wire. Copper (II) ions from the solution move to the copper electrode and get neutralized. A KCl salt bridge is used to connect the two half-cells. Negatively charged chloride ions from the salt bridge flow to the Zn/Zn^{2+} half-cell, whereas potassium ions flow to Cu/Cu^{2+} half-cell to maintain electrical neutrality.

The salt bridge allows the charge to move from one half-cell to the other half-cell, but prevents mixing of the solutions.

In Daniel cell, zinc electrode is called anode because oxidation takes place at the zinc electrode and copper electrode is called cathode because reduction takes place there.

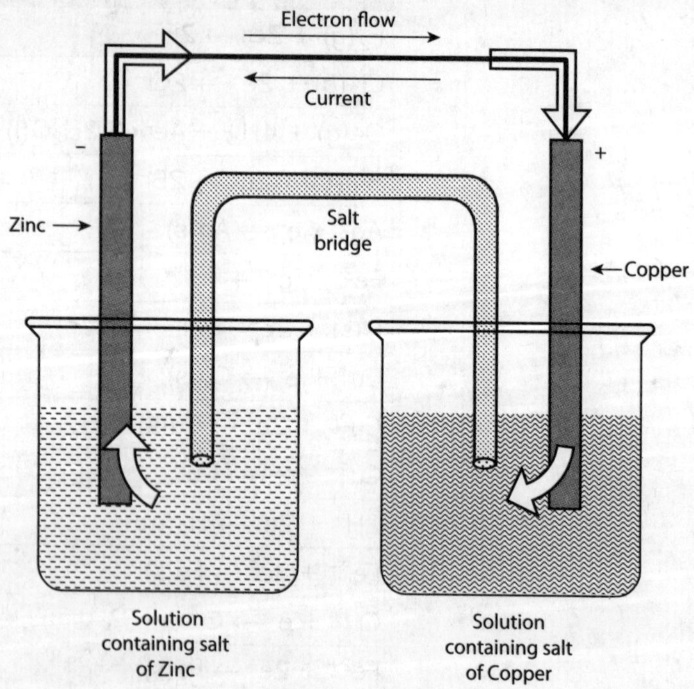

Figure 3.6 Schematic representation of Daniel cell

Half-cell Reactions

$$Zn \rightarrow Zn^{2+} + 2e^-$$

$$Cu^{2+} + 2e^- \rightarrow Cu$$

Net Reaction

$$Zn + Cu^{2+} \rightarrow Zn^{2+} + Cu$$

Representation of Cell

According to the IUPAC convention, oxidation half-cell is written first by writing metal followed by metal ion separated by a single vertical line. The reduction half-cell is written later by writing metal ion followed by metal. The two half-cells are separated by a double vertical line that indicates salt bridge.

Examples: Daniel cell

$$Zn(s)\,|\,Zn^{2+}(aq)\,||\,Cu^{2+}(aq)\,|\,Cu(s)$$

Applications of Electrochemical Series: Prediction of Cell Reaction

By coupling the standard electrodes whose potentials are known, the standard emf of the cell can be calculated. Since the emf of a cell is always positive, accordingly RHE and LHE are chosen. RHE involves oxidation half-reaction and LHE involves reduction half-reaction. Therefore, the cell reaction can be predicted from the relative positions of the electrodes in the electrochemical series.

Selective Discharge of Ions During Electrolysis

The cations with lower discharge potential get discharged at the cathode in preference to one with higher discharge potential.

Examples:

1. If Cu^{2+} and H^+ are present in the solution, Cu^{2+} will be discharged due to its lower discharge potential.
2. If Na^+ and H^+ are present in the solution, H^+ will be discharged due its lower discharge potential.

Similarly, the anions with lower discharge potential get discharged at the anode due to increasing ease of oxidation from top to bottom of the electronegative series.

Examples:

Between Cl^- and OH^-, OH^- gets discharged at the anode due to its lower discharge potential than that of Cl^-.

Electrolysis of Acidulated Water Using Platinum Electrodes

Electrolytic Cell: Hoffmann's voltameter

Electrolyte: H_2O + dil H_2SO_4 (small amount)

Electrodes: Platinum electrodes as cathode and anode

Current: 12 V (from a battery)

Dissociation Reaction: $2H_2O \rightarrow H_3O^+ + OH^-$

Ions Present: OH^- and H_3O^+, SO_4^{2-}, H^+ (H_3O^+)

Electrode Reaction:

At cathode: $H^+ + e^- \rightarrow H$

$H + H \rightarrow H_2\uparrow$

At anode: $4OH^- - 4e^- \rightarrow 2H_2O + O_2$

Products Obtained: H_2 and O_2

(**net reaction:** $2H_2O \rightarrow 2H_2 + O_2$)

Volumetric Analysis

On electrolysis, water gives 2 volumes of H_2 and 1 volume of O_2. Hence, ratio of H_2 and O_2 formed is 2 : 1.

Apart from the position of an electrode in the electrochemical series, other factors also affect the preferential discharge of ions at the respective electrodes.

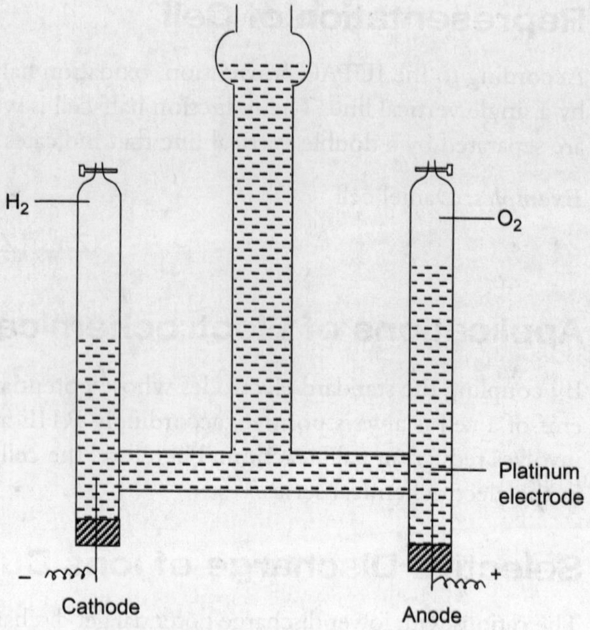

Figure 3.7 Hoffman's voltameter

Table 3.3 Electrolysis of $CuSO_4$

	Electrolysis of $CuSO_4$ (aq) using active anode (Cu)	Electrolysis of $CuSO_4$ (aq) using inert anode (Pt)
Electrolytic cell	Iron crucible at normal temperature	Iron crucible at normal temperature
Electrolytic reactions	Electrolytic dissociation: $CuSO_4 \rightarrow Cu^{2+} + SO_4^{2-}$ $H_2O \rightarrow H^+ + OH^-$ At cathode: $Cu^{2+} + 2e \rightarrow Cu$ At anode: $Cu - 2e^- \rightarrow Cu^{2+}$	Electrolytic dissociation: $CuSO_4 \rightarrow Cu^{2+} + SO_4^{2-}$ $H_2O \rightarrow H^+ + OH^-$ At cathode: $Cu^{2+} + 2e \rightarrow Cu$ At anode: $4[OH^- - e^- \rightarrow OH] \rightarrow 2H_2O + O_2$
Procedure	(i) Electric current is passed through $CuSO_4$ solution keeping copper as anode (ii) Cu^{2+}, H^+, SO_4^{2-}, and OH^- ions are formed (iii) SO_4^{2-} and OH^- ions migrate towards the anode. Ionization potential of copper is less than the discharge potential of SO_4^{2-} and OH^- copper anode itself ionizes	(i) Electric current is passed through $CuSO_4$ solutions keeping platinum as anode (ii) Cu^{2+}, H^+, SO_4^{2-}, and OH^- ions are formed (iii) SO_4^{2-} and OH^- migrate towards the anode but OH^- is discharged in preference to SO_4^{2-} ions due to the low discharge potential
Observation	Blue color of $CuSO_4$ solutions does not fade as concentration of Cu^{2+} does not change	Blue color of $CuSO_4$ fades away as the concentration of $CuSO_4$ decreases
Schematic Diagram	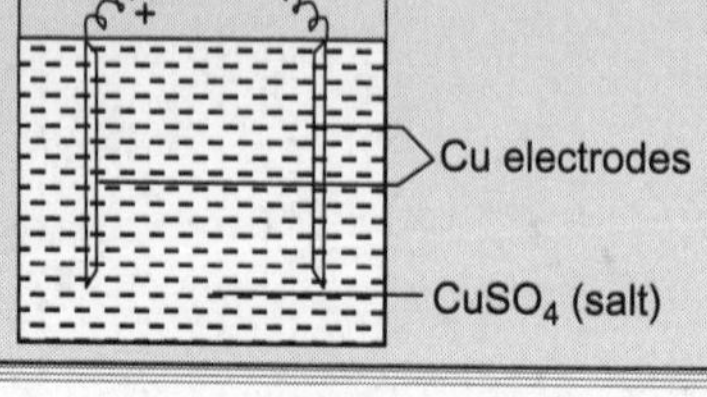	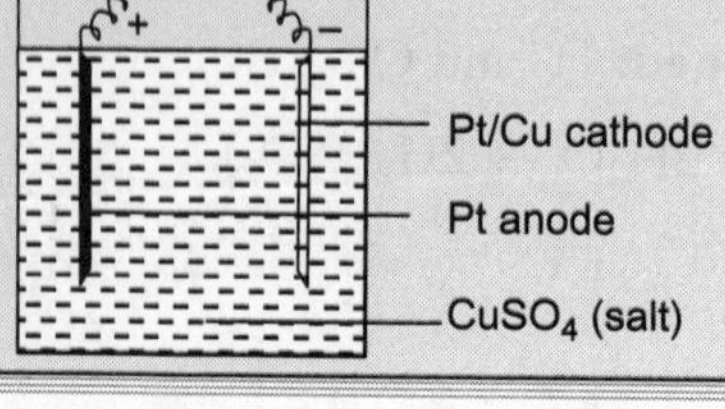

EXAMPLE 3.6 How does aqueous and acidified $CuSO_4$ dissociate on the passage of current? Also write the electrode reactions at the respective electrodes.

SOLUTION

Aqueous acidified copper sulphate dissociates as shown below.

$CuSO_4 \rightarrow Cu^{2+} + SO_4^{2-}$; $H_2O \rightarrow H^+ + OH^-$; $H_2SO_4 \rightarrow 2H^+ + SO_4^{2-}$

Reaction at Cathode: Copper gets discharged at the cathode because of lower discharge potential than that of hydrogen.

$Cu^{2+} + 2e^- \rightarrow Cu$

Reaction at Anode

(i) If anode is platinum or graphite (inactive anode)
OH^- is discharged at the anode because its discharge potential is lower than that of SO_4^{2-} ion.
$4OH^- \rightarrow 2H_2O + O_2 + 4e^-$

(ii) If the anode is copper itself (active anode)
$Cu - 2e^- \rightarrow Cu^{2+}$
No product is formed at anode.

EXAMPLE 3.7 When concentrated solution of cupric chloride is taken, chlorine gets liberated at anode, in contrast to a dilute solution where oxygen is liberated. However, when aqueous solution of $CuSO_4$ is taken, only oxygen is liberated at anode irrespective of concentration. How do you account for this?

SOLUTION

An aqueous solution of cupric chloride contains Cl^- ions, OH^- ions, Cu^{2+} ions and H^+ ions. Due to lower discharge potential of OH^- than Cl^-, oxygen gas is liberated at anode in preference to chlorine. However, in the concentrated solution, as the concentration of OH^- ions is very low, only chlorine gets liberated at anode. This is possible because the difference between discharge potentials of Cl^- and OH^- is only marginal. An aqueous solution of $CuSO_4$ contains Cu^{2+}, H^+, OH^- and SO_4^{2-} ions. Due to large difference in discharge potentials between SO_4^{2-}, and OH^-, only OH^- ions get discharged at anode irrespective of the concentration of the electrolyte.

EXAMPLE 3.8 In the electrolysis of a mixture of sodium chloride and sulphuric acid using inert electrodes, why is hydrogen, and not sodium, evolved at the cathode? Relate this observation to the discharge potential and standard reduction potential (SRP) values of the involved ions.

SOLUTION

During electrolysis, both H^+ ions (from (H_2SO_4) and Na^+ ions compete for reduction at the cathode. The discharge potential is influenced by SRP values. H^+ ions have a higher SRP than Na^+ ions, indicating they are more likely to be reduced. Thus, despite sodium having a lower discharge potential, hydrogen is evolved at the cathode because its SRP makes it more favourable for reduction.

Applications of Electrolysis

The concept of electrolysis finds applications in various industries for various purposes.

The concept of electrochemical cells is made use in different types of batteries. The hydrogen—oxygen fuel cells are also based on the same concept. The most important applications are listed below:

1. Electroplating of metals
2. Electrolytic refining of metals
3. Extraction of metals (electrometallurgy)

Info Bytes!

Electrochemistry has numerous applications. These range from metallurgical processes like electroplating to medical devices such as pacemakers. It's also used for water treatment and corrosion prevention.

Electroplating

Electroplating is an electrolytic process of depositing a thin film of a metal like gold, silver, nickel, etc., on other metals like iron, copper, etc., for different purposes. Applications of electroplating are:

(a) Anti-corrosion: To induce anti-corrosive properties by coating a metal with other metal.

(b) Decoration: To give a pleasing appearance, less valuable metals are electroplated with costly ones. ***Example:*** gold over brass.

Conditions to be Maintained During Electroplating

(a) The article to be electroplated is always made the cathode in electrolysis since the metal is deposited at the cathode.

(b) The metal (like Ni, Ag, Au, etc.), which is to be electroplated on the given metal is always placed at anode. Since the metal at anode continuously dissolves in the solution, it has to be replaced periodically.

(c) The electrolyte solution must contain the metal ions like Ag, Au, Ni, etc., since these ions travel towards cathode and get deposited on the metal placed at cathode.

(d) Less amount of current is supplied for longer time. It helps to reduce the uneven deposition of metal.

(e) Only direct current is to be used because alternating current causes discharge or ionization on alternate electrode. No effective coating takes place on cathode.

Table 3.4 Comparative study of electroplating of brass spoon and iron

Parameters	Electroplating of a brass spoon with silver	Electroplating of iron with nickel metal
Electrolyte	$AgCN + KCN + HCN$ Silver cyanide + Potassium cyanide + Hydrogen cyanide	$NiSO_4 + H_2SO_4$ Nickel sulphate + Sulphuric acid
Electrodes	Brass spoon (cathode) Pure silver (anode)	Iron article (cathode) Nickel metal (anode)
Electrolytic dissociation reaction	$AgCN \rightarrow Ag^+ + CN^-$ $KCN \rightarrow K + CN^-$ $HCN \rightarrow H^+ + CN^-$ $K^+ + Ag^+ + CN^- \rightarrow KAg(CN)_2$ The formation of potassium argentocyanide controls the deposition of silver on the cathode so that the coating becomes thin, uniform, and adheres properly over the cathode	Electrolytic reaction $NiSO_4 \rightarrow Ni^{2+} + SO_4^{-2}$ $H_2SO_4 \rightarrow 2H^+ + SO_4^{-2}$ $H_2O \rightarrow H^+ + OH^-$
	At cathode: $Ag^+ + e^- \rightarrow Ag$ At anode: $Ag - e^- \rightarrow Ag^+$	At cathode: $Ni^{2+} + 2e^- \rightarrow Ni$ At anode: $Ni - 2e^- \rightarrow Ni^{2+}$
Procedure	(i) A highly cleaned brass spoon that has to be electroplated is taken (ii) Due to electrolytic dissociation, Ag^+, K^+, H^+, OH^-, and CN^- ions are formed (iii) CN^- and OH^- ions are not discharged at the anode due to higher reduction potential than Ag (iv) Silver gets deposited on brass spoon. $AgNO_3$ is also used an electrolyte	(i) A highly cleaned iron article that has to be electroplated is taken (ii) Due to electrolytic dissociation, Ni^{2+}, H^+, SO_4^{2-}, and OH^- are formed (iii) SO_4^{2-} and OH^- are not discharged at the anode due to higher reduction potential than Ni (iv) Hence, Ni metal gets deposited on iron article

(Continued.)

Table 3.4 Continued

Parameters	Electroplating of a brass spoon with silver	Electroplating of iron with nickel metal
Schematic diagram	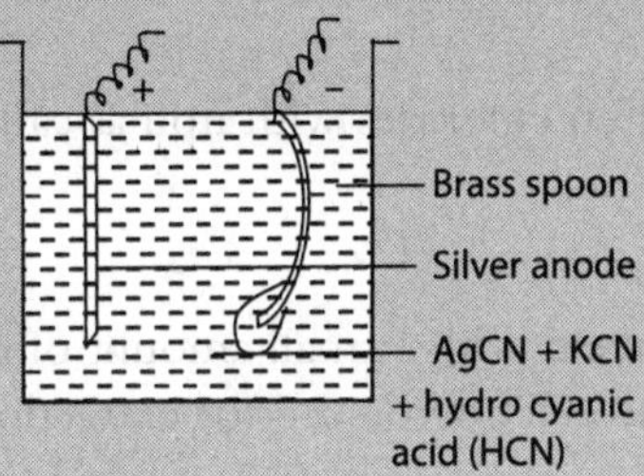	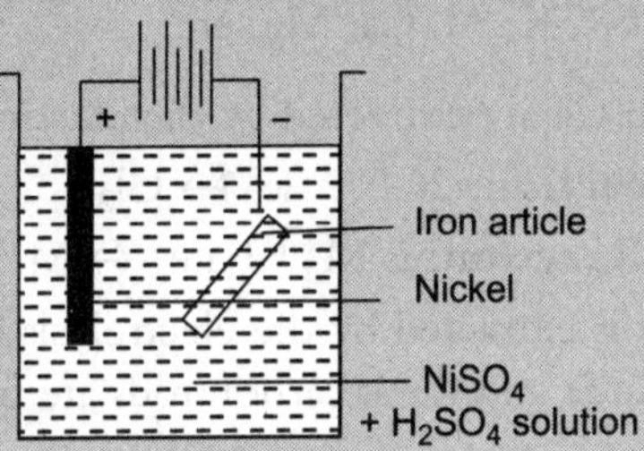

Electrolytic Refining

Electrolysis can also be used for refining metals containing impurities. They can be purified electrolytically. For example, purification of copper.

Electrolytic Refining of Copper Metal

Electrolyte: Acidified copper sulphate ($CuSO_4 + H_2SO_4$) solution

Electrodes: Impure copper rod as anode and thin strip of pure copper rod as cathode.

Dissociation of electrolyte takes place in the following ways:

$$CuSO_4 \rightleftharpoons Cu^{2+} + SO_4^{2-}$$
$$H_2SO_4 \rightleftharpoons 2H^+ + SO_4^{2-}$$
$$H_2O \rightleftharpoons H^+ + OH^-$$

Reaction at the Cathode:

$$Cu^{2+} + 2e^- \rightarrow Cu$$

The Cu^{2+} ions in the solution get attracted to cathode and are deposited there by reduction.

Reaction at the Anode:

$$Cu - 2e^- \rightarrow Cu^{2+}$$

The impure copper rod gets oxidized and hence forms Cu^{2+} ions and dissolves in the solution. These Cu^{2+} ions get deposited at the cathode. As a result, gradually the cathode increases in size. The copper obtained at the cathode is 99.9% pure.

Anode Mud: The impurities like silver, gold, mercury, etc., settle down as anode mud (slime).

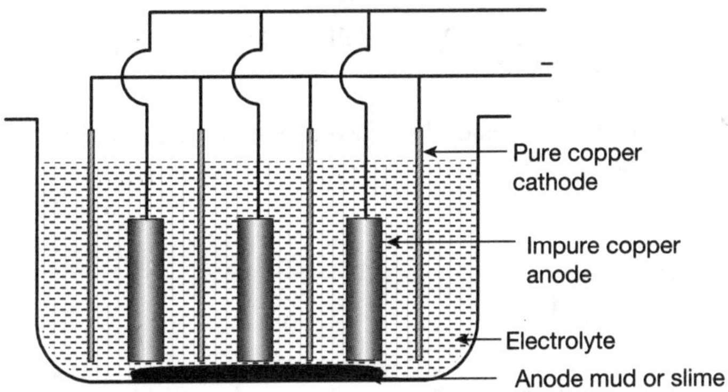

Figure 3.8 Electrolytic refining of copper

Electrometallurgy

Electrolysis can also be used in the extraction of metals which are at the top of electrochemical series.

Examples: Na, K, Al, Ca, Mg, etc.

Na, Mg and Ca are extracted by the electrolysis of their molten chlorides with iron as cathode and graphite as anode.

Anodic Reaction: $2Cl^- - 2e^- \rightarrow Cl_2\uparrow$

Cathodic Reaction: is $M^{+n} + ne^- \rightarrow M$, where M is the metal.

Aluminium is extracted by the electrolysis of fused Al_2O_3 mixed with a small amount of cryolite. Gas carbon lining is made the cathode and thick carbon rods are made anodes in the electrolytic cell for extraction of aluminium.

Reactions At Cathode: $2Al^{3+} + 6e^- \rightarrow 2Al$

Reactions At Anode: $3O^{2-} - 6e^- \rightarrow 3O_2\uparrow$

Batteries

Various types of batteries are used in watches, transistor radios, cars and other automobiles. Some batteries can be recharged and some cannot be recharged.

The most common type of battery consists of zinc rod dipped in a paste of zinc chloride and ammonium chloride. This entire set up is kept in contact with a graphite rod surrounded by a mixture of MnO_2 and graphite powder. Emf of this cell is around 1.5 V. Other type of batteries includes button-shaped cells having an emf of 1.6 V. A common car battery consists of PbO_2 in contact with H_2SO_4.

Info Bytes!

A battery is essentially a collection of one or more Galvanic cells arranged in series or parallel. Batteries can be rechargeable (like your phone battery) or non-rechargeable (like many AAA batteries).

Fuel Cell

A **fuel cell** is a type of electrochemical cell that uses chemical energy of a fuel and produce electricity from it.

Example: Hydrogen–oxygen fuel cell.

In the hydrogen–oxygen fuel cell, platinum electrodes are placed in a solution of an alkali. Electricity is generated by means of the following cell reactions.

Cell Reactions Involved:

$$2H_2(g) + 4OH^-(aq) \rightarrow 4H_2O(l) + 4e^-$$

$$O_2(g) + 2H_2O(l) + 4e^-(aq) \rightarrow 4OH^-$$

Net Reaction: $2H_2(g) + O_2(g) \rightarrow 2H_2O(l)$

Info Bytes!

Unlike batteries which store chemical energy, fuel cells convert fuel (often hydrogen) directly into electricity. They are efficient, produce fewer emissions than combustion engines, and are being researched extensively for future green energy applications.

EXAMPLE 3.9

Explain the electrometallurgical process for the extraction of potassium using fused potassium chloride.

SOLUTION

Electrolyte: Fused potassium chloride

Cathode: Iron

Anode: Graphite (inert anode)

Dissociation of electrolyte: $KCl \rightarrow K^+ + Cl^-$

Reactions at the cathode: $K^+ + e^- \rightarrow K$

Reactions at the anode: $[Cl^- - e^- \rightarrow Cl^-] \times 2$

$Cl + Cl \rightarrow Cl_2$

EXAMPLE 3.10

With reference to the position of various metals in the electrochemical series, identify and justify the method of extraction followed for the metals given below:

(i) Zinc (ii) Copper (iii) Magnesium

SOLUTION

(i) Zinc is a metal present in the middle of the electrochemical series. Zinc has negative SRP value that is why it can be reduced by normal reducing agents such as hydrogen, carbon monoxide and carbon. This is because these reducing agents possess the ability to break ionic bonds between metal ion and oxide ion.

(ii) Copper is a metal present above hydrogen in the electrochemical series. It has positive value for SRP that indicates the lesser thermal stability of its oxide. Thus, it can be extracted by reduction with other metals that have lower SRP than Cu.

(iii) Magnesium is a metal present at the bottom in the electrochemical series. It has very high value of negative SRP value. That means, it itself is a strong reducing agent and hence, cannot be reduced by any other reducing agents. It is therefore extracted by the electrolytic reduction of its molten salt.

EXAMPLE 3.11

Why do platinum and gold occur in free state in nature?

SOLUTION

Platinum and gold have high negative values of oxidation potentials. They do not possess tendency to form positive ions at all. Therefore, they do not occur in combined state unlike other metals and hence, they occur free in nature.

POINTS TO REMEMBER

- ✔ The interconversion of electrical energy and chemical energy by the means of oxidation–reduction reactions come under the purview of electrochemistry.
- ✔ The substances that allow the passage of electric current through them are called electrical conductors.
- ✔ In metallic conductors, conduction takes place due to the flow of free electrons.
- ✔ Some compounds conduct electricity because of the movement of ions in their molten state or in aqueous solution. These types of conductors are called electrolytic conductors.
- ✔ The process due to which an ionic solid dissociates into ions, in the fused state or in dissolved state is called electrolytic dissociation.
- ✔ The process of formation of oppositely-charged ions from the molecules of polar covalent compound is called ionization.
- ✔ The process of electrolysis takes place in an electrochemical cell called electrolytic cell or voltameter.
- ✔ The amount of substance that undergoes electrode reaction by the passage of one faraday (96,500 C) of electricity is equal to the equivalent weight of the substance.
- ✔ The equivalent weight of an element or radical is calculated by dividing its atomic weight/formula weight by its valency. The unit of equivalent weight is atomic mass unit.
- ✔ The electrochemical cell used for the purpose of conversion of chemical energy into electrical energy is also known as a galvanic cell or voltaic cell.
- ✔ This potential developed at the interface of metal rod and the solution of its own ions is called single electrode potential. It is denoted by E.
- ✔ The electrode potential measured under these standard conditions is called standard electrode potential. It is denoted by E°.
- ✔ The arrangement of the electrodes in the order of their standard electrode potentials is called electrochemical series.

DW

PRACTICE QUESTIONS CLASSROOM WING

Very Short Answer Type Questions

Directions for questions from 1 to 5:
Fill in the blanks.

1. _____ of electrolyte gets oxidized in electrolysis.
2. Pure metal in electroplating gets deposited at _____.
3. _____ electrodes do not take part with deposited or liberated materials.
4. During electrolysis, the cations get discharged at cathode in _____ order of their discharge potential.
5. For uniform deposition of a metal during electroplating _____ amount of current is supplied for _____ time.

Directions for questions from 6 to 25:
Answer the following questions.

6. The addition of which aluminium molecule to water makes it a feeble conductor of electricity. Why?
7. Which reaction takes place at the anode when the aqueous solution of $CuSO_4$ is electrolyzed using platinum as anode?
8. What is Daniel cell?
9. What is cell emf? Write down the cell reactions involved in Daniel cell.
10. What are the electrodes used in electrorefining of copper?
11. Define electrochemical equivalent.
12. What do you mean by standard hydrogen electrode?
13. Write the cell representation of Daniel cell.
14. Define standard electrode potential with an example.
15. What is the principle of fuel cells?
16. How many electrons constitute one Faraday?
17. Write the cell reaction for the following cell representation.
    $Zn \mid Zn^{2+}(aq) \mid\mid Ag^{+}(aq) \mid Ag(s)$
18. What is the smallest possible charge existing?
19. Why do polar covalent molecules conduct electricity in aqueous solutions?
20. Why do anions move towards anode and cations move towards cathode in electrolysis?
21. Why are electrolytes in solid state not good conductors?
22. How many Faradays of charge are required to deposit 1 g atomic weight of Cu metal from Cu (II) solution of 1 mole concentration?
23. Write the electrolytic products of electrolysis of
    (i) aq $NaOH_{(conc)}$ (Pt electrodes)
    (ii) aq $NaCl_{(conc)}$ (Pt electrodes)
    (iii) aq $AgNO_{3(conc)}$ (Ag electrodes)
24. What happens when a bulb is connected in series with two electrolytic cells containing aqueous $CuSO_4$ and aqueous sucrose solution?
25. How much charge is required to deposit one equivalent of any substance?

Short Answer Type Questions

26. Arrange the following ions in the ascending order of tendency to get discharged at the respective electrodes.

    (A) Copper (B) Potassium
    (C) Iron (D) Zinc
    (E) Hydrogen

27. The standard oxidation potential of an element 'X' is 2.84 V. It is connected to an electrode 'Y' with SRP value of 0.8 V. Identify the true statements corresponding to the above mentioned electrochemical cell.

    (i) X gets deposited by losing electrons.
    (ii) Y undergoes oxidation.
    (iii) X can displace hydrogen from acids.
    (iv) Y gets deposited at the cathode when connected to a hydrogen electrode.

28. Calculate the strength of the current which when passed through copper sulphate solution for 20 min deposits 6.375 g of copper.

29. Addition of which of the strong or weak electrolytes increases the conductance of water to the maximum extent? Give an example.

30. The deposition of one mole of a metal at the cathode requires a 3 F electric charge. If its atomic weight is 'M', what is its equivalent weight?

31. Define the following terms with examples.
   (i) Electrolysis
   (ii) Electrolytic cell
   (iii) Electrochemical cell
   (iv) Ions and electrodes
   (v) 1 Faraday

32. What is degree of ionization and ionization constant or dissociation constant?

33. What are the different types of electrolytes? Give examples for each.

34. On what factor does selectivity of ion to be discharged depends? Explain.

35. K^+ and H^+ ions are present in an electrolyte. Which would get discharged at cathode? Why?

36. What are noble electrodes? Explain their use.

37. Write down the procedure for electroplating iron.

38. The products obtained at electrodes vary as the electrodes used in electrolysis. Justify.

39. What do you mean by spectator ions? Give an example.

40. Write down applications of electrolysis with examples.

Essay Answer Type Questions

41. Considering the properties of electroplating, is it possible to electroplate non-metallic items? If so, how might this be done and what could be its applications?

42. How might the anode mud, which consists of precious metals like gold and silver, be processed further to extract these valuable components?

43. Can you think of any ethical implications surrounding the widespread use of batteries, especially considering their components and disposal challenges?

44. What is meant by electrometallurgy? Explain the extraction of Na, Mg, and Al. State the reactions involved.

45. Explain the standard electrode potential of an electrode. How is it measured?

PRACTICE QUESTIONS COMPETITION WING

Level 1: Apply your Concepts

Direction for questions from 1 to 7:
State whether the following statements are true or false.

1. Electrolysis brings about a chemical change.
2. Batteries are voltaic cells.
3. During electrolysis, cations move towards the positive terminal.
4. The negative sign of the reduction potential indicates that reduction occurs at that electrode when connected to the standard hydrogen electrode.
5. In the electrochemical series, ions are arranged in an increasing order of discharge potentials.
6. The salt bridge permits movement of charge and mixing of the solution.
7. The deposition of different ions at electrodes stops when the supply of electricity is stopped.

Direction for questions from 8 to 19:
Fill in the blanks.

8. Dissociation of a substance by passing electricity is called _____.
9. Conversion of chemical energy to electrical energy is done in _____.
10. The cell in which electrolysis is carried out is called _____.
11. Current enters or leaves the electrolyte through _____.
12. Conversion of electrical energy to chemical energy is the principle involved in _____.
13. The extent to which an electrolyte can dissociate into ions is called _____.
14. Zn^{2+} and Ag^{+} are present in a solution to be electrolysed. The metal that is deposited first at cathode is _____.
15. The thickness of _____ increases in the electrorefining of copper.
16. During electrolysis of molten $PbBr_2$, _____ fumes are liberated at the anode.
17. The electrode potential of standard hydrogen electrode is assigned a value of _____.
18. Thick sheets of pure copper are obtained at _____ in electrorefining.
19. In cell representation, oxidation half-cell is represented on the _____.

Direction for question 20:
Match the entries given in column A with the appropriate ones in column B.

20. Match the values of Column A with those of Column B.

Column A (No. of Faradays of Electricity Passed)	Column B (Amount of Substance Deposited)
(i) 1	(A) 24 g magnesium
(ii) 0.5	(B) 27 g aluminium
(iii) 2	(C) 4 g oxygen
(iv) 0.1	(D) 35.5 g chlorine
(v) 3	(E) 10.8 g silver

Direction for questions from 21 to 42:
For each of the questions, four choices have been provided. Select the correct alternative.

21. **Assertion (A):** Passage of 96,500 coulombs through saturated copper chloride solution results in the liberation of 22.4 L of chlorine at STP at the anode.

    Reason (R): Passage of 1 F through any solution liberates 1 g equivalent of the substance at the respective electrode.

    (a) Both A and R are true and R is the correct explanation of A.
    (b) Both A and R are true, but R is not the correct explanation of A.
    (c) A is true and R is false.
    (d) A is false and R is true.

22. **Assertion (A):** Passage of 1 F of electricity deposits 1 mole of silver at the cathode.

Reason (R): The number of equivalents of any substance deposited at the electrode is equal to the number of faradays of electricity passed through the electrolyte.

(a) Both A and R are true and R is the correct explanation of A.

(b) Both A and R are true, but R is not the correct explanation of A.

(c) A is true and R is false.

(d) A is false and R is true.

23. **Assertion (A):** Galvanic cell is used to generate electricity.

Reason (R): In galvanic cell, electrical energy is converted to chemical energy.

(a) Both A and R are true and R is the correct explanation of A.

(b) Both A and R are true, but R is not the correct explanation of A.

(c) A is true and R is false.

(d) A is false and R is true.

24. A current of 4.825 A is passed through fused magnesium chloride for 100 s. Amounts of cathodic and anodic products, respectively, are ________.

(a) 0.12 g; 0.355 g (b) 0.06 g; 0.355 g

(c) 0.12 g; 0.1775 g (d) 0.06 g; 0.1775 g

25. Electrolysis of aqueous $CuSO_4$ with inert electrodes gives ______.

(a) Cu at cathode, anode gets dissolved

(b) Cu at cathode, O_2 at anode

(c) O_2 at anode, H_2 at cathode

(d) O_2 at anode, cathode gets dissolved

26. The amount of copper deposited by the passage of 1 mole of electrons during the electrolysis of aqueous $CuSO_4$ solution is:

(a) 63.5 g (b) 31.75 g

(c) 159.5 g (d) 79.75 g

27. Negative sign in the standard electrode potential indicates

(a) greater ease of oxidation compared to that of hydrogen

(b) greater ease of reduction compared to that of hydrogen

(c) lesser ease of oxidation compared to that of hydrogen

(d) none of the above

28. The products of electrolysis of dilute aqueous solution of sodium hydride are:

(a) Na at cathode and H_2 at anode

(b) H_2 at cathode and O_2 at cathode

(c) Na at cathode and O_2 at anode

(d) H_2 at both cathode and anode

29. In a Daniel cell, if A ($E^0 = -0.76$ V) and B (= −2.36 V) half-cells are taken then

(a) B acts as an anode

(b) A acts as an anode

(c) B acts as a cathode

(d) cannot be predicted

30. In the electroplating of iron by nickel, nickel sulphate solution is taken as an electrolyte. What is the acid that is added to the electrolyte during the process?

(a) HCl (b) HCN

(c) HNO_3 (d) H_2SO_4

31. Equimolar solutions of zinc sulphate and ferric sulphate are subjected to electrolysis. What is the ratio of Faradays of electricity required for deposition of one mole each of zinc and iron?

(a) 1 : 2 (b) 2 : 3

(c) 1 : 3 (d) 3 : 2

32. Emf of a voltaic cell can be given by ______.

(a) SRP of anode – SRP of cathode

(b) SRP of cathode + SRP of anode

(c) SOP of cathode – SOP of anode

(d) SOP of cathode + SOP of anode

33. The process used in purifying metals by electrolysis is called ______.

(a) electroplating

(b) electrometallurgy

(c) electrorefining

(d) electrodeposition

34. In a voltaic cell, if iron and silver electrodes are connected with each other, then current flows:

(a) from iron to silver outside the cell

(b) from silver to iron within the cell

(c) from silver to iron outside the cell

(d) current does not flow in this cell

35. The amount of sodium produced by passage of 2 moles of electrons in the electrolysis of fused NaCl is ______.

(a) 23 g (b) 46 g
(c) 11.5 g (d) 58.5 g

36. The standard electrode potentials of the electrodes are given below. Arrange them in decreasing order of ease of oxidation.

(1) Electrode – I, E° = −2.89 V
(2) Electrode – II, E° = −0.16 V
(3) Electrode – III, E° = 0.77 V
(4) Electrode – IV, E° = −2.93 V
(5) Electrode – V, E° = −1.67 V

(a) 3 2 5 1 4 (b) 4 1 5 2 3
(c) 3 5 1 4 2 (d) 3 2 1 4 5

37. Pairs of electrodes and their corresponding standard electrode potentials are given. Arrange the cells constructed by these electrodes in increasing order of emf values.

(1) Electrode → A, E° = −2.92 V and Electrode → B, E° = −2.71 V
(2) Electrode → C, E° = −0.760 V and Electrode → D, E° = −0.44 V
(3) Electrode → B, E° = −2.71 V and Electrode → D, E° = −0.44 V
(4) Electrode → A, E° = −2.92 V and Electrode → C, E° = −0.76 V

(a) 2 1 4 3 (b) 1 2 4 3
(c) 2 4 1 3 (d) 2 4 3 1

38. The amounts of metals deposited when 965 C of electricity is passed through NaCl and $AgNO_3$ solutions are ______ and ______, respectively.

(a) 23 g, 108 g (b) 11.5 g, 54 g
(c) 0.23 g, 1.08 g (d) 2.3 g, 10.8 g

39. Ratio of number of Faradays of electricity required to deposit magnesium, aluminium, and sodium in equimolar ratio on electrolysis of their respective molten salts is ______.

(a) 2 : 3 : 2 (b) 2 : 1 : 1
(c) 2 : 3 : 1 (d) 4 : 6 : 1

40. The ratio of volumes of H_2 and O_2 liberated on electrolysis of water is ______.

(a) 1 : 2 (b) 1 : 3
(c) 2 : 1 (d) 3 : 1

41. **Assertion (A)**: Passage of 48,250 C of electricity through cupric sulphate and ferrous sulphate solutions result in the deposition 0.5 moles each of iron and copper at the respective cathodes.

Reason (R): Number of equivalents of a metal deposited at cathode is equal to the number of faradays of electricity passed through the electrolyte.

(a) Both 'A' and 'R' are true and 'R' is the correct explanation of 'A'.
(b) Both 'A' and 'R' are true and 'R' is not the correct explanation of 'A'.
(c) 'A' is correct and 'R' is wrong.
(d) 'A' is wrong and 'R' is correct.

42. 100 mL of 0.05 M aqueous $CuSO_4$ solution is subjected to electrolysis. Calculate the quantity of electricity required for the deposition of entire copper at the cathode.

(a) 0.005 F (b) 0.01 F
(c) 0.1 F (d) 0.05 F

Level 2: Review Your Concepts

43. The standard reduction potential of the two electrodes are −x V and y V, respectively. Calculate the emf of the cell in terms of x and y.

44. Which reaction takes place at the anode when $CuSO_4$ solution undergoes electrolysis using copper as anode?

45. *x* g of bivalent metal gets deposited at the cathode by passing 1 F of electric charge. Calculate its atomic weight.

46. Arrange the following ions: SO_4^{-2}, F^{-1}, Br^{-1}, OH^- in the decreasing order of ease of oxidation.

47. Identify the cathode, anode and calculate cell emf when a cell is constructed with A (E^0 = −0.44 V) and B (E^0 = 0.337 V).

48. What is the role of moisture in rusting of iron?

49. An external voltage opposing the cell potential is applied to a Daniel cell with zinc and copper electrodes. What happens when the external emf is increased from 0.8 V to 1.1 V and then 1.54 V?

50. What should be used as the anode, cathode and electrolyte in the process of electroplating of iron by nickel and why?

51. During the electrolysis of silver nitrate using copper anode, the color changes to blue and the intensity of the color increases. Explain with the help of electrochemical series. What would you observe if $ZnSO_4$ is taken instead of $AgNO_3$?

52. How does galvanization of iron protect iron from rusting even when protective zinc coating is partially worn away?

53. If a metal is to be electroplated with silver, what would happen if a solution of silver nitrate alone is used as an electrolyte? What is the preferable electrolyte and why is it used?

54. A current 5.00 A liberates 0.252 g of hydrogen in certain time. How many grams of oxygen, aluminium and sodium can be liberated or deposited by the same current in the same time?

55. Two monovalent metals A and B are treated with dilute sulphuric acid. A liberates hydrogen and metal B does not. Predict the half-cell reactions and cell representation when these metals are coupled with H-electrode. Justify your answer with respect to standard electrode potential.

56. The standard oxidation potential of silver electrode is given as –0.799 V. The standard reduction potential of copper electrode is given as 0.337 V. Find out the emf of the cell constituted by these two electrodes. Also, write the half-cell reactions involved in the cell and give cell representation.

57. Why is it not possible to measure the single electrode potential of any electrode? Justify.

58. Electrolysis of molten magnesium chloride results in the formation of 0.4 g magnesium. Calculate the vol ume of chlorine liberated during the reaction at STP. When an electrolytic cell consisting of molten $AlCl_3$ and molten NaCl are connected in series with the above cell, calculate the amount of aluminium and sodium deposited at cathode.

59. What is the amount of silver deposited by passing 2 A for 20 min through molten silver nitrate? If the same quantity of electricity is passed through a molten salt solution of gold, 1.6 g of gold is deposited at cathode, then find out its equivalent mass and oxidation state of gold in gold salt (atomic weight of Au = 197, Ag = 108).

60. A brass strip of dimensions 4 cm and 6 cm has to be coated with a silver layer of 2 mm thickness. Calculate the amount of charge required for the deposition of silver and the amount of magnesium deposited in another electrolytic cell when same amount of charge is passed (density of Ag = 10.5 g/cc.).

61. An aqueous solution of ferrous sulphate is taken and subjected to electrolysis. Calculate the number of electrons flowing through the circuit when 0.7 g of iron is deposited at cathode (atomic mass of Fe = 56).

62. Compare the conductivity of same amount of NaCl dissolved in water and in alcohol (assume that volumes of solvents are equal).

63. Why does conductivity of metallic conductor decrease with an increase in temperature, whereas in case of electrolytic conductors the conductivity increases with an increase in temperature?

64. Three electrolytic cells A, B, and C are connected in series that consist of concentrated aqueous solution of sodium chloride (brine solution), fused zinc sulphate and aqueous silver nitrate solution. If 1.4 *l* of chlorine is produced at STP in A at the anode, calculate the volumes of all gaseous products liberated in B and C at their respective electrodes at STP and the charge required for the deposition.

65. During electrolysis of aqueous copper sulphate solution using platinum electrodes, the blue color of the electrolytic solution fades and towards the end of the process bubbles appear at the cathode. Why? Also, comment on the change in pH of solution due to electrolysis.

66. Little litmus is placed in the cathode and the anode compartments of Hoffmann's voltameter containing acidulated water and then electrolysis is carried out. What do you observe and why?

67. An aqueous solution of copper sulphate is subjected to electrolysis using platinum electrodes. Calculate the number of electrons flowing through the circuit when 0.3175 g of copper is deposited. Also, calculate the number of molecules present in anodic product (atomic mass of copper = 63.5).

Level 3: Assess Your Concepts

68. Two electrodes 'X' and 'Y' are connected to hydrogen electrodes separately. The electrode reactions corresponding to X and Y are $X^{+2} + 2e^- \rightarrow X$ and

$Y \rightarrow Y^{+3} + 3e^-$ in the respective electrochemical cells. Which of the following statements are false regarding the abovementioned cells?

(i) X can displace hydrogen from acids.

(ii) Hydrogen is liberated at the anode in the cell in case of Y.

(iii) X has a positive standard reduction potential value.

(iv) X has a higher standard reduction potential value than Y.

69. An electrochemical cell is represented as $x\,|\,x^{+n}\,||\,y^{+n}\,|\,y$. Can of the following pair of electrode potentials (SRP) correspond to x and y?

$x \rightarrow$ -0.76 V, $y \rightarrow$ -0.34 V

70. Some batteries are rechargeable, whereas others must be thrown away after they get discharged. Justify with respect to the concept of electrochemical cells.

71. Explain the effect of change in temperature on the conductivity of the following conductors. Justify with appropriate reasons.

(a) Copper rod

(b) Aqueous solution of $CuSO_4$

(c) Aqueous solution of acetic acid

72. Why does single electrode potential depend upon the concentration of the electrolyte?

73. Thermal stability of metal oxides can be compared using electrochemical series. Explain.

74. How does magnesium connected by a wire to buried iron pipeline protect it from corrosion?

75. How does dilution affect the conductivity of strong electrolytes and weak electrolytes?

76. What do you observe when electrolysis of copper sulphate is done using iron strip as anode? Give reasons.

77. Rusting is an electrochemical process. Justify. If two iron articles are coated with tin and zinc respectively, in which case will the rusting of iron be more rapid, if the coating is worn out in one place. Give reason.

AT

PRACTICE QUESTIONS JEE-NEET SPECIAL WING

Multiple-Answer Type Questions

Directions for questions 1 to 5:

Select one or more correct alternative(s) from the given choices.

1. A voltaic cell is represented as

   $A(s) \mid A^{2+}(aq) \parallel B^{2+}(aq) \mid B(s)$

   If A and B are metal electrodes, identify which of the following statements are incorrect with respect to the given cell.

   (a) A is anode and B is cathode

   (b) The cell reactions are represented as $A^{+2} + 2e^- \rightarrow A$ and $B^{+2} + 2e^- \rightarrow B$.

   (c) Movement of electrons is from electrode A to electrode B.

   (d) A^{2+} ions are undergoing oxidation while B^{2+} are undergoing reduction.

2. Observe the given figure related to the electrolysis of acidified aqueous solution of the electrolyte mentioned in the diagram and identify the correct statements.

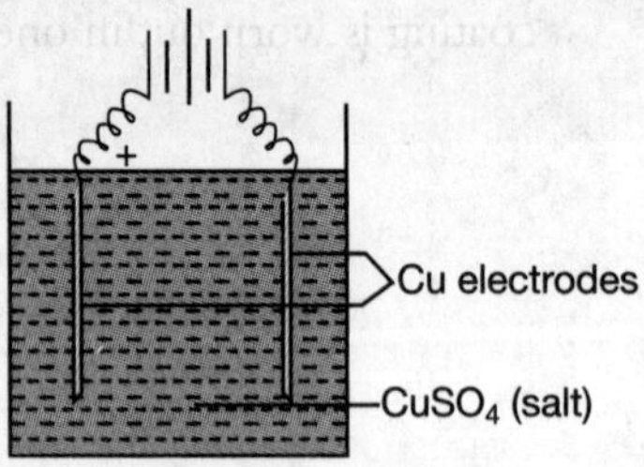

   (a) Copper undergoes oxidation at anode.

   (b) Blue colour of $CuSO_4$ fades away

   (c) OH^- is discharged in preference to SO_4^{2-} ions due to the low discharge potential.

   (d) No product formation takes place at anode.

3. During electrolysis, selective discharge of ions at electrodes is influenced by which parameters?

   (a) The nature of electrodes used.

   (b) The relative reduction potential of ions.

   (c) The relative concentration of ions present in the electrolyte.

   (d) The magnitude of charge that ions carry.

4. Identify the true statements regarding standard hydrogen electrode.

   (a) Its standard electrode potential is assigned a value of zero volts.

   (b) It can be used as either anode or cathode in a voltaic cell

   (c) The concentration of electrolyte in this electrode is 0.1 M

   (d) When coupled with magnesium electrode the EMF of the cell is negative

5. Which of the following statements do not align with the characteristics of fuel cells.

   (a) The oxidant used in the fuel cells undergoes reduction.

   (b) Fuel cells can be employed for providing power to only small electronic devices.

   (c) Fuel cells typically generate electricity in the form of AC (alternating current).

   (d) The standard cell potential (E° cell) of a hydrogen-oxygen fuel cell is always greater than zero.

Comprehension-Based Questions

Directions for Questions 6 to 11:

Read the following passage and answer the questions given below.

In numerous chemical and biological processes, ions play a crucial role in redox (reduction-oxidation) reactions. These reactions can be studied using electrochemical cells, which consist of two electrodes (conductors) immersed in an electrolyte solution containing ions. The behavior of ions in these cells is influenced by their concentration in the solution. The Nernst Equation relates this concentration to the electric potential (voltage) developed across the cell. It essentially tells us how the concentration of ions affects the voltage of the cell.

The general mathematical expression of Nernst Equation is given as follows:

$$E = E^\circ - \frac{2.30RT}{nF} \times \log_{10}\frac{[\text{Products}]}{[\text{reactants}]}$$

- E is the emf of the cell in Volts.
- E° is the standard emf of the cell.

- F is Faraday constant ($96487 \approx 96500$ C mol^{-1})
- R is the Universal Gas constant = 8.314 $J.K^{-1}.mol^{-1}$.
- T is the temperature in the Kelvin scale
- n is the number of electrons transferred in the redox reaction (from the balanced reaction).
- [Reactants]- concentration of the reactants
- [Product]- concentration of the products.

Nernst equation tells us how changes in ion concentration affect the cell's voltage.

Applying Nernst equation to the following cell reaction of a Daniel cell,

$Zn(s) + Cu^{2+}(aq) \rightarrow Zn^{2+}(aq) + Cu(s)$, expression to calculate EMF of the cell is given by,

$$E = E° - \frac{2.303RT}{nF} \times \log \frac{[Zn^{2+}]}{[Cu^{2+}]}$$

At the standard temperature of 298K,

$$E = E° - \frac{0.0591}{n} \times \log \frac{[Zn^{2+}]}{[Cu^{2+}]}$$ - x log (by substituting the values of R, F)

The key part of the above equation is the logarithmic term $\log \frac{[Zn^{2+}]}{[Cu^{2+}]}$ As this term indicates that as the concentration of one form of the ion increases relative to the other, the voltage of the cell changes.

A standard reduction potential table provides voltage values under specific standard conditions, such as a 1M concentration for solutions and 1 atm pressure for gases. However, the Nernst equation enables the determination of the cell potential (E) under different conditions, allowing for calculations at various concentrations of solutions and gas pressures. This capability holds great significance across a diverse spectrum of applications, spanning from the advancement of improved batteries to gaining insights into biological processes and environmental monitoring such as the pH level (related to hydrogen ions) or the concentration of pollutants in water.

6. Consider the voltaic cell represented as follows:

   A | A^{2+}(aq) (M) || B^{+}(aq) (M_1) | B.

   Observe the given cell representation and answer the following questions related to this cell.

   (i) Write the balanced equation for the overall cell reaction occurring in this voltaic cell.

   (ii) Apply the Nernst equation to the derived cell reaction and give the expression for calculating the cell's EMF.

   (iii) The value of n in the above equation is ______.

   (iv) Calculate the EMF of the cell at 25°C if M and M_1 are 1M and 0.1M respectively and standard EMF of the cell, E° is 1.56V.

7. $P(s) + Q^{2+}(aq) \rightarrow P^{2+}(aq) + Q(s)$; E cell = 1.179V, E° cell = 1.12 V at standard temperature conditions. Which of the following graphs, showing Ecell versus the logarithm of the ratio of $[P^{2+}]$ to $[Q^{2+}]$, approximately correlates Ecell as the function of concentrations of ions for the above given cell reaction? Explain your choice.

(a)

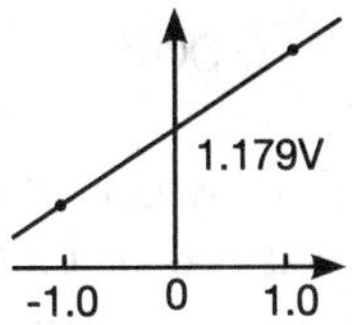

(b)

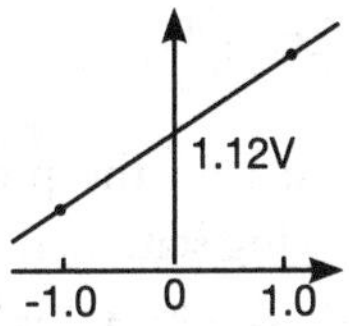

(c)

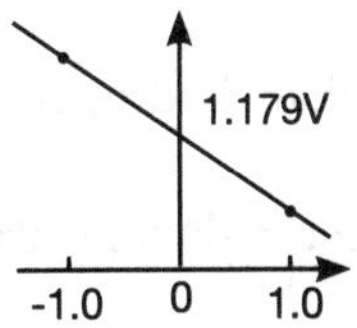

(d)

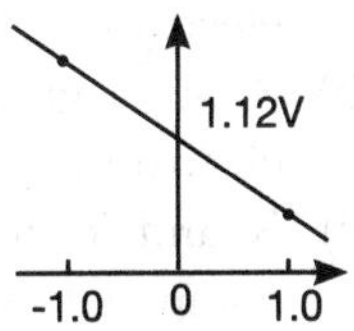

8. Predict the numerical value of the slope of the curve plotted for the graph mentioned in the question 7.

   (a) 10.0 (b) -0.0295

   (c) 100 (d) -0.01

9. "The key part of the above equation is the logarithmic term $\log([Zn^{2+}])/([Cu^{2+}])$. As this term indicates that as the concentration of one form of the ion increases relative to the other, the voltage of the cell changes". Illustrate with an example.

10. Labels and representations of the Daniel cells (List - I) with their corresponding cell EMFs (List - II), considering that $E_1 > E_2 > E_3 > E_4$ are matched.

List – I Label and Representation of Daniel cell	List – II Cell EMF
(A) Zn | Zn^{2+}(1M) || Cu^{2+}(1M) | Cu	(i) E_4
(B) Zn | Zn^{2+}(0.01M) || Cu^{2+}(1M) | Cu	(ii) E_3
(C) Zn | Zn^{2+}(1M) || Cu^{2+}(0.1M) | Cu	(iii) E_1
(D) Zn | Zn^{2+}(0.1M) || Cu^{2+}(1M) | Cu	(iv) E_2

Find the correct match.

	(A)	(B)	(C)	(D)
(a)	(iv)	(i)	(iii)	(ii)
(b)	(ii)	(iii)	(iv)	(i)
(c)	(i)	(iv)	(ii)	(iii)
(d)	(ii)	(iii)	(i)	(iv)

Directions for Questions 11 to 15:

Read the following passage and answer the questions given below.

Study the details of hypothetical electrodes and their standard reduction potentials.

Electrode	Standard reduction potential
X^{2+} | X	0.44V
Y^{2+} | Y	0.33V
Z^{2+} | Z	–0.44V
$2H^+$| H	0.00V

11. Based on the provided information, which of the following statements can be considered a correct inference?

(a) Z has a higher tendency than hydrogen to lose electrons.

(b) Z has a greater tendency than hydrogen to gain electrons.

(c) X and Y demonstrate better reducing properties compared to Hydrogen

(c) X, Y and Z display stronger oxidizing characteristics than Hydrogen

12. Reduction takes place at Hydrogen gas electrode when coupled with which of the following electrodes?

(a) Y (b) X

(c) Z (d) Both X and Y

13. The reaction, $A + B^{2+} \rightarrow A^{2+} + B$ will be spontaneous when

(a) A = X, B = Z

(b) A = X, B = Y

(c) A = Hydrogen gas electrode, B = Y

(d) A = Z, B = Hydrogen gas electrode

14. An electrochemical cell 'M' is constructed by coupling hydrogen gas electrode with electrode X. Identify the correct representation of anode half-cell of M.

(a) $H^+(aq) | H_2(g) | Pt$ (b) $Pt | H_2(g) | H^+(aq)$

(c) $X(s) | X^{2+}(aq)$ (d) $X^{2+}(aq) | X$

15. Satish constructed a galvanic cell with highest EMF using the combination of the electrodes given in the table. Predict the correct combination of cathode and anode of the cell constructed by Satish.

(a) Y, Hydrogen gas electrode

(b) X, Z

(c) Z, X

(d) X, Y

Match the Columns

Direction for Question 16:

Read the following passage and match the Following.

When the same quantity of electricity passes through different electrolytes, the substances deposited at the electrodes are in the ratio of their respective equivalent weights. In this scenario, a current of 9.65 A passes through the aqueous solutions of the salts of metals A, B, and C separately for 30 seconds. The atomic masses of B and C are 5 times and 3 times the atomic mass of A, respectively.

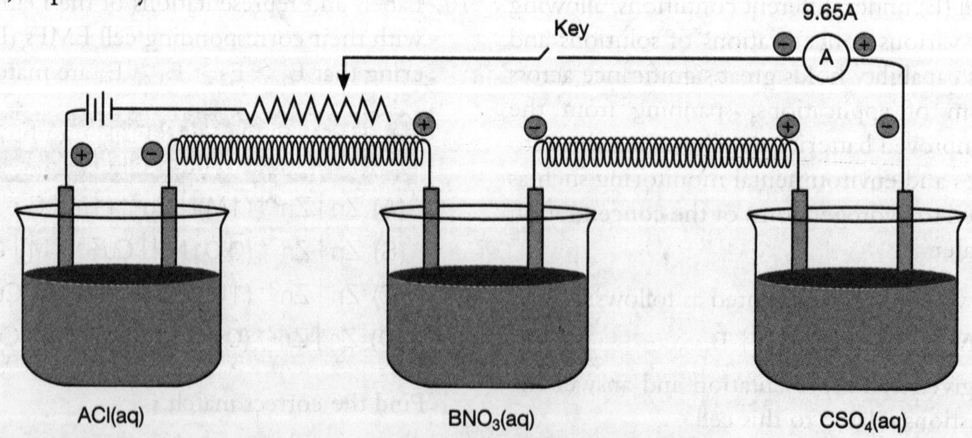

16.

List – I Metal	List – II Mass of the metal deposited at cathode
(a) A	(i) 0.27x
(b) B	(ii) 0.18x
(c) C	(iii) 0.9x

ANSWER KEYS

Crossword

Across

2. Daniel cell 5. Reduction 7. Electrometallurgy 11. Fluorine 12. Salt bridge 13. Galvanic cell 17. Voltmeter 18. Coulomb 19. Platinum 20. Oxidation

Down

1. Oxygen 3. Electrochemical series 4. Faraday 6. Cell potential 8. Battery 9. Anodising 10. Voltameter 14. Anode mud 15. Conductor 16. Zero

Classroom Wing

Very Short Answer Type Questions

1. anion 2. cathode 3. inert 4. decreasing 5. lesser, longer

Competition Wing

Level 1: Apply your Concepts

1. True 2. True 3. False 4. True 5. True 6. False 7. True 8. Electrolysis 9. Batteries 10. voltameter 11. electrodes 12. electrochemical cell 13. Degree of dissociation 14. Zinc 15. Cathode 16. Bromine 17. 0 volt 18. Cathode 19. Left-hand side 20. (i) - (D); (ii) - (C); (iii) - (A); (iv) - (E); (v) - (B) 21. (d) 22. (a) 23. (c) 24. (d) 25. (b) 26. (b) 27. (a) 28. (d) 29. (a) 30. (d) 31. (b) 32. (a) 33. (c) 34. (c) 35. (b) 36. (b) 37. (b) 38. (c) 39. (c) 40. (c) 41. (a) 42. (c)

JEE-NEET Special Wing

Multiple-Answer Type Questions

1. (b, d) 2. (a, d) 3. (a, b, c) 4. (a, b) 5. (b, c)

Comprehension-Based Questions

7. (d) 8. (b) 10. (d) 11. (a) 12. (c) 13. (c) 14. (b) 15. (b)

Match the Columns

16. (a)-(ii), (b)-(iii), (c)-(i)

Hints and Explanations

Classroom Wing

Very Short Answer Type Questions

1. anion
2. cathode
3. inert
4. decreasing
5. lesser, longer
6. The addition of $Al(OH)_3$ to water makes it a feeble conductor of electricity since it is a very weak electrolyte.
7. Hydroxyl ions get oxidized to oxygen at the anode when an aqueous solution of $CuSO_4$ is electrolyzed using platinum as an anode.
8. Electrochemical cell used for the conversion of chemical energy to electrical energy.
9. When two half cells are connected through a voltmeter, the reading of the voltmeter gives the emf of the cell.

   emf of cell = $E^{\circ}_{RHE} + E^{\circ}_{LHE}$

   Cell reactions of Daniel cell

   $Zn \rightarrow Zn^{2+} + 2e^-$

   $Cu^{2+} + 2e^- \rightarrow Cu$

   $Zn + Cu^{2+} \rightarrow Zn^{2+} + Cu$

10. Pure copper → Cathode

    Impure copper → Anode
11. Electrochemical equivalent can be defined as the mass of substance which undergoes electrode reaction at an electrode by the passage of one coulomb of electricity through the electrolyte.
12. Hydrogen gas at 1 atm pressure in contact with platinum surface and HCl solution of molar concentration at 25°C temperature.
13. $Zn(s)\,|\,Zn^{2+}(aq)\,||\,Cu^{2+}(aq)\,|\,Cu(s)$
14. When any electrode is connected to the standard hydrogen electrode, the potential difference between the two electrodes is called of that electrode. For example, Zn = – 0.76V
15. Generation of electricity by means of cell reactions
16. 6.023×10^{23} electrons
17. $Zn \rightarrow Zn^{2+} + 2e^-$

    $Ag^+ + e^- \rightarrow Ag$
18. $e = 1.6 \times 10^{-19}$ C
19. Polar covalent molecules ionize in aqueous solution.
20. Anions are negatively charged hence, they move towards positive plate (anode), cations are positively charged, hence move towards (cathode) negatively charged plate.
21. Strong electrostatic force of attraction.
22. Equivalent weight of Cu ∵ 96,500

    $Cu^{+2} + 2e^- \rightarrow Cu$

    For the deposition of atomic weight of Cu, 2 × 96,500 C is required, 2 Faraday.
23. (i) Aqueous NaOH

    Cathode: Na

    Anode: O_2

    (ii) Cathode: Na

    Anode: Cl_2

    (iii) Cathode: Ag

    Anode: Ag^+
24. Does not glow.
25. 96,500 C

Short Answer Type Questions

26. (B) Potassium (D) Zinc

    (C) Iron (E) Hydrogen

    (A) Copper

    Increasing order of SRP values shows the ascending order of discharge at the respective electrodes.
27. Since Y has a higher SRP value than X, X undergoes oxidation and Y undergoes reduction. This means that X gets liberated at the anode by losing electrons ($X \rightarrow X^{+2} + 2e^-$). Since X undergoes oxidation, it can displace hydrogen from acids. Y has a positive SRP

value and undergoes reduction when connected to the hydrogen electrode and gets deposited at the cathode. Statements (i) and (ii) are true.

28. $Cu^{+2} + 2\ e\text{-} \rightarrow Cu$

31.75 g Cu $\rightarrow$ 1 F

6.375 g Cu $\rightarrow 6.375/31.75 = 0.2$ F

Current strength × time of follow = Quantity of electricity

$t = 20 \times 60 = 1200$ s

$Q = 0.2\ F = 0.2 \times 96{,}500$ C

$C \times 1200 = 0.2 \times 96500$

$C = 0.2 \times 96500/1200 = 16$ A

29. Addition of NaOH increases the conductance of water to the maximum extent since it is a strong electrolyte.

30. Since 3 F electric charge is required, its valency is 3.

∴ Equivalent weight = M/3.

31. (i) Conversion of energy
   (ii) Process of electrolysis
   (iii) Conversion of energy
   (iv) Nature of particles
   (v) Charge of 1 mole of electrons

32. An acid or base's strength refers to its degree of ionization. Ionization constant (K_a) for the ionization of an acid is called the acid.

33. Refer table 3.1

34. It depends on three factors :
   (i) The relative position of ions in the electrochemical series.
   (ii) The relative concentration of ions.
   (iii) The nature of the electrodes.

35. It depends on the position of ions in electrochemical series.

36. Electrodes made from noble metals with less reactivity are called noble electrodes.

37. Electroplating is an electrolytic process in which a thin film of a metal like gold, silver, nickel, etc., is deposited on other metals like iron, copper, etc., for different purposes.

38. The amount of substance deposited or liberated or dissolved at an electrode is directly proportional to the quantity of electricity passing through the electrolyte.

39. A spectator ion does not take part in a chemical reaction.

For example: When a solution of sodium hydroxide, NaOH, is mixed with hydrochloric acid, HCl, the compounds dissociate into the ions Na^+, OH^-, H^+ and Cl^-. The hydrogen and hydroxide ions react to form water, but the sodium and chlorine ions stay in solution unchanged, these two are spectator ions in this instance.

40. (i) Production of hydrogen by electrolysis of water.
   (ii) Manufacture of heavy water.
   (iii) The metals like K, Mg, Al, etc., are obtained by electrolysis of fused electrolytes.
   (iv) Non-metals like hydrogen, fluorine, chlorine are obtained by electrolysis.
   (v) In this method pure metal is deposited at cathode from a solution containing the metal ions, etc.
   (vi) Compounds like NaOH, KOH, white lead, etc., are synthesized by electrosynthesis method.

Essay Answer Type Questions

41. At its most basic, electroplating involves using electricity to reduce the cations of a desired metal onto a surface, resulting in metal deposition on that surface. A conductive surface is required for the process. Plastics, glass, and ceramics, for example, are insulators and thus non-conductive. As a result, direct electroplating is not an option.

However, there are methods to make these non-metallic surfaces conductive:

1. *Conductive Coating:* Coating the non-metallic item with a thin layer of conductive material is a common technique. This can be accomplished through a variety of methods, including: (i) spraying the item with conductive paint or ink containing metal particles. (ii) Immersion in a solution containing conductive particles and a binder, followed by solvent evaporation.
2. *Activation:* Another method is to 'activate' the non-metallic surface by immersing it in solutions containing catalytic metals (like palladium). This layer then enables electroless plating of a metal, which can then be built upon with electroplating.

Applications:

a. *Decorative Purposes:* Non-metallic items can be given a metallic finish using electroplating, increasing their aesthetic appeal. Plastic car parts or jewellery, for example, can be electroplated for a 'chrome' finish.

b. *Electronics:* Electroplating can be used to deposit metal on non-metallic substrates used in electronics, thereby creating electrical current pathways.

c. *Wear Resistance:* A metal coating can be applied to non-metallic items that are prone to wear, providing an additional layer of protection.

42. The residue that forms at the bottom of the electrolytic cell during the electrolytic refining of metals, particularly copper, is known as anode mud (or slime). This residue frequently contains valuable precious metals such as gold, silver, and platinum group metals.

To extract these metals, several steps can be employed:

1. *Physical Separation:* To separate larger impurities, the anode mud is first subjected to physical processes such as filtration or sedimentation.
2. *Pyrometallurgical Treatment:* In the presence of fluxes, the filtered anode mud can be heated in a furnace, resulting in the formation of a molten metallic phase and slag. During the metallic phase, precious metals accumulate.
3. *Hydrometallurgical Treatment:* The mud is treated with leaching agents such as acids or cyanide solutions. Gold, for example, can be leached with a cyanide solution to form a soluble complex, which can then be reduced back to metallic gold with chemicals such as zinc.
4. *Electrorefining:* The extracted metals from anode mud can be purified using electrolysis in the same way that copper was. Using an electrorefining process, for example, gold can be refined to 99.999 per cent purity.

43. The usage of batteries, particularly in large quantities, raises several ethical concerns:

1. *Environmental Impact:* Batteries contain potentially hazardous chemicals and metals like cadmium, lead, mercury, and lithium. If not properly disposed of, these can leach into the soil and water, contaminating the environment and posing risks to aquatic life and human health.
2. *Resource Extraction:* Mining for metals used in batteries has the potential to have serious environmental consequences. Local ecosystems can be harmed by habitat destruction, soil erosion, and chemical runoff. Furthermore, the extraction of rare metals such as cobalt frequently involves exploitative labour practices, including child labour in some areas.
3. *E-waste and Disposal:* As we become more reliant on electronic devices, so does the production of electronic waste (e-waste), which includes used batteries. Many parts of the world lack adequate e-waste management infrastructure. This can lead to improper disposal or informal recycling, putting workers' health at risk from hazardous chemicals.
4. *Consumerism and Planned Obsolescence:* Some electronics manufacturers create products with non-replaceable batteries or that quickly become obsolete. This encourages a throwaway culture, which leads to more waste and resource exploitation.
5. *Recycling Challenges:* While recycling can help alleviate some of the problems associated with battery disposal, it is not always simple. Effective recycling necessitates adequate infrastructure, technology, and knowledge, all of which may be lacking in many areas. Even where recycling facilities exist, consumers may be unaware of them or find it inconvenient to recycle.

44. (i) Process of extraction of metals.
(ii) Cathodic and anodic reaction.

45. (i) Potential across metal rod and solution under standard conditions.
(ii) Reference electrodes.

Competition Wing

Level 1: Apply your Concepts

20. (i) → (D); 1 F → 35.5 g Cl_2 ($2Cl^- \rightarrow Cl_2 + 2e^-$)

(ii) → (C); 0.5 F → 4 g O_2 ($4OH^- \rightarrow O_2 + 2H_2OI + 4e^-$)

(iii) → (A); 2 F → 24 g Mg ($Mg^{+2} + 2e^- \rightarrow Mg$)

(iv) → (E); 0.1 F → 10.8 g Ag ($Ag^+ + e^- \rightarrow Ag$)

(v) → (B); 3 F → 27 g Al ($Al^{+3} + 3e^- \rightarrow Al$)

21. (d) Passage of 96500 coulombs (1 F) through saturated copper chloride solution results in the liberation of 1 g equivalent of chlorine that occupies

11.2 l volume at STP ($2Cl^- \rightarrow Cl_2 + 2e^-$).

So, A is false and R is true.

Hence, the correct option is (d)

22. The number of equivalents of any substance deposited at the electrode is equal to the number of faradays of electricity passed through the electrolyte. Since gram equivalent mass of silver is equal to the molecular mass, 1 equivalent of silver is equal to 1 mole. A and R are both true and R is the correct explanation of A.

Hence, the correct option is (a)

23. In galvanic cell, chemical energy is converted to electrical energy.

∴ It is used to generate electricity.

Hence, the correct option is (c).

24. $MgCl_2 \rightarrow Mg^{+2} + 2Cl^-$

$Mg^{+2} + 2e^- \rightarrow Mg$ (cathode reaction)

$2Cl^- \rightarrow Cl_2 + 2e^-$ (anode reaction)

C = 4.825 A t = 100 s

Q = C t = 4.825 × 100 = 482.5 C

96,500 c → 1 F

482.5 c → 482.5/96500 = 0.005 F

1F → 12 g Mg

0.005 F → ? g of Mg

= 0.005 × 12

0.06 g of Mg

2 F → 71 g of Cl_2

0.005 → ?

= 0 005 × 71/2 = 0.1775 g of Cl_2

Hence correct option is (d)

36. The electrode with greater negative value of standard reduction potential acts as anode. The electrode with greater positive value of standard reduction potential acts as cathode. Oxidation takes place at anode and reduction takes place at cathode. X

(i) Electrode – IV E° = –2.93 V

(ii) Electrode – I, E° = –2.89 V

(iii) Electrode – V E° = –1.67 V

(iv) Electrode – II, E° = –0.16 V

(v) Electrode – III E° = 0.77 V

Hence, the correct answer is (b).

37. (i) Electrode – A, E° = –2.92 V and

Electrode – B, E° = –2.71 V

(ii) Electrode – C, E° = –0.760 V and

Electrode – D, E° = –0.44 V

(iii) Electrode – B, E° = –2.71 V and

Electrode – D, E° = –0.44 V

(iv) Electrode – A, E° = –2.92 V and

Electrode – C, E° = –0.76 V

Hence, the correct answer is (b).

38. $W = \frac{M.c.t}{n.96,500}$ or $\frac{MQ}{n96,500}$

$W_{Na} = \frac{23 \times 965}{1 \times 96,500}$ g, $W_{Ag} = \frac{108 \times 965}{1 \times 96,500}$ g

$W_{Na} = 0.23$ g, $W_{Ag} = 1.08$ g

Hence, the correct answer is (c).

39. Electrode reactions involved are

$Mg^{2+} + 2e^- \rightarrow Mg$

$Al^{3+} + 3e^- \rightarrow Al$

$Na^+ + e^- \rightarrow Na$

1 mole of Mg requires 2 Faradays.

1 mole of Al requires 3 Faradays.

1 mole of sodium requires 1 Faraday.

Ratio of number of Faradays = 2 : 3 : 1.

Hence, the correct answer is (c).

40. $H_2O \rightarrow H^+ + OH^-$

Cathode: $4OH^- \rightarrow 2H_2O + O_2 + 4e^-$

Anode: $4H^+ + 4e^- \rightarrow 2H_2$

$\therefore$ The ratio of volumes of H_2 and O_2 is 2 : 1

Hence, the correct answer is (c).

41. 48,250 C is equal to 0.5 Faraday. Number of equivalents of metal deposited is equal to the number of faradays of electricity passed through the electrolyte and that means 0.5 equivalents of copper and iron are deposited. Since they are bivalent ions, 0.5 equivalents correspond to 0.25 moles.

Hence, the correct answer is (a).

42. $\frac{W_{Cu}}{63.5} \times \frac{1000}{100} = 0.05M$

$\Rightarrow W_{Cu} = \frac{0.05 \times 63.5}{10} = 0.3175$ g

No. of equivalents $= \frac{0.3175}{31.75} = 0.01$

$\therefore$ No. of Faradays is 0.01 F

Hence, the correct answer is (c).

Level 2: Review your Concepts

43. The cell emf = E° of R.H.S − E° of L.H.S

$= \{y - (-x)\}$ V $= (y + x)$ V

44. Reaction that takes place at the anode when $CuSO_4$ solution undergoes electrolysis using copper as the anode is $Cu - 2e^{-1} \rightarrow Cu^{+2}$.

45. Equivalent weight wt = x, valency = 2

$\therefore$ Atomic weight = $2x$

46. The decreasing order of ease of oxidation is $OH^- > Br^{-1} > F^{-1} > SO_4^{-2}$.

47. (i) Comparison of standard electrode potentials of A and B.

(ii) Relation between standard reduction potential of a metal and its tendency to get oxidized/reduced.

(iii) Identification of anode and cathode based on the relative tendency of getting oxidized/reduced.

(iv) Calculation of cell emf.

48. (i) Formation of Iron (II) hydroxide.

(ii) Composition of rust.

(iii) Comparison of form in which iron is present in pure metal and rust.

(iv) Change undergone by iron during the rusting process.

(v) Requisite for an electrochemical cell.

(vi) Identification of electrode and electrolyte in the process of rusting.

(vii) Component of air that plays a significant role.

49. (i) A voltaic or galvanic cell is constructed by combining two electrode systems wherein the potential difference between the two electrode systems can be measured by means of an voltmeter and this potential difference of the given cell is called cell emf or cell potential.

(ii) Calculation of cell emf.

(iii) Comparison of the cell emf with the external voltage applied.

(iv) Determination of direction of current depending on the magnitude of the external voltage.

50. Metal to be electroplated is taken as cathode.

51. (i) Comparison of electropositivity of copper and silver.

(ii) Identification of the product obtained at the electrode.

(iii) Nature of the anode.

(iv) Reaction that takes place between the anode and the electrolyte.

(v) Ions responsible for blue color.

52. (i) Relative reactivity of zinc and iron.

(ii) Change undergone by iron during rusting.

(iii) Comparison of oxidation potentials of zinc and iron.

(iv) Mode of prevention of rusting by zinc if the coating is partially worn away.

53. (i) Purpose of silver plating.

(ii) Solubility of silver nitrate.

(iii) Quantity of ions present in the electrolyte.

(iv) Relation between the quantity of ions present in the electrolyte and the quality of coating.

(v) Soluble salt of silver that can form a complex with NaCN.

(vi) Ions produced from the complex.

(vii) Change in the concentration of ions due to the complex formation.

(viii) Effect of change in concentration of ions on quality of plating.

54. (i) The number of gram equivalents is same when the same amount of charge is passed through.

(ii) Calculation of total charge required to produce 0.252 g of hydrogen.

(iii) Calculation of the amounts of other products based on the quantity of charge passed through the respective electrolytes.

55. (i) Comparison of electropositivity of A and B with hydrogen.

(ii) Identification of anode and cathode of the electrochemical cells.

(iii) Half-reactions that take place at the electrodes of the respective cells.

56. (i) Difference in standard electrode potentials of the electrodes

(ii) Difference between oxidation and reduction potentials.

(iii) Comparison of standard electrode potentials of the respective metals.

(iv) Identification of anode and cathode in the electrochemical cell.

(v) Calculation of emf of the cell.

57. (i) Process of measurement of potential.

(ii) The particles present on metal rod and electrolyte.

(iii) The reason for origin of potential difference between the electrode and electrolyte.

(iv) The mode of measurement of single electrode potential.

(v) The changes associated with the system while carrying out the process.

58. $MgCl_2 \rightarrow Mg^{2+} + 2C^-$

For the deposition for 12 g of Mg (equivalent weight of magnesium) one faraday is required.

$\therefore$ 12 g requires 1 faraday

0.4 g requires?

$$= \frac{0.14}{12} = 0.03 \text{ Faraday}$$

1 Faraday gives 11.2 L of Cl_2 at STP; therefore, 0.03 faradays gives?

= 0.336 l L of Cl_2 at STP

1 faraday required to deposit 9 g of Al

$\therefore$ 0.03 faraday required to deposit? = 0.27 g

1 faraday required to deposit 23 g of Na

$\therefore$ 0.03 faraday required to deposit?

$= 0.03 \times 23 = 0.69$ g

59. Number of gram equivalents $= \dfrac{\text{current} \times \text{time}}{96500}$

$$= \frac{2 \times 20 \times 60}{96,500} = 0.0248$$

Amount of silver deposited $= 0.0248 \times 108$

= 2.68 g

Let the equivalent weight of Au be E_{Au}.

$$\therefore \frac{E_{Au}}{E_{Hg}} = \frac{W_{Au}}{W_{Ag}}$$

$$\Rightarrow \frac{E_{Au}}{108} = \frac{1.6}{2.68} \Rightarrow E_{Au} = 64.47$$

$\therefore$ Oxidation state of gold $= \dfrac{\text{Atomic weight}}{\text{Equivalent weight}}$

$$= \frac{197}{64.47}$$

$$= 3.05 \approx 3$$

Gold is present in Au^{3+} state in the salt

60. Density of Ag = 10.5 g/cc

Mass of silver required for coating brass spoon $= 10.5 \times 4 \times 0.2 \times 6 = 50.4$ g

108 g of Ag requires 1 faraday of charge. Therefore, 50.4 g of Ag require

$$= \frac{50.4}{108} = 0.466 \text{ faradays}$$

1 faraday of charge deposits 12 g of Mg. Therefore, 0.466 faradays charge deposits

$= 0.466 \times 12 = 5.6$ g

61. Equivalent mass of iron $= \dfrac{56}{2} = 28$

$(Fe^{2+} + 2e^- \rightarrow Fe)$

1 faraday of electricity is required to deposit 28 g of iron.

1 faraday charge is required to deposit 6.023×10^{23} electrons.

$\therefore$ 28 g of Fe required to deposit 6.023×10^{23} electrons.

0.7 g of Fe required to deposit

$$= \frac{6.023 \times 10^{23} \times 0.7}{28} = 1.5 \times 10^{22} \text{ electrons}$$

62. The conductivity of an electrolyte depends on the nature of solvent. A solvent having high dielectric constant like water has greater ability to weaken the strong

electrostatic force of attraction between Na^+ and Cl^- ions when it is dissolved in water. Therefore, aqueous solution of NaCl contains free ions that conduct electricity. When the same substance is dissolved in alcohol that has low dielectric constant, the electrostatic forces cannot be weakened to a large extent. As a result, there are few mobile ions in the solution. Hence, it is a poor conductor of electricity.

63. With an increase in temperature the degree of dissociation of an electrolyte increases, thus more number of ions is produced and rate of migration of ions towards respective electrodes also increases due to increase in the mobility of ions. Therefore, conductivity increases. However, conductivity decreases with decrease in temperature in case of metallic conductors because as temperature increases the vibration of positive kernels and free electrons increases but there is net increase in the KE of electrons, thereby the speed or flow of electrons is hindered or obstructed by increased movement of positive kernels. The obstruction caused by positive kernels to the flow of electrons is called resistance and due to the increase in resistance with increase in temperature, conductivity of a metal decreases.

64. $2Cl^- \rightarrow Cl_2 + 2e^-$

∴ 11.2 L of chlorine is liberated by passing 96,500 C of electricity

11.2 L of Cl_2 is produced by 96,500 C

1.4 L of Cl_2 is produced by ?

$$= \frac{1.4 \times 96500}{11.2} = 12062.5\text{C of charge is required.}$$

Electrolytic cell A (aqueous NaCl)

$2H^+ + 2e^- \rightarrow H_2$

$2Cl \rightarrow Cl_2 + 2e^-$

Cathodic product is H_2 and anodic product is Cl_2

11.2 l L of H_2 is produced by 96,500 C

? is produced by 12,062.5 C

$$= \frac{12062.5 \times 11.2}{96{,}500} = 1.4\text{ L}$$

Electrolytic cell B (fused $ZnSO_4$)

Cathode: Zn

Anode: $SO_4^{2-} \rightarrow SO_2 + O_2 + 2e^-$

$2 \times 96{,}500$ C gives 22.4 L of SO_2 and 22.4 L of O_2 at STP

12,062.5 C gives ? of SO_2 and ? of O_2 at STP

$$= \frac{12062.5}{2 \times 96{,}500}\text{ L of } SO_2 \text{ and } \frac{22.4 \times 12062.5}{2 \times 96{,}500}\text{ L of } O_2$$

= 1.4 L of SO_2 and 1.4 L of O_2

$V_{SO_2} + V_{O_2} = 2.8$ L

Electrolytic cell C (Aq. $AgNO_3$)

Cathode: Ag;

Anode: O_2

$4OH^- \rightarrow 2H_2O + O_2 + 4e^-$

$4 \times 96{,}500$ C gives 22.4 L of O_2 at STP;

therefore, 12,062.5 C gives ? at STP

$$= \frac{12062.5 \times 22.4}{4 \times 96{,}500} = 0.7\text{ L of } SO_2$$

65. Dissociation of electrolyte:

$CuSO_4 \rightarrow Cu^{2+} + SO_4^{2-}$

$H_2O \rightarrow H^+ + OH^-$

Cathode: $Cu^{2+} + 2e^- \rightarrow Cu$

Anode: $4OH^- - 4e^- \rightarrow 2H_2O + O_2$

Cu^{2+} discharges in preference to H^+ due to low discharge potential. Due to this the blue color of the solution fades as Cu^{2+} ions gradually migrate or discharge at cathode and as the electrolyte or whole Cu^{2+} ions are exhausted, H^+ ions get discharged and are liberated as H_2 gas at the cathode.

∴ Bubbles appear at cathode.

$H^+ + e^- \rightarrow H$

$H + H \rightarrow H_2$

In the beginning OH^- ions get discharged at anode and H^+ ions remain in the solution. Therefore, pH of the solution decreases. Once all Cu^{2+} ions are consumed, H^+ ions start getting discharged at cathode. Therefore, pH of the solution increases.

66. If blue litmus is added to the water in Hoffmann's voltameter, the color of litmus is not changed in cathode compartment since the solution remains alkaline due to increase in OH^- ions in the solution due to the discharge of H^+ ions at the cathode to give H_2 gas. But blue litmus changes to red in the anode compartment since the OH^- ions get discharged at anode and the solution becomes rich in H^+ ions. Thus, after electrolysis, in cathode compartment, the solution is blue and in anode compartment it is red.

67. $CuSO_4 \rightarrow Cu^{2+} + SO_4^{2-}$

$H_2O \rightarrow H^+ + OH^-$

Among the cations Cu^{2+} and H^+, Cu^{2+} requires lesser discharge potential compared to H^+ so Cu is discharged at cathode.

At cathode: $Cu^{2+} + 2e^- \rightarrow Cu$

For the deposition of 63.5 g of Cu, $2 \times 6.023 \times 10^{23}$ e^- have to flow through the circuit; therefore, 0.3175 g of Cu requires ? electrons

$$= \frac{0.3175 \times 2 \times 6.023 \times 10^{23}}{63.5}$$

$= 6.023 \times 10^{21}$ electrons are required

At anode: $4OH^- \rightarrow 2H_2O + 4e^- + O_2$

For the formation of 1 mole of oxygen 4 moles of electrons are required.

$$96{,}500 \text{ C} = \frac{N}{4} \text{ moles of oxygen}$$

$$= \frac{6.023 \times 10^{23}}{4} \text{ molecule}$$

(6×10^{21} electrons = 965 C)

No. of molecules of oxygen liberated for 965 C

$$= \frac{965 \times 6.023 \times 10^{23}}{4 \times 96{,}500} = 1.5 \times 10^{21} \text{ molecule}$$

Level 3: Assess Your Concepts

68. 'X' undergoes reduction when connected to a hydrogen electrode. This indicates that X is above hydrogen in the electrochemical series. That means, 'X' has a positive SRP value. 'Y' undergoes oxidation when connected to a hydrogen electrode. This means that Y has a negative SRP value. Since X undergoes reduction, it can- not displace hydrogen from acids. Y undergoes oxidation at the anode and hydrogen is liberated at the cathode.

Statements (i) and (ii) are true.

69. X represents anodic half-cell and Y represents a cathodic half-cell. This means that oxidation takes place at X and reduction takes place at Y. The SRP value of X should be lower than that of Y. SRP values of -0.76 V for X and 0.34 V for Y correspond to a lower value for X than Y. Therefore, it represents the given cell reaction.

70. (i) Reversible cell reaction

(ii) Requisite for an electrochemical cell.

(iii) Change taking place in a battery as electrochemical cell.

(iv) Effect of this change on the working of battery.

(v) Requisite for the revival of the function.

(vi) Change that takes place during the above process.

71. (i) Mechanism of conduction of electricity in the given conductors.

(ii) Requisite for a solid substance to conduct electricity.

(iii) Type of bond present in metal.

(iv) Changes that take place in the movement of the constituent particles of metal due to the change in temperature.

(iv) Particles that conduct electricity in an electrolyte.

(v) Comparison of number of ions present in equimolar $CuSO_4$ solution and acetic acid solution.

(vi) Effect of change of temperature on the concentration of ions in the above solutions.

(vii) Relation between conductivity of an electrolyte and the concentration of ions in it.

72. (i) Effect of concentration on direction of equilibrium

(ii) The particles present on metal rod and electrolyte.

(iii) The reason for the origin of difference in potential between the electrode and electrolyte.

(iv) The factor responsible for the potential difference.

(v) Effect of concentration on the above factor.

73. Elements with higher standard reduction potential have lesser tendency of losing electrons. They are less electropositive and form oxides that are less stable towards heat. These metals are generally placed on the top in electrochemical series when they are arranged in decreasing order of reduction potential (+ve) values and form unstable oxides towards heat, that is, these oxides are decomposed on heating. In case of weak electrolytes, degree of dissociation increases with dilution.

74. Magnesium preferentially gets reduced to Mg^{2+} ions over iron. Therefore, iron does not produce Fe^{2+} ions. Magnesium acts as cathode and iron acts as anode. Due to this reason, iron is protected from corrosion when it is connected to magnesium.

75. In case of strong electrolytes, when the concentration of the solution is high, the number of solvent molecules is few and the oppositely charged ions are close to each other. This results in strong electrostatic forces of attraction between the ions and lesser mobility of the ions. This accounts for increase in conductivity with dilution. In case of weak electrolytes, degree of dissociation increases with dilution.

76. Electrolyte: $CuSO_4$

$$CuSO_4 \rightarrow Cu^{2+} + SO_4^{2-}$$

Cathode (Reduction)	Anode (Fe) (Oxidation)
$Cu^{2+} + 2e^- \rightarrow Cu$	$Fe - 2e^- \rightarrow Fe^{2+}$
	Compared to SO_4^{2+}, Fe ionizes to give Fe^{2+} due to low reduction potential

$\therefore$ Cu and Fe^{2+} are products at cathode and anode, respectively.

77. Iron when exposed to humid atmosphere gets converted to Fe^{2+} due to the formation of $Fe(OH)_2$ and this is in presence of air (O_2) to form rust.

$Fe_2O_3 . xH_2O$.

When tin coating on iron is broken, iron gets exposed to atmosphere. Since iron has greater oxidation potential than tin, iron acts as anode and tin acts as cathode. Iron gets oxidized to Fe^{2+} ions in preference to tin. Consequently rusting becomes rapid when tin coating on iron is broken. Since Zn has greater oxidation potential than Fe, though Zinc is worn out, Zn present on the rest of the article gets oxidized in preference to Fe. Hence, rusting of Fe is slow.

JEE-NEET Special Wing

Multiple-Answer Type Questions

1. In the given voltaic cell representation,
$A(s) | A^{2+} (aq) || B^{2+} (aq) | B(s)$

A(s) is changing to $A^{2+}(aq)$ and $B^{2+}(aq)$ is changing to B(s)

$\Rightarrow$ B^{+2} ions are reduced to B by gaining electrons while metal atoms of A are undergoing oxidation by losing electrons to form A^{2+} ions (that enters into the electrolyte).

$\Rightarrow$ at electrode A, half-cell reaction will be $A \rightarrow A^{+2} + 2e-$ and at electrode B, half-cell reaction will be $B^{+2} + 2e- \rightarrow B$.

$\Rightarrow$ Oxidation of A is taking place at electrode A and reduction of B^{2+} ions at electrode B.

Therefore, A is acting as anode while B as cathode in the given cell.

In a voltaic cell, electrons move from oxidation half-cell (anode) to reduction half-cell (cathode).

2. Aqueous acidified copper sulphate dissociates as shown below.

$CuSO_4(aq) \rightarrow Cu^{2+} + SO4^{2-}$; $H_2O \rightarrow H^+ + OH^-$; $H_2SO_4 \rightarrow 2H^+ + SO_4^{2-}$

Reaction at Cathode:

Copper gets discharged at the cathode because of lower discharge potential than that of hydrogen.

$Cu^{2+} + 2e^- \rightarrow Cu$

Reaction at Anode:

(i) If anode is inert (platinum or graphite)

OH^- is discharged at the anode because its discharge potential is lower than that of SO_4^{2-} ion.

$4OH^- \rightarrow 2H_2O + O_2 + 4e^-$

(ii) If the anode is copper itself (active anode)

$Cu - 2e^- \rightarrow Cu^{2+}$

No product is formed at anode.

3. In the presence of multiple ions carrying the same charge within an electrolyte solution under identical conditions, one of them is selectively discharged at the electrode, a phenomenon known as selective ion discharge. And it depends on the following factors:

Factors	Explanation
Nature of electrode	Electrode's material and its interaction with the ions present in the electrolyte solution (like its affinity for ions, its reduction potential etc) affects the selective discharge of ions
Relative concentration of ions	Ions with higher concentration gets deposited first
Relative reduction potential of ions	The relative position of ions in the electrochemical (activity) series. In case of cation, the species having high reduction potential get discharged first. In case of anion, the species having low reduction potential get discharged first.

The magnitude of charge on the ions (e.g., +1, +2, -1, etc.) is important for determining the overall charge balance in the electrochemical cell, but it does not directly dictate which ions will be selectively discharged.

4. The concentration of electrolyte in this electrode is 1 M. The emf of the cell is positive. This is the only incorrect statement regarding the hydrogen electrode.

5. Fuell cell are electrochemical cells that convert chemical energy to electrical energy, typically in the form of direct current (DC) but not alternating current (AC). In these cells fuel undergo oxidation at anode while the oxidant, generally oxygen undergoes reduction at cathode. Small portable fuel cells can be employed for providing power to any electronic device. As the chemical reaction in hydrogen oxygen fuel cell is spontaneous, its standard cell potential (E° cell) will be always greater than zero.

Comprehension-Based Questions

6. (i) A(s) + $2B^+$(aq) → A^{2+}(aq) + 2B(s)

(ii) $E = E^\circ - \dfrac{2.303RT}{nF} \times \log\dfrac{[A^{2+}]}{[B^+]^2}$

(iii) The value of *n* in the above equation is 2. (This is because two moles of electrons are involved in the balanced cell reaction)

(iv) At 25°C, Nernst equation for the cell reaction of the given cell is:

E = E° - x log

Given data:

E° is 1.56V, $[A^{2+}]$ = 1M and $[B^+]$ = 0.1M.

Substituting these values in the above expression,

$$E = 1.56 - \frac{0.0591}{2} \times \log\frac{1}{(0.1)^2}$$

$$E = 1.56 - \frac{0.0591}{2} \times \log\frac{1}{0.01}$$

$$E = 1.56 - \frac{0.0591}{2} \times \log(100)$$

$$E = 1.56 - \frac{0.0591}{2} \times \log 10^2$$

$$E = 1.56 - \frac{0.0591}{2} \times 2(\log 10) \quad \text{Since } \log 10 = 1$$

E =1.5008V

7. Given data:

P(s) + Q^{2+}(aq) → P^{2+}(aq) + Q(s)

E cell = 1.179V, E°cell = 1.12 V

Applying Nernst equation,

$$E_{cell} = E^\circ_{cell} - \frac{2.303RT}{nF} \times \log\frac{[P^{2+}]}{[Q^{2+}]}$$

Plotting graph of Ecell versus the $\log\dfrac{[P^{2+}]}{[Q^{2+}]}$ on Y and X-axis respectively,

We should get a straight line with an intercept on Y-axis as it is of the form y = *mx* + *c*.

$$E = E^\circ + \{\frac{2.303RT}{nF} \times \log\frac{[P^{2+}]}{[Q^{2+}]}\}$$

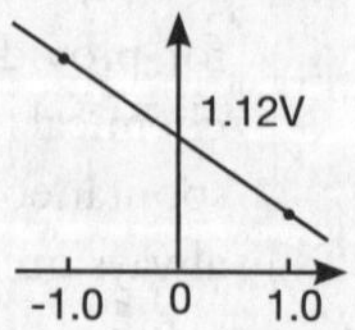

Y = *c* + *mx*. ⇒ *y* = E_{cell} and *x* = log,

$m(\text{slope}) = -\dfrac{2.303RT}{nF}$, *c* (*y* intercept)= E°cell

So, as slope is negative and *c* (*y* intercept)= E°cell = 1.12

8. Slope = $m = -\dfrac{2.303RT}{nF}$

⇒ At standard temperature,

$m = -\dfrac{0.0591}{2} = -0.0295$ (Since *n* = 2)

9. The cell reaction of a Daniel cell is,

Zn(s) + Cu^{2+}(aq) → Zn^{2+}(aq) + Cu(s),

For illustration, let's consider the impact of changing the concentration of copper ions ($[Cu^{2+}]$) while keeping the concentration of zinc ions ($[Zn^{2+}]$) constant on the cell's voltage (Ecell).

Let's assume that the concentrations and Cell EMF are as follows:

	Initial concentration	Changed concentration	EMF of the cell
$[Zn^{2+}]$	1M	1M (Unchanged)	E_1
$[Cu^{2+}]$	1M	10M	E_2 =?

Applying Nernst equation, expression to calculate EMF of the cell is given by,

$$E = E^\circ - \frac{2.303RT}{nF} \times \log\frac{[Zn^{2+}]}{[Cu^{2+}]}$$

At initial concentration, $E = E^\circ - \dfrac{2.303RT}{nF} \times \log\dfrac{1}{1}$

⇒ E = E°- 0 = E_1(given)

With changed concentration of Cu^{2+} as 10M, keeping the $[Zn^{2+}]$ same, i.e., 1M,

$$E_2 = E^\circ - \frac{2.303RT}{nF} \times \log\frac{1}{10}$$

$$E_2 = E^\circ - \frac{2.303RT}{nF} [\log 1 - \log 10]$$

$$E_2 = E^\circ - \frac{2.303RT}{nF} \times [0 - 1]$$

$$E_2 = E^\circ + \frac{2.303RT}{nF} \Rightarrow E_2 > E_1$$

With the increased concentration of $[Cu^{2+}]$, the logarithmic term $\log([Zn^{2+}]/[Cu^{2+}])$ becomes more negative. Consequently, the voltage of the cell (E) increases compared to the initial voltage E_1.

So, by increasing the concentration of one form of the ion (in this case, Cu^{2+}) relative to the other (Zn^{2+}), we see that the voltage of the cell changes, and it increases. This illustrates the impact of the logarithmic term in the Nernst equation and how changes in ion concentrations can influence the cell potential.

10. Cell reaction of a Daniel cell is written as:

$Zn(s) + Cu^{2+}(aq) \rightarrow Zn^{2+}(aq) + Cu(s)$,

According to the Nernst equation,

$$E = E^\circ - \frac{0.0591}{n} \times \log\frac{[Zn^{2+}]}{[Cu^{2+}]}, \text{where}$$

E = EMF of the cell at the given conditions

E° = EMF of the call at standard conditions.

$n = 2$ (number of electrons transferred in the redox reaction (from the balanced reaction)

$$\Rightarrow E = E^\circ - \frac{0.0591}{2} \times \log\frac{[Zn^{2+}]}{[Cu^{2+}]}$$

$$\Rightarrow E = E^\circ - 0.0295 \times \log\frac{[Zn^{2+}]}{[Cu^{2+}]}$$

List – I Label and Representation of Daniel cell	Calculated cell EMF	List – II Cell EMF
(A) $Zn \mid Zn^{2+}(1M) \parallel Cu^{2+}(1M) \mid Cu$	$E = E^\circ - 0.0295 \times \log\frac{1}{1}$ $E(A) = E^\circ - 0 = E^\circ$	(ii) E_3
(B) $Zn \mid Zn^{2+}(0.01M) \parallel Cu^{2+}(1M) \mid Cu$	$E = E^\circ - 0.0295 \times \log\frac{0.01}{1}$ $E = E^\circ - 0.0295 \times \log\frac{1}{100}$ $E = E^\circ - 0.0295\ [\log 1 - \log 10^2]$ $E = E^\circ - 0.0295\ [0 - 2]$ $E(B) = E^\circ + 0.059$	(iii) E_1
(C) $Zn \mid Zn^{2+}(1M) \parallel Cu^{2+}(0.1M) \mid Cu$	$E = E^\circ - 0.0295 \times \log\frac{1}{0.1}$ $E = E^\circ - 0.0295\ [\log 10]$ $E = E^\circ - 0.0295\ [1]$ $E(C) = E^\circ - 0.0295$	(i) E_4
(D) $Zn \mid Zn^{2+}(0.1M) \parallel Cu^{2+}(1M) \mid Cu$	$E = E^\circ - 0.0295 \times \log\frac{0.1}{1}$ $E = E^\circ - 0.0295 \times \log\frac{1}{10}$ $E = E^\circ - 0.0295\ [\log 1 - \log 10]$ $E = E^\circ - 0.0295\ [0 - 1]$ $E(D) = E^\circ + 0.0295$	(iv) E_2

Hence, the correct match is as follows:

	(A)	(B)	(C)	(D)
(d)	(ii)	(iii)	(i)	(iv)

11. High standard reduction potential(SRP) values indicate the greater tendency of an element to undergo reduction. Elements that readily undergo reduction serve as strong oxidizing agents, while those that easily undergo oxidation act as strong reducing agents.

- If SRP value < 0, it indicates a stronger tendency to lose electrons (undergo oxidation) compared to hydrogen.
- SRP value > 0 , it indicates a stronger tendency to gain electrons (undergo reduction) compared to hydrogen.

So, the correct inferences that can be made from the given information is:

Z has a higher tendency than hydrogen to lose electrons (i.e. greater reducing properties) while X and Y have a greater tendency to gain electrons(i.e., lesser reducing properties) than hydrogen.

12. From the information given in the table, electrode Z has a lesser value of standard reduction potential compared to that of Hydrogen gas electrode (E°cell = 0.00V). Which means that hydrogen can gain electrons readily i.e., undergo reduction compared to Z. So, when coupled with electrode Z, reduction occurs at Hydrogen gas electrode and oxidation at electrode Z.

13. In this reaction, $A + B^{2+} \rightarrow A^{2+} + B$, A is undergoing oxidation to form A^{2+} ions while B^{2+} ions are getting reduced to B. In a galvanic cell, oxidation occurs at the anode while reduction at the cathode. The Cell reaction is spontaneous if E° cell is > 0 i.e., positive.

Option	Anode (A)	Cathode(B)	E° cell = E° (cathode) – E° (anode) Volts
(a)	X	Z	E° cell = (–0.44) – (0.44)V = –0.88V < 0 ⇒ Nonspontaneous
(b)	X	Y	E° cell = (0.33) – (0.44) V = -0.11V < 0 ⇒ Nonspontaneous
(c)	Hydrogen	Y	E° cell = (0.33) – (0.00) V = 0.33V > 0 ⇒ Spontaneous
(d)	Hydrogen	Z	E° cell = (–0.44) – (0.00) V = 0.44V < 0 ⇒ Nonspontaneous

In the above given option E° cell is positive only in the case where A is hydrogen gas electrode (E° of hydrogen is 0.00V) and B is electrode Y.

14. SRP of electrode 'X' is greater than that of hydrogen gas electrode. So, when hydrogen gas electrode is coupled with electrode X, oxidation occurs at hydrogen electrode and reduction at electrode 'X'. Hence hydrogen electrode acts as anode. Representation of hydrogen gas electrode when it is acting as anode half-cell is: $Pt|H_2(g)|H^+(aq)$

15. Greater is the difference in SRP values of the electrodes, greater will the Emf of the cell.

SRP of X and Z is +0.44V and -0.44V respectively. So, electrochemical cell constructed with Z as anode and X as cathode generates an EMF of 0.88V

Match the Columns

16.

Metal solutions subjected to electrolysis	Valency of metal	Atomic mass of the metal	Equivalent weight of the metal Atomic mass/Valency
ACl	1	X	X
BNO_3	1	5X	5X
CSO_4	2	3X	1.5X

'When the same quantity of electricity passes through different electrolytes, the substances deposited at the electrodes are in the ratio of their respective equivalent weights'. From this it is clear that, if *m*1, *m*2, and *m*3 represent the masses of different substances, and *E*1 , *E*2, and *E*3 denote the equivalent weights of these substances, then the ratio *m*1: *m*2: *m*3 = *E*1: *E*2: *E*3 when the quantity of electricity remains constant.

Ratio of given masses of metals deposited at their respective electrodes in List-II is:

0.27X : 0.18X : 0.9X = 1.5X : X : 5X.

By comparing this ratio with the equivalent weights of the metals, it is clear that 0.27X, 0.18X and 0.9X should correspond to the mass of metal C, A, B respectively deposited at the cathodes of their respective electrochemical cell. So, the correct match is: (a)-(ii), (b)-(iii), (c)-(i)

CHAPTER

4

Periodic Table

Remember

Before beginning this chapter, you should be able to:

- understand earlier versions of classification of elements with emphasis on Mendeleev's periodic table.
- describe modern periodic table.

Key Ideas

After completing this chapter, you should be able to:

- understand the historical aspects of the development of periodic table.
- explain different periodic laws and the arrangement of elements into groups and periods in the periodic table.
- describe the trends of atomic size, ionization energy, electron affinity, electropositivity, oxidizing, and reducing property, etc., among the elements in the periodic table.
- compare different elements based on their periodic properties.

Scientific Crypt

A Tribute to H.G.J Moseley (1887–1915)

The history of classification of elements dates back to 17th century. Many scientists like Dobereiner, Newland and Mendeleev did a lot of pioneering work in this field. However, the work done by Henry Moseley in this area was a major break-through in the history of chemistry.

Henry Gwyn Jeffreys Moseley was a great English scientist born on 23rd November in 1887 in Weymouth, Great Britain. As a son of professor in biology, his earlier interest was biology. But, he excelled in mathematics in Eton College on King's scholarship. After he graduated from Trinity college with high honours in Mathematics and sciences, he acquired the position of a research assistant under Earnest Rutherford at University of Manchester. There, his studies of X-ray diffraction on various elements led to the discovery of atomic number as the most fundamental characteristic property of elements instead of being simply an arbitrary sequential number as was thought earlier. This discovery ultimately culminated in the development of Modern Periodic table.

Unfortunately, Moseley left his research work to join British Army during First World war in which he was shot and killed on 10th August 1915 at a very early age of 27. This early demise of such an eminent scientist was a great loss not only to the scientific community, but to the society as such.

FUN TIME

CROSSWORD

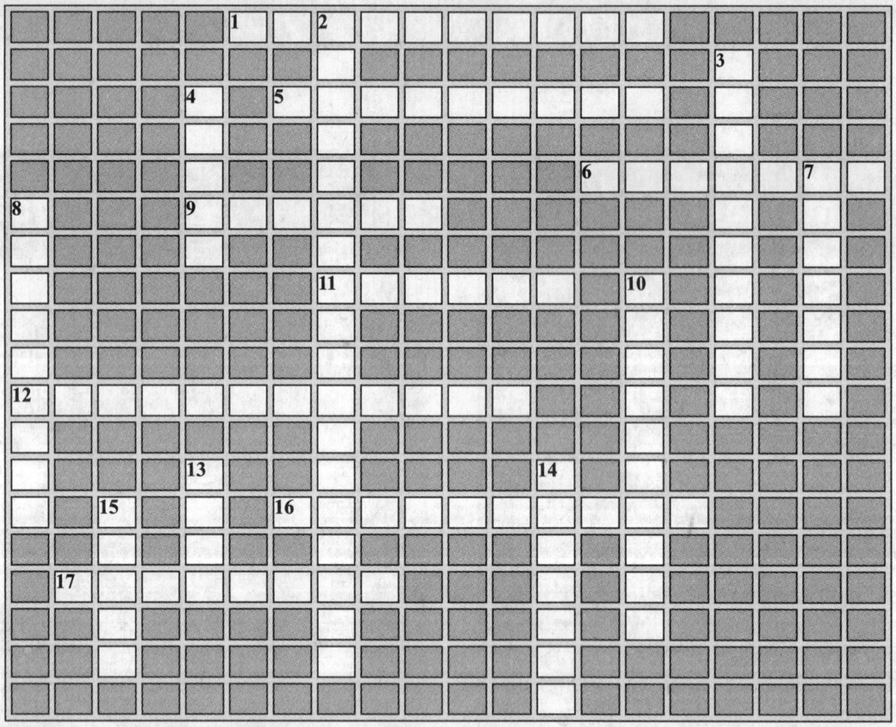

Across

1. elements which show properties of both metals and non-metals
5. element with atomic number 25
6. modern name for eka-aluminium
9. radioactive element in IIA group (2nd group)
11. halogen in fifth period of periodic table is
12. these group elements have highest reducing nature in the complete periodic table
16. nature of oxide of aluminium is
17. most electronegative element in the periodic table

Down

2. d-block elements are also called as
3. unreactive gases with zero electron affinity are called as
4. phosphorus is present in this period
7. radioactive element with atomic number 92
8. moving down the group metallic nature
10. last name of scientist who gave law of triads
13. valency of 18th group elements
14. last name of the scientist who gave law of octaves
15. most of the metals exist in this physical state

INTRODUCTION

Chemistry deals with the study of various elements and their compounds which are essential as they invariably find numerous applications in variety of fields in industries. The discovery of elements is a continuous process with new elements being added to the existing ones. There are 118 authorized elements at present and few more have been discovered however yet to be authorized. The study of 100 odd elements and the innumerable compounds formed by them is a tedious task. Therefore, classification of elements has been necessitated for a systematic study. This idea of classification of elements ultimately culminated into the arrangement of elements into a periodic table.

The periodic table of elements can be considered as a single document that reflects the behavior of elements in a simple and logical way. That means, just by knowing the position of an element in the periodic table, it is possible to predict the nature and behavior of the elements. In fact, the organization of the elements into a periodic table was a major breakthrough in the history of chemistry.

Mendeleev's Periodic Table

According to Mendeleev, the properties of elements were related to their atomic weights. On this basis, he formulated his periodic law. Mendeleev's periodic law states that the physical and chemical properties of the elements are the periodic functions of their atomic weights. Therefore, the elements have been arranged in the increasing order of their atomic weights. He compiled a periodic table by arranging the 63 elements known then in eight vertical columns called **groups** and seven horizontal rows known as **periods**. Later, when the noble gases were discovered, Mendeleev gave a modified periodic table by including the noble gases in zero group. He categorized the table into eight (columns) groups and seven periods (rows). The groups range from zero to eight and these except the zero and eighth group were further subdivided into two subgroups A and B. He numbered the periods from 1 to 7 of which the seventh period is incomplete.

Historical Aspects

Classification of elements into metals, non-metals and metalloids could not serve the purpose, as the elements within a category also show characteristic differences in their properties. One of the earliest attempts of classification was made by Döbereiner on the basis of atomic weights. According to this classification, the elements are grouped into triads in which the atomic weight of the middle element is the approximate average of the atomic weights of the other two elements. This classification had a major drawback in that as only a few elements could be grouped into triads, which could reflect proper trends in properties.

Another similar attempt was made by Newland, who proposed the famous law of octaves. According to Newland's law of octaves, the properties of every eighth element are a kind of repetition of the first. This classification could hold good only up to atomic weight 40 but failed beyond that. The first systematic classification of all the then known elements was made by Mendeleev by taking atomic weight as the fundamental characteristic property.

Info Bytes!

Mendeleev's intuition and scientific insight were so spot-on that he accurately predicted the properties of three missing elements in his table. When these elements (Gallium, Germanium, and Scandium) were eventually discovered, their properties closely matched Mendeleev's predictions, solidifying his Periodic Table's significance in the annals of scientific history.

Merits of Mendeleev's Periodic Table

1. Mendeleev left some gaps for some undiscovered elements in the periodic table. The properties of these elements could be predicted based on the properties of other elements present in the same group. He named these missing elements as Eka boron, Eka aluminium, and Eka silicon that were later discovered and named as scandium, gallium, and germanium, respectively.
2. Mendeleev corrected the doubtful atomic weights of some elements like indium, beryllium, and uranium.

Limitations of Mendeleev's Periodic Table

1. In certain parts of the periodic table, elements with a higher atomic weight were placed before that of the lower atomic weight in order to maintain the gradation in properties. These are known as **anomalous pairs**. Examples of anomalous pairs are the following:

(i) Co	58.9	(ii) Te	127.6	(iii) Ar	39.94
Ni	58.6	I	126.9	K	39.10

2. Isotopes of an element have different atomic weights. However, there is no position for the isotopes in Mendeleev's periodic table.

3. Three groups of three transition elements are placed in group VIII of the periodic table. They should have been given separate positions.

4. Transition elements were placed with other elements under the same group.

5. Coinage metals were placed along with alkali metals.

Table 4.1 Periodic system of the elements in groups and periods

	Groups of elements								
Series	O	I	II	III	IV	V	VI	VII	VIII
1	—	Hydrogen H 1.008	—	—	—	—	—	—	
2	Helium He 4.0	Lithium Li 7.03	Beryllium Be 9.1	Boron B 11.0	Carbon C 12.0	Nitrogen N 14.04	Oxygen O 16.00	Fluorine F 19.0	
3	Neon Ne 19.9	Sodium Na 23.05	Magnesium Mg 24.3	Aluminium Al 27.0	Silicon Si 28.4	Phosphorus P 31.0	Sulphur S 32.06	Chlorine Cl 35.45	
4	Argon Ar 38	Potassium K 39.1	Calcium Ca 40.1	Scandium Sc 44.1	Titanium Ti 48.1	Vanadium V 51.4	Chromium Cr 52.1	Manganese Mn 55.0	Iron Fe 55.9
									Cobalt Co 58.9
									Nickel Ni 58.7 (Cu)
5		Copper Cu 63.6	Zinc Zn 65.4	Gallium Ga 70.0	Germanium Ge 72.3	Arsenic As 75	Selenium Se 79	Bromine Br 79.95	
6	Krypton Kr 81.8	Rubidium Rb 85.4	Strontium Sr 87.6	Yttrium Y 89.0	Zirconium Zr 90.6	Niobium Nb 94.0	Molybdenum Mo 96.0	—	Ruthenium Ru 101.7
									Rhodium Rh 103.0
									Palladium Pd 106.5 (Ag)

(Continued.)

Table 4.1 Continued

Series	Groups of elements 0	I	II	III	IV	V	VI	VII	VIII
7		Silver Ag 107.9	Cadmium Cd 112.4	Indium In 114.0	Tin Sn 119.0	Antimony Sb 120.0	Tellurium Te 127	Iodine I 127	
8	Xenon Xe 128	Caesium Cs 132.9	Barium Ba 137.4	Lanthanum La 139	Cerium Ce 140	—	—	—	—
9	—	—	—	—	—	—	—	—	—
10	—	—	—	Ytterbium Yb 173	—	Tantalum Ta 183	Tungsten W 184	—	Osmium Os 191
									Iridium Ir 193
									Platinum Pt 194.9 (Au)
11		Gold Au 197.2	Mercury Hg 200.0	Thallium Tl 204.1	Lead Pb 206.9	Bismuth Bi 208	—	—	
12	—	—	Radium Rd 224	—	Thorium Th 232	—	Uranium U 239		
Higher saline oxides									
	R	R_2O	RO	R_2O_3	RO_2	R_2O_5	RO_3	R_2O_7	RO_4
Higher gaseous hydrogen compounds									
					RH_4	RH_3	RH_2	RH	

Owing to these limitations and the later discovery of atomic structure, Mendeleev's periodic table has no practical significance at present. Nevertheless, its significance lies in the fact that the concept of periodicity in properties and the resultant arrangement of elements into a periodic table originated from Mendeleev's classification of elements.

After the discovery of fundamental particles, it has been established that only electrons take part in chemical reactions. Therefore, Moseley considered atomic number as the fundamental characteristic of elements.

Modern Periodic Table—The Long Form of the Periodic Table

In this, the atomic number, that is, the total nuclear charge is used as the basis of the periodic table instead of the atomic weight. This observation led to the modern periodic law. The modern periodic law states that 'the physical and chemical properties of elements are the periodic functions of their atomic numbers or electronic configurations'.

Thus, according to the modern periodic law, if the elements are arranged in the order of their increasing atomic numbers, the elements with similar properties are repeated after certain regular intervals.

The periodic table consists of seven horizontal rows called **periods** and 18 vertical columns called **groups**. The groups are numbered from I to VIII and the zero group. The groups from I to VII are further divided into A and B. VIII group consists of three vertical columns. All the noble gases are kept in the zero group.

Table 4.2 Description of periods

Periods	Description
1	This is a very short period consisting of only two elements, hydrogen and helium. The elements have only one shell.
2	This is a short period. These elements have two shells. It has eight elements, i.e., from Li to Ne. These are called **bridge elements**.
3	This is a short period. It has 8 elements ranging from Na to Ar. These are called the **typical elements**.
4	This is a long period. It has 18 elements, i.e., from K to Kr. It consists of first transition series elements, i.e., from Sc to Zn.
5	This is the second long period. It has 18 elements, i.e., from Rb to Xe. It consists of second transition series elements, i.e., from Y to Cd.
6	This is a very long period. It has 32 elements, i.e., from Cs to Rn. It has the third transition series elements, i.e., from La to Hg and also the 14 inner transition elements, i.e., from Ce to Lu.
7	Incomplete period. The elements are radioactive in nature. The elements succeeding uranium are all artificial elements. These are called **transuranic elements**. This period includes the elements of fourth transition series that is incomplete and the 14 inner transition series elements, i.e., from Th to Lr.

Division of Periodic Table into Blocks

Depending on the subshell into which the differentiating electron enters, the elements are categorized into four blocks. The newly added electron in an atom of an element is called the **differentiating electron**.

Table 4.3 Description of blocks

Blocks	Description	Groups
s-block	The differentiating electron enters the valence s-subshell.	Group I A → alkali metals Group II A → alkaline earth metals Left part of the periodic table. It consists of only metals.
p-block	The differentiating electron enters the valence p-subshell	III A IV A V A VI A VII A (halogens) Zero group It consists of metals, non-metals, metalloids, and noble gases. p-block constitutes right part of the periodic table. s- and p-block elements except zero group are called representative elements.
d-block	The differentiating electron enters the penultimate d-subshell	III B, IV B,V B,VI B,VII B,VIII, I B, II B These are called transition elements. It consists of only metals placed in between left and right parts of the periodic table.
f-block	The differentiating electron enters the antepenultimate f-subshell	III B These are the inner transition elements kept separately at the bottom of the periodic table. It consists of only metals.

Table 4.4 Modern periodic table

Key: 1 — Atomic number, *Z*; H — Element symbol; 1.008 — Relative atomic mass, *A*

1	2	3	4	5	6	7	8	9	10	11	12	13	14	15	16	17	18
1 **H** 1.008																	2 **He** 4.00
3 **Li** 6.94	4 **Be** 9.01											5 **B** 10.81	6 **C** 12.01	7 **N** 14.01	8 **O** 16.00	9 **F** 19.00	10 **Ne** 20.18
11 **Na** 22.99	12 **Mg** 24.31											13 **Al** 26.98	14 **Si** 28.09	15 **P** 30.97	16 **S** 32.06	17 **Cl** 35.45	18 **Ar** 39.95
19 **K** 39.10	20 **Ca** 40.08	21 **Sc** 44.96	22 **Ti** 47.90	23 **V** 50.94	24 **Cr** 52.01	25 **Mn** 54.94	26 **Fe** 55.85	27 **Co** 58.93	28 **Ni** 58.69	29 **Cu** 63.54	30 **Zn** 65.41	31 **Ga** 69.72	32 **Ge** 72.59	33 **As** 74.92	34 **Se** 78.96	35 **Br** 79.91	36 **Kr** 83.80
37 **Rb** 85.47	38 **Sr** 87.62	39 **Y** 88.91	40 **Zr** 91.22	41 **Nb** 92.91	42 **Mo** 95.94	43 **Tc** 98.91	44 **Ru** 101.07	45 **Rh** 102.91	46 **Pd** 106.42	47 **Ag** 107.87	48 **Cd** 112.40	49 **In** 114.82	50 **Sn** 118.71	51 **Sb** 121.75	52 **Te** 127.60	53 **I** 126.90	54 **Xe** 131.30
55 **Cs** 132.91	56 **Ba** 137.34	**La–Lu**	72 **Hf** 178.49	73 **Ta** 180.95	74 **W** 183.85	75 **Re** 186.21	76 **Os** 190.23	77 **Ir** 192.22	78 **Pt** 195.08	79 **Au** 196.97	80 **Hg** 200.59	81 **Tl** 204.37	82 **Pb** 207.19	83 **Bi** 208.98	84 **Po** 210	85 **At** 210	86 **Rn** 222
87 **Fr** 223	88 **Ra** 226.03	**Ac–Lr**	104 **Rf** [261]	105 **Db** [262]	106 **Sg** [266]	107 **Bh** [264]	108 **Hs** [277]	109 **Mt** [268]	110 **Ds** [271]	111 **Rg** [272]	112 **Cn** [285]	113 **Nh** [286]	114 **Fl** [289]	115 **Mc** [286]	116 **Lv** [293]	117 **Ts** [294]	118 **Og** [294]

Lanthanoids	57 **La** 138.91	58 **Ce** 140.12	59 **Pr** 140.91	60 **Nd** 144.24	61 **Pm** 146.92	62 **Sm** 150.36	63 **Eu** 151.96	64 **Gd** 157.25	65 **Tb** 158.92	66 **Dy** 162.50	67 **Ho** 164.93	68 **Er** 167.26	69 **Tm** 168.93	70 **Yb** 173.04	71 **Lu** 174.97
Actinoids	89 **Ac** 227.03	90 **Th** 232.04	91 **Pa** 231.04	92 **U** 238.03	93 **Np** 237.05	94 **Pu** 239.05	95 **Am** 241.06	96 **Cm** 244.07	97 **Bk** 249.08	98 **Cf** 252.08	99 **Es** 252.09	100 **Fm** 257.10	101 **Md** 258.10	102 **No** 259	103 **Lr** 262

Merits of the Long Form of the Periodic Table

1. The classification is based on the atomic number of elements, which is more fundamental than the atomic weight.
2. Elements belonging to the same group have same number of electrons in their valence shells and show similar chemical characteristics.
3. Variation of chemical properties along a period is correlated with gradual filling of electrons in a particular shell in the period.
4. Placement of inert gases at the end of each period is logical as it represents completion of corresponding valence shells. Inertness of these elements could also be explained on the basis of electronic configuration.
5. Certain types of elements like
   (a) active metals,
   (b) transition metals,
   (c) noble gases, and
   (d) inner transition elements (lanthanides and actinides) have their specific locations in this periodic table.
6. This arrangement of the elements is easy to remember and to reproduce since it is based on electronic configuration.

Info Bytes!

The Modern Periodic Table is not fixed. As new elements are discovered, the table continues to grow. As of my last training data, it had 118 known elements. But who knows? There might be new ones added soon.

Defects of the Long Form of the Periodic Table

1. The position of hydrogen in the periodic table is controversial because hydrogen with one electron in its valence shell shows similarities with both alkali metals and halogens. Therefore, placing hydrogen in IA group is not completely justifiable.
2. The elements lanthanides and actinides could not be placed in the main body of the modern periodic table.
3. This periodic table does not reflect the exact distribution of electrons of some of the transition and inner transition elements.

Konnect

The positioning of hydrogen in the long form of the periodic table has always been a point of debate. Even though it's placed with the alkali metals, it doesn't truly belong there. Hydrogen can form a positive ion like alkali metals, but it also forms a negative ion and shares some properties with halogens.

EXAMPLE 4.1 What are the key distinctions between Mendeleev's periodic law and the Modern Periodic Law?

SOLUTION

(i) *Basis:* Mendeleev's law arranges elements by increasing atomic weight, while the Modern Periodic Law uses atomic number.

(ii) *Prediction:* Mendeleev's table had gaps for undiscovered elements; the modern table doesn't prioritize such predictions.

(iii) *Position of Elements:* In Mendeleev's table, certain anomalies like the positioning of isotopes couldn't be addressed, while the modern table resolves such issues due to its atomic number basis.

(iv) *Blocks:* The modern table divides elements into blocks (s, p, d, f) based on the last electron's orbital, a feature absent in Mendeleev's arrangement.

EXAMPLE 4.2 In the modern periodic table, magnesium is surrounded by elements with atomic numbers 4, 11, 13, and 20. Identify the elements. Which of these have chemical properties resembling magnesium?

SOLUTION

The element ^{12}Mg is present in the centre of the elements having atomic numbers 4, 11, 13, and 20. The atomic number 4 and 20 resemble magnesium because they belong to same group having same number of valence electrons.

	Be = 4 (2, 2)	
Na = 11 2, 8, 1	Mg = 12 (2, 8, 2)	Al = 13 (2, 8, 3)
	Ca = 20 (2, 8, 8, 2)	

EXAMPLE 4.3 Why was the placement of noble gases not incorporated into Mendeleev's periodic table initially?

SOLUTION

Mendeleev's periodic table was proposed before the discovery of noble gases. Once the noble gases were discovered, their unique properties did not fit well with Mendeleev's arrangement based on atomic masses. The modern periodic table, with its basis on atomic numbers and clear distinction of periods and groups, provided an appropriate place for noble gases in a separate group, ensuring the periodicity of properties was maintained.

Periodicity

The regular gradation in the properties of elements and their repetition at regular intervals is called **periodicity**. The properties that show such regular trends are called **periodic properties**.

Periodic Properties

Atomic Size

Atomic size is defined in terms of atomic radius, which is the distance between the nucleus and the valence shell. However, it is not possible to measure the atomic radius directly as an individual atom cannot be isolated.

There are two different ways of measuring the atomic radius:

(a) Covalent Radius: The atomic size of the non-metals is determined by taking half the distance between the nuclei of two like atoms bonded together by a single covalent bond.

(b) Metallic Radius: It is determined by taking half the distance between the nuclei of two adjacent metal atoms in a metallic crystal.

Variation of Atomic Size

(a) Period: The atomic size generally decreases from left to right along the period. This is because along a period the electrons are added to the same energy level, which leads to an increase in the effective nuclear charge on the outermost shell, thereby decreasing the size of the atom.

Exception: In the noble gases, due to interelectronic repulsions, the size is larger than the corresponding halogen.

(b) Group: On going down the group, a new shell is being added from one element to the other. As the electron is added to a shell farther from the nucleus, the effective nuclear force of attraction on the valence shell decreases thereby increasing the size of the atom.

Exception: Atomic sizes of the 5th period elements do not show much increase from the corresponding 4th period elements of same groups. This is because of the addition of 14 electrons in the antepenultimate 'f' subshell of lanthanide elements. The contraction in atomic size among lanthanide elements is called **lanthanide contraction**.

Ionization Energy

Ionization energy of an element is the minimum amount of energy required to remove the outermost electron from an isolated neutral gaseous atom of that element in its lowest energy state to form a cation. This is called the first ionization potential.

The minimum amount of energy required to remove the electron from a gaseous atom is called its **first ionization potential**. The **second ionization potential** is the energy required to remove the electron from the outermost shell of a unipositively charged gaseous ion. Similarly, we can define the third and the fourth ionization energies or ionization potentials. If the first ionization energy is considered as I_1 and the second as I_2 and so on then, $I_1 < I_2 < I_3 < I_4 < \ldots\ldots$ Theoretically, an atom can have as many ionization potentials as there are electrons in it.

> **Konnect**
>
> This successive increase in the values of ionization potential is due to increase in effective nuclear charge from the neutral atom to the respective ions.

Variation of Ionization Potential

(a) Period: Ionization energy generally increases from left to right along a period. This is because along a period, the atomic size decreases and the valence shell is closer to the nucleus. Thus, more energy is required to remove an electron from the valence shell.

(b) Group: The ionization energy decreases from top to bottom in a group because the atomic size increases down the group, thus, resulting in decrease in the effective nuclear force of attraction.

Graphical Representation of Variation of IP with Atomic Numbers

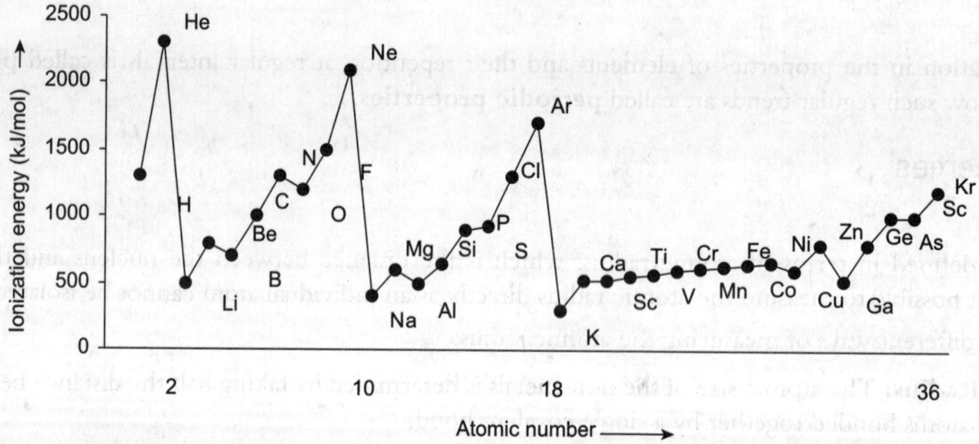

Figure 4.1 The ionization energies of the elements (hydrogen to krypton)

Conclusions

(a) The noble gases occupy the highest positions indicating that they have exceptionally high ionization potential values.

(b) Variation of ionization potential from nitrogen to oxygen and phosphorus to sulphur does not follow the regular trend.

(c) The variation of IP in transition metals is more regular and marginal in comparison to the representative elements.

Electron Affinity

The amount of energy released when an electron is added to an isolated neutral gaseous atom in its lowest energy state to produce an anion is called the **electron affinity**.

Variation of Electron Affinity

(a) Period: As the atomic size decreases and nuclear charge increases from left to right across the period, the electron affinity values generally increase.

(b) Group: The electron affinity gradually decreases from top to bottom due to the steady increase in atomic radius and the resultant decrease of effective nuclear charge.

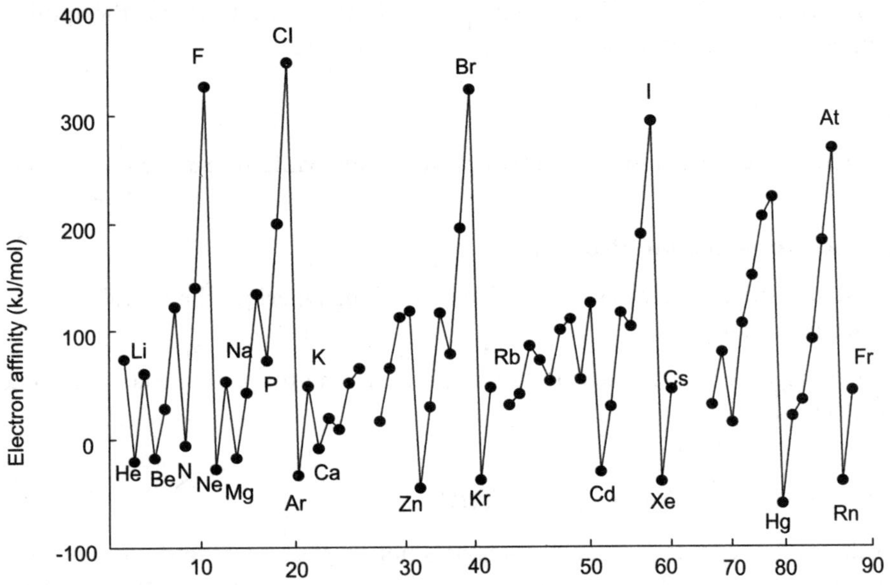

Figure 4.2 Graphic representation of electron affinity with atomic numbers.

Conclusions

(a) The noble gases show zero electron affinity values indicating that the addition of an electron to those atoms is not possible.

(b) The elements of IIA group show negative values for electron affinity, which indicates that the addition of electron is associated with the absorption of energy.

(c) Halogens occupy the highest positions in the curve, which show maximum tendency to form negative ions.

Electronegativity

Electronegativity of an element is defined as the tendency of an atom to attract the shared pair of electrons towards itself in a bonded molecule.

Since electronegativity is a relative value, measurement of absolute value is not possible. One way of measurement of electronegativity is to take an average of ionization potential and electron affinity. On the other method, fluorine is taken as standard and the electronegativity values of other elements are calculated with respect to fluorine.

Variation of Electronegativity

(a) Period: Electronegativity increases along a period from left to right. This is due to the increase in nuclear charge and decrease in atomic size.

(b) Group: Electronegativity decreases from top to bottom in a group due to increase in the atomic size.

Electropositive Character

Electropositive character of an element is its ability to lose one or more electrons to form a positively charged ion.

The electropositive character of an element depends on its ionization potential. An element in which the atom has greater ability to lose an electron means that it has low ionization potential and high electropositivity. Such an element acts as a good reducing agent. An element that has a high ionization potential has low electropositivity and hence cannot give out electron easily. Such an element acts as a good oxidizing agent.

Variation of Electropositive Character

(a) Period: The electropositive character decreases (the oxidizing capacity increases and the reducing capacity decreases) from left to right along a period due to the increase in ionization potential.

(b) Group: Due to the decrease of ionization potential and electron affinity down the group, the electropositivity increases, oxidizing capacity decreases and reducing capacity increases.

Metallic and Non-metallic Property

Metals can generally give away electrons easily and form positive ions while non-metals generally accept electrons and form negative ions.

Variation of Metallic and Non-metallic Properties

(a) Period: As the electronegativity increases from left to right along a period, the metallic character decreases and the non-metallic character increases.

(b) Group: As the electronegativity decreases from top to bottom in a group, the metallic character increases and non-metallic character decreases.

Position of Elements in Periodic Table

Thus, the right side of the periodic table (p-block) comprises non-metals, metalloids, and metals. The left side of the table is completely occupied by metals. The middle portion (d-block) as well as the bottom portion (f-block) comprises metals.

This kind of distribution shows that though the periodic table comprises metals, non-metals, and metalloids, 75% of the elements are metals. Since the metals have certain characteristic properties that clearly distinguish them from the rest of the elements, the study of metals gained significance. The metals also differ among themselves in their properties and hence they are placed in the respective positions in the periodic table.

For example, alkali metals that possess one electron in their valence shells are grouped together in group IA of the modern periodic table. Similarly, the alkaline earth metals that possess two electrons in their valence shells are placed in Group IIA of the periodic table. These two categories of metals belong to 's-' block of the periodic table.

The other two categories are transition metals and inner transition metals. These metals have certain specific properties that are not exhibited by any other groups of elements. Some of the specific properties of transition metals that clearly distinguish them from the other metals are paramagnetic nature of the atoms and ions, formation of colored compounds, and exhibition of variable oxidation states in their compounds.

Formation of Colored Compounds

All the compounds of alkali and alkaline earth metals are colorless. However, many compounds of transition metals have their characteristic colors due to the presence of incomplete d-subshells.

Examples:

$CuSO_4 . 5H_2O$	Blue
$K_2Cr_2O_7$	Orange
$KMnO_4$	Violet
$CuCl_2$	Bluish green
$FeSO_4$	Light green

These elements also do not show a regular trend in the common periodic properties. Therefore, these are placed in the 'd-' block of the periodic table and are studied separately.

Comparative Study of Alkali Metals and Alkaline Earth Metals

Alkali metals and alkaline earth metals belong to 's-' block of the periodic table and they show regular gradation in the properties.

Melting and boiling points of alkali metals are lower than those of alkaline earth metals as well as transition metals to their right.

Reaction with Water

Alkali metals react vigorously with water and liberate hydrogen gas. Reaction of lithium is less vigorous:

$$M + 2H_2O \rightarrow MOH + H_2$$
(M = alkali metal)

Alkaline earth metals also react with water to liberate hydrogen gas:

$$M + 2H_2O \rightarrow M(OH)_2 + H_2$$
(M = alkaline earth metal)

Konnect

Out of all the Alkaline Earth Metals, magnesium and calcium are essential for our bodies. Magnesium plays a crucial role in the synthesis of DNA, RNA, and the antioxidant glutathione, while calcium is vital for bone and teeth formation.

Reaction with Oxygen

Alkali and alkaline earth metals burn in the presence of O_2 to give their corresponding oxides:

$$4M + O_2 \rightarrow 2M_2O$$
(M = alkali metals)

$$2M + O_2 \rightarrow 2MO$$
(M = alkaline earth metals)

Sodium (alkali metal) and barium (alkaline earth metal) also give their stable peroxides along with the oxides:

$$2Na + O_2 \rightarrow Na_2O_2$$

$$Ba + O_2 \rightarrow BaO_2$$

Reaction with Hydrogen

Alkali metals and alkaline earth metals react with H_2 and form their stable hydrides:

$$2M + H_2 \rightarrow 2MH$$
(M = alkali metals)

$$M + H_2 \rightarrow MH_2$$
(M = alkaline earth metals)

Info Bytes!

Beryllium hydride is unstable.

All the hydrides of alkali and alkaline earth metals get readily hydrolysed by water and liberate hydrogen gas.

$$2MH + 2H_2O \rightarrow 2MOH + 2H_2\uparrow$$
(M = alkali metals)

$$MH_2 + 2H_2O \rightarrow M(OH)_2 + 2H_2\uparrow$$
(M = alkaline earth metals)

Reaction with Chlorine

All the alkali metals and alkaline earth metals react with chlorine to give their corresponding chlorides:

$$2M + Cl_2 \rightarrow 2MCl$$
(M = alkali metals)

$$M + Cl_2 \rightarrow MCl_2$$
(M = alkaline earth metals)

EXAMPLE 4.4 (a) Why do fluorine and chlorine show similar chemical properties, but differ significantly in their reactivities? Name an element that might also behave similarly.

(b) Arrange the elements from that group in decreasing order of electron affinity. Give reason.

SOLUTION

(a) Fluorine and chlorine both belong to Group 17, known as the halogens. They have similar chemical properties due to possessing seven valence electrons. However, fluorine is much more reactive than chlorine because of its smaller atomic size and higher electronegativity. Bromine is another element from this group that would show similar chemical properties.

(b) Decreasing order of electron affinity is F > Cl > Br > I > At. This is because as we move down the group, atomic size increases, causing the incoming electron to be farther from the nucleus, resulting in decreased electron affinity.

EXAMPLE 4.5 Teacher explained periodicity of ionization potential in a period and group with reasons. She then drew a curve of IP vs atomic number for elements with Z = 11 to Z = 20. On the basis of the curve, she asked the following questions to students.

(a) Identify the elements occupying peaks and bottom-most points.

(b) Also identify 'X' and 'Y' marked in the curve.

(c) In what respect 'X' and 'Y' deviate from their preceeding elements?

When students answered these correctly, she was satisfied and told – "Now, I will give you a brain teaser to get me answer by next chemistry class". Students enthusiastically said – "yes"! Then teacher wrote the following question on board __

(d) 'Why do "X" and "Y" show deviations from their preceeding elements in the trend of IP values'? What explanation would you give if you were there in the class?

SOLUTION

(a) Peak is occupied by noble gas, Ar. Bottom-most point is occupied by alkali metal, K.

(b) 'X' is aluminium and 'Y' is sulphur.

(c) Generally, with increase in atomic number, IP value should also increase. However, from magnesium to aluminium, IP value decreases. Similarly, from phosphorus to sulphur, IP value decreases.

(d) In magnesium, there is a pair of electrons in 3s orbital. Removal of electron is slightly more difficult. Moreover, since the electron to be removed belongs to 's' subshell having greater penetrating power, the IP value is relatively higher. In case of aluminium, there is an unpaired 'p' electron, whose removal is easier. Hence, IP value is less.

EXAMPLE 4.6 Why does ionization energy generally increase across a period from left to right on the periodic table?

SOLUTION

As we move from left to right across a period, the number of protons in the nucleus increases, leading to a stronger nuclear attraction for the electrons. Even though electrons are also added, they are in the same energy shell and don't shield the nuclear charge effectively. This makes it harder to remove an electron, thus increasing the ionization energy.

EXAMPLE 4.7 (a) One mole of atoms of an element 'x' absorb 800 kJ of energy for the formation of unipositive ions. For the conversion of one mole of 'X' atoms into tripositive ions, 6800 kJ of energy is required. Second and third ionization energies are in 2 : 3 ratio. Calculate the second and third ionization energies.

(b) First and second ionization energies of Be(g) are 900 and 1750 kJ/mol, respectively. Calculate approximate percentage of Be^{2+}(g) ions, if 1 g of Be(g) absorbs 150 kJ of energy (Be atomic weight is 9).

SOLUTION

(a) $x \rightarrow x^+$, 800 kJ/mol (IP_1)

$x \rightarrow x^{+3}$, 6800 kJ

$\therefore IP_1 + IP_2 + IP_3 = 6800 \text{ kJ} \Rightarrow IP_2 + IP_3 = 6800 - 800 = 6000$

$x^+ \rightarrow x^{+2}\ IP_2;\ x^{+2} \rightarrow x^{+3}\ IP_3$

$\because IP_2 : IP_3 = 2 : 3 \Rightarrow \frac{IP^2}{IP_3} = \frac{2}{3}$

$\Rightarrow IP_2 = \frac{2}{3}.\ IP_3 \text{ or } IP_3 = \frac{3IP_2}{2}$

$\Rightarrow IP_2 + IP_3 = 6000$

$\Rightarrow IP_2 + \frac{3}{2}.\ IP_2 = 6000 \Rightarrow 2\ IP_2 + 2\ IP_3 = 6000 \times 2$

$IP_2 = \frac{6000}{5} \times 2 = 2400 \text{ kJ/mol};\ IP_3 = \frac{6000}{5} \times 3 = 3600 \text{ kJ/mol}$

(b) 1 mole (9 g) of beryllium requires 900 kJ to dislodge the first electron.

$\therefore$ 1 g of Be requires $= \frac{1 \times 900}{9} = 100$ kJ

$\therefore$ Difference in the amount of energy absorbed = 150 – 100 = 50 kJ

To dislodge the second electron from 1 mole of Beryllium ion, 1750 kJ is required.

50 kJ is sufficient for $\frac{50}{1750} \times 3 = 0.25 = 25\%$

Percentage of Be^{2+}(g) ions is 25%.

EXAMPLE 4.8 The ionic size of Cl^- is greater than that of K^+ ion, though they are isoelectronic. Explain.

SOLUTION

Nuclear forces of attraction on valence electrons are higher in K^+ ion than in Cl^-. This is due to the greater nuclear charge of K^+ ion. So, the ionic size of Cl^- ion is greater than that of K^+ ion.

EXAMPLE 4.9 A sharp change in the atomic radius is observed from lithium to potassium but a gradual change in the atomic radius is observed from potassium to caesium. Explain.

SOLUTION

A sharp increase in the atomic radius is observed from lithium to potassium due to increase in the number of shells. But a gradual change is observed from potassium to caesium due to filling up of d electrons in the penultimate shell that increases the effective nuclear charge. Hence, increase in size is gradual and not sharp.

POINTS TO REMEMBER

- ✔ Mendeleev's periodic law states that the physical and chemical properties of the elements are the periodic functions of their atomic weights.
- ✔ The modern periodic law states that the physical and chemical properties of elements are the periodic functions of their atomic numbers or electronic configurations.
- ✔ The periodic table consists of seven horizontal rows called periods and 18 vertical columns called groups.
- ✔ The regular gradation in the properties of elements and their repetition at regular intervals is called periodicity. The properties that show such regular trends are called periodic properties.
- ✔ Atomic size is defined in terms of atomic radius, which is the distance between the nucleus and the valence shell.
- ✔ Ionization energy of an element is the minimum amount of energy required to remove the outermost electron from an isolated neutral gaseous atom of that element in its lowest energy state to form a cation.
- ✔ The amount of energy released when an electron is added to an isolated neutral gaseous atom in its lowest energy state to produce an anion is called the electron affinity.
- ✔ Electronegativity of an element is defined as the tendency of an atom to attract the shared pair of electrons towards itself in a bonded molecule.
- ✔ Electropositive character of an element is its ability to lose one or more electrons to form a positively-charged ion.

DW

PRACTICE QUESTIONS CLASSROOM WING

Very Short Answer Type Questions

Directions for questions from 1 to 9:
Fill in the blanks.

1. The valence electronic configuration of the best oxidising agent along a period is ________.
2. General electronic configuration of chalcogens is ____________.
3. The elements present in ______ and ______ periods can exhibit diagonal relationship.
4. Ionization potential value of Cs is equal to the electron affinity value of its corresponding ______.
5. ______ block elements can exhibit variable number of oxidation states.
6. In the long form of periodic table ________ group contains the maximum number of elements.
7. Anion size is always ______ than the parent atom.
8. In the f-block elements differentiating electron enters f-orbital of ______ shell.
9. _____ group elements are the strongest reducing agents.

Directions for questions from 10 to 24:
Answer the following questions.

10. The valence electronic configuration of four elements is given as $2s^22p^3$, $2s^2$, $2s^22p^4$, $2s^22p^1$. Which element has the highest ionization energy?
11. An element has 3 electrons in the 3d subshell. Which group and period does it belong to?
12. Among the electronic configurations: [Kr] $5s^1$, [Ne] $3s^1$, [Xe] $6s^1$, [Ar] $4s^1$. Which among them has the maximum metallic character?
13. Describe the trend of atomic size along a period and a group in the periodic table.
14. Which periods are called the short periods and which are called the long periods? Why?
15. Describe the trend of ionization potential along a period and a group in the periodic table.
16. Why are the chemical properties of the elements belonging to the same group similar?
17. Why is it that hydrogen can be placed in both I A group and VII A group of the modern periodic table?
18. What do you mean by representative elements? Give an example.
19. Which group contains the noble gases and what are the special characteristics of these gases?
20. Describe the trend of ionization potential down the group in the periodic table.
21. Describe how the metallic and non-metallic characters vary along a period and group of the periodic table.
22. What is a covalent radius?
23. How does the electron affinity vary in the first transition series?
24. What is metallic radius? Give the implication of measuring a metallic radius.

Short Answer Type Questions

25. An element has 18 electrons more than the number of electrons present in xenon. Which block does the element belong to?
26. An element has two electrons in the 3p shell. Which group does it belong to?
27. The number of electrons in an element is four times the number of electrons in helium. Which block does the element belong to?
28. Among the groups: IA, IIIA, IIA, IVA, which of them results in an endothermic process on the addition of an electron?
29. The atomic numbers of four elements 'A', 'B', 'C' and 'D' are (Z − 1), (Z − 2), Z, and (Z + 1), respectively. If C is an inert gas (not helium). What is the correct order of ionization energies of these elements?

30. Among the metals: Na, K, Mg, Ca, which of them acts as the best-reducing agent?

31. A^{+2}, B^{+1}, C^{-1} and D^{-2} are the stable ions formed by the elements 'A', 'B', 'C' and 'D'. Arrange A, B, C and D in the increasing order of their group numbers in the periodic table.

32. The order of ionization energies of three elements is X >>> Y > Z. What could be the elements 'X', 'Y' and 'Z'?

33. An element 'X' belongs to the 5th period and the 2nd group in the modern periodic table. Calculate the number of electrons present in s-orbits.

34. What is the basic difference between Mendeleev's periodic table and modern periodic table?

35. Among all the periods, which one is incomplete and what are the main important properties exhibited by all the elements present in this period?

36. What is the difference between electronegativity and electropositivity?

37. Mention different categories of elements in the long form of the periodic table.

38. What is the difference between transition and inner transition elements?

39. How does filling of valence electrons takes place in p-block, d-block, and f-block elements?

Essay Answer Type Questions

40. The energy of an electron in the 2nd orbit of a single electron species is −54.4 eV. The neutral atom of that species belongs to ________.

41. Describe briefly Mendeleev's periodic table along with its merits.

42. What are the limitations of Mendeleev's periodic table?

43. Explain briefly the periods of the modern periodic table.

44. Explain briefly about the groups of the modern periodic table and also classify the elements depending on electron filling in s-, p-, d-, and f-subshells along with the position in the periodic table.

45. (a) Assuming that 113 elements are present in the present periodic table, how many more elements can be accommodated in the 7th period?

(b) An element has atomic number 48. Identify the true statements regarding this element.

(A) d – block element

(B) Transition element

(C) Two incomplete shells

(D) No variable valency

(E) Differentiating electron enters into d subshell

PRACTICE QUESTIONS COMPETITION WING

Level 1: Apply your Concepts

Direction for questions from 1 to 10:
State whether the following statements are true or false.

1. Modern periodic table is based on atomic number.
2. In a period, the first element has the smallest size.
3. 's' and 'p' block elements except zero group are known as representative elements.
4. The inert gas present in the second long period is Xe.
5. Among the isoelectronic ions Na^+, Mg^{2+}, and Al^{3+}, Na^+ ion have the largest size.
6. Alkali metals act as strong reducing agents by undergoing reduction.
7. Electronegativity is the property of an atom in a bonded molecule.
8. Mendeleev stated that the properties of elements are the periodic functions of their atomic weight.
9. The properties of elements beyond atomic weight 40 cannot be explained by Newland's law.
10. The 's-' and 'p-' blocks elements called transition elements

Direction for questions from 11 to 19:
Fill in the blanks.

11. An element has a total of 4 electrons with l = 2. The element is a/an ________.
12. The valence electronic configuration of the best-reducing agent along a period is ________.
13. An element has 11 electrons with l = 1, the element is a/an ________.
14. The order of electron affinity of Be, B and C is ________.
15. The ascending order of the first ionization potential of C, N, O, and F is _____.
16. The total number of inner transition elements present in the 7th period are ________.
17. Amongst the species Br^-, Br, Br^+, the smallest one in size is _____.
18. In most of the lanthanides, the penultimate shell contains ________ electrons in ______orbitals.
19. Metals exhibit _____ oxidation states in their compounds.

Direction for question 20:
Match the entries in Column A with the appropriate ones in Column B.

20. Match the entries of Column A with those of Column B.

Column A	Column B
(i) Maximum metallic character	(A) Cl
(ii) Maximum electronegativity	(B) Na
(iii) Maximum ionization energy	(C) Cs
(iv) Maximum electron affinity	(D) He
	(E) F

Direction for questions from 21 to 39:
For each of the questions, four choices have been provided. Select the correct alternative.

21. Among the following metals which has the maximum metallic character?
    a. Na b. Mg
    c. K d. Ca
22. Among the four given metals which has the maximum reducing property?
    a. Na b. Li
    c. K d. Rb
23. **Assertion (A):** Na and Ca show different chemical properties.

    Reason (R): Both Na and Ca belong to the same group.

    (a) Both A and R are true and R is the correct explanation of A.
    (b) Both A and R are true, but R is not the correct explanation of A.
    (c) A is true and R is false.
    (d) A is false and R is true.

24. **Assertion (A):** Chemical properties of the elements belonging to the same group are the same.

Reason (R): Elements belonging to the same group possess the same number of valence electrons.

(a) Both A and R are true and R is the correct explanation of A.

(b) Both A and R are true, but R is not the correct explanation of A.

(c) A is true and R is false.

(d) A is false and R is true.

25. Predict the formula of a compound formed between a metal 'M' that has 1st, 2nd, 3rd IP values as 518, 7314, 9820 kJ/mol, respectively and a halogen 'X.'

(a) MX_2 (b) M_2X_3
(c) MX_3 (d) MX

26. In a period, from the left to right the electron affinity increases, but alkaline earth metals have lower electron affinity than alkali metals because:

(a) alkaline earth metals have lesser atomic radius than alkali metals.

(b) alkaline earth have higher electronegativity than alkali metals.

(c) alkaline earth metals have completely filled 's-' orbitals.

(d) alkaline earth metals have lesser electronegativity than alkali metals.

27. 5f series elements are known as:

(a) lanthanides

(b) representative elements

(c) transition elements

(d) actinides

28. The first ionization energies of Li, Be, B, and C are in the order:

(a) Li > Be < B < C

(b) Li < Be > B < C

(c) Li > Be > B > C

(d) Li < Be > B > C

29. Predict the powerful oxidizing agent in the 3rd period:

(a) sulphur

(b) sodium

(c) chlorine

(d) bromine

30. A neutral atom with 32 protons will belong to:

(a) 4th period, VIA group

(b) 3rd period, IVA group

(c) 4th period, IVA group

(d) 5th period, VA group

31. The element having the electronic configuration [Kr] $4d^{10}\ 4f^{14}\ 5s^2\ 5p^6\ 5d^2\ 6s^2$ belongs to

(a) s-block (b) p-block
(c) d-block (d) f-block

32. The number of valence electrons that can be present in the second element of any period is:

(a) 1 (b) 2
(c) 5 (d) 7

33. Transition metals can exhibit variable valency. It is because of:

(a) the smaller atomic radius

(b) the high screening effect

(c) the very less energy difference between (n – 1) d-subshell and ns-subshell

(d) the high nuclear charge

34. Arrange O, F, Cl and N in the descending order of their electronegativity:

(a) O > F > Cl > N

(b) F > O > Cl > N

(c) F > N > O > Cl

(d) Cl > F >O > N

35. In the sixth period, the orbitals that are completely filled are:

(a) 6s, 6p, 5d, 5f

(b) 6s, 6p, 6d, 6f

(c) 6s, 5f, 6d, 6p

(d) 6s, 4f, 5d, 6p

36. Which of the following sequence of explanation is appropriate for explaining the reason for the periodicity of reducing property in a period or group?

(1) Tendency to undergo oxidation decreases in a period and increases in a group.

(2) In a period ionization energy increases and in a group it decreases.

(3) In a period the atomic size decreases and in a group it increases.

(4) The elements present in the left side of the periodic table have strong reducing property.

(a) 3 2 1 4 (b) 3 4 2 1

(c) 4 3 1 2 (d) 4 2 1 3

37. Which of the following triads does not follow Dobereiner's law of triads?

(a) Li, Na, K (b) Ca, Sr, Ba

(c) Be, Mg, Ca (d) Cu, Ag, Au

38. X belongs to IA or 1st group and 5th period and Y succeeds X in the group. Z succeeds Y in the period. Arrange the following statements in the correct sequence in order to arrange X, Y and Z in the increasing order of their atomic sizes.

(1) Effect of number of valence electrons and number of shells on the atomic size.

(2) Identification of the elements X, Y and Z.

(3) Determination of the number of shells and the number of valence electrons present in X, Y, and Z.

(4) Determination of the positions of Y and Z in the periodic table based on the position of X.

(a) 4 2 3 1 (b) 2 4 3 1

(c) 3 1 4 (d) 4 3 1

39. Which of the following sets of atomic numbers corresponds to elements belonging to s–, d–, f–, p-blocks, respectively?

(a) 35, 37, 29, 70 (b) 35, 29, 70, 37

(c) 37, 29, 70, 35 (d) 37, 29, 35, 70

Level 2: Review Your Concepts

40. Why is the atomic radius of oxygen slightly more than that of nitrogen?

41. Predict the position of an element with atomic number 55 in the periodic table and explain the chemical behavior of that element.

42. (a) Why is electron affinity of chlorine more than that of fluorine?

(b) Two elements X and Y have electronic configuration $ns^2\ np^5$. They belong to 2nd period and 3rd period respectively. Compare their electron affinity values. Give reason in support of your answer.

43. Why do most of the inner transition elements exhibit stable +3 oxidation state?

45. Xenon has an octet configuration in the valence shell but it shows variable valency with the highly electronegative elements like oxygen and fluorine. Comment.

45. Though oxygen and sulphur belong to the same group, sulphur shows many oxidation states, whereas oxygen does not show a higher oxidation state than that of –2. Comment.

46. First and second ionization energies of Be(g) are 900 kJ mol^{-1} and 1750 kJ mol^{-1} approximately. Calculate approximate percentage of Be^{2+}(g) ions, if 1 g of Be(g) absorbs 150 kJ of energy [atomic weight of Be is 9].

47. The separation of one lanthanide from another is an extremely difficult task, almost as difficult as the separation of isotopes of one element. Justify.

48. In a particular transition series, the atomic radius reaches minimum up to group VIII elements, then again increases towards the end of the series. Give appropriate reasons.

49. Ionization potential decreases down the group in representative elements while transition elements of the 6th period have greater ionization potential values compared to the elements of the 5th period. Justify.

50. (a) The densities of transition metals are greater than the alkali and alkaline earth metals. Justify.

(b) Identify the element which cannot be oxidized by any other element and also the halogens which can be oxidized by the above element. Give reason in support of your answer.

51. Successive ionization potentials of an element 'X' are IP_1 = 520 kJ mol^{-1}, IP_2 = 7,298 kJ mol^{-1} and IP_3 = 10,815 kJ mol^{-1}. Give the probable formulae of chloride and oxide of 'X.'

52. An element 'A' has atomic number 28. What is the electronic configuration of the elements below it in the periodic table? Predict their chemical properties.

Directions for questions from 53 to 62:
Application-Based Questions.

53. When a Dobereiner triad is considered, the sum of atomic weights of extreme elements X and Z is 177.6 and difference of Z and Y is five times the number of protons present in a neon atom. Identify X, Y, and Z.

54. Iron can form two types of ions. Compare the ionic sizes of the respective ions.

55. Three elements A, B, and C have atomic numbers as x, $x + 1$, and $x + 2$. The atomic size of C is greater

than that of B but atomic size of B is less than that of A. Predict the positions of A, B, and C in the periodic table and justify the trend in atomic size.

56. A teacher while explaining the definition of ionization potential gave an example: Ionization potential value of sodium is 140 kJ/mol. That means, 140 kJ of energy is required to remove the lone electrons from '3s' orbitals of one mole of gaseous sodium atoms. Then, a student Rinku stood up immediately and asked: sodium is a solid metal. Why should we consider it in gaseous state? What explanation would have been given by the teacher?

57. Formation of X^- ion from 'X' is associated with the release of 144 kJ/mol energy. However, formation of X^{-2} ion from X^- is associated with the absorption of 840 kJ of energy. How do you account for this?

58. A tripositive ion of element 'X' has six electrons with $l = 0$ and five electrons with $l = 2$.

(a) Predict the group and period to which 'X' belongs.

(b) Does the element show variable valencies? Justify.

59. Identify the position of the elements having outer electronic configuration:

(a) $ns^2\ np^5$ for $n = 3$

(b) $(n - 1)d^2\ ns^2$ for $n = 4$

60. The steady decrease in size of lanthanide elements and their ions is called lanthanide contraction. In lanthanide elements, the differentiating electron enters into antepenultimate 'f-' subshell.

(a) How does the entry of differentiating electron into antepenultimate shell affect the atomic and ionic sizes?

(b) Densities of 6th period elements are double to those of 5th period elements. Why?

61. An element 'X' has three completely filled shells and forms a stable uninegative ion and the total number of electrons in the third and fourth shells is same. Identify the elements that form unipositive and dipositive ions that are isoelectronic with X^- ion. Compare the reactivities of these two elements with water. Give a reason in support of your answer.

62. Why are the electron affinities of alkaline earth metals positive?

$$M(g) + e^- \rightarrow M^-(g)\ \Delta H = +\ (\text{Electron affinity})$$

Level 3: Assess Your Concepts

63. The radius of the 3rd orbit of a single electron species is 4.761 A°. Identify the element.

64. The first ionization energy of magnesium is greater than that of sodium, whereas the reverse is true for second ionization energy. Explain.

65. Why do some of the periodic properties like atomic size, electronegativity and ionization potential of transition and inner transition elements not show as much variation as the representative elements?

66. Why are the electron affinities of IIA group and IIB group elements less than zero?

67. The density of elements belonging to the 3rd transition series is double that of the elements belonging to the 2nd transition series provided they are in the same group unlike alkali and alkaline earth metals. Comment.

Directions for questions from 68 to 72:
Application-Based Questions.

68. In the d-block elements as we move along a period the atomic radius decreases in the beginning, reaches minimum and then increases towards the end of the series. Explain with appropriate reasons.

69. Why are the values of electron affinity of the IIA group and IIB group elements less than zero?

70. Why do some of the periodic properties like atomic size, electronegativity, and ionization potential of transition and inner transition elements do not show as much variation as the representative elements?

71. Three elements X, Y and Z have atomic numbers 22, 40, and 72, respectively. Comment on the trend of change in ionization potential values from X to Y and Y to Z.

72. There is a sharp decrease in the ionization energies from boron to aluminium but it is almost the same from aluminium to gallium. Justify.

73. IE values of ceasium and barium (6th period) are lower than rubidium and strontium (5th period). However, hafnium (6th period) has greater IE value than zirconium (5th period). How do you account for this discrepancy?

AT

PRACTICE QUESTIONS JEE-NEET SPECIAL WING

Multiple-Answer Type Questions

Directions for Questions number 1 to 5:

Select one or more correct alternative(s) from the given choices.

1. Which of the following will affect the energy required for the given process:

   $X_{(g)} \rightarrow X^+_{(g)}$

   (a) Number of valence electrons in X

   (b) Reactivity of X.

   (b) No of electron shells in X.

   (d) Total number of nucleons in X.

2. Given that the stable ion M^{a+} is isoelectronic with the stable ion of N^{b-}, and M and N are elements, which of the following options is not consistent with this statement.

   (a) M and N belong to the same period.

   (b) The magnitudes of a and b are equal.

   (c) M^{a+} and N^{b-} have same number of valence electrons

   (d) M^{a+} and N^{b-} have the same electronic configuration.

3. Choose false statements regarding Mendeleev's periodic table.

   (a) Elements are organized based on recurring trends in their physical properties.

   (b) It allowed for the prediction of future new elements.

   (c) It effectively accommodated the isotopes of the known elements of that time.

   (d) It consists of 7 rows and 8 columns.

4. Identify the correct sets arranged in the increasing order of their ionic radii.

   (a) Cl^-, K^+ (b) Al^{3+}, Mg^{2+}

   (c) O^{2-}, F^- (d) Ca^{2+}, S^{2-}

5. Study the following changes related to the formation of stable oxide ion and pick the correct interpretations.

   $O(g) + e^- \rightarrow O^-(g)$; $\Delta H = -141$ kJ mol^{-1} ....(i)

   $O^-(g) + e^- \rightarrow O^{2-}(g)$; $\Delta H = +780$ kJ mol^{-1} ....(ii)

   (a) Step(i) is more favourable as it is exothermic.

   (b) Step(ii) is unfavourable as it is endothermic.

   (c) Though addition of electron is taking place in both the steps, electron entering O^- is facing more inter electronic repulsions compared to the one entering in the neutral atom of oxygen.

   (d) Formation of O^{2-} from O requires an energy of 639KJ/mole.

Comprehension-Based Questions

Directions for questions 6 to 12:

Read the following passage and answer the questions given below.

Transition metals are characterized by partially filled d-orbitals with general electronic configuration of outer orbitals $(n-1)d^{1-10}$ ns^{1-2}. However, this generalisation has several exceptions because of very little energy difference between (n-1)d and ns orbitals. Furthermore, half, and completely filled sets of orbitals are relatively more stable. The 3d, 4d, and 5d transition series elements, although studied alongside other transition elements, aren't considered transition metals due to their full d-shell configurations in the ground state and common oxidation states. These metals form colourful compounds through d-d transitions, forms stable complexes with diverse ligands, and can display various oxidation states. The highest oxidation number/state in the transition metal oxides coincides with the group number. The maximum oxidation state that an element can exhibit is determined by the number of unpaired electrons it possesses in its excited state.

The f-block elements involve (n-2)f orbitals with general outer electronic configuration $(n-2)$ $f^{1-14}(n-1)$ d^{0-1} ns^2. In these **elements**, the differentiating electron enters into f-orbital of anti-penultimate shell. Two series of the third group, the lanthanides, and actinides, represent these elements. Lanthanides exhibit different oxidation states, mainly +3, and undergo a consistent decrease in ion size as atomic number increases, a phenomenon known as lanthanide contraction.

Given below is the outline of long form of periodic table. Study the table and answer the questions given below. Letters do not represent the actual symbols

of the elements. Use these letters when answering the following questions.

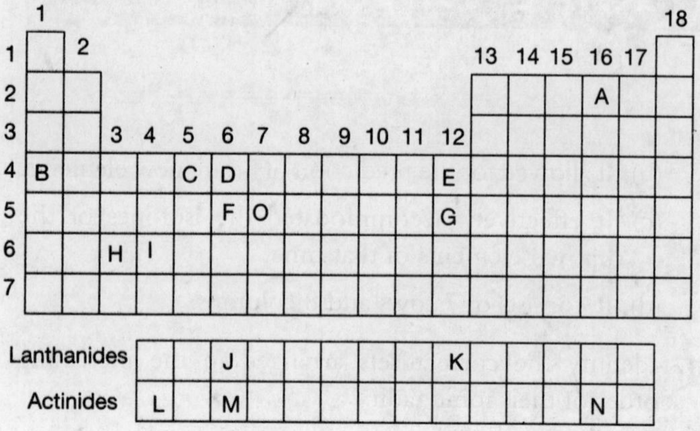

6. Which of the given elements will have the outer orbital electronic configuration $4d^5\ 5s^1$.
(a) C (b) D
(c) F (d) O

7. Of the following, the elements that belong to same group are:
(a) AN (b) EGK
(c) HJM (d) KLMN

8. Choose the correct formula of the compound formed by C and A with C in its highest oxidation state.
(a) C_5A_2 (b) C_3A_2
(c) C_2A_5 (d) CA

9. Identify the element in which the outermost d orbital is completely filled in its ground state.
(a) G (b) L
(c) H (d) I

10. Choose the correct increasing order of the elements with respect to the size of their stable tripositive ions.
(a) HIJ (b) JLM
(c) KJH (d) LMN

11. Why do transition elements form coloured compounds?
(a) Due to d-d transitions
(b) Because of variable oxidation states
(c) Because of the complex structure of their compounds
(d) Because of very less energy difference between their (n-1) d subshell and ns subshell.

12. Match the following:

List – I	List – II Symbol of the element as given in the above model periodic table
(A) Ground state outer electronic configuration-$5f^3 6d^1 7s^2$	(i) B
(B) Stability due to half-filled 3d orbitals	(ii) E
(C) Element that exhibits highest oxidation number	(iii) M
(D) Forms colourless complex compounds	(iv) O
	(v) D
	(vi) F
	(vii) L

Find the correct match.

	(A)	(B)	(C)	(D)
(a)	(vi)	(vi)	(iii)	(ii)
(b)	(vi)	(v)	(iv)	(i)
(c)	(iii)	(v)	(iv)	(ii)
(d)	(iii)	(iv)	(vi)	(v)

Directions for questions 13 to 17:

Given below is a part of the long form of periodic table. Study the table, description of the elements given in the table and answer the questions given below. Letters do not represent the actual symbols of the elements. Use these letters when answering the following questions.

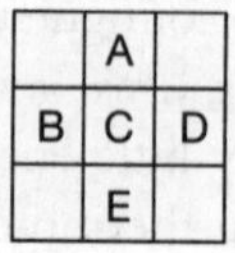

Element A and D are the first and last elements in their group and period respectively. Elements B, C and D differ in their atomic numbers by one.

13. Magnitude of the first electron gain enthalpies in kJ/mol of the elements A, B, C and E are given. Choose the value that corresponds to element C.

(a) 349 (b) 324

(c) 322 (d) 200

14. If X and Y are the elements above and below element D, identify the correct increasing order with respect to their ionization energy

(a) XDYC (b) CXDY

(c) CYDX (d) XCDY

15. Stable ion of an element Z is iso electronic with the stable ion of an element B. Valency of Z is 2, and it forms a compound 'M' with the first element of the group to which element B belong. Identify the correct statement/s with respect to M.

(a) It is crystalline at room temperature

(b) It is sparingly soluble in water

(c) pOH of its aqueous solution is > 7

(d) All the above

16. Identify the element with highest effective nuclear charge on its valence electrons.

(a) B (b) D

(c) C (d) A

17. Statement 1: The element preceding B in the periodic table exhibits a higher ionization energy than B.

Statement II: Ionization energy increases from left to right in a period

Option	Statement I	Statement II
(a)	False	True
(b)	False	False
(c)	True	False
(d)	True	True

Match the Column

18. The energy required to separate one mole of an ionic solid into the gaseous form of its ions is known as lattice energy. lattice energy of an ionic compound is determined by the magnitude of the charges and the distance between the ions in the crystal lattice. Higher is the magnitude of the charge and smaller is the size of the ion, greater will be its lattice energy. Usually, a difference in charge has a greater effect on the lattice energy than a difference in the distance. If P, Q, R, S represents the compounds of sodium with element A, B, C and E respectively, match the entries of list-I with that of List-II

List – I Compounds of sodium	List – II Lattice energy kJ/mol
P	(i) -7.86X
Q	(ii) -9.26X
R	(iii) -7.52X
S	(iv) -21.92X

ANSWER KEYS

Crossword

Across

1. Metalloids 5. Manganese 6. Gallium 9. Radium 11. Iodine
12. Alkali metals 16. Amphoteric 17. Fluorine

Down

2. Transition elements 3. Noble gases 4. Third 7. Uranium 8. Increases
10. Dobereiner 13. Zero 14. Newland 15. Solid

Classroom Wing

Very Short Answer Type Questions

1. $ns_2\ np_5$ 2. $ns^2\ np^4$ 3. second; third 4. Cs^+ 5. d–
6. first 7. larger 8. anti-penultimate 9. first

Competition Wing

Level 1: Apply your Concepts

1. True 2. False 3. True 4. True 5. False
6. True 7. True 8. True 9. True 10. False
11. transition elements 12. ns^1 13. halogen 14. C>B>Be 15. C, O, N, F
16. 14 17. Br^+ 18. 8, s, p 19. Positive
20. (i) - (C), (ii) - (E), (iii) - (D), (iv) - (A) 21. (c) 22. (d) 23. (c)
24. (a) 25. (d) 26. (c) 27. (d) 28. (b)
29. (c) 30. (c) 31. (c) 32. (b) 33. (c)
34. (b) 35. (d) 36. (a) 37. (d) 38. (d)
39. (c)

JEE-NEET Special Wing

Multiple-Answer Type Questions

1. (a, b, c) 2. (c, d) 3. (a, c) 4. (b, c) 5. (a, b, c, d)

Comprehension-Based Questions

6. (b) 7. (d) 8. (c) 9. (a) 10. (c)
11. (a) 12. (c) 13. (a) 14. (c) 15. (a)
16. (b) 17. (d)

Match the Columns

18. (P) – (ii), (Q) – (iv), (R) – (i), (S) – (iii)

Hints and Explanations

Classroom Wing

Very Short Answer Type Questions

1. VII A or 17th group elements are the best oxidizing agents. ∴ The valence electronic configuration is ns^2np^5.
2. ns^2 np^4
3. second; third
4. Cs^+
5. d–
6. first
7. larger
8. anti-penultimate
9. first
10. Among the given elements, the electronic configuration of the element with the highest ionization energy is $2s^2$ $2p^3$ because of its half-filled configuration in the p subshell.
11. Since the element has 3 electrons in the 3d sub-shell, it belongs to V B or the 5th group and the 4th period. Filling up of electrons in the 3d subshell starts after 4s.
12. [Kr] $5s^1 \rightarrow$ Rb, [Ne] $3s^1 \rightarrow$ Na, [Xe] $6s^1 \rightarrow$ Cs, [Ar] $4s^1 \rightarrow$ K

    Down the group, metallic character increases due to the decrease in ionization energy.
13. Atomic size along a period – decreases

    Down the group – Increases.
14. Short periods – II and III with 8 elements each

    Long periods – IV and V with 18 elements each
15. Along a period, ionization potential increases
16. Elements of a group have same number of valence electrons.
17. Similarity in properties with both IA and VII A groups.
18. Elements of s- and p- block except zero group (18th group)
19. 18th group elements are the noble gases.

    Special characteristics are attributed to the presence of 8 electrons in the outer most shell (except He)
20. Down the group, ionization potential decreases.
21. Metallic properties

    Along a period – decreases

    Down the group – increases

    Non-metallic Properties

    Along a period – increases

    Down the group – decreases
22. Half the internuclear distance between two atoms bonded by a single covalent bond.
23. Electron affinity decreases from Sc to Zn.
24. Half the internuclear distance between the adjacent metal atoms in a metallic crystal. Properties of metals like hardness, malleability, ductility can be known.

Sort Answer Type Questions

25. There are 54 electrons present in xenon.

    ∴ The given element has (54 + 18) = 72 electrons. Hence, the electronic configuration is [Xe] $6s^2$ $4f^{14}$ $5d^2$ and this is a 'd' block element.
26. An element has two electrons in the 3p shell. Hence, it has 4 valence electrons ($3s^23p^2$). Therefore, it belongs to the IV-A group or the 14th group.
27. Helium has four electrons. Therefore, the given element has 8 electrons. The valence electronic configuration is $2s^2$ $2p^4$.

    ∴ The element belongs to the p block.
28. Due to stable ns^2 valence electronic configuration, the addition of electrons to IIA group elements is an endothermic process.
29. A → VII A group, B → VI A group, C → 0 group D → I A group and next period. A, B, and C belong to the same period.

    Ionization energy increases across the period and decreases down the group. Hence, the order is C > B > A > D.

30. Reducing property increases down the group and decreases across the period. Hence, K acts as a good reducing agent.

31. $A \rightarrow A^{+2} + 2e \Rightarrow 2^{nd}$ group

$B \rightarrow B^{+1} + e \Rightarrow 1^{st}$ group

$C + e \rightarrow C^{-1} \Rightarrow 17^{th}$ group

$D + 2e \rightarrow O^{-2} \Rightarrow 16^{th}$ group.

32. In a given period, inert gases possess the highest ionization energy. Hence, X → Ar, Y → Mg, Z → Na.

33. $X \rightarrow 2, 8, 18, 8, 2 \Rightarrow 1s^2\, 2s^2\, 2p^6\, 3s^2\, 3p^6\, 3d^{10}\, 4s^2\, 4p^6\, 5s^2$

∴ Total s electrons are 10.

34. (i) Mendeleev's classification based on atomic weight of elements.

(ii) Modern periodic law based on atomic numbers.

35. (i) Seventh period

(ii) Radioactivity

36. The elements that can easily lose electrons to form positive ions are called electropositive elements, for example, metals. Electropositivity is the measure of the ability of elements (mainly metals) to donate electrons to form positive ions.

The elements that can easily accept electrons to form negative ions are called electronegative elements, for example, non-metals. Electronegativity is the measure of the ability of an element (mainly non-metals) to attract electrons towards itself.

37. (i) Active metals

(ii) Transition metals

(iii) Non-metals

(iv) Metalloids

(v) Noble gases and

(vi) Inner transition elements

38. (i) In transition elements, differentiating electron enters (n − 1)d subshell.

(ii) In inner transition elements, differentiating electron enters (n − 2)f subshell.

39. (i) 'p'-block, 'p'-subshell - valence shell.

(ii) 'd'-block, 'd'-subshell - penultimate shell.

(iii) 'f'-block, 'f'-subshell - anti- penultimate shell.

Essay Answer Type Questions

40. $E_n = \dfrac{kz^2}{n^2} = \dfrac{13.6 \times z^2}{2^2}$ eV

$\therefore \dfrac{13.6 \times z^2}{4} = 54.4$

$\therefore z^2 = \dfrac{54.4 \times 4}{13.6} = 16$

∴ The element is beryllium and it is present in 2nd period and II A (2) group.

41. (i) Basic arrangement of elements

(a) Vertical columns

(b) Horizontal rows

(ii) Merits

(a) Gaps for undiscovered elements

(b) Correction of some doubtful atomic weights

42. (i) Anomalous pairs

(ii) Position of hydrogen

(iii) Position of isotopes

(iv) Position of lanthanides and actinides

(v) Position of elements of group 8

(vi) Anomalous placing of transition metals and coinage metals.

43. (i) Number of elements in each period.

(ii) Other name for the period

(iii) Starting and ending element

(iv) Number of energy levels in each period

44. (i) Different group

(ii) Position of group

(iii) Blocks

(iv) Position of blocks

(v) Types of elements in each block

45. (a) The last noble gas in the present periodic table is radon with Z = 86. The next noble gas element to be discovered is expected to have the atomic number 118 (86 + 32). That means the number of elements to be added to the 7th period is 5.

(b) The element having atomic number 30 belongs to d – block. But, it is the last element in 4d-series having the electronic configuration [Ar] $3d^{10}4s^2$. Since it has only 4th shell incomplete, it does not come under transition elements. As 2 electrons are there in the valence shell, it can form bivalent ion and does not show variable valency A, D, E are correct choices.

Competition Wing

Level 1: Apply your Concepts

11. Since the element has 4 electrons in the 3d orbital, it is a transition element.

12. Group IA (or) 1 elements are the best-reducing agents. The general electronic configuration of group IA or 1 elements is ns^1.

13. The valence electronic configuration of the element is $3s^2 3p^5$. Hence, it is a halogen.

14. Across the period, electron affinity values increase. Hence, the order is C > B > Be.

20. Maximum metallic character → Cs

 Maximum electronegativity → F

 Maximum ionization energy → He

 Maximum electron affinity → Cl.

21. Na → 1st group and 3rd period

 Mg → 2nd group and 3rd period

 K → 1st group and 4th period

 Ca → 2nd group and 4th period

 Down the group, the metallic character increases and across the period decreases. Hence, K has the maximum metallic character.

 Hence, the correct option is (c).

22. Down the group, reducing property increases. Hence, Rb possesses the maximum reducing property.

 Hence, the correct option is (d).

23. Na and Ca belong to different groups and hence, they show different chemical properties. Hence, the correct option is (c).

24. Elements belonging to the same group possess the same number of valence electrons. Hence, they possess the same chemical properties. Hence, the correct option is (a).

36. 3 In a period the atomic size decreases and in a group it increases.

 2 In a period ionization energy increases and in a group it decreases.

 1 Tendency to undergo oxidation decreases in a period and increases in a group.

 4 The elements present in the left side of the periodic table have strong reducing property.

 Hence, the correct answer is (a).

37. Since the atomic weight of Ag is not equal to the mean of the atomic weights of Cu and Au, (Cu, Ag, and Au) triad do not follow Dobereiner's law of triads.

 Hence, the correct answer is (d).

38. 4 Determination of the positions of Y and Z in the periodic table based on the position of X.

 3 Determination of the number of shells and the number of valence electrons present in X, Y, and Z.

 1 Effect of number of valence electrons and number of shells on atomic size.

 Hence, the correct answer is (d).

39. Electronic configuration of an element with atomic number

 37 is [Kr] $5s^1$.

 29 is [Ar] $3d^{10} 4s^1$,

 70 is [Xe] $4f^{14} 5d^0 6s^2$.

 35 is [Ar] $3d^{10} 4s^2 4p^5$.

 Hence, 37, 29, 70 and 35 belong to s, d, f, and p, respectively.

 Hence, the correct answer is (c).

Level 2: Review Your Concepts

40. (i) comparing electronic configuration of nitrogen and oxygen

 (ii) electronic arrangement in the valence shell of nitrogen and oxygen

 (iii) relation between the electronic arrangement and the stability of the atom

 (iv) effect of stability on size of the atom

41. (i) electronic configuration of the element and predict group and period

 (ii) correlation between the position of the element in the periodic table and its chemical behavior

42. (a) (i) factors affecting electron affinity

 (ii) electronic configuration of chlorine and fluorine

 (iii) comparison of the number of valence electrons with respect to the atomic size between chlorine and fluorine

 (b) The given elements X and Y should be fluorine and chlorine respectively. Chlorine has a greater electron affinity than fluorine. Normally, from top to bottom in a group, the electron affinity decreases. That means, the electron affinity should decrease from fluorine to chlorine. However, due to stronger interelectronic repulsions in small sized fluorine atom some amount of energy is utilized to overcome the repulsions. Therefore, the net energy released is less than that of chlorine.

43. (i) electronic configuration of inner transition elements, entry of differentiating electron
(ii) comparison of energy of valence shell and that of penultimate shell
(iii) participation of penultimate shell electrons in bonding

44. (i) Xenon belongs to the 5th period
(ii) atomic size of xenon in comparison to the other noble gases
(iii) comparison of influence of electronegativity of fluorine and oxygen

45. (i) comparison of electronic configuration of oxygen and sulphur
(ii) presence of vacant 'd' subshell and scope for excited state configuration

46. (i) amount of energy absorbed by1 g of Be to form Be^+ and Be^{2+}
(ii) energy required for conversion of 1 g Be(g) into Be^+ ions
(iii) calculation of additional amount of energy
(iv) conversion of Be^+ ions to Be^{2+} ions
(v) 25%.

47. (i) differentiating electron of lanthanides
(ii) lanthanide contraction and its effect on atomic and ionic sizes of lanthanide elements
(iii) dependence of chemical properties on the atomic sizes
(iv) properties exploited for separation of different elements

48. (i) electron filling in transition elements
(ii) effect on effective nuclear charge
(iii) relation between effective nuclear charge and atomic radius
(iv) comparison of electronic configuration in (n – 1)d subshell of the transition elements of each group
(v) effect on atomic size

49. (i) factors effecting ionization potential
(ii) comparison of the screening effects of s, p, d, and f-electrons

50. (a) (i) factors affecting density
(ii) comparison of electron filling in alkali, alkaline earth, and transition metals
(iii) effect on atomic size
(iv) comparison of mass with respect to atomic volume among alkali, alkaline earth, and transition metals

(b) Fluorine is the element which cannot be oxidized by any other element. All halogens, chlorine, bromine and iodine can be oxidized by fluorine. Fluorine is the most electronegative element and hence cannot lose electron at all. It has high affinity to take up electron. Hence, it is the best oxidizing agent.

51. (i) comparing IP values; valency of X
(ii) abrupt change in IP value
(iii) valence electronic configuration of stable ion
(iv) valencies of the corresponding positive and negative radicals

52. (i) electronic configuration of element A
(ii) electronic configuration corresponding to Z = 28
(iii) position of A in the periodic table
(iv) position of the element present below A in the periodic table and its electronic configuration
(v) determination of the properties from its position

53. $x + z = 177 \times 6$

$z - y = 5 \times 10$ 177.6

(–)(+)   –   50.0

$x + y = 127.6$ 127.6

As X, Y, and Z form Dobereiner triad

$y = \frac{x+z}{2}$, where x, y and z are atomic masses of X, Y, and Z, respectively.

$$y = \frac{177.6}{2} = 88.8$$

$x = 127.6 - 88.8 = 38.8$

$z = 177.6 - 38.8 = 138.8$

$x = 38 \times 8 \approx 40$

$X = 40 \Rightarrow Ca$

$Y = 88 \times 80 \Rightarrow Sr$

$Z = 138 \times 6 \Rightarrow Ba$

54. Both Fe^{2+} and Fe^{3+} have the same number of protons but the number of electron in Fe^{3+} is less than that of Fe^{2+}. Hence the effective nuclear charge is more in the case of Fe^{3+} and thereby the ionic size of Fe^{3+} is less than that of Fe^{2+}.

55. As the atomic numbers of A, B and C differ by 1 unit each they must be belonging to adjacent groups. Along a period the atomic size decreases till the VII A group and then increases till the zero group. As the atomic size of C is greater than B though it differs by one unit in its atomic number it must be a zero group element. Though the atomic number of B is greater than A, it has smaller size than B and this shows that B is a halogen, that is, VII A group and A is a chalcogen, that is, VI A group.

56. For any element, ionization potential is considered for gaseous state only. Ionization potential corresponds to the energy required to overcome the force of attraction exerted by the nucleus on the electron without considering any other kinds of attractions. In gaseous state, the intermolecular forces of attractions being negligible, removal of electron from a neutral gaseous atom involves an amount of energy equal to IP only. In solid and liquid states, the intermolecular forces of attraction are stronger and the energy required to remove electron involves not only IP but also the energy required to overcome the other forces. Thus, for any element, IP is considered only for the isolated gaseous atoms irrespective of the state in which it exists.

57. During the addition of an electron to a neutral atom, work is done towards the nuclear force of attraction. Hence, energy is released. After the addition of an electron, the uninegative species formed, repels the 2nd electron. Hence during the addition of the second electron, work is done against the force of repulsion that requires supply of energy.

58. (a) l = 0 corresponds to 's' subshell and l = 2 corresponds to 'd' subshell. Further, six electrons in 's' subshell and five electrons in 'd' subshell means the ion should have the electronic configuration $1s^2\ 2s^2\ 2p^6\ 3s^2\ 3p^6\ 3d^5$. Since it is a tripositive ion, the atom could have lost two electrons from 4s subshell and one electron from 3d subshell. Therefore, atomic number is 26. Electronic configuration is [Ar] $3d^6\ 4s^2$. It belongs to the VIII group and 4th period.

(b) Yes. Since Fe is a transition element it shows variable oxidation state. In transition elements, the electrons enter into the penultimate shell instead of valence shell. Energy difference between ns and (n – 1)d-orbitals is very less. Hence, both ns and (n – 1)d-electrons are available for chemical bond formation. So, they exhibit variable valency.

59. (a) ns^2, np^5 for n = 3

$1s^2, 2s^2, 2p^6, 3s^2, sp^5$

So, the period is 3rd and the group is 17th (VII A).

(b) (n – 1) $d^2\ ns^2$ for n = 4

$1s^2, 2s^2, 2p^6, 3s^2, 3p^6, 4s^2, 3d^2$

So, the period is 4th and the group is 4th (IV B).

60. (a) In lanthanide elements, the newly added electron enters into anti-penultimate shell keeping the configuration of penultimate and valence shells same. The addition of electrons to inner shell should result in increased screening effect. But the 'f-' subshell has a very poor screening effect. So, the addition of electrons to the inner 'f-' subshell does not result in corresponding increase in atomic size. Therefore, the increasing nuclear charge from cerium to lutetium (71) results in drastic decrease in atomic and ionic sizes.

(b) Between the 5th and 6th periods, the intervening lanthanides increase the nuclear charge and lanthanide contraction results in decrease of atomic size. As a result of this, mass of atom increases and atomic size decreases. This results in drastic increase in density of elements from the 5th to 6th periods.

61. The element 'X' must be a halogen since it forms the stable X^- ion. As there are three completely filled shells in 'X,' the electronic configuration of 'X' could be 2, 8, 18, 18, 7 and X^- is 2, 8, 18, 18, 8. Since there are 54 e^-s in X^-, the corresponding elements that form unipositive and dipositive ions should be cesium (55) and barium (56). Cesium reacts more vigorously with water than barium. This is because reactivity of alkali metals is more due to their greater atomic size when compared with alkaline earth metals. Moreover, alkaline earth metals have greater IP values than alkali metals. Hence, they react slowly with water.

62. All the electrons present in alkaline earth metals are paired. Therefore to add one extra electron to these atoms, work has to be done against the force of repulsion. Hence, electron affinity of an alkaline earth metal is a positive.

Level 3: Assess Your Concepts

63. $r_n = 0.529 \times \dfrac{n^2}{z}$

$\therefore\ 4.761 = 0.529 \times \dfrac{3^2}{z}$

$\therefore\ Z = \dfrac{4.761}{0.529} = 1$

The element is hydrogen. Hence, it has similarities with alkali metals as well as halogens.

64. (i) electronic configuration of sodium and magnesium

(ii) comparison of atomic size of sodium and magnesium

(iii) effect of atomic size on first ionization energy

(iv) electronic configuration of stable ions of sodium and magnesium

(v) relation between the stability of ion and the respective ionization energy

65. (i) shell into which the differentiating electron enters

(ii) general electronic configuration of representative elements

(iii) comparison with general electronic configurations of transition and inner transition elements

(iv) comparison of effective nuclear charge and its effect on the periodic properties

66. (i) electronic configuration of II A and II B

(ii) change in energy that takes place due to the addition of electron to the neutral atom of the elements belonging to the Groups IIA and IIB

(iii) relation between change in energy and electron affinity values

67. (i) factors affecting density

(ii) general trend of atomic sizes in groups of transition elements

(iii) effect of inclusion of lanthanide elements on the atomic size of the elements belonging to the 3rd transition series

(iv) factors affecting the density of an atom

(v) change in atomic size of alkali and alkaline earth metals along the group

(vi) comparison of change of densities along the group among alkali, alkaline earth, and transition metals

68. In a particular series of d-block elements, electron filling takes place in the penultimate shell. Hence their atomic size decreases up to the 7th group and reaches minimum and then again increases because with the pairing of electrons, repulsive force also increases. The repulsion among the added electrons exceeds the increased force of attraction (due to the increase of nuclear charge) after the 8th group. Hence, atomic radius increases slightly.

69. Electronic configuration of II A and II B group elements is ns^2np^0. Addition of an electron to these elements requires energy to overcome repulsive forces between completely filled ns electrons and electron going to be added. Hence, electron affinity values are less than zero.

70. In case of representative elements, from left to right in a period, the nuclear charge increases with increase in atomic number. Since the number of inner shells and inner electrons remain constant, the increased effective nuclear charge decreases the atomic size proportionately.

In case of transition and inner transition elements, the electrons are being added to the penultimate and anti-penultimate shells, respectively. There is slight increase in screening effect that counterbalances the increased nuclear charge to some extent and hence the decrease in atomic size is less pronounced than in representative elements. Since the other properties in turn depend on atomic size, they also show the same trend as atomic size.

71. The respective elements X, Y, and Z are Ti, Zr and Hf. They belong to IVB group of 3d, 4d, and 5d series of transition elements, that is, 4th period, 5th period and 6th period. As they belong to same group and the value of ionization potential decreases down the group, the same trend follows from Ti to Zr. However, the IP value of Hf is double to that of Zr. This is because of intervening lanthanide elements that cause lanthanide contraction. As there is no pronounced increase in atomic size due to lanthanide contraction, the increased nuclear charge increases the effective nuclear force of attraction drastically. Thus, there is a drastic increase in IP value.

72. Among IIIA group elements, boron has the highest ionization potential due to smaller size. The sharp decrease in ionization energy from boron to aluminium is due to increase in atomic radius. The atomic radius increases due to decrease in effective nuclear charge. In gallium contraction in atomic size is significant due to the presence of completely filled d-electrons in the penultimate shell. Thus, the effective nuclear charge increases. Hence, both aluminium and gallium have almost equal ionization energy values.

73. $Z = 7$ corresponds to nitrogen atom having the valence electronic configuration $2s^2\ 2p^3$. Addition of 3 electrons results in the formation of N^{3-} ion with configuration $2s^2\ 2p^6$ $Z = 8$ corresponds to oxygen atom having the valence electronic configuration $2s^2\ 2p^4$. Addition of 2 electrons results in the formation of O^{2-} ion with configuration $2s^2\ 2p^6$ $Z = 9$ corresponds to fluorine atom with valence electronic configuration $2s^2\ 2p^7$ and can form a stable F^- ion with $2s^2\ 2p^6$ configuration. $Z = 11$, $Z = 12$ and $Z = 13$ correspond to sodium, magnesium, and aluminium with valence configurations $3s^1$, $3s^2$ and $3s^2\ 3p^1$ respectively. These atoms lose 1, 2 and 3 electrons to form Na^+, Mg^{2+} and Al^{3+} respectively. All the said ions possess 10 electrons each and hence are considered to be isoelectronic. With increase in nuclear charge from $Z = 7$ to $Z = 13$ the effective nuclear force of attraction increases and the ionic size decreases.

JEE-NEET Special wing

Multiple-Answer Type Questions

1. The energy required to convert $X_{(g)} \rightarrow X^{+}{}_{(g)}$ is said to be first ionization energy of X.

   It depends on:

   The reactivity of X, its electronic configuration, Number of inner shell electrons(their shielding effect) but not on the total number of nucleons (mass number)

2. Stable ion M^{a+} is isoelectronic with the stable ion of N^{b-} means,

   The total number of electrons in both are ions are same

   ⇒ Both have same electronic configuration and hence the same number of valence electrons.

3. Mendeleev organized the known elements based on the recurring trends in their chemical properties, following his periodic law that states, 'Element properties are a periodic function of their atomic weight.' Isotopes, which are atoms of the same element with different masses, were not accommodated in Mendeleev's periodic table despite his law suggesting that different isotopes of an element should have distinct positions.

4. The factor that governs the radii of ionic species is the ratio between the atomic number "Z" and the number of electrons "n." This ratio is referred to as the Z/e^- ratio.

   As Z/e^- ratio increases, ionic radius decreases.

   (a) Cl^-, K^+ ---- $\frac{17}{18}, \frac{19}{18}$ ⇒ Ionic radius of $Cl^- > K^+$

   (b) Al^{3+}, Mg^{2+} ---- $\frac{13}{18}, \frac{12}{18}$ ⇒ Ionic radius of $Al^{3+} < Mg^{2+}$

   (c) O^{2-}, F^- ---- $\frac{8}{10}, \frac{9}{10}$ ⇒ Ionic radius of $O^{2-} > F^-$

   (d) Ca^{2+}, S^{2-} ---- $\frac{20}{18}, \frac{16}{18}$ ⇒ Ionic radius of $Ca^{2+} < S^{2-}$

   the correct sets arranged in the increasing order of their ionic radii are, $Al^{3+} < Mg^{2+}$ and $Ca^{2+} < S^{2-}$

5. The enthalpy change (ΔH) is negative in step (i) and positive in step (ii). This indicates that step (i) is exothermic, meaning it releases energy, which is typically considered favourable. In contrast, step (ii) is endothermic, absorbing energy, which is less favourable in most cases.

   Both steps involve the addition of electrons to oxygen species. However, in step (ii), the energy is absorbed, suggesting that the electron entering O-experiences more inter-electronic repulsions compared to the electron entering the neutral oxygen atom. This increased repulsion requires more energy to overcome than the energy released due to the addition of the electron, resulting in a net absorption of energy. Also, the formation of O^{2-} from O requires an energy of 639kJ/mol.

Comprehension-Based Questions

6. For transition metals, the general electronic configuration of outer orbitals $(n - 1)d^{1-10}\, ns^{1-2}$.

   For the given outer orbital electronic configuration of $4d^5\, 5s^1$, n = 5

   ⇒ element should be of 5th period.

   Total number of electrons:

   5 of d orbital +1 of s orbital = 6. ⇒ the element should belong to 4th period, 6th group i.e., D.

7. Elements of Lanthanides and Actinides belong to 3rd group. H, J, K, L, M and N belong to same group. Hence KLMN is the correct answer

8. Element C belongs to 4th period, 5th group, and element A belongs to 2nd period 16th group.

   ⇒ Highest oxidation state that C can exhibit is +5 and A can exhibit (18 – 16 = 2) -2 oxidation state

   ⇒ Compound is formed between C^{+5} and A^{-2} ions.

   ⇒ Using cris-cross method formula can be written as C_2A_5.

9. Elements belonging to 12 group contains the general electronic configuration $(n - 1)d^{1-10}ns^{1-2}$.

   ⇒ E and G will have completely filled d orbitals in their ground state.

10. Lanthanides exhibit +3 stable oxidation state and show lanthanide contraction.

    ⇒ Lanthanides undergo a consistent decrease in ion size as atomic number increases.

    ⇒ with respect to ionic size, K<J<H

11. Transition elements show variable oxidation states because of very less energy difference between their (n-1) d subshell and ns subshell but they form coloured compounds because of d-d transitions. This is because d-d transitions, which involve the movement of electrons between partially filled d orbitals, are responsible for the absorption of certain wavelengths of light and the production of colour in compounds.

12.

List – I	Explanation	List – II Symbol of the element as given in the above model periodic table
(A) Ground state outer electronic configuration-$5f^3 6d^1 7s^2$	This of general outer electronic configuration: $(n-2)\ f^{1-14}(n-1)\ d^{0-1}\ ns^2$. ⇒ The element is inner transition element with $n = 7$. *f* orbital contains 3. Hence the element belongs to 7th period, 3rd group, and it is the 3rd element of lanthanide series.	(iii) M
(B) Stability due to half-filled 3d orbitals	Elements in group 7 have half-filled orbitals. However, because half-filled d orbitals are more stable, group 6 elements gain one electron from their ns orbital. As a result, element 'D' in group 6, and elements 'F' and 'O' in group 7, contain half-filled 3d and 4d orbitals, respectively.	(v) D
(C) Element that exhibits highest oxidation number	The maximum oxidation state that an element can exhibit is determined by the number of unpaired electrons it possesses in its excited state. Element 'O'($[Ar]4d^5\ 5S^2$) possesses seven unpaired electrons in its excited state [Ar] [1 1 1 1 1] (3d) [1] (4s) [1 1 1] (4p)	(iv) O
(D) Forms colourless complex compounds	Elements with completely filled d orbitals do not show d-d transitions and, as a result, form colourless compounds.	(ii) E

Correct match is:

	(A)	(B)	(C)	(D)
(c)	(iii)	(v)	(iv)	(ii)

13. The electron gain enthalpies of elements generally decrease along the group. However, the first electron gain enthalpy of second-period elements tends to be slightly lower than that of their corresponding third-period elements due to their smaller size and higher electron densities. Among the given elements, element C is expected to possess the highest electron gain enthalpy.

14. Ionization energy generally increases along the period and decreases along the group. So, the correct increasing order is CYDX.

15. Given Z is isoelectronic with B. It means Z should be an alkaline earth metal. Given that the valency of Z is 2. First element that belongs to group B is oxygen. So, the compound M formed between Z and Oxygen is ZO (CaO). Alkali and alkaline metal oxides are crystalline at room temperature and are water soluble. When dissolved in water it forms a basic solution with pH >7. Hence its pOH should be <7.

16. More is the atomic number and lesser is the atomic size, greater is the Effective nuclear charge experienced by the valence electrons.

17. Ionization energy increases along the period. But the preceding element of B in the periodic table has higher Ionization energy compared to B because of its half-filled p orbitals. Half-filled p-orbitals imparts extra stability to the atom. Hence, both the given statements are true.

Match the Columns

18. As the cation is same in all the given compounds, lattice energy of these compounds depends on the size and charge of the anion. Stable ions of A, B, C and E follows the order $A<C^{-}<B^{-2}<E$. But magnitude of charge on B is double that of other ions. Given that difference in charge has a greater effect on the lattice energy than a difference in the distance. So, the compound of sodium with B should have the highest value of lattice energy.

CHAPTER

5

Chemical Bonding

Remember

Before beginning this chapter, you should be able to:

- understand the relation between electronic configuration and bond formation.
- represent bonds by Lewis dot structures.

Key Ideas

After completing this chapter, you should be able to:

- explain the concept of ionic character in covalent bond and covalent character in ionic bond.
- describe the properties of ionic and covalent compounds in correlation with the type of bond present in them.
- explain Lewis theory of covalent bond formation on the basis of octet rule and exceptions to octet rule.
- understand the concept of orbital overlapping to overcome the drawbacks of Lewis theory.
- illustrate the theory of hybridization.
- correlate the shapes of molecules with the concept of VSEPR theory.
- compare various types of non-bonded forces of attraction and their relative strengths.
- understand the concept of metallic bond and its effect on properties of metals.
- describe the electronic concept of oxidation and reduction.

Scientific Crypt

A Tribute to Linus Pauling (1901–1994)

Linus Pauling was considered as one of the greatest chemists of 20th century. He was a distinguished American chemist who integrated chemistry with quantum theory. He was the first to make quantum theory and chemical experiment to work together. Pauling added the concepts of hydrogen bonding, resonance, and valence bond approach to his work on the structure of molecules. In 1939, he gathered his research papers to form a book "the nature of chemical bond and the structure of molecules". In 1954 he was awarded Noble prize in chemistry for his work on chemical bonding. Prior to this, he was also awarded Noble prize for peace in 1952. He is the only person in the world to have won two unshared Noble prizes. Because of his consistent work on the power of vit-C, which can fight cancer and common cold, he was best known as vit-C advocate.

This distinguished American scientist was born on 28th February in 1901 in Portland, Oregon, in USA. He took his last breath in 1994 in California, in USA at the age of 93. His long life had lot of significant contributions to the field of modern chemistry.

FUN TIME

CROSSWORD

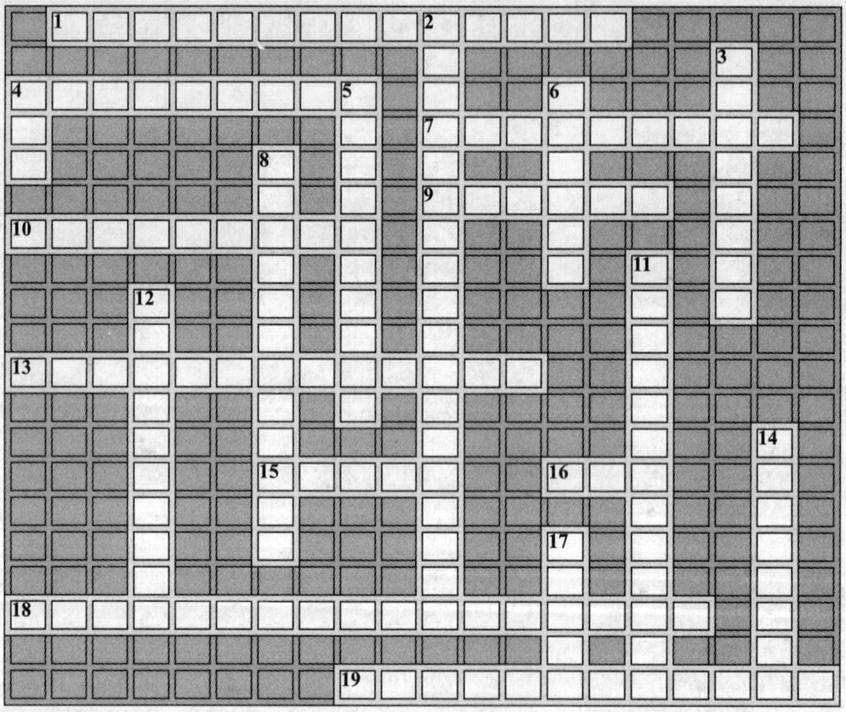

Across

1. Shape of boron trichloride molecule
4. Covalent bond formed by the axial overlapping of atomic orbitals
7. Bond formed by the transfer of electrons
9. Covalent molecule having two opposite charge centers
10. Shape of ammonia molecule
13. Energy released in the formation of ionic compound
15. Presence of eight electrons in the valence shell of an atom
16. Electrovalency of calcium in calcium oxide
18. Weak forces of attraction existing among nonpolar molecules
19. Bond formed by sharing of electrons

Down

2. Structures representing the picture of bonding in ions and molecules
3. Electron pair present in the valence shell but is not involved in bond formation
4. Number of electrons around boron in BCl_3 molecule
5. Covalent bond formed by sharing of two electron pairs
6. Covalent bond formed by the sidewise overlapping of orbitals
8. The attractive force between hydrogen atom of one molecule and highly electronegative atom of other molecule
11. Covalent compounds that conduct electricity
12. The other name for coordinate covalent bond
14. Donor atom in the formation of ammonium ion
17. Covalency of nitrogen in ammonia

INTRODUCTION

Nature is invariably associated with a number of chemical reactions. We all are aware of the fact that an atom is the smallest particle that takes part in a chemical reaction. Nevertheless, most of the elements exist in combined state in the form of molecules. Only in case of very few elements namely noble gases, the atom has an independent existence. The existence of these elements in atomic state is attributed to the high stability associated with the completely filled octet or duplex configuration in their valence shells. Obviously, the atoms of other elements have an inherent tendency to attain the above configuration by means of bond formation. This is known as an octet rule envisaged by Lewis theory. The process of bond formation is associated with the decrease in the energy of the system. This lowest energy state corresponds to the most stable state of the system. Different types of bond formation takes place depending on the nature of participant atoms.

Ionic Bond

An ionic bond is formed between two atoms which differ much in electronegativities. One atom loses one or more electrons and the other atom gains these electrons to attain the noble gas configuration. The atom losing the electrons forms a positively charged ion **(cation)** and the atom gaining electrons forms a negatively charged ion **(anion)**. The cation and anion are held together by the electrostatic force of attraction. The electrostatic force of attraction existing between the oppositely charged ions is called an **ionic bond**. Compounds that contain ionic bonds are known as ionic compounds.

Info Bytes!

Salt, or sodium chloride (NaCl), is one of the most common examples of an ionic compound.

Energy Changes Involved in the Formation of Ionic Compounds

Ionic compounds are formed due to the transfer of one or more electrons from one atom to the other. Hence, two oppositely charged ions are formed in this process and an electrostatic force of attraction is developed between them.

In addition to the force of attraction between the individual pair, force of attraction also exists among the oppositely charged ions of different pairs that bring them close to each other. As a result of this, repulsive forces are also generated between similar ions of different pairs.

However, the cation–cation distance and the anion–anion distance (measured from their centre) of different pairs are greater than the cation–anion distance of different pairs. Hence, the force of attraction is greater than the repulsive forces and the ions arrange themselves in such a way that their potential energy becomes minimum. The arrangement of ions associated with minimum potential energy gives the crystalline structure of the ionic compound.

The potential energy of the ions is assumed to be zero when they are separated by an infinite distance. When the ions approach each other, each of them releases a certain amount of energy.

The amount of energy released when the oppositely charged gaseous ions are brought closer from an infinite distance to form one mole of ionic crystal is called **lattice energy**.

Covalent Bond

When the elements do not differ much in their electronegativities, transfer of electrons is not possible between the atoms. In this case, sharing of electrons takes place.

A **covalent bond** is formed when two atoms attain their nearest noble gas configuration by sharing one or more electron pairs. Each of the atoms contributes equal number of electrons towards the bond formation.

Info Bytes!

The simplest covalent molecule is H_2, where two hydrogen atoms share their electrons to form a molecule.

Energy Changes During Covalent Bond Formation

Considering an example of the formation of hydrogen molecule. When two hydrogen atoms are brought close together, two types of forces start acting as listed hereunder:

1. Proton–proton and electron–electron repulsion
2. Proton–electron attraction.

Bond formation between two H-atoms takes place at a distance where the proton–electron attraction just balances the electron–electron repulsion and proton–proton repulsion.

At this stage, the system becomes stable because it possesses the lowest possible energy, and H_2 molecule is formed. The distance between the nuclei of the hydrogen atoms, after the formation of the bond, is called the **bond length**.

The total energy of this system is a function of the distance between hydrogen nuclei as shown in Figure 5.1. This is the way covalent bond formation takes place between two atoms.

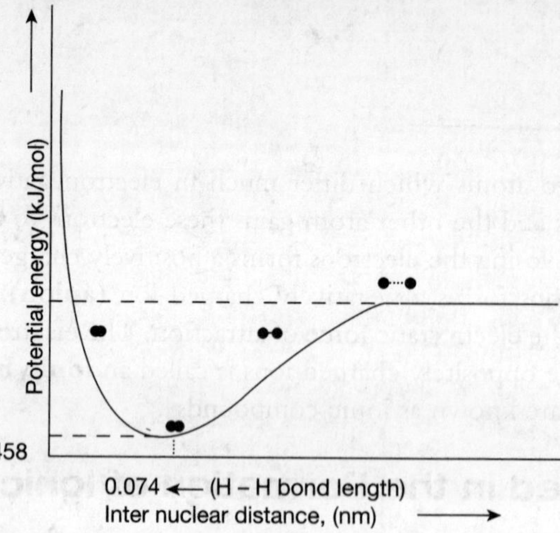

Figure 5.1 Potential energy curve representing the formation of covalent bond in hydrogen molecule

Non-polar Covalent Bond

In a bond between two identical atoms, the electrons are shared equally between the atoms. No separation of charge takes place in the molecule. This type of bond is called **non-polar covalent bond.**

> **Konnect**
>
> A covalent bond can be formed between two identical atoms (atoms of same element) as well as between the atoms of two different elements.

Polar Covalent Bond

A polar covalent bond is formed between non-identical atoms, which differ in electronegativities. Since the two atoms differ in their capacity to attract the shared electron pair, unequal sharing of electron density results. As a result, polarity is developed in the bond and the bond is said to have dipole moment. **Dipole moment** is the quantitative measure of the polarity of the molecule. A slight ionic character is imparted to this type of bond due to the difference in electronegativity between the bonded atoms and such type of bond is called **polar covalent bond.**

The relative tendency of non-identical atoms to form ionic bond or polar covalent bond depends upon the ease of the formation of cation and anion by the respective elements.

Easier the formation of cation and anion, more is the tendency of the formation of ionic bond. Larger size of the atom favors cation formation, whereas smaller atoms have greater tendency of attracting electrons towards it that leads to the formation of anion.

Ionic bonds are associated with some covalent character due to the attractive forces acting between the cation and the electron cloud of the anion.

The relative proportions of ionic character and covalent character of an ionic compound can be explained on the basis of the concept of polarization and **Fajan's rules.**

Concept of Polarization and Fajan's Rules

During the formation of an ionic compound, when a cation and anion approach each other, the nucleus of cation exerts some attractive force on the electron cloud. As a result of this, the symmetry of the electron cloud gets distorted and it shifts slightly towards the cation. This phenomenon is called **polarization**. This results in the partial sharing of electron cloud between the bonded atoms that is considered as a covalent character. This ability of a cation to distort the electron cloud of the anion is called **polarizing power** of the cation and the tendency of the anion to get distorted by the influence of the cation is called the **polarizability** of the anion.

The relative proportions of ionic and covalent characters of an ionic compound depend upon the polarizing power and polarizability of the respective cation and anion that can be explained on the basis of **Fajan's rules**.

1. **Size of Cation and Anion**

   (a) A large cation and a small anion result in maximum ionic character for the bond.
   Example: Cs^+ and F^-

   (b) A small cation and a large anion result in maximum covalent character for the bond.
   Example: Li^+ and I^-

2. **Charge of Cation and Anion**

   (a) Low charge on cation and anion results in maximum ionic character for the bond.
   Example: Na^+ and Cl^-

   (b) High charge on cation and anion results in greater proportion of covalent character for the bond.
   Example: Al^{3+} and O^{2-}

Theories of Covalent Bond Formation

Many theories have been proposed in order to explain covalent bond formation and the stability of the resultant molecules.

Octet Rule

Octet rule states that the atoms of the elements have a tendency to attain the nearest inert gas configuration either by the transfer of electrons or by the sharing of electrons.

Some examples of covalent molecules, the stability of which can be satisfactorily explained with the help of the octet rule are provided in the following table:

Table 5.1 Explanation of stability of covalent molecules by octet rule

Molecules	No. of valence electrons	Structures
Hydrogen (H_2)	1	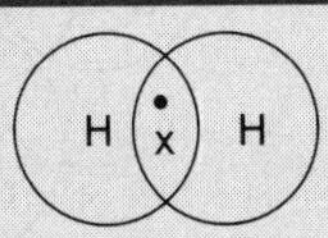 1 shared pair
Oxygen (O_2)	6	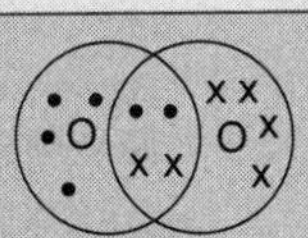 2 shared pairs

(Continued.)

Table 5.1 Continued

Molecules	No. of valence electrons	Structures
Nitrogen (N_2)	5	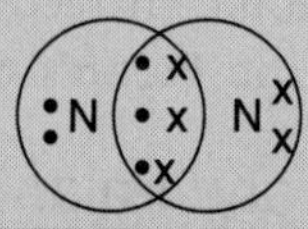 3 shared pairs
Chlorine (Cl_2)	7	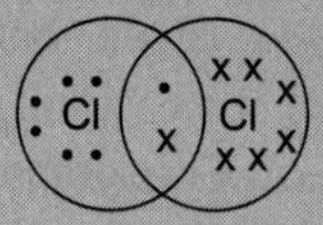 1 shared pair
Water (H_2O)	$H \rightarrow 1, O \rightarrow 6$	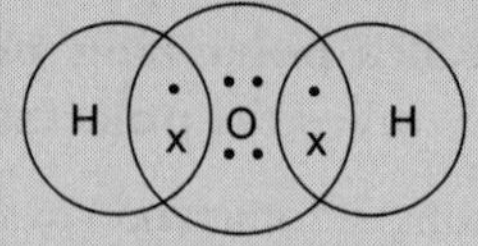 2 shared pairs
Methane (CH_4)	$C \rightarrow 4, H \rightarrow 1$	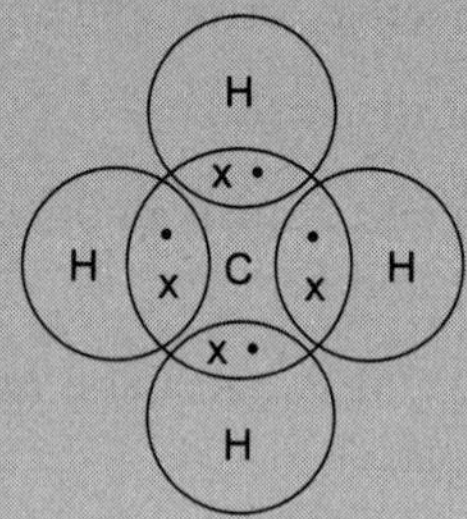 4 shared pairs

All the above molecules are found to obey the octet rule that is visualized by writing their Lewis dot structures. Therefore, it is justified that the atoms acquire stability by gaining the octet configuration. However, some molecules are also found in which the central atom does not acquire the octet configuration. But the fact that their stability is comparable with the stability of molecules that obey the octet rule indicates that the octet rule itself cannot completely justify formation and stability of covalent molecules.

Exceptions to the Octet Rule

The molecules may contain less than eight or more than eight electrons around the central atom. These are considered as deviations from the octet rule.

Incomplete Octet or Contracted Octet: Molecules in which the central atom possesses less than eight electrons in its valence shell.

Examples: BF_3, $BeCl_2$

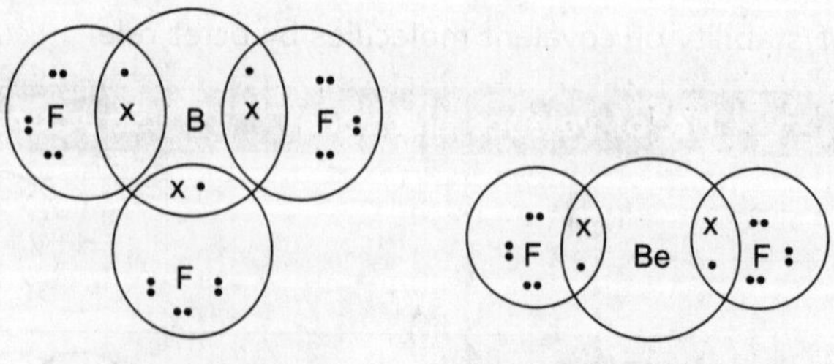

B has 6 electrons in its valence shell in BF_3

Be has 4 electrons in its valence shell in BeF_2

Figure 5.2 Incomplete octet or contracted octet

Expanded Octet: Molecules in which the central atom possesses more than eight electrons in its valence shell.

Examples: PCl_5, SF_6, IF_7

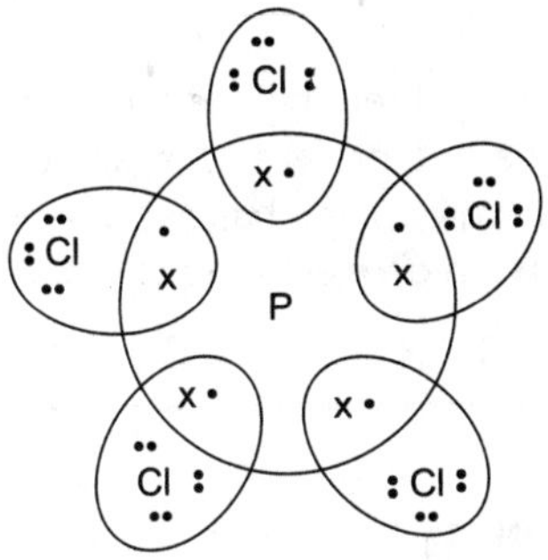

Figure 5.3 Expanded octet

P has 10 electrons in its valence shell in PCl_5.

Lewis theory explains the formation of covalent bond through sharing of electrons, but this theory does not explain the mechanism of sharing of electrons that leads to the stability of molecules. The mechanism of sharing of electrons was interpreted with the help of the concept of orbital overlapping after the quantum mechanical model of atom was proposed.

EXAMPLE 5.1 Between MgO and NaCl, which has a stronger ionic bond? Why?

SOLUTION

MgO consists of Mg^{2+} and O^{2-} ions, whereas NaCl has Na^+ and Cl^- ions. The magnesium ion (Mg^{2+}) has a greater charge than the sodium ion (Na^+), and the oxide ion (O^{2-}) has a greater charge than the chloride ion (Cl^-). Additionally, due to a higher effective nuclear charge, Mg^{2+} is smaller in size compared to Na^+, and similarly, O^{2-} is smaller than Cl^-. Given these factors, the electrostatic attraction between Mg^{2+} and O^{2-} is stronger than that between Na^+ and Cl^-. Therefore, MgO has a stronger ionic bond than NaCl.

EXAMPLE 5.2 Between AgCl and AgBr, which is more covalent and why?

SOLUTION

Between AgCl and AgBr, AgBr is more covalent. Since the cation (Ag^+) is the same in both, the anion's size determines the extent of polarization. Among Cl^- and Br^- ions, Br^- ion is larger and more polarizable. A higher degree of polarizability leads to increased covalent character in the compound. Hence, AgBr has a greater covalent character compared to AgCl.

EXAMPLE 5.3 Distinguish between ionic and covalent compounds with respect to:

(i) electrical conductivity
(ii) melting and boiling points
(iii) state at room temperature.

SOLUTION

(i) Ionic compounds conduct electricity when dissolved in water or a molten state due to the movement of free ions. Covalent compounds generally do not conduct electricity as they lack free-moving ions.

(ii) Ionic compounds typically have high melting and boiling points due to strong electrostatic forces between ions. Covalent compounds usually have lower melting and boiling points because of weaker intermolecular forces.

(iii) Most ionic compounds are solid at room temperature because of their closely packed lattice structure. Covalent compounds can be solids, liquids, or gases at room temperature depending on the strength of their intermolecular forces.

EXAMPLE 5.4 Carbon does not form an ionic bond with chlorine, but magnesium does. Give reason.

SOLUTION

Carbon, being a non-metal, has four electrons in its outer shell and requires four more electrons to achieve a full octet, making it unfavourable to lose or gain electrons. Instead, it prefers to share electrons with chlorine, leading to a covalent bond. Magnesium, on the other hand, belongs to the II A group and has two valence electrons. It can easily lose these two electrons to achieve a noble gas configuration. Chlorine, with a high electronegativity, can accept these electrons, resulting in the formation of an ionic bond between magnesium and chlorine.

Concept of Orbital Overlapping

According to this concept, covalent bond is formed when an overlap takes place between the orbital of one atom with the orbital of another atom.

Conditions required for orbital overlapping:

1. The orbitals belonging to the valence shell only take part in overlapping.
2. Each of the overlapping orbitals should contain an unpaired electron.
3. The electrons in the overlapping orbitals should have an opposite spin.

Konnect

If the atom possesses more than one atomic orbital having unpaired electrons, then more than one covalent bond can be formed.

Different Types of Overlapping

s–s overlapping

Example: H_2 molecule

Each hydrogen atom has only one electron ($1s^1$) that is available for bonding.

In the formation of H_2 molecules, 1s orbital of one atom overlaps with that of the other forming a single covalent bond.

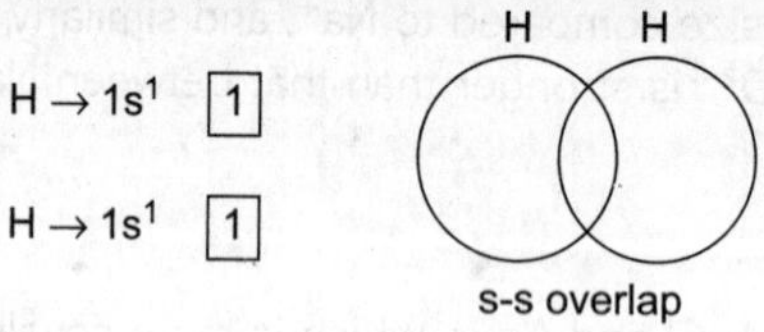

s–p overlapping

Example: HF molecule

It is formed by the overlapping of 1s orbital of hydrogen atom and $2p_z$ orbital of fluorine atom, that is, by s–p overlapping.

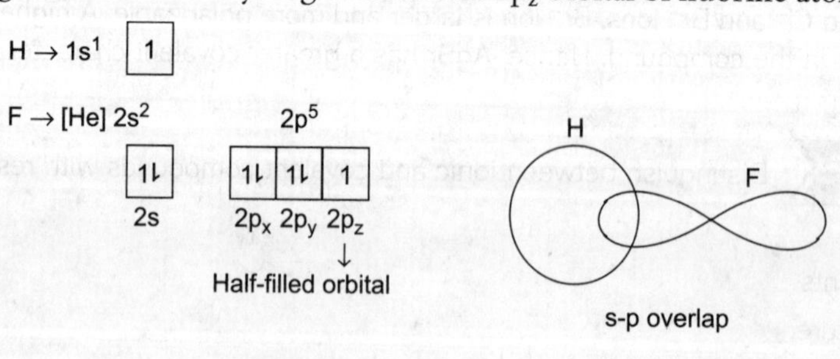

p–p overlapping

Examples: Cl_2, F_2, Br_2 molecules, etc.

Cl_2 molecule is formed by the overlapping of $3p_z$ orbitals of two chlorine atoms.

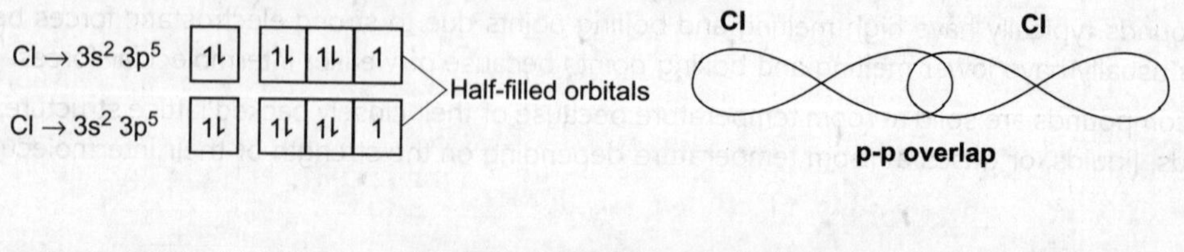

In the above examples (H_2, HF, and Cl_2), orbitals of two atoms, each having one unpaired electron, overlap to form a single covalent bond.

Strength of a Covalent Bond

The strength of a covalent bond is related to the extent to which the two combining atomic orbitals can overlap. The greater the extent of overlap between the atomic orbitals, the greater is the strength of the resulting covalent bond.

Sigma (σ) Bond

Sigma bond is a covalent bond formed as a result of maximum overlapping (end-to-end overlapping) of s–s, s–p and p–p orbitals along the internuclear axes. Due to the greater extent of overlapping, this type of overlapping results in a strong bond.

Pi (π) Bond

A covalent bond formed between two atoms by lateral overlapping of orbitals perpendicular to the internuclear axis is called a **pi bond**. Due to the less extent of overlapping, this type of overlapping results in a weak bond.

Table 5.2 Comparative study of sigma and pi bonds

Sigma bond	Pi bond
It is a strong covalent bond formed due to end-to-end overlapping of orbitals.	It is a weak covalent bond formed by lateral overlapping of orbitals.
It is denoted by σ.	It is denoted by π.
It has an independent existence.	It does not have any independent existence as it can be formed only after the formation of a σ bond.
Bond dissociation energy is high.	Bond dissociation energy is low.
Orbitals s, p, and d are capable of forming this type of bond.	Orbitals other than 's' are capable of forming a π bond.
The bonded electron cloud is distributed in a cylindrically symmetrical way around the internuclear axis.	The bonded electron cloud is distributed in two banana-shaped regions above and below the internuclear axis.

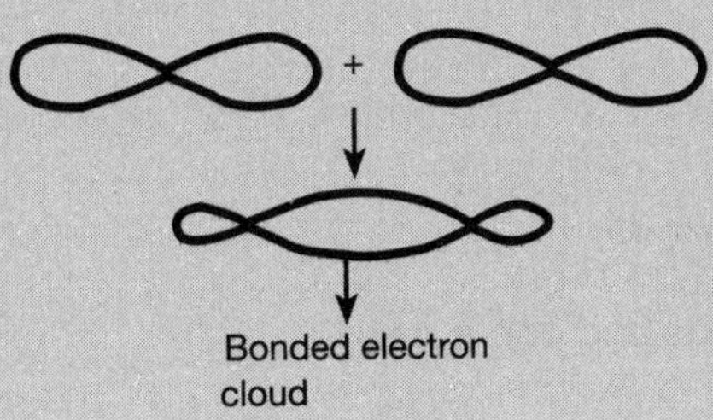

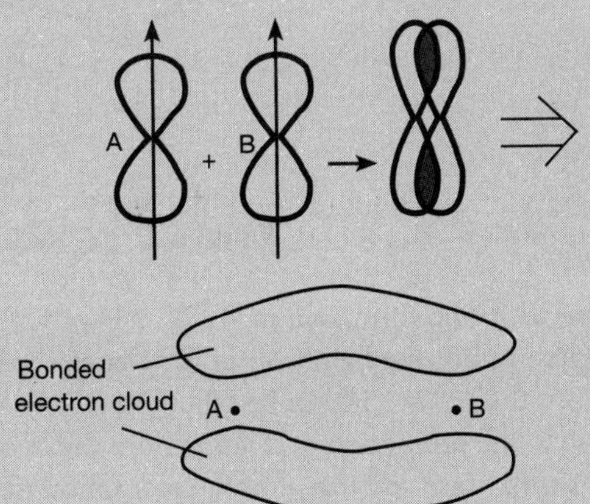

Some examples showcasing formation of pi bonds

1. **O_2 molecule**: The electronic configuration of an oxygen atom is $1s^2\ 2s^2\ 2p_x^2\ 2p_y^1\ 2p_z^1$. Hence, the oxygen atom has two unpaired electrons. Singly occupied $2p_z$ orbital of one oxygen atom overlaps (end-to-end) with the same orbital of another oxygen atom to give rise to a sigma bond. Singly occupied $2p_y$ orbitals of both the oxygen atoms overlap (sidewise) along a line perpendicular to *z*-axis (molecular axis) to give a pi bond. Thus, a double bond is formed.

   Thus, an O_2 molecule has a double bond between the atoms: one is a p_z–p_z sigma bond and the other p_x–p_x pi bond called **double bond.**

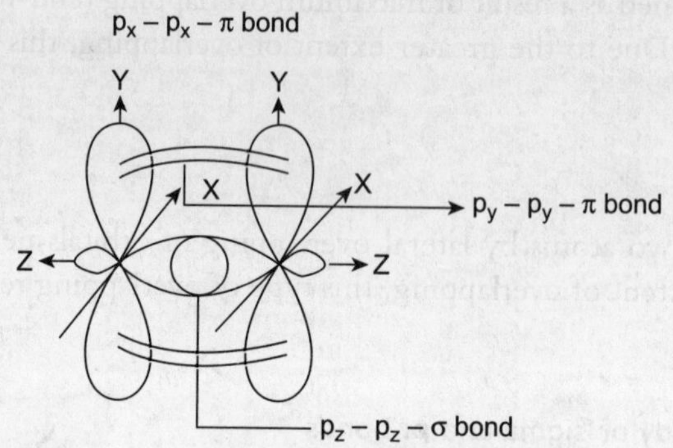

Figure 5.4 O_2 molecule (one σ bond and one π bond)

2. **N_2 molecule**: The electronic configuration of a nitrogen atom: $1s^2 2s^2 2p_x^1 2p_y^1 2p_z^1$. Hence, a nitrogen atom has three singly occupied orbitals. One $2p_z$–$2p_z$ sigma bond is formed. The other two pi bonds are $2p_x$–$2p_x$ and $2p_y$–$2p_y$. Thus, N_2 molecule has three bonds—one (p_z–p_z) sigma bond and other two (p_x–p_x and p_y–p_y) pi bonds, which are perpendicular to each other and perpendicular to the *z*-axis, that is, the axis of the sigma bond (molecular axis). Hence, a triple bond is formed.

   The concept of orbital overlapping gives satisfactory explanation for the formation of covalent bond and the stability of the molecule. However, the bond formation in certain molecules such as $BeCl_3$, BF_3, CH_4, etc., cannot be explained only on the basis of this concept.

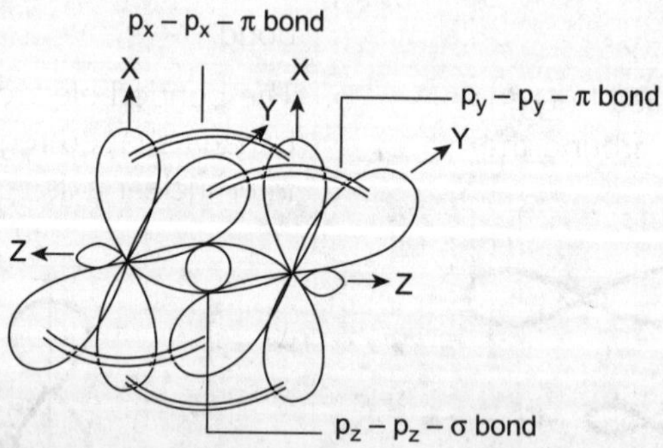

Figure 5.5 N_2 molecule (two π bonds and one π bond)

However, the bond formation in $BeCl_2$, BF_3, CH_4, etc., can be explained by using the concept of excitation of electrons. Beryllium has no unpaired electron in its valence shell, boron has only one unpaired electron and carbon has two unpaired electrons. But the bicovalency of beryllium in $BeCl_2$; tricovalency of boron in BF_3 and tetracovalency of carbon in CH_4 are possible due to the promotion of electron from the 's' orbital to 'p' orbital. The state of atom before the promotion of electron is called **ground state** and that after the promotion of electron is called **excited state**.

However, in the excited state of beryllium, one of the two unpaired electrons is present in '2s' orbital and the other one is in '2p' orbital. Hence, during the formation of $BeCl_2$, the overlapping of orbitals should take place between s–p and p–p orbitals that are non-identical.

But the bonds in $BeCl_2$ are found to be identical in all respects. Similarly in BF_3, the three B–F bonds and in CH_4, the four C–H bonds are identical.

In order to explain the identical nature of the bonds, concept of hybridization and hybrid orbitals has come into existence.

Hybridization

Hybridization is a process of intermixing of two or more atomic orbitals of almost equal energies (belonging to the valence shell) of an atom and their redistribution into an equal number of identical orbitals. The resultant orbitals are called **hybrid orbitals**.

sp-Hybridization

Mixing up of one s-orbital and one p-orbital to give two new identical orbitals is called sp hybridization and the two orbitals formed are called `sp' hybrid orbitals.

> **Info Bytes!**
>
> There are different types of hybridization like sp, sp^2, sp^3, sp^3d, and sp^3d^2, each explaining the geometry of molecules.

Structure of $BeCl_2$

We will study the sp hybridization with the help of an example of $BeCl_2$.

Electronic configuration of beryllium is: $1s^2\ 2s^2\ 2p^0$.

Valence shell configuration of Be is: $2s^2\ 2p^0$.

Ground state configuration of Be is: | ↑↓ | | | | |

Excited state configuration of Be is: | ↑ | | ↑ | | |

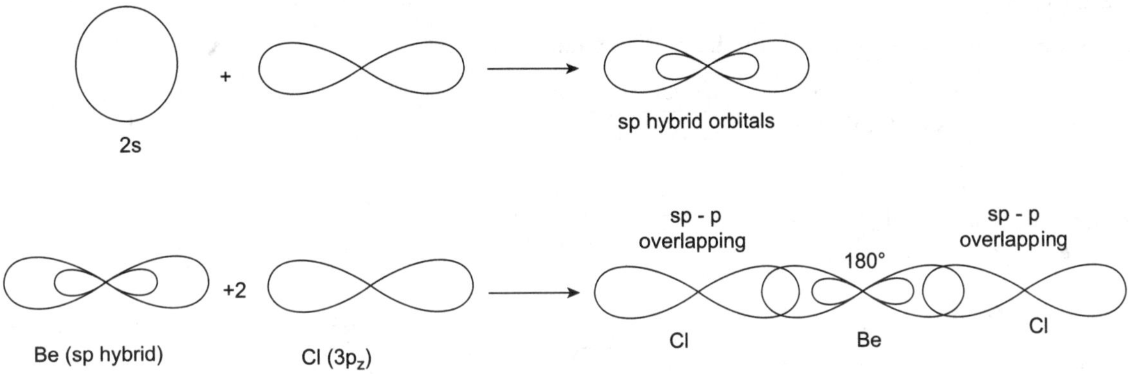

Figure 5.6 Formation of $BeCl_2$ molecule

sp^2-Hybridization

Mixing up of one s-orbital and two p-orbitals to form three new identical orbitals is called **sp^2 hybridization**. The orbitals so formed are called **sp^2 hybrid orbitals**.

Structure of BCl_3

We will study the sp^2 hybridization with the help of an example of BCl_3.

Ground state electronic configuration of B: 2s | ↓↑ | 2p | ↑ | | |

Excited state electronic configuration of B: 2s | ↑ | 2p | ↑ | ↑ | |

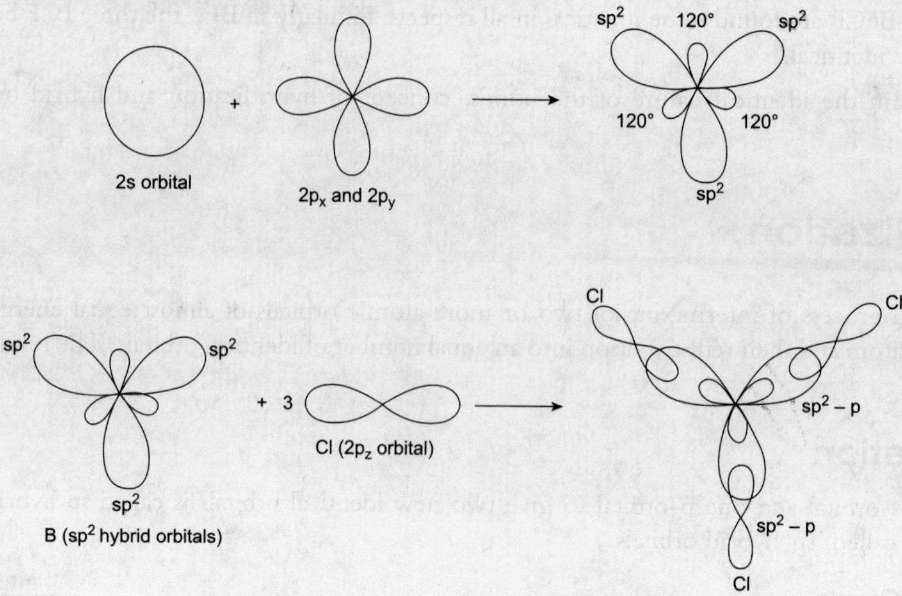

Figure 5.7 Formation of BCl_3 molecule

sp³-Hybridization

Mixing up of one s-orbitals and three p-orbitals to form four identical orbitals is called **sp³ hybridization**. These three orbitals are called **sp³ hybrid orbitals**.

Structure of CH_4

We will study the sp^3 hybridization with the help of an example of CH_4.

Ground state electronic configuration of C:

2s	2p		
↑↓	↑	↑	

Excited state electronic configuration of C:

2s	2p		
↑	↑	↑	↑

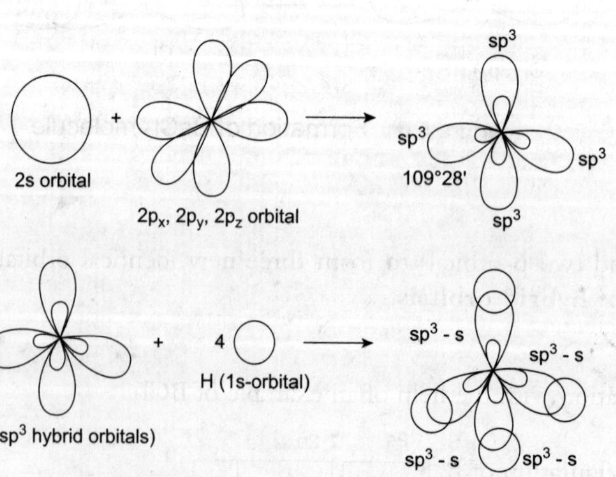

Figure 5.8 Formation of CH_4 molecule

Valence Shell Electron Pair Repulsion (VSEPR) Theory

On the basis of valence shell electron pair repulsion (VSEPR) theory, the geometry and the shapes of the covalent molecules can be explained.

Postulates of the Valence Shell Electron Pair Repulsion Theory

- Different geometrical shapes of the covalent molecules are generated due to the repulsion between the electron pairs present in the valence shell of the central atom of the molecules.
- These electron pairs arrange themselves in such a way that the repulsion among them becomes minimum.
- The electron pairs involved in bond formation are called **bonded electron pairs**. The electron pairs, which are present in the valence shell of central atom but not involved in bond formation are called **lone electron pairs**.
- Repulsion between two lone pairs is greater than the repulsion between a lone pair and a bond pair, which is in turn greater than the repulsion between two bond pairs. Therefore, the shape of the molecule not only depends on the number of electron pairs but also depends upon the number of bonded electron pairs and lone electron pairs on the central atom in that molecule.

Table 5.3 Shapes of the molecules without lone pair of electrons

Molecules	Number of bond pairs	Shapes
$BeCl_2$	2	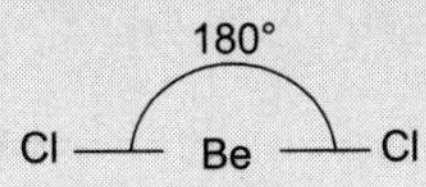 linear
BF_3	3	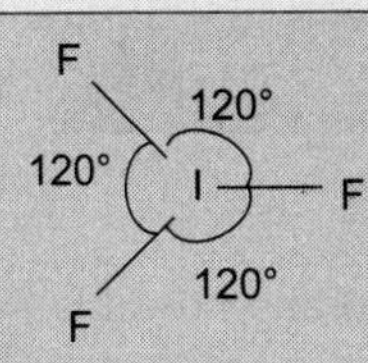 trigonal planar
CH_4	4	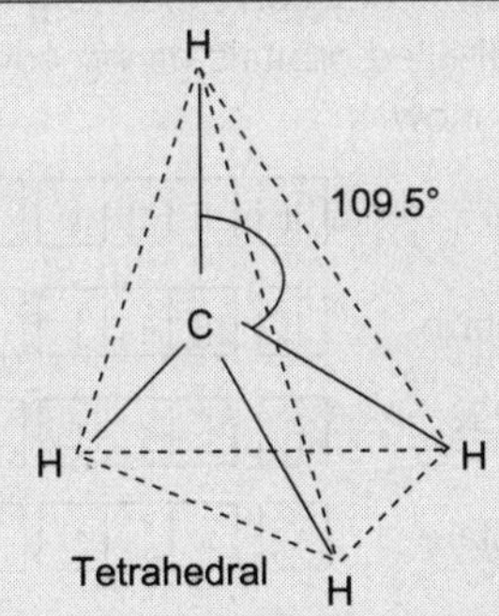 Tetrahedral
PCl_5	5	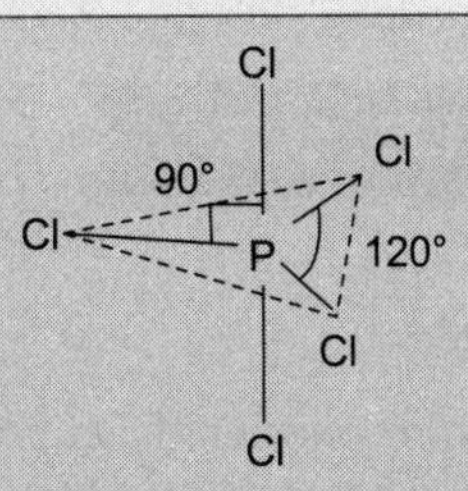 trigonal bipyramidal

Table 5.4 Shapes of molecules having lone pair(s) of electrons

Molecules	Number of bond pairs	Number of lone pairs	Shapes
NH_3	3	1	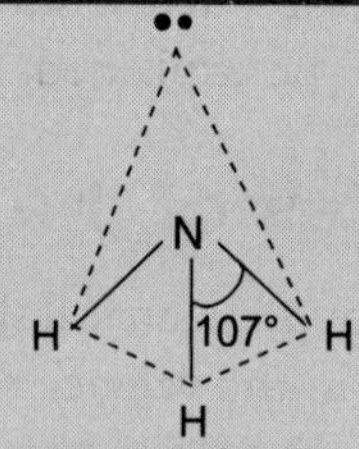 (pyramidal)
PCl_3	3	1	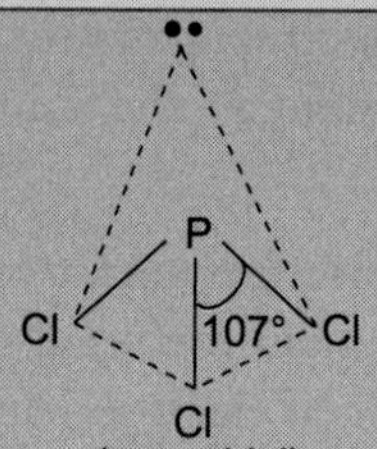 (pyramidal)
H_2O	2	2	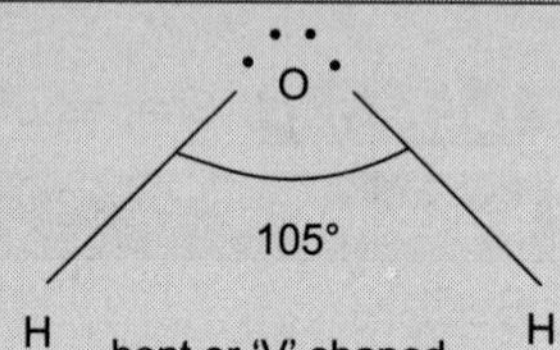 bent or 'V' shaped

EXAMPLE 5.5

Explain how chlorine exhibits a maximum covalency of 7.

SOLUTION

Electronic configuration of Cl is [Ne] $3s^2 3p^5$. In third shell, there are vacant d orbitals.

The paired electrons of 3s and 3p orbitals can be excited to 3d orbitals. Therefore, the number of unparied electrons increases. As a result, covalency corresponding to the number of unparied electrons is exhibited. In the fully excited state of Cl atom, there are seven half-filled orbitals giving covalency of 7. As there is no scope for further excitation, it is the maximum covalency that chlorine can show.

State	3s	3p	3d	
Ground state :	↑↓	↑↓ ↑↓ ↑		⇒ Covalency of 1
1st excited state :	↑↓	↑↓ ↑ ↑	↑	⇒ Covalency of 3
2nd excited state :	↑↓	↑ ↑ ↑	↑ ↑	⇒ Covalency of 5
3rd excited state :	↑	↑ ↑ ↑	↑ ↑ ↑	⇒ Covalency of 7

EXAMPLE 5.6

Both Neon (Ne) and Magnesium (Mg) have filled s-orbitals in their respective outermost shells. However, Magnesium forms compounds like MgO, while neon does not form compounds. Explain.

SOLUTION

Both neon and magnesium have filled s-orbitals in their valence shells. Magnesium has a configuration ending in $3s^2$ and can lose two electrons to achieve a stable noble gas configuration, forming Mg^{2+} ions. Neon, with a configuration ending in $2s^2 2p^6$, already has a full valence shell resembling a noble gas configuration, making it inert and unreactive. Hence, magnesium can form compounds while neon cannot.

EXAMPLE 5.7 Why is the repulsion between two lone pairs of electrons more than that between a lone pair and a bond pair or a bond pair and a bond pair of electrons?

SOLUTION

Lone pair of electrons is under the sole influence of the nucleus of one atom, but the bond pair of electrons is under the influence of the nuclei of the two atoms. There is spreading of the electron cloud of the lone pair of electrons that is much closer to the central atom. Hence, they occupy a broader orbital with greater electron density and exert greater repulsion on the adjacent electrons.

Special Types of Bonds and Non-Bonded Forces of Attraction

Co-ordinate Covalent Bond

It is a special type of covalent bond in which only one of the participating atoms contributes to the electron pair for sharing. The atom that gives the electron pair for sharing is called the **donor** and the other atom that accommodates the shared pair of electrons is called an **acceptor**. In this mechanism, the contribution of electron pair is one-sided, and slight polarity develops in the molecule. A co-ordinate bond is represented by '→,' pointing from the donor to the acceptor atom. It is also called a **dative bond**. A co-ordinate bond is explained below with the help of an example.

Example: Formation of $NH_3 \rightarrow BF_3$

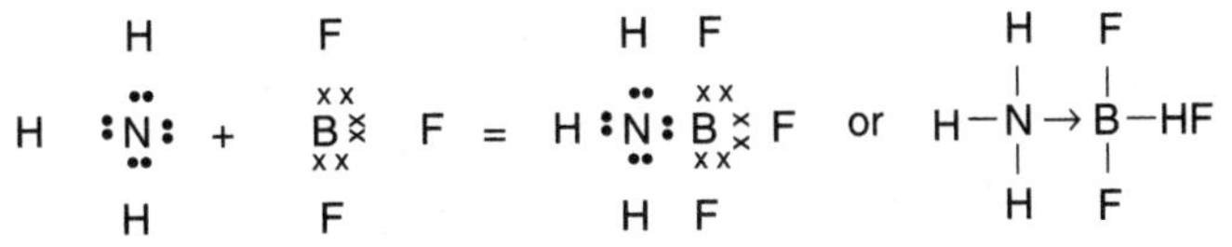

Nitrogen atom of ammonia has a lone pair of electrons and these are accepted by the vacant p-orbital of the boron atom of BF_3. Hence, nitrogen atom is the donor and boron atom is the acceptor.

Other examples with co-ordinate covalent bond formation are H_3O^+, $[Fe(H_2O)_6]^{2+}$, etc.

Metallic Bond

Each atom in a metal crystal loses all its valence electrons. The electrons thus obtained form an electron pool. The resulting positively charged metal ions are believed to be held together by the electron pool. The positively charged metal ions have a definite position in the crystal lattice of the metal. The valence electrons are not attached to any individual ions, they belong to the crystal as a whole and are free to move throughout the metal crystal.

The electrostatic force of attraction that binds metal ions to the mobile electrons within its sphere of influence is known as a **metallic bond**.

EXAMPLE 5.8 Hydrogen bond is nothing but strong dipole–dipole attraction. Justify.

SOLUTION

When a covalent bond is formed between atoms of different elements, partial charges are developed on the bonded atoms. This molecule is called dipole. Due to the presence of opposite partial charges on the atoms, dipole–dipole attractions exist between the molecules. In case of polar covalent bond between hydrogen and highly electronegative atom, the magnitude of partial charges will be much greater. As a result, the dipole–dipole attractions become stronger and this is called hydrogen bond.

EXAMPLE 5.9 Why do NH_3 and H_2O act as electron pair donors?

SOLUTION

Ammonia molecule possesses one lone pair on nitrogen atom. Water molecule possesses two lone pairs on oxygen atom. They can therefore donate the excess electron pair to any ion or atom or molecule that has electron defficiency.

EXAMPLE 5.10 Between van der Waals forces and dipole–dipole attractions, which are stronger and Why?

SOLUTION

Dipole–dipole attractions are stronger as they exist between opposite partial charges. van der Waals forces are weaker as they exist between the nucleus of one atom and the electrons of the other atom.

EXAMPLE 5.11 Some metals like sodium can be cut with a knife. How do you explain with respect to metallic bond?

SOLUTION

Sodium has one electron in its valence shell. Being the first element of that period, it has large size. The force of attraction binding the metal ions with electrons, that means, metallic bond is weaker when compared to the other metals. Therefore, sodium is soft metal and can be cut with a knife.

POINTS TO REMEMBER

- ✔ The atom losing the electrons forms a positively-charged ion (cation) and the atom gaining electrons forms a negatively-charged ion (anion).
- ✔ The electrostatic force of attraction existing between the oppositely-charged ions is called an ionic bond.
- ✔ Ionic compounds are formed due to the transfer of one or more electrons from one atom to the other.
- ✔ The amount of energy released when the oppositely charged gaseous ions are brought closer from an infinite distance to form one mole of ionic crystal is called lattice energy.
- ✔ A covalent bond is formed when two atoms attain their nearest noble gas configuration by sharing one or more electron pairs.
- ✔ The distance between the nuclei of the hydrogen atoms, after the formation of the bond, is called the bond length.
- ✔ The ability of a cation to distort the electron cloud of the anion is called polarizing power of the cation and the tendency of the anion to get distorted by the influence of the cation is called the polarizability of the anion.
- ✔ Octet Rule states that the atoms of the elements have a tendency to attain the nearest inert gas configuration either by the transfer of electrons or by the sharing of electrons.
- ✔ Covalent bond is formed when an overlap takes place between the orbital of one atom with the orbital of another atom.
- ✔ Sigma bond is a covalent bond formed as a result of maximum overlapping (end-to-end overlapping) of s–s, s–p and p–p orbitals along the internuclear axes.
- ✔ A covalent bond formed between two atoms by lateral overlapping of orbitals perpendicular to the internuclear axis is called a pi bond.
- ✔ Hybridization is a process of intermixing of two or more atomic orbitals of almost equal energies (belonging to the valence shell) of an atom and their redistribution into an equal number of identical orbitals.
- ✔ Mixing up of one s-orbital and one p-orbital to give two new identical orbitals is called sp hybridization and the two orbitals formed are called 'sp' hybrid orbitals.
- ✔ Mixing up of one s-orbital and two p-orbitals to form three new identical orbitals is called sp^2 hybridization. The orbitals so formed are called sp^2 hybrid orbitals.
- ✔ Mixing up of one s-orbitals and three p-orbitals to form four identical orbitals is called sp^3 hybridization. These three orbitals are called sp^3 hybrid orbitals.
- ✔ The electron pairs involved in bond formation are called bonded-electron pairs. The electron pairs, which are present in the valence shell of central atom but not involved in bond formation are called lone electron pairs.
- ✔ Co-ordinate covalent bond is a special type of covalent bond in which only one of the participating atoms contributes to the electron pair for sharing.
- ✔ The atom that gives the electron pair for sharing is called the donor and the other atom that accommodates the shared pair of electrons is called an acceptor.
- ✔ The electrostatic force of attraction that binds metal ions to the mobile electrons within its sphere of influence is known as a metallic bond.

PRACTICE QUESTIONS CLASSROOM WING

Very Short Answer Type Questions

Directions for questions from 1 to 9:
Fill in the blanks.

1. In metallic bonds, there are no ___________.
2. If the electron pair is unequally shared between the bonded atoms, it results in ______ bond.
3. In the formation of a Br_2 molecule, the overlapping of ______ orbitals takes place.
4. Metallic bond is devoid of ___________.
5. The electrostatic forces of attraction between the metallic ions and free electrons is called ______.
6. Among the following molecules: BCl_3, CH_4, H_2O, CCl_4 which molecule has sp^3-p overlapping?
7. The shape of $BeCl_2$ is ______.
8. The forces of attraction between the elemental gaseous molecules are called ______.
9. The shape of BF_3 molecule is ________.

Directions for questions from 10 to 25:
Answer the following questions.

10. Among the following molecules: NH_3, ClF_3, BF_3, PCl_3 which molecule is non-polar?
11. During the formation of NH_3, HI, H_2O and NaH, in which of these molecules, does hydrogen gain an electron?
12. Why do polar covalent compounds dissolve in water?
13. What would be the shape of XY_3 molecule if there is no lone pair on the central atom?
14. Why is the H–O–H bond angle in H_2O smaller than H–N–H bond angle in NH_3?
15. How many lone pair of electrons are present on the central atom of CH_4, H_2O, NH_3, PCl_3, and PCl_5 molecules?
16. What type of bond formation takes place between the atoms of Group IA and Group VIIA?
17. Although the number of bond pair of electrons in the valence shell of phosphorus in a PCl_3 molecule is 3, its shape is not trigonal planar. Why?
18. What are the donors in a hydronium ion and ammonium ion?
19. Why do metals conduct electricity?
20. Why does the presence of a lone pair change the shape of the molecule?
21. Why are the participating atoms of a co-ordinate bond called the donor and the acceptor?
22. How many electrons are present in the valence shells of the central atoms in the molecules of $BeCl_2$, BF_3, and PCl_5?
23. Write the order of repulsions among the electron pairs.
24. How are the hybrid orbitals arranged in the molecules?
25. How many new hybrid orbitals are formed in sp, sp^2, and sp^3 hybridizations?

Short Answer Type Questions

26. 'Among the following molecules: Hypochlorous acid, Hydrochloric acid, Hydrogen chloride gas, and Ammonium chloride, which one has a dative bond absent?
27. Among the following molecules: CCl_4, NaCl, BCl_3, NCl_3 which one is associated with dipole-dipole interaction?
28. Among the following molecules: CO_2, $BeCl_2$, OF_2, C_2H_2 which one is the odd one out with respect to hybridization?
29. Why is a nitrogen molecule less reactive than an oxygen molecule?
30. Explain the role of electron affinity and ionization potential during the ionic and covalent bond formation?

31. How is the metallic or non-metallic character of an atom related to bond formation?

32. (a) Explain the structure of $BeCl_2$ with the help of hybridization.
(b) The solubilities of four compounds (fluorides) AF, BF, CF and DF, (A, B, C and D are four metals) in water are in the following order:
BF < DF < AF < CF.
If their hydration energies are assumed to be same, arrange them in the order of their melting points.

33. Why is $BeCl_2$ molecule linear, but BF_3 is trigonal planar?

34. Write a note on the energy changes during the formation of a hydrogen molecule.

35. Write about the partial covalent nature of ionic bond and explain it on the basis of Fajan's rules.

36. 'The orbitals of two different shells of an atom combine and form one hybrid orbital.' State whether the statement is true or false and justify your answer.

37. Explain the structure of CH_4 with the help of hybridization.

38. Explain the formation of hydrogen, oxygen, and nitrogen molecules.

39. Mention two main striking differences between sigma and pi bonds.

40. Explain different types of bond formation in $H_3N \rightarrow BF_3$.

Essay Answer Type Questions

41. 'A', 'B', 'C' and 'D' are four metals belonging to group 2 (IIA) and 3rd, 4th, 5th and 6th periods, respectively. Arrange their chlorides in the increasing order of covalent character.

42. (a) The strength of a covalent bond depends on which factor/factors?
(b) Classify covalent bonds depending on the strength. Compare those bonds.

43. What are the factors on which the geometrical shapes of covalent molecules depend? Explain with suitable examples.

44. (a) What are the conditions required for the overlapping of the orbitals during covalent bond formation?
(b) Describe the different types of orbital overlapping with suitable examples.

45. (a) What is hybridization?
(b) What are the conditions for an atom to undergo hybridization?
(c) How can we explain the shapes and bond angles of $BeCl_2$, BCl_3, and CH_4 with hybridization?

46. The element with the highest electronegativity reacts with the noble gas of 5th period. How many compounds are possible? Predict their shapes.

PRACTICE QUESTIONS COMPETITION WING

Level 1: Apply your Concepts

Direction for questions from 1 to 7:
State whether the following statements are true or false.

1. Ionic compounds are soluble in organic solvents.
2. All covalent compounds possess co-ordinate covalent bonds.
3. BF_3 does not obey the octet rule.
4. The bond angle in ammonia is 109°28′.
5. A sigma (σ) bond is stronger than a pi (π) bond.
6. The hydrogen bond is always formed between the molecules of the same substance.
7. Covalent bonds are non-directional bonds.
8. Atoms form molecules to attain stability.
9. Attractive forces are generated between similar ions of different pairs.
10. Electrostatic forces of attraction are present between ions.
11. Strength of σ bond is less than that of π bond.

Direction for questions from 12 to 19:
Fill in the blanks.

12. Sharing of three electron pairs between two atoms results in the formation of a ________ bond.
13. In CaF_2, the number of electron(s) transferred from calcium to fluorine atoms is _______.
14. The bond formed by end on overlap is _______ than the bond formed by side on overlap.
15. Linear overlapping of any two pure atomic p-orbitals lead to ________ bond formation.
16. Cl–C–Cl bond angle in CCl_4 is ______.
17. Among the hydrogen halides _____ has maximum ionic character.
18. The shape of $BeCl_2$ molecule is _______.
19. In ammonia–boron trifluoride complex, the donor molecule is _______.

Direction for question 20:
Match the entries given in Column A with appropriate ones from Column B.

20. Match the entries of Column A with those of Column B.

Column A	Column B
(i) MgO	(A) Hydrogen bond
(ii) HI (B)	(B) Non-polar covalent bond
(iii) NH_3	(C) Ionic bond
(iv) NH_4Cl	(D) Polar covalent bond
(v) Cl_2(E)	(E) Co-ordinate covalent bond

Direction for questions from 21 to 44:
For each of the questions, four choices have been provided. Select the correct alternative.

21. In which of the following molecules, does the transfer of electron(s) take place?
    (a) PCl_3 (b) CsCl
    (c) BCl_3 (d) $BeCl_2$
22. Which of the following molecules is polar?
    (a) CH_4 (b) CO_2
    (c) KCl (d) $CHCl_3$
23. Which of the following molecules has sp^2–p overlapping?
    (a) CO_2 (b) CCl_4
    (c) BCl_3 (d) C_2H_4
24. **Assertion (A):** A substance constituted of non-polar covalent molecules mostly exists in gaseous states.

    Reason (R): van der Waals' force of attraction is the strongest among the non-bonded forces of attraction among molecules.

    (a) Both A and R are true and R is the correct explanation of A.
    (b) Both A and R are true, but R is not the correct explanation of A.

(c) A is true and R is false.

(d) A is false and R is true.

25. **Assertion (A):** Ammonia gas is easily liquefiable at room temperature.

Reason (R): H-bond formation takes place among the molecules constituted of hydrogen and a highly electronegative element of smaller size.

(a) Both A and R are true and R is the correct explanation of A.

(b) Both A and R are true, but R is not the correct explanation of A.

(c) A is true and R is false.

(d) A is false and R is true.

26. Which of the following statements is wrong?

(a) KCl is soluble in water.

(b) HCl conducts electricity in its aqueous solution.

(c) Acetic acid is soluble in water.

(d) The bond formed between aluminum and fluorine is covalent.

27. NH_4^+ is isostructural with:

(a) PCl_3 (b) CH_4

(c) BF_3 (d) NO_3^-

28. In water molecule, the bond angle of 104.5° around oxygen is accounted due to

(a) high electron affinity of oxygen.

(b) very high repulsions between lone pair and bond pair of electrons.

(c) very high repulsion between lone pair and lone pair electrons.

(d) small size of hydrogen.

29. Which of the following bonds is more polar when compared to others?

(a) O–H (b) N–H

(c) C–H (d) H–H

30. The number of sigma and pi bonds in benzene are

(a) 6σ and 3π bonds

(b) 12σ and 3π bonds

(c) 9σ and 3π bonds

(d) 6σ and 6π bonds

31. Which among the following pairs of molecules possess same geometry?

(a) $BeCl_2$, SiO_2 (b) CO_2, SiO_2

(c) BF_3, PCl_3 (d) F_2O, H_2S

32. The number of σ and π bonds in C_2H_2 is ________.

(a) 0 and 4 (b) 2 and 2

(c) 3 and 2 (d) 4 and 2

33. A species H_3O^+ pyramidal in shape. The number of lone pairs of electrons is:

(a) 0 (b) 1

(c) 2 (d) 3

34. The shape of H_2O molecule is ________.

(a) linear (b) tetrahedral

(c) V-shaped (d) trigonal planar

35. The covalency of 'N' in NH_4^+ ion is equal to number of

(a) covalent bonds.

(b) co-ordinate bonds.

(c) covalent bonds and co-ordinate bonds.

(d) valence electrons.

36. Two substances X and Y are dissolved in water under suitable conditions. X is a gas while Y is a solid under normal conditions. Solution of Y is found to conduct electricity but not 'X.' Based on the conclusion identify the nature of bond present in X and Y with appropriate reasons as given below.

Arrange the steps given below in a sequence.

(1) Y is a solid at room temperature and its aqueous solution conducts electricity. This shows that it is an ionic compound.

(2) X on dissolution in water does not conduct electricity and is a gas at room temperature. Hence it should be a non-polar covalent molecule.

(3) Aqueous solutions of both ionic compounds and polar covalent compounds conduct electricity because of the presence of free ions.

(4) All ionic compounds are solids and most of the non-polar covalent molecules are gases or solids at room temperature. Polar covalent compounds are liquids or gases.

(a) 3 4 2 1 (b) 1 4 3 2

(c) 1 3 2 4 (d) 3 1 2 4

37. The formation of double bond in an oxygen molecule is explained below. Arrange the given points in a sequential order.

(1) $2p_y$ orbitals of each oxygen atom overlap laterally/sidewise to form a pi bond.

(2) Thus, double bond between two oxygen atoms in which one p_z–p_z sigma bond and p_y–p_y pi bond is formed.

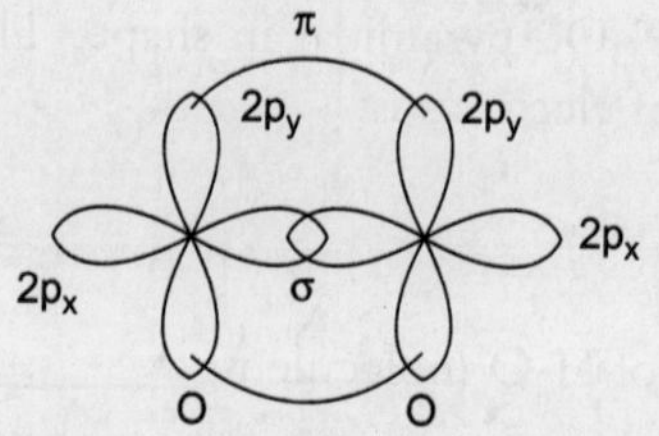

(3) All the three 2p orbitals are perpendicular to each other. Hence, $2p_z$ orbitals of each oxygen atom overlap end to end to form a sigma bond.

(4) The electronic configuration of oxygen is O: $1s^2 2s^2 2p_x^1 2p_y^2 2p_z^1$.

(a) 3 1 4 2 (b) 4 3 1 2
(c) 3 4 2 1 (d) 3 4 1 2

38. The necessary steps required to show the formation of CCl_4 by Lewis electron dot diagram have been jumbled. Arrange them in a sequence.

(1) Thus, an electron pair is shared between C and Cl. This is the Lewis electron dot diagram for CCl_4.

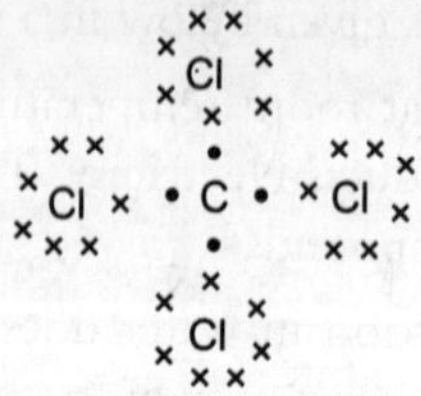

(2) Write the symbol of chlorine and represent its valence electrons with the help of crosses, that is,

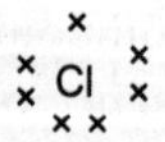

(3) Write the symbol of carbon and represent its valence electrons with the help of dots, that is,

(4) When carbon combines with four chlorine atoms, the carbon atom contributes four electrons for sharing, whereas each chlorine atom contributes only one electron for sharing. Thus, both the atoms in CCl_4 attain an octet.

(a) 1 3 2 4 (b) 2 1 3 4
(c) 4 3 2 1 (d) 3 2 4 1

39. Which among the following substances does not conduct electricity in its aqueous solution state?

(a) glucose
(b) alcohol
(c) hydrochloric acid
(d) common salt

40. The ease of formation of which of following chlorides is maximum?

(a) NaCl (b) KCl
(c) RbCl (d) CsCl

41. During the formation of sodium chloride from its constituents,

(a) Na undergoes oxidation and acts as an oxidizing agent.
(b) Na undergoes reduction and Cl undergoes oxidation.
(c) Cl undergoes reduction and acts as a reducing agent.
(d) Na acts as a reducing agent and Cl acts as an oxidizing agent.

42. The valence electronic configurations of two elements are $4s^1$ and $3s^2\ 3p^5$, respectively. The type of bond expected to be present between them is:

(a) polar covalent bond
(b) non-polar covalent bond
(c) metallic bond
(d) ionic bond

43. The angular shape of water molecule is due to:

(a) high electron affinity of oxygen
(b) very high repulsions between lone pair and bond pair of electrons
(c) very high repulsion between lone pair and lone pair electrons
(d) small size of hydrogen

44. The element that has the strongest metallic bond among ${}_{11}A^{23}$, ${}_{12}B^{24}$, ${}_{13}C^{27}$ and ${}_{19}D^{39}$ is ______.

(a) A (b) B
(c) C (d) D

Level 2: Review Your Concepts

45. Based on the geometry of the molecules: SO_2, Cl_2O, H_2O, Na_2O, which among these molecules has an angle of 105°?

46. Among the following molecules: $AlCl_3$, $MgCl_2$, KCl, CsCl in which does interionic attraction not exist?

47. Among the following molecules: PCl_5, NCl_3, Al_2Cl_6, C_2H_6 which molecule has a dative bond present?

48. Find out the hybridization of: XeF_2, CH_2Cl_2, PCl_5, SF_4

49. (a) Between NF_3 and BF_3, which is the more polar molecule? Why?
    (b) Arrange CaO, KF, MgS, MgO and Al_2S_3 in ascend ing the order of their covalent character.

50. Noble gases do not usually form chemical bonds. But xenon forms a number of stable compounds. Account for this.

51. Just like H_2O, there are two lone pairs in Cl_2O molecule. But bond angle in Cl_2O is 111°. Explain.

52. Though sulphur has only two unpaired electrons it exhibits covalency of 2, 4, 6. Explain.

53. Phosphorous can form PCl_5 molecule in the excited state of phosphorous atom. But the formation of PH_5 is not possible in the same state. Account for this.

54. Between LiF and LiI, which has the higher lattice energy and why?

55. Which among the following geometries is most preferred with respect to ClF_3 molecule and why?

(a)
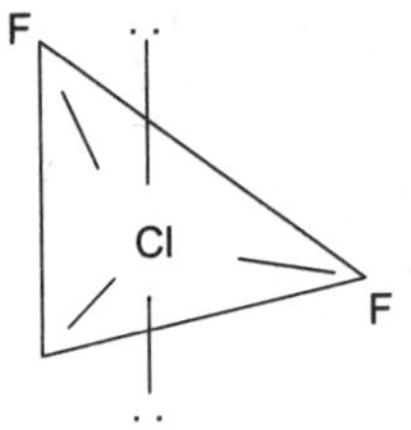

(b)
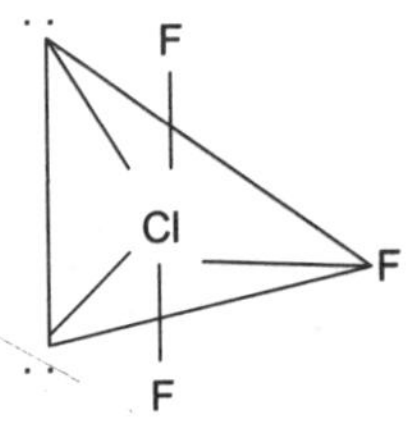

(c)
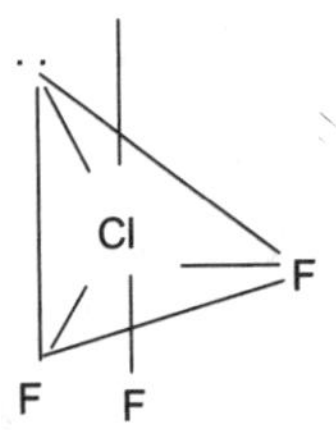

56. Explain and give reasons for the changes in potential energy after the bond formation in a diatomic molecule from the given graph.

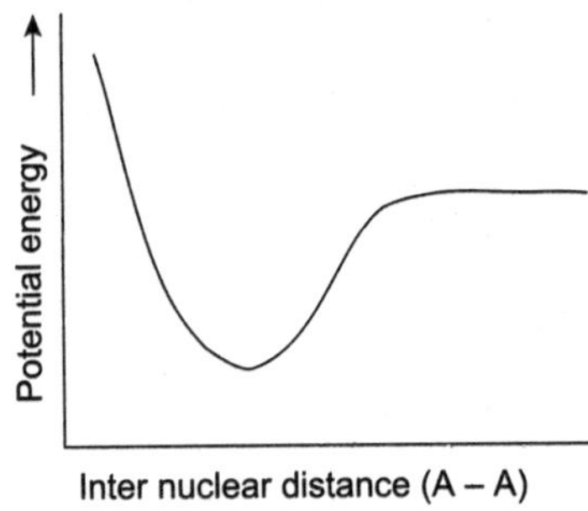

57. (a) In comparison with sodium salts, ammonium salts are more soluble in water. Explain.
    (b) Mercury exists in liquid state at room temperature although it is a metal. Give reason.

Directions for questions from 58 to 65:
Application-Based Questions

58. Compare NaCl and CsCl with respect to ease of formation and also strength of ionic bond.

59. Comment on the intensity of charge of an electric field when HF and dry air are placed between two charged parallel plates.

60. Phosphorous can form PCl_5 molecule in the excited state of phosphorous atom. But the formation of PH_5 is not possible in the same state. How do you account for this?

61. Predict hybridization and shape of SF_4 molecule.

62. All halides of sodium are ionic. Fluorides and chlorides of magnesium are ionic. But among halides of aluminum, only AlF_3 is ionic. How do you account for this variation?

63. The nitrogen atom of NH_3 acts as a donor during the formation of a co-ordinate covalent bond while the central nitrogen atom in NO_2 cannot act as a donor. Explain.

64. Increase in temperature decreases the conductivity of metallic conductors. Give a reason.

65. Why are metals malleable and ductile?

Level 3: Assess Your Concepts

66. Water has a higher boiling point than hydrogen fluoride. What is the reason?

67. Why does H_2S have higher vapour pressure than H_2O in their liquid states?

68. XeF_2 is also a linear molecule like $BeCl_2$. But they differ in their formation and structural aspects. How can you justify this?

69. A molecule has an octahedral geometry. So how many number of valence electrons should the central atom possess and are the number of valence electrons is the same if one, two bond pairs are successively replaced by lone pairs? What are the geometries of the molecules with one and two lone pairs? Explain with the help of hybridization.

70. Thallous compounds are more common and stable than thallic compounds. Justify this statement.

Directions for questions from 71 to 75:
Application-Based Questions

71. Lattice energies of fluoride, chloride, bromide and iodide compounds are 766.5, 597.5, 537.5, and 437.03 kJ/mol, respectively. Compare the oxidizing capacities of the halogens on the basis of the lattice energies of these compounds with an appropriate reason.

72. A molecule 'AB$_5$' has five bond pairs around the central atom 'A.' If the bond pair of electrons are successively replaced by one, two, and three lone pair of electrons, then what would be the preferred shapes of the molecules and how do they differ from actual geometry of AB$_5$?

73. Though covalent character increases from lithium fluoride to lithium iodide, lithium fluoride is insoluble in water while lithium iodide is soluble. Justify the above statement.

74. Identify the consequences of hydrogen bonding.
A. Anomalous expansion of water
B. Dehydrarting nature of conc. H_2SO_4
C. Dissolution of sugar in water
D. Dimerisation of acetic acid

75. The atomic number of tin is 50 and chlorine is 17. What should be the shape of $SnCl_2$ molecule in its vapor state?

AT

PRACTICE QUESTIONS JEE-NEET SPECIAL WING

Multiple-Answer Type Questions

Directions for Questions number 1 to 5:

Select one or more correct alternative(s) from the given choices.

1. Identify the correct set with respect to the increasing order of covalent character.

   (a) LiI, CsF (b) LiF, CsF

   (c) NaCl, $MgCl_2$ (d) KF, K_2O

2. Observe the following figure and choose correct interpretations from the given options:

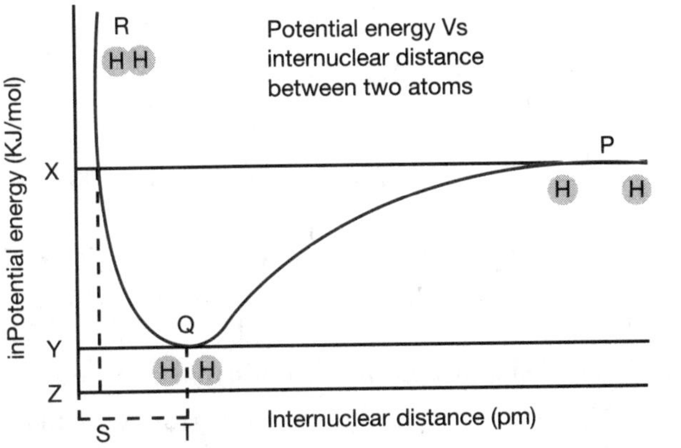

   (a) P to Q, proton and electron forces of attraction dominates over proton-proton and electron-electron forces of repulsion.

   (b) (T-S) pm indicates bond length in hydrogen molecule.

   (c) (Y-Z)KJ/mole gives bond energy

   (d) Hydrogen attains highest stability at an internuclear distance of T pm.

3. 'According to the concept of orbital overlapping, covalent bond is formed when an overlap takes place between the orbital of one atom with the orbital of another atom'.

   Choose the statements that does not comply with the conditions required for orbital overlapping:

   (a) Overlapping orbitals should possess more than one unpaired electron.

   (b) Only orbitals of similar energy from the valence shell and the penultimate shell participate in overlapping.

   (c) Electrons in the overlapping orbitals should possess opposite spins.

   (d) There must be sufficient energy to overcome the electrostatic repulsion between electrons in the overlapping orbitals.

4. Choose the sets that are incorrectly matched.

   (a) Br_2----------3p-3p overlap.

   (b) $BeCl_2$----- 2s-3p overlap.

   (c) SF_6---------sp^3d^2-p overlap.

   (d) HF----------1s-2p overlap.

5. Identify the statements that comply with the bonding in N_2O_5 molecule.

   (a) Two nitrogen atoms are bonded with a triple bond.

   (b) Two oxygen atoms are bonded with a double bond.

   (c) Two N-O bonds are dative bonds.

   (d) All N-O bonds are polar bonds.

Comprehension-Based Questions

Directions for Questions number 6 to 10:

Read the following passage and answer the questions given below.

One of the fundamental theories that aids us in predicting the geometries of molecules is the Valence Shell Electron Pair Repulsion (VSEPR) theory. This theory provides insight into why molecules adopt specific shapes and why these shapes are significant. It is grounded in the idea that valence electrons experience repulsion, leading atoms to arrange themselves in a manner that minimizes this repulsion. This atomic arrangement ultimately dictates the molecular geometry.

Key postulates of the VSEPR theory include:

- The shape of a molecule is determined by the number of valence shell electron pairs (whether bonded or nonbonded) around the central atom (typically the least electronegative or most electropositive atom).

- Valence electron pairs repel each other due to their negatively charged electron clouds and tend to position themselves in a way that minimizes repulsion and maximizes the distance between them.
- The valence shell is visualized as a sphere, and electron pairs are situated on the spherical surface to maximize their separation.
- Multiple bonds are treated as single electron pairs, with two or three electron pairs from a multiple bond regarded as a single "super pair."
- Repulsive interactions between electron pairs follow this order: Lone pair (lp) – Lone pair (lp) > Lone pair (lp) – Bond pair (bp) > Bond pair (bp) – Bond pair (bp).
- Presence of a lone pair on the central atom causes slight distortion of the bond angles from their ideal values.
- The electronegativity difference between the central atom and the other atoms determines the magnitude of repulsion between the bonding pair of electrons.
- Triple bonds cause more repulsion than the double bonds. Similarly double bond causes more repulsion than a single bond.

Chemists employ the concept of the steric number to predict these shapes. The steric number reveals the total count of electron pairs, encompassing both bond pairs and lone pairs, surrounding the central atom. It plays a crucial role in the VSEPR theory, aiding in the determination of molecular geometry.

Following are the formulas used to find the steric numbers:

For neutral molecules:

Steric Number = (number of lone pairs on the central atom) + (number of atoms bonded to the central atom)

For molecules or ions that have a net charge:

Steric Number = ½ × [(number of valence electrons on the central atom) + (number of monovalent atoms attached to the central atom) – (cationic charge) + (anionic charge)]

And the formal charge on an atom is calculated using the formula,

Formula charge on an atom =

[valence electrons of that atom – nonbonding electrons or (lone pair) on the atom- ½ (bonding electrons of that atom)]

Or

Steric Number-S.N. = ½[V+M±I] where V = *n*(*e*–), the number of valence electrons of central atom, M=n(atom), the number of monovalent atoms directly bonded to it, and 'I' is the number of positive or negative charges present (subtract it if the charge is positive, and add it if the charge is negative).

Once the steric number is calculated, we can quickly assess the molecule's shape.

S No.	Steric Number	Shape of the molecule
1	2	Linear
2	3	Trigonal Planar
3	4	Tetrahedral
4	5	Trigonal Bipyramidal
5	6	Octahedral
6	7	Pentagonal Bipyramidal

6. Study the following molecules and answer the question that follows.

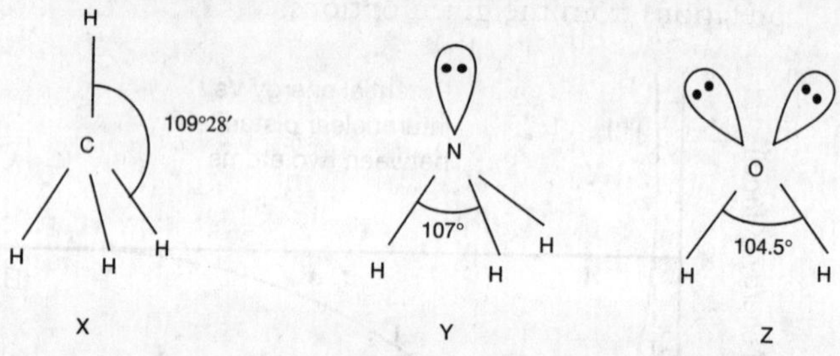

Identify the main reason for difference in bond angles in X, Y, Z.

(a) Difference in the hybridisation of central atoms.
(b) Difference in the electronegativity of the central atoms
(c) Difference in the number of lone pairs on the central atom
(d) Difference in their Steric Numbers

7. Find the formal charge on the most electropositive element in SO_4^{-2} if the number of lone pair electrons on it is zero:

(a) -2 (b) -1
(c) +1 (d) +2

8. Observe the shape of the given molecule and find its steric number.

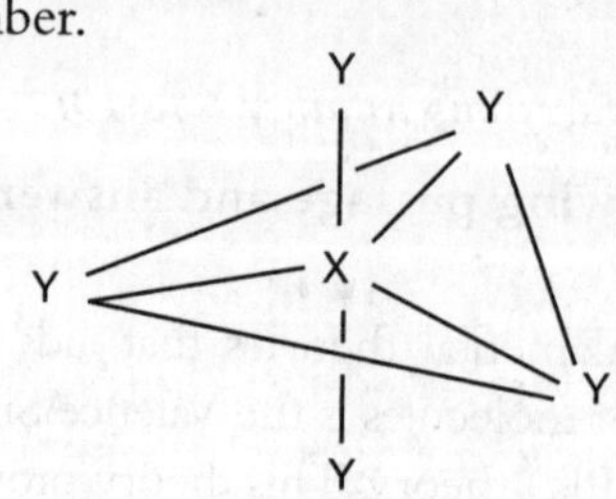

(a) 7 (b) 5
(c) 3 (d) 6

9. Identify the correct statements with respect to the hydrocarbons, C_nH_{2n+2}, C_nH_{2n} and C_nH_{2n-2}.
   (1) C_nH_{2n-2}, C_nH_{2n}, C_nH_{2n+2}, is the correct increasing order of arrangement with respect to their steric number.
   (2) C_nH_{2n-2}, C_nH_{2n}, C_nH_{2n+2}, is the correct increasing order of arrangement with respect to the repulsion between the C-C bond pair and C-H bond pair.
   (3) C_nH_{2n-2}, C_nH_{2n}, C_nH_{2n+2}, is the correct decreasing order of arrangement with respect to their steric number.
   (4) C_nH_{2n-2}, C_nH_{2n}, C_nH_{2n+2}, is the correct decreasing order of arrangement with respect to the repulsion among the C-C bond pairs and C-H bond pair.
   (a) 2, 4 (b) 2, 3
   (c) 1, 3 (d) 1, 4

10. Match the following:

List – I	List – II Shape of the molecule
(A) NH_4^+	(i) Tetrahedral
(B) NO_3^-	(ii) Linear
(C) O_3	(iii) Trigonal Bipyramidal
(D) CO_2	(iv) Trigonal Planar

Find the correct match.

	(A)	(B)	(C)	(D)
(a)	(i)	(iv)	(iv)	(ii)
(b)	(iii)	(i)	(iv)	(ii)
(c)	(iv)	(ii)	(iii)	(iv)
(d)	(iii)	(iv)	(iii)	(ii)

Directions for Questions number 11 to 16:

Read the following passage and answer the questions given below

Nitrogen, oxygen, and fluorine, being highly electronegative elements, form dipoles when they bond with hydrogen. This leads to the hydrogen atom gaining a partial positive charge while the electronegative atom gains a partial negative charge. This partially positive hydrogen atom forms a weak bond with another nearby highly electronegative atom, illustrated as a dotted line, known as a hydrogen bond.

$$\overset{+\delta}{H}-\overset{-\delta}{X}\cdots\cdots\overset{+\delta}{H}-\overset{-\delta}{X}\cdots\cdots\overset{+\delta}{H}-\overset{-\delta}{X}$$

For the formation of a hydrogen bond, the electronegative atom needs to be small. Atoms with similar or greater electronegativity than nitrogen but larger in size do not engage in hydrogen bonding. These bonds typically range in strength from 4 kJ to 50 kJ per mole of hydrogen bonds, weaker than covalent and ionic bonds but stronger than van der Waals forces.

There are two types of hydrogen bonds:

- Intermolecular hydrogen bonds: These occur between different molecules of the same or different compounds.
- Intramolecular hydrogen bonds: These form when a hydrogen atom is positioned between two highly electronegative atoms within the same molecule.

Effects of hydrogen bonding encompass:

- Dissociation: In water, HF separates, releasing the difluoride ion instead of the fluoride ion due to hydrogen bonding.
- Association: Carboxylic acid (ex. acetic acid) molecules create dimers through hydrogen bonding, effectively doubling their molecular weights compared to what's derived from their basic formulas

Study the above given passage and answer the following questions. Choose all the options that apply.

11. Intramolecular hydrogen bonding in a compound results in:
    (a) increased solubility in water
    (b) Elevated boiling point
    (c) Decreased viscosity and surface tension of the substance
    (d) None of the mentioned effects

12. **Assertion(A):** The bond energy of O-H is greater than that of the N-H bond in their respective hydrides.
    Reason(R): Intermolecular hydrogen bonding in the hydride of oxygen is stronger compared to that in the hydride of nitrogen.
    (a) Both Assertion and Reason are true, and reason is the correct explanation of assertion.
    (b) Both Assertion and Reason are true, and reason is not the correct explanation of assertion.
    (c) A is true and R is false
    (d) A is false and R is true

13. Which of the following phenomena is primarily unrelated to hydrogen bonding. Choose all the options that are correct.
    (a) The merging of two ice cubes into one when pressed together.
    (b) Anomalous expansion observed in water

(c) Comparison of the acidic strength between HF and HCl

(d) Dimerization of acetic acid

14. 'The extent of H–bonding depends upon electronegativity and the number of H–atoms available for bonding'. Identify the set arranged in the correct order with respect to the extent of H-bonding.

(a) $H_2O_2 > H_2O > HF > H_2S$

(b) $HF > H_2O_2 > H_2O > H_2S$

(c) $H_2O_2 > H_2O > HF > H_2S$

(d) $HF > H_2S > H_2O\ H_2O_2$

15. Which of the provided molecules, exhibit the tendency to form a linear polymeric arrangement due to hydrogen bonding?

(a) HCl (b) NH_3

(c) HF (d) H_2O

16. Match the following:

List – I	List – II Approximate boiling point values at standard atmospheric pressure in Fahrenheit scale
(A) H_2O	(i) $-6.25x$
(B) PH_3	(ii) $10.6x$
(C) NH_3	(iii) $4.35x$
(D) HF	(iv) $-1.4x$

ANSWER KEYS

Crossword

Across

1. Trigonal planar
4. Sigma bond
7. Ionic bond
9. Dipole
10. Pyramidal
13. Lattice energy
15. Octet
16. Two
18. van der Waals forces
19. Covalent bond

Down

2. Lewis dot structures
3. Lone pair
4. Six
5. Double bond
6. Pibond
8. Hydrogen bond
11. Polar covalent
12. Dative bond
14. Nitrogen
17. Three

Classroom Wing

Very Short Answer Type Questions

1. neutral atom
2. polar covalent
3. p – p
4. anions
5. metallic bond
6. equatorial; axial
7. linear
8. Van der Waals forces of attraction
9. trigonal planar

Competition Wing

Level 1: Apply Your Concepts

1. False
2. False
3. True
4. False
5. True
6. False
7. False
8. True
9. False
10. True
11. False
12. Triple bond
13. Two
14. Stronger
15. Sigma
16. 109°28’
17. HF
18. Linear
19. Ammonia
20. (i) - (C), (ii) - (D), (iii) - (A), (D), (iv) - (C), (D), (E), (v) - (B)
21. (d)
22. (d)
23. (c)
24. (c)
25. (a)
26. (d)
27. (b)
28. (c)
29. (a)
30. (b)
31. (d)
32. (c)
33. (b)
34. (c)
35. (c)
36. (a)
37. (b)
38. (d)
39. (a)
40. (d)
41. (d)
42. (d)
43. (c)
44. (c)

JEE-NEET Special Wing

Multiple-Answer Type Questions

1. (c, d)
2. (a, d)
3. (a, b)
4. (a, c)
5. (c, d)

Comprehension-Based Questions

6. (c)
7. (d)
8. (b)
9. (a)
10. (a)
11. (d)
12. (b)
13. (c)
14. (a)
15. (c)
16. (A) - (ii), (B) - (i), (C) - (iv), (D) - (iii)

Hints and Explanations

Classroom Wing

Very Short Answer Type Questions

1. Neutral atom

   In metallic bonds, no neutral atoms are present. Valence electrons of metal atoms form a pool of electrons and positively charged metal ions remain embedded in that pool in fixed positions.

2. polar covalent
3. p – p
4. Metallic bond is devoid of anions. It is constituted of free electrons and positively charged metal ions.
5. metallic bond
6. In CCl_4, sp^3 hybridized orbitals of C overlap with the p-orbital of chlorine.
7. linear.
8. Van der Waals forces of attraction
9. trigonal planar
10. BF_3 is non-polar because its shape is trigonal planar and no lone pair of electrons is present on the central atom.
11. During the formation of NaH, hydrogen gains 1 electron from sodium.
12. Presence of partial charges on polar covalent compounds.
13. Trigonal planar.
14. Difference in the number of lone pair of electrons around the central atom.
15. PCl_5, $CH_4 \Rightarrow 0$

    $H_2O \Rightarrow 2$

    NH_3, $PCl_3 \Rightarrow 1$
16. Ionic bond
17. Presence of lone pair of electrons on phosphorous.
18. $H_3O^+ \longrightarrow$ Oxygen of H_2O

    $NH_4^+ \longrightarrow$ Nitrogen of NH_3
19. Presence of mobile electrons
20. Lone pair of electron is not taken into consideration in the shape of molecule as it occupies more space.
21. One of the participating atoms contributes the electrons for the bond formation and is called the donor and the other one is called acceptor.
22. $BeCl_2 \Rightarrow 2$

    $BF_3 \Rightarrow 3$

    $PCl_5 \Rightarrow 5$
23. Lone pair – lone pair > lone pair – bond pair > bond pair – bond pair.
24. Hybrid orbitals are arranged in such a way so as to minimize the repulsions between them.
25. $sp \Rightarrow 2$

    $sp^2 \Rightarrow 3$

    $sp^3 \Rightarrow 4$

Short Answer Type Questions

26. In hypochlorous acid, the dative bond is present between Cl and O atoms. In hydrochloric acid, dative bond formation takes place between H^+ and H_2O molecules. In NH_4Cl, a dative bond forms between the N atom and H^+. In HCl gas, there is no dative bond.
27. In NCl_3, the intermolecular force of attraction which exists is called dipole-dipole interaction because it is a polar covalent molecule.
28. $BeCl_2$, C_2H_2, and CO_2 molecules have sp hybridization. OF_2 has sp^3 hybridization.
29. (i) Triple bond

    (ii) Very stable

31. (i) Losing or gaining of electrons

    (ii) Formation of ions

32. (a) (i) Ground state configuration of Be
(ii) Excited state configuration of Be
(iii) Hybrid orbitals
(iv) Overlapping of sp-p orbitals
(v) Shape of $BeCl_2$

(b) The higher the lattice energy, the lower is the solubility of the solute in water. Lattice energy, strength of ionic bond and melting point are directly proportional to each other. Hence the order of melting points is: CF < AF < DF < BF.

33. (i) Ground state configuration of Be, B
(ii) Excited state configuration of Be, B
(iii) Hybridization
(iv) Shape

34. (i) Forces of attraction
(ii) Forces of repulsion
(iii) Bond length
(iv) Graph

35. (i) Concept of polarization and polarizability
(ii) Size of ions
(iii) Charges on ions

36. Hybridization is a process of intermixing of two or more atomic orbitals of almost equal energies (belonging to the valence shell) of an atom and their redistribution into an equal number of identical orbitals. The resultant orbitals are called hybrid orbitals.

37. (i) Ground state configuration of carbon
(ii) Excited state configuration of carbon
(iii) Hybridization
(iv) Overlapping of orbitals
(v) Structure

38. (i) Electronic configuration
(ii) Orbitals with unpaired electrons
(iii) Overlapping of orbitals

39. Sigma Bond: It is a strong covalent bond formed due to end-to-end overlapping of orbitals, has an independent existence and orbitals s, p, and d are capable of forming this type of bond.

Pi Bond: It is a weak covalent bond formed by lateral overlapping of orbitals, does not have any independent existence as it can be formed only after the formation of an s bond and orbitals other than "s" are capable of forming a pi bond.

40. (i) Bond formation between N and H
(ii) Bond formation between B and F
(iii) Bond formation between NH_3 and BF_3.

Essay Answer Type Questions

41. The polarizing power of the cation is directly proportional to the charge possessed by it and inversely proportional to the radius. The charge possessed by A, B, C, and D is the same because they belong to the same group. However, their radii increase in the order A < B < C

< D. Hence, the order of polarizing ability is A

> B > C > D. The more the polarizing ability, the greater the covalent character.

∴ The order of covalent character of chlorides of four metals is D < C < B < A.

42. (i) Type of overlapping
(ii) Extent of overlapping
(iii) Strength of bonds

43. (i) VSEPR theory
(ii) Postulates
(iii) Electron pair repulsions.

44. (i) s – s
(ii) s – p
(iii) p – p (Sigma and Pi)

45. (i) Hybridization is a process of intermixing of two or more atomic orbitals of almost equal energies (belonging to the valence shell) of an atom and their redistribution into an equal number of identical orbitals. The resultant orbitals are called hybrid orbitals.
(ii) Valence electrons (excitation)
(iii) Hybrid orbitals, shapes

46. Ground state

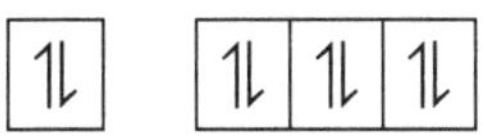

$5s^2$ $5p^6$

Excited state 1:

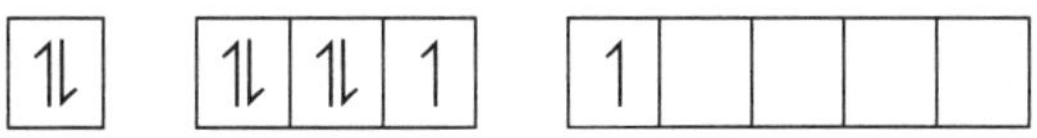

$5s^2$ $5p^5$ $5d^1$

Excited state 2:

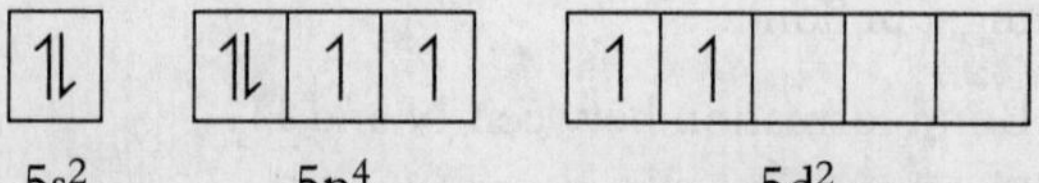

$5s^2$ $5p^4$ $5d^2$

Excited state 3

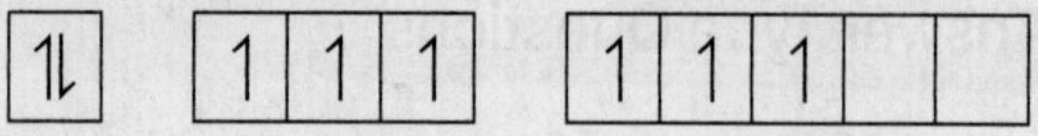

$5s^2$ $5p^3$ $5d^3$

Highest electronegative element is fluorine. In the first excited state, xenon undergo sp^3d hybridization and the molecule formed is XeF_2 and the shape is linear.

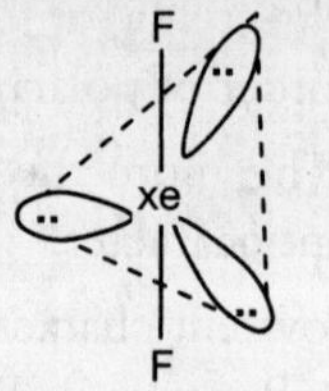

In the second excited state, xenon undergoes sp^3d^2 hybridization, and the molecule formed is XeF_4 and the shape is square planar.

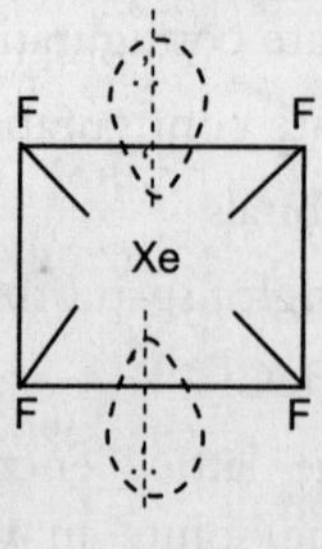

In the third excited state, xenon undergoes sp^3d^3 hybridization and the molecule is formed is XeF_6 and shape is distorted octahedral.

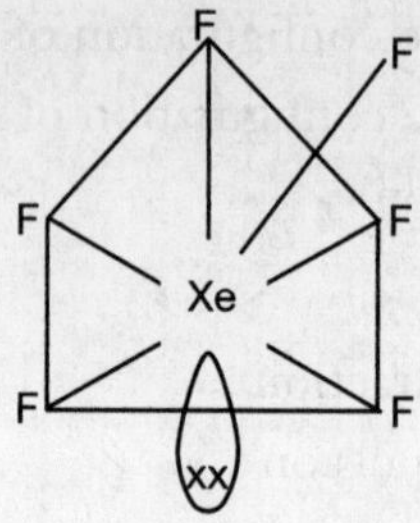

Competition Wing

Level 1: Apply your Concepts

20. MgO → Ionic bond; (i) → (C)

HI → Polar covalent bond; (ii) → (D)

NH_3 → Polar covalent bond, H bond;

(iii) → (A), (D)

NH_4Cl → Polar covalent bond, co-ordinate covalent bond, and ionic bond; (iv) → (C), (D), (E)

Cl_2 → Non-polar covalent bond; (v) → (B)

21. Among the given molecules, transfer of electron(s) takes place only in CsCl as it is an ionic compound.

Hence, the correct option is (b).

22. CH_4,

CO_2 → Non-polar

KCl → Ionic

$CHCl_3$ → Polar

Hence, the correct option is (d).

23. CO_2 → sp - p overlapping

CCl_4 → sp^3 - p overlapping

BCl_3 → sp^2 - p overlapping

C_2H_4 → sp^2 - sp^2 and sp^2 - s overlapping

Hence, the correct option is (c).

24. The non-bonded force of attraction among the non-polar covalent molecules is known as Van der Waals' forces of attraction. Since it is the weakest force of attraction, non-polar covalent substances mostly exist in a gaseous state.

Hence, the correct option is (c).

25. Ammonia gas is easily liquefiable because of the presence of strong H-bonding among NH_3 molecules. H-bonding takes place if the molecules are constituted of hydrogen and a highly electronegative element of smaller size. Hence, the correct option is (a).

36. 3 Aqueous solutions of both ionic compounds and polar covalent compounds conduct electricity because of the presence of free ions.

4 All the ionic compounds are solids and most of the non-polar covalent molecules are gases or solids at room temperature. Polar covalent compounds are liquids or gases.

2 As aqueous solution of X doesn't conduct electricity and moreover it is a gas at room temperature. It should be a non-polar molecule. Hence, it is a covalent molecule.

1 Y is a solid at room temperature in which its aqueous solution conducts electricity shows that it is an ionic compound.

Hence, the correct answer is (a).

37. 4 The electronic configuration of oxygen is O: $1s^2\ 2s^2\ 2p_x{}^2\ 2p_y{}^1\ 2p_z{}^1$.

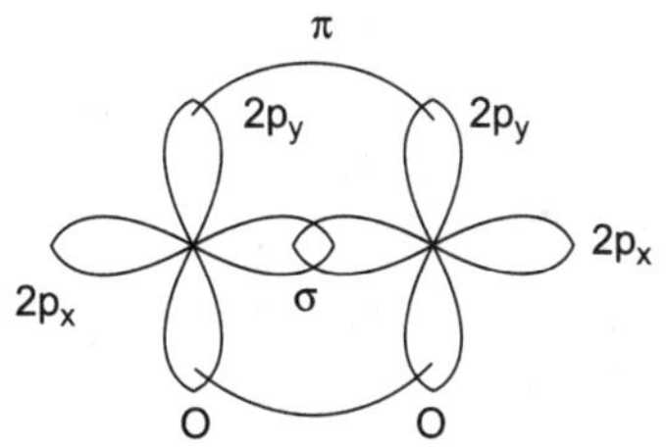

3 All the three 2p orbitals are perpendicular to each other.

Hence, $2p_z$ orbitals of each oxygen atom overlap end to end to form a strong sigma bond.

1 $2p_y$ orbitals of each oxygen atom overlap laterally/sidewise to form a weak pi bond.

2 Thus, double bond between two oxygen atoms in which one p_y–p_y pi bond is formed.

Hence, the correct answer is (b).

38. 3 Write the symbol of carbon and represent its valence electrons with the help of dots, that is,

2 Write the symbol of chlorine and represent its valence electrons with the help of crosses, that is,

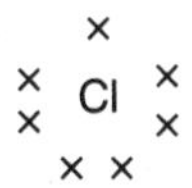

4 When carbon combines with four chlorine atoms, the carbon atom contributes four electrons for sharing, whereas each chlorine atom contributes only one electron. Thus, both the atoms in CCl_4 attain an octet.

1 Lewis electron dot diagram for CCl_4. Thus, an electron pair is shared between C and Cl.

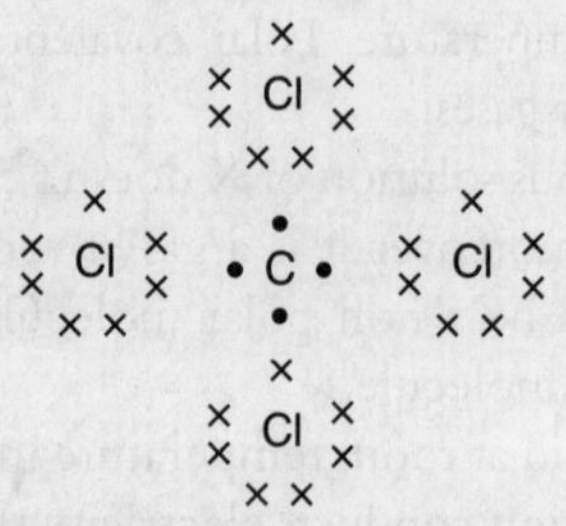

Hence, the correct answer is (d).

39. Since glucose does not ionize in water, it does not conduct electricity in its aqueous solution sate.

Hence, the correct answer is (a).

40. The ease of formation of ionic bond is directly proportional to the size of metal atom and inversely proportional to the size of non-metallic atom. Hence, the ease of formation of ionic bond is maximum in CsCl.

Hence, the correct answer is (d).

41.

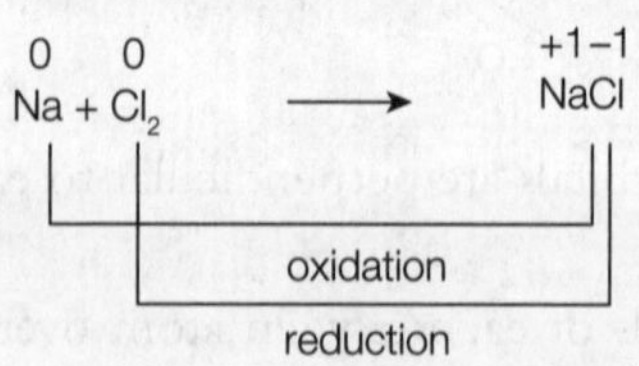

During the formation of NaCl, Na undergoes oxidation and Cl undergoes reduction. Hence, Na is the reducing agent and Cl is the oxidizing agent.

Hence, the correct answer is (d).

42. The two elements are potassium and chlorine, respectively. Hence, the bond formed between them is an ionic bond.

Hence, the correct answer is (d).

43. In a water molecule, oxygen has sp^3 hybridization. Two of these hybrid orbitals have lone pair of electrons, and the other two overlap with s-orbital of hydrogen to form sigma bonds. The expected shape is tetrahedral. However, due to lone pair–lone pair repulsions, the shape becomes angular.

Hence, the correct answer is (c).

44.

Elements	Atomic numbers	Electronic configurations
A	11	2, 8, 1
B	12	2, 8, 2
C	13	2, 8, 3
D	19	2, 8, 8, 1

A and D can lose one electron and become stable, B loses two electrons and C loses 3. Strength of metallic bond depends on the charges on metal kernels and radii. As C has the maximum charge and is the smallest in size among the given elements, the metallic bond is the strongest in C.

Hence, the correct answer is (c).

Level 2: Review Your Concepts

45. Na_2O is an ionic compound.

SO_2

Cl_2O

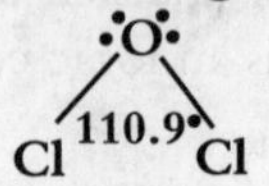

H_2O

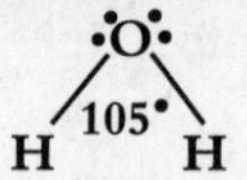

Hence, H_2O is the correct answer.

46. Among the given compounds, only $AlCl_3$ is a polar covalent compound; the rest are ionic compounds. Hence, interionic attraction does not exist in $AlCl_3$.

47.

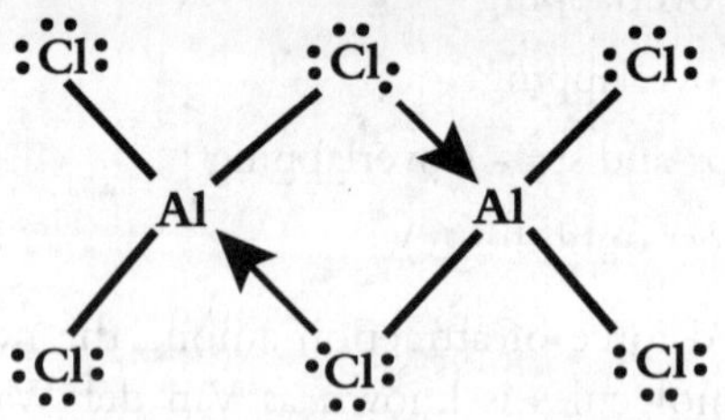

A dative bond is present in Al_2Cl_6.

48. $XeF_2 \rightarrow sp^3d$ hybridization

$CH_2Cl_2 \rightarrow sp^3$ hybridization

$PCl_5 \rightarrow sp^3d$ hybridization

$SF_4 \rightarrow sp^3d$ hybridization

49. (a) (i) comparison of shape of BF_3 and NF_3

(ii) number of lone pairs and bond pairs present in the valence shell of the central atom of respective molecules

(iii) shapes of the respective molecules

(iv) influence of shape on the polarity of the molecule

(b) Covalent character is directly proportional to the polarizing power of the cations and the polarizabilities of the anions.

Ascending order of the polarizing powers of the given cations is

$$K^+ < Ca^{2+} < Mg^{2+} < Al^{3+}$$

Ascending of the polarizabilities of given anions is

$$F^- < O^{2-} < S^{2-}.$$

∴ The ascending order of the covalent character is

$$KF < CaO < MgO < MgS < Al_2S_3.$$

50. (i) comparison of atomic size of xenon with other noble gases
(ii) electronic configuration of xenon and atomic size of xenon
(iii) scope for excited state configurations
(iv) types of hybridization possible

51. (i) comparison of electrons present in the valence shell in Cl in Cl_2O and H in H_2O
(ii) comparison of size between chlorine and hydrogen
(iii) comparison of the valence electronic configuration between hydrogen and chlorine

52. (i) valence shell of 'S.'
(ii) number and type of orbitals present in the valence shell
(iii) number of unpaired and paired electrons present in valence shell in ground state
(iv) number of unpaired electrons possible in different exited states
(v) relation between number of unpaired electrons and covalency

53. (i) valence electronic configuration of hydrogen and chlorine
(ii) type of hybridization in PCl_5
(iii) comparison of electronegativities between hydrogen and chlorine
(iv) the difference between the energies of overlapping orbitals

54. (i) comparison of the size of the anions
(ii) factors affecting the lattice energy

55. (i) order or intensity of repulsions between different electron pairs
(ii) preferred positions of an electron pair that causes more repulsion
(iii) geometry based on arrangement of different electron pairs

56. (i) relation between the energy of the system and its stability
(ii) kind of force exerted on the atoms when they approach each other after bond formation
(iii) interrelation among work, force and energy
(iv) effect of the amount of force on the rate of change of energy

57. (a) (i) requisite of a substance to be soluble in water
(ii) type of forces of attraction in between the compounds of NaCl and NH_4Cl
(iii) effect of this on solubility

(b) According to electron pool theory the strength of metallic bond depends on the number of free electrons. The higher the number of free electrons, the stronger is the metallic bond. This is due to the stronger electrostatic forces of attraction. In mercury, electron pool is very thin because of very high effective nuclear charge due to lanthanide contraction. Hence metallic bond is not strong enough to fix the position of the metal kernels and thus mercury exists in liquid state.

58. Ionic compounds are formed easily between larger cation and smaller anion. This is because an atom whose atomic radius is large can form a cation easily and an atom that has a small atomic radius can form an anion easily. Cs^+ ion can be formed more easily than Na^+ ion. Formation of CsCl is easier than the formation of NaCl. Between NaCl and CsCl, as the anion is the same, that is, Cl^-, the sizes of the cations are compared. Cs^+ has a larger ionic radius than Na^+. Thus, the strength of ionic bond is more in NaCl than CsCl.

59. When a polar molecule like HF is placed between charged parallel plates, the molecule orients in such a way that the positive end of the molecule is directed towards the negatively charged plate and the negative end of the molecule is directed towards the positively charged plate. As a result of this, the intensity of the charge on each plate is diminished. However, when dry air (nitrogen, oxygen), which is non-polar in nature is placed, there would be no change in the intensity of the charge.

60. The valence electronic configurations of phosphorous is $3s^23p^3$. Though there are only three half-filled orbitals for bonding, in the excited state five half-filled orbitals are available for bond formation. Among these five orbitals, three are 'p-' orbitals and two are 'd-' orbitals. These orbitals overlap with the half-filled '3p' orbitals of five chlorine atoms forming PCl_5 molecule. Such a situation is not possible with hydrogen atoms since there is wide variation in energies between '3d' orbitals of phosphorous and '1s' orbitals of hydrogen.

61. Electronic configuration of sulphur is $[Ne]3s^23p^43d^0$ electronic configuration of excited state of sulphur is $[Ne]3s^23p^33d^1$

SF_4 is formed when four half-filled sp^3d hybrid orbitals of sulphur atom overlap with half-filled 'p' orbitals of fluorine atoms. Hence, there exist four bond pairs and one lone pair in SF_4 molecule. According to the VSEPR theory, expected structure of SF_4 is trigonal bipyramidal but as the lone pair and two bond pairs of the molecule lie on the plane and other two bond pairs present above and below the plane and the structure of SF_4 is 'see saw' structure. This deviation is due to the lone pair of electrons.

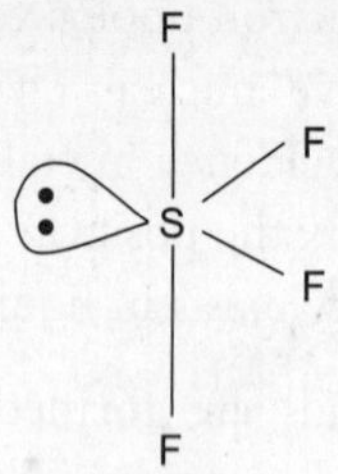

See-saw shape

62. Polarizing power of the cation depends on its size and the charge present on it. The smaller the size and the higher the charge of the cation, the greater the polarizing power. Among Na^+, Mg^{2+} and Al^{3+}, Al^{3+} has least ionic size and the charge present on it is maximum. Hence, polarizing power of Al^{3+} is maximum. Among the halides AlF_3 is ionic, but other halides of aluminium are covalent. Polarizing power of magnesium is less than aluminium. Hence, chloride and fluoride of magnesium are ionic. But Na^+ has the least polarizing power. Hence, all the halides of sodium are ionic.

63. The central nitrogen atom of ammonia has lone pair of electrons on it that can be donated to form co-ordinate covalent bond, which is obvious from the nature of bonding present in NH_3. Thus, the central N atom of NH_3 acts as a donor.

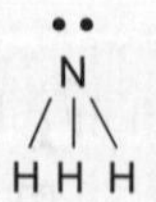

The central 'N' atom of NO_2 doesn't participate in co-ordinate covalent bond formation due to the lack of lone electron pair on nitrogen. The central 'N' participates in co-ordinate covalent bond formation with oxygen during the formation of NO_2 and thus it cannot further act as donor and forms co-ordinate covalent bond with other species that is obvious from the nature of bonding present in NO_2.

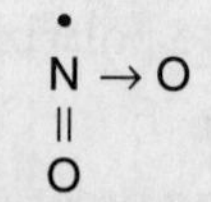

64. Being more electropositive in nature, metals have a tendency to lose their valence electrons. Due to the presence of these free electrons metals act as good conductors. But increase in temperature increases the vibrations of metal kernels in the metal lattice. Increase in the vibrations obstructs the path of the electrons that in turn increases the resistance of the metal. Therefore, the conductivity decreases.

65. When a large amount of shearing force is applied to a metal, the metal kernels of one layer slide over the other. After getting displaced, the metal kernels again get stabilised there due to the uniform distribution of free electrons throughout the metal. Hence metals can be permanently deformed without breaking and exhibit malleability and ductility.

Level 3: Assess Your Concepts

66. Fluorine being more electronegative than oxygen, HF has a stronger hydrogen bond than water. However, each water molecule can form 4 hydrogen bonds, whereas each HF molecule can form 2 hydrogen bonds. Therefore, H_2O has a higher boiling point than HF.

67. Due to the presence of hydrogen bonding in water, water has a higher boiling point and therefore, preferably exists in a liquid state. Hence, it has lower vapour pressure. H_2S, on the other hand, has no hydrogen bonding in it and preferably exists in a gaseous state. As a result, in a liquid state, it has higher vapour pressure.

68. (i) comparison of electronic configuration of beryllium and xenon
(ii) type of hybridization in XeF_2 and $BeCl_2$
(iii) the number of lone pairs and bond pairs present in the valence shell of the central atom

69. (i) relation between number of valence electron pairs (bond pairs and lone pairs) and geometry
(ii) number of valence electrons around central atom for octahedral geometry

70. (i) valence electronic configuration of thallium
(ii) difference in the electronic configuration of thallous and thallic ions

(iii) comparison of the ease of formation of thallous and thallic ions

(iv) relation between the ease of formation of ion and availability of the compound in nature containing that ion

71. The more the lattice energy, the stronger the ionic bond which in turn depends on the ease of formation of anion if the cation is the same. The easier the formation of the anion, the more the oxidizing capacity. Hence, from the given lattice energies it can be concluded that the increasing order of the oxidizing capacities of halogens is:

$$I_2 < Br_2 < Cl_2 < F_2$$

72. In AB_5 molecule, central atom A is surrounded by five electron pairs and no lone pairs. Hence, the structure is a trigonal bipyramid and as there are no lone pairs, so the structure is not distorted. Here in this structure three bonded atoms occupy equatorial positions of the triangle and other two axial positions (top and bottom) of the equilateral triangle. When one of the bond pairs is replaced by a lone pair, the preferred position of the lone pair is equatorial and the geometry is distorted trigonal bipyramid because in this structure it experiences less number of repulsions and hence stable.

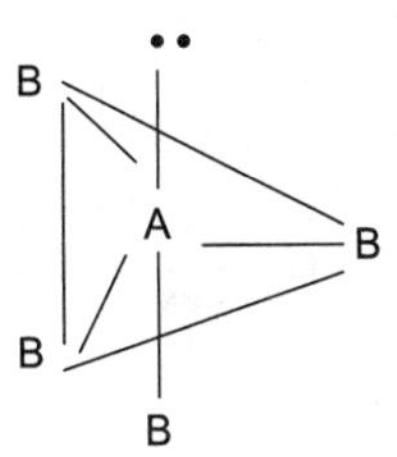

(i) Wrong structure

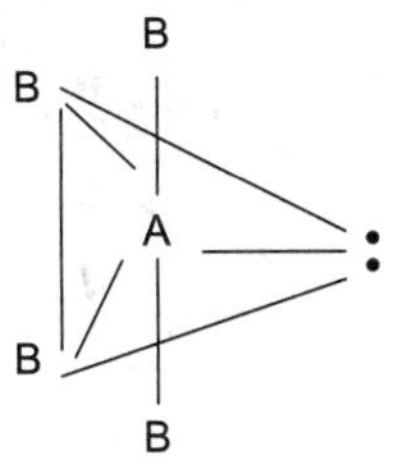

(ii) Right structure

When two bond pairs are replaced by lone pair of electrons, then the preferred geometry will be the one of lowest energy with minimum repulsions.

When two lone pairs are present among five electron pairs allowed the central atom then the molecule experiences three types of repulsions and their order is:

l.p - l.p > l.p - b.p > b.p - b.p.

The structure that has lesser repulsions is

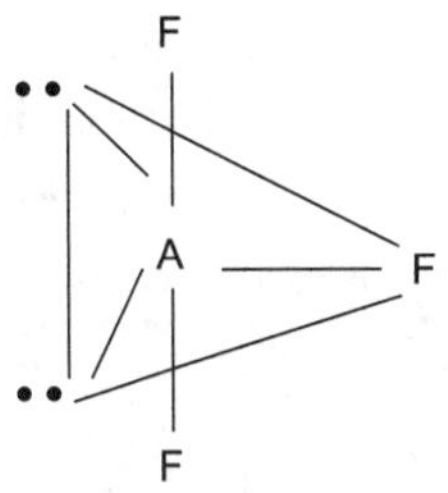

The two lone pairs are separated by maximum bond angle of 120° and hence, the above structure is most preferred geometry that is T-shape with minimum repulsions. When three bond pairs are replaced by a lone pair, then the preferred geometry is the one where three lone pairs occupy equatorial positions with maximum separation of bond angle and hence the shape is linear.

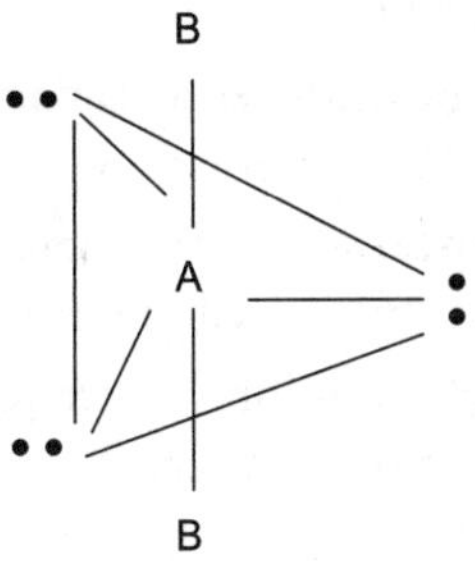

73. Since the size of halide ion increases down the group, the ease of getting polarized by a cation also increases. Thus, Li^+ ion can polarize I^- ion to a greater extent and thus from LiF to LiI covalent character increases. Hence, we expect that LiF is more soluble in water and LiI is less soluble or not soluble in water. The solubility of an ionic compound in water depends on the relative values of lattice energy and hydration energy. The substance becomes soluble in water if hydration energy exceeds lattice energy. From LiF to LiI, lattice energy decreases while hydration energy increases. Since lattice energy of LiF is much greater than hydration energy, it is insoluble in water and thus solubility in water increases from LiF to LiI.

74. Anomalous expansion of water results due to the partial breakage of hydrogen bonds during melting of ice. Dissolution of sugar in water is also due to the formation of hydrogen bonding between sugar and water. Two molecules of acetic acid bound by hydrogen bond together form dimer. Dehydrating nature of conc H_2SO_4 is not due to hydrogen bonding.

A, C and D are correct choices

75. The electronic configuration of Sn is $1s^22s^22p^63s^23p^6 3d^{10}4s^24p^64d^{10}5s^25p^2$ and chlorine is $1s^22s^22p^63s^23p^5$. Hence, in $SnCl_2$ molecule in vapor state, there is one lone pair of electrons and two bond pairs of electrons in the valence shell of tin. Therefore, the expected shape is trigonal planar. But due to presence of the lone pair, its shape is bent and bond angle is 88°.

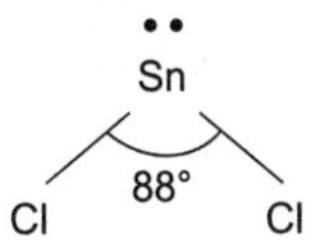

JEE-NEET Special Wing

Multiple-Answer Type Questions

1. The energy required to convert $X(g) \rightarrow X^+ (g)$ is said to be first ionization energy of X.

It depends on:According to Fajan's rule, compound with comparatively small cation and large anion will be more covalent in nature.

⇒ **For compounds with same anion:** Compound with smaller size cation will be more covalent.

⇒ **For compounds with same cation:** Compound with larger size anion will be more covalent.

And for different anion and cation: Compound with a small size cation and large size anion will be more covalent in nature.

Following are the criteria used to compare sizes of atoms and ions.

1. The greater the number of electron shells of atoms or ions the greater the size of the atom/ion.
2. For atoms or ions with the same number of electron shells, the fewer the proton number of the atom/ion the bigger the atom or ion

For the given sets, the correct order of covalent character is,

Order of covalent character	Reason
(a) LiI > CsF	Size of $Li^+ < Cs^+$ and $I^- > F^-$
(b) LiF > CsF	Same anion and size of $Li^+ < Cs^+$
(c) NaCl < $MgCl_2$	Same anion and size of $Mg^{+2} < Na^+$
(d) KF < K_2O	Same cation and $O^{-2} > F^-$

So, the sets NaCl, $MgCl_2$ and KF, K_2O are arranged in the correct increasing order.

2. From the figure, it is clear that potential energy of the system decreases as the two hydrogen atoms approach each other. Bond formation between two H-atoms takes place at a distance where the proton–electron attraction just balances the electron–electron repulsion and proton–proton repulsion i.e., at point Q when the internuclear distance is T pm. At this stage, the system becomes stable because it possesses the lowest possible energy, and H_2 molecule is formed. The distance between the nuclei of the hydrogen atoms, after the formation of the bond, is called the bond length i.e., T pm. Amount of potential energy decreased from point P to point Q gives bond energy i.e., Y-X kJ/mol. Hence only choice a and d interpretations are correct

3. For orbital overlapping, the orbitals belonging to the valence shell only take part in the overlapping and they should possess at least one unpaired electron. So, choice (a) and (b) does not comply with the conditions required for orbital overlapping.

4. Valence shell electronic configuration of:

Br- $4s^2 4p^5$, Cl- $3s^2 3p^5$, F- $2s^2 2p^5$, S- $3s^2 3p^4$, Be- $2s^2 2p^2$, H- $1s^1$

So, the correct match will be:

(a) Br_2-----------4p-4p overlap.

(b) $BeCl_2$----- sp-p overlap.(Be undergoes sp hybridization)

(c) SF_6--------- sp^3d^2-P overlap.(S undergoes sp^3d^2 hybridization)

(d) HF----------1s-2p overlap.

Choice (a) and (c) are incorrectly matched.

5. N_2O_5 contains all N-O bonds (both covalent and dative bonds). All N-O bonds in this compound are polar bonds (as both covalent and dative bonds are polar).

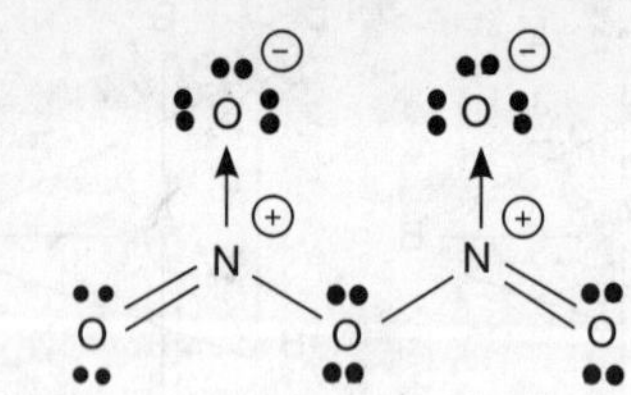

Comprehension-Based Questions

6. All the three molecules possess same steric number 4 and their central atoms are sp^3 hybridized. Difference in electronegativity between O-H > N-H > C-H. Main reason for the deviation in the bond angle is due to the difference in the no. of lone pairs on the central atom but not the difference in the electronegativities of their central atoms. Repulsion between l.p-l.p > l.p-b.p > b.p-b.p.

7. Most electropositive element in SO_4^{-2} is the central atom sulphur (S).

Formula charge on an atom = [valence electrons – nonbonding electrons- ½ (bonding electrons)]

- Valence electrons of sulphur = 6
- Bonding electrons = 4 single bonds = 4(2) = 8 electrons
- Non-bonding electrons = no. of lone pair electrons = 0 electrons
- Formula charge on sulphur = [6 – 0 - ½ (8)] = +2

8. Shape of the given molecule is Trigonal Bipyramidal. Hence its steric number will be 5.

9. According to the postulates of VSEPR theory,

'Triple bonds cause more repulsion than the double bonds. Similarly double bond causes more repulsion than a single bond'.

Hence, the repulsion between the C-C bond pair and C-H bond pair in alkynes > alkenes > alkanes.

According to the passage, for neutral molecules,

Steric Number = (number of lone pairs on the central atom) + (number of atoms bonded to the central atom)

Steric number (S.N.):

For Alkynes each C is bonded to two atoms (1C, 1H) and no of lone pairs zero ⇒ S.N. = 0 + 2 = 2

For Alkenes each C is bonded to three atoms (1C, 2H) and no of lone pairs zero ⇒ S.N. = 0 + 3 = 3

For Alkanes each C is bonded to two atoms (1C, 3H) and no of lone pairs zero ⇒ S.N. = 0 + 4 = 4

So, S.N. of alkynes < alkenes < alkanes.

Hence C_nH_{2n-2}, C_nH_{2n} , C_nH_{2n+2}, is the correct increasing order of arrangement with respect to the repulsion between the C-C bond pair and C-H bond pair.

10. Formula:

Steric Number N = ½[V + M ± I] where V = n(e−), the number of valence electrons of central atom, M = n(atom), the number of monovalent atoms directly bonded to it, and I is the number of positive or negative charges present (subtract it if the charge is positive and add it if the charge is negative).

List – I	Steric number S.N. =½[V+M±I]	List – II Shape of the molecule based on its steric number
(A) NH_4^+	= ½[5 + 4 – I] = 4	(i) Tetrahedral
(B) NO_3^-	= ½[5 + 0 + I] = 3	(iv) Trigonal Planar
(C) O_3	½[6 + 0 – 0] = 3	(iv) Trigonal Planar
(D) CO_2	= ½[4 + 0 – 0] = 2	(ii) Linear

Correct match is

	(A)	(B)	(C)	(D)
(a)	(i)	(iv)	(iv)	(ii)

11. Intramolecular hydrogen bonding may not significantly impact certain physical properties like boiling point or melting point, but it can have a noticeable impact on other properties such as solubility, viscosity, and surface tension. The internal bonding within the molecule can hinder interactions with other substances, reducing solubility. Additionally, it can contribute to increased viscosity (resistance to flow) and higher surface tension (resistance to changes in surface area) due to the strengthened internal cohesion caused by these intramolecular hydrogen bonds.

12. Bond energy is the energy needed to separate one mole of gaseous molecules into individual atoms. Bond energy depends on the strength of the covalent bond but not on the intermolecular bonding. When the electronegativity difference between bonded atoms is smaller, both the strength of the covalent bond and intermolecular hydrogen bonding tend to be greater. As oxygen has a higher electronegativity compared to nitrogen, the O-H bond exhibits greater bond energy than the N-H bond.

13.

Phenomenon	Correct reason
(a) The merging of two ice cubes into one when pressed together	The temporary bonding between water molecules due to hydrogen bonding allows the cubes to merge.
(b) Anomalous expansion observed in water	As water cools from room temperature, hydrogen bonds become more ordered, leading to increased spacing between molecules, and causing water to expand as it freezes
(c) Comparison of the acidic strength between HF and HCl	The smaller size of fluorine in HF results in a stronger covalent bond between hydrogen and fluorine compared to the bond in HCl, leading to a weaker acidic behavior of HF compared to HCl.
(d) Dimerization of acetic acid	It is because of hydrogen bonding.

14. Extent of hydrogen bonding is influenced by both electronegativity and the availability of hydrogen atoms for bonding. Correct order of electronegativity is F>O>S. Sulphur, because of its large size cannot form hydrogen bonding. H_2O_2 (hydrogen peroxide) has more hydrogen atoms available for bonding compared to water (H_2O), despite having a similar electronegative oxygen atom. Hence, H_2O_2 comes first in the order.

Though electronegativity of fluorine is greater compared to oxygen, as H_2O contains a greater number of hydrogen atoms compared to in HF, the extent of bonding(number of hydrogens formed per molecule) in H_2O is greater than that compared to in HF. Hence the correct order is $H_2O_2 > H_2O > HF > H_2S$.

15. HF and H_2O can form polymeric structures through hydrogen bonding. HF forms a linear polymeric structure, while H_2O forms a tetrahedral polymeric structure. On the other hand, NH_3, despite its ability to engage in hydrogen bonding, does not exhibit a polymeric structure due to the weaker nature of its N−H bonds. In HCl, although chlorine has electronegativity almost equal to that of nitrogen, it cannot form hydrogen bonding due to its larger size.

16. The strength and extent of hydrogen bonding impact a molecule's boiling point. Despite fluorine's higher electronegativity than oxygen, water (H_2O) forms more hydrogen bonds per molecule than hydrogen fluoride (HF). While HF typically forms two hydrogen bonds on average, water forms four due to its two lone oxygen pairs. Consequently, water has a higher boiling point than HF because of its extensive hydrogen bonding, creating a robust structure needing substantial energy to break these bonds. Additionally, HF exists as a dimer in its gaseous state, resulting in fewer hydrogen bonds to break during its liquid-to-gas transition. Phosphorus lacks hydrogen bonding, hence, should possess the lowest boiling point of all the given molecules. The correct order based on hydrogen bonding strength is: $H_2O > HF > NH_3 > PH_3$, reflecting the corresponding boiling point order.

List – I	List – II Approximate boiling point values at standard atmospheric pressure in Fahrenheit scale
(A) H_2O	(ii) $10.6x$
(B) PH_3	(i) $-6.25x$
(C) NH_3	(iv) $-1.4x$
(D) HF	(iii) $4.35x$

CHAPTER

6

Metallurgy

Remember

Before beginning this chapter, you should be able to:

- understand the concept of chemical bonding for metals and non-metals.
- know occurrence of metals in our surroundings.

Key Ideas

After completing this chapter, you should be able to:

- understand the characteristics, properties of metals, non-metals, and metalloids.
- explain the processes of extraction of magnesium, zinc, aluminium, iron, and copper from their respective ores and their uses.
- understand about the composition, properties, and uses of important alloys and amalgams.
- describe the properties of copper, aluminium, zinc, iron, and magnesium.

Scientific Crypt

A Tribute to Karl Josef Bayer (1847–1904)

Karl Josef Bayer, an Austrian chemist is known for his contribution to the economical production of aluminium that brought a revolutionary change in the industrial world. Karl Josef Bayer was born in Bielitz, near Cracow in Silesia (a province of the Austrian Empire) now located in Poland. He obtained his Doctorate in Chemistry at the University of Heidelberg under Robert Bunsen. After completing his Doctorate, Bayer went to saint Petersburg and there he worked in Tentlev chemical plant. He worked there on the problems of extraction of alumina which was required in textile industries as a fixing agent for dyeing of cotton, wool, etc. In 1887, he found that the precipitation followed by filtration of aluminium hydroxide from alkaline solution is more convenient and easier than the conventional method of precipitating aluminium hydroxide from an acid medium by neutralization. In 1888, he developed and patented a process of extracting alumina from bauxite ore and this process is popularly known as Bayer's process. Aluminium extraction was too energy intensive before the introduction of Bayer's process. The first aluminium plant where Bayer's process was used was established in 1893.

Aluminium was highly expensive in 19th century. In 1855 a bar of aluminium was exhibited alongside the Crown Jewels in Paris Exhibition whereas since twentieth century aluminium is being extensively used in diversified fields from simple household utensils to aircraft frames and automobiles. The Austrian chemical society has started giving Bayer medal in his honour since 1961, for the contribution made by him to industrial world.

FUN TIME

CROSSWORD

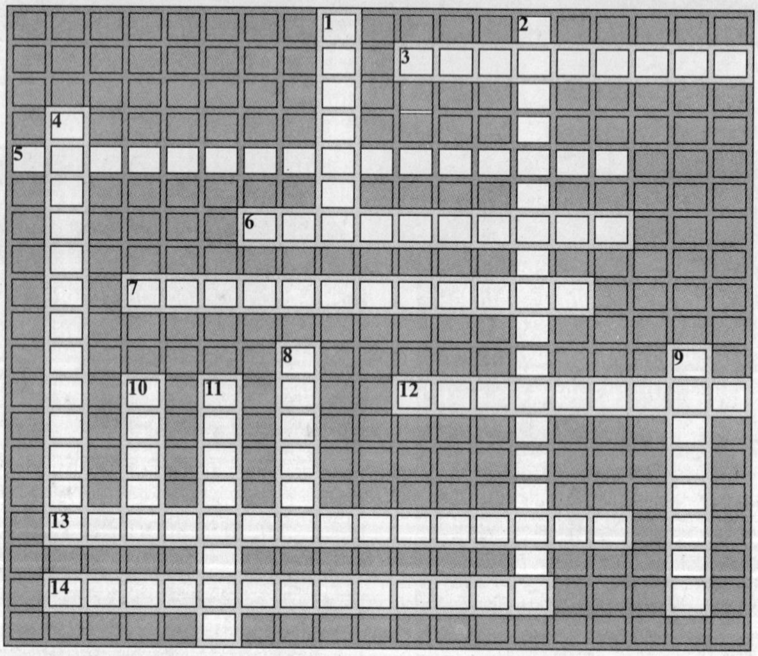

Across

3. The alloy of aluminium used for manufacturing aircraft frames, automobiles etc.
5. The process of heating steel to a temperature of 1000 K to 1250 K and cooling suddenly by plunging it into cold water or oil is called ______.
6. The lower region of blast furnace which is used for the extraction of iron from ferric oxide is known as ______ zone.
7. The process in which bauxite is made to react with sodium carbonate in order to concentrate it
12. Element which exhibits the properties of both metals and nonmetals
13. Coloured gas formed when cupric nitrate is heated
14. The process by which the small pieces of ore are ground to a fine powder

Down

1. A special class of alloy containing mercury as the essential component is called ______.
2. This method is employed for the concentration of ores in which either the ore or the gangue is attracted by a magnet and other is not.
4. The process of coating of zinc on the surface of iron is called ______.
8. Impurities present in ore is known as ______.
9. Sulphide ore of mercury
10. Purity of gold is stated in terms of ______.
11. The gas produced when zinc reacts with steam.

INTRODUCTION

The periodic table of elements comprises 118 elements that have been discovered and authorised till now. All these elements are broadly categorized as metals and non-metals. In addition to these, there is another category of elements known as metalloids. However, over 75% of the elements are metals as the left and middle portions of the periodic table are completely occupied by metals. Owing to the large number and also to their widespread use in day-to-day life ranging from tools to sophisticated electronic devices, the study of metals gained a lot of significance.

The history of the study of metals dates back to 6000 BCE, a period when gold, silver, and copper were the only metals known. These metals occurred in their native state in the sands and gravels of river beds. However, the metals that were discovered in the later period were found to exist in combined state in the form of minerals. Owing to the significant ornamental and utilitarian values attributed to these metals, attempts were made not only for the discovery of new metals but also for the development of methods for the extraction of these metals from their compounds.

Thus, the branch of metallurgy, probably one of the oldest applied sciences, contributed much to the cultural and technological development of human society. Metallurgy is treated as the art and science of extracting the metals from the ores in the most profitable way. The other aspects of metallurgy include the transformation of these metals into various usable forms and also understanding the physical and chemical nature of metals.

Metals and Non-metals

Generally, metals are considered as elements possessing 1–3 electrons in their valence shells and non-metals as the elements possessing 4–7 electrons in their valence shells. Due to the difference in the number of valence electrons, metals and non-metals differ widely in their characteristic properties.

Physical Properties of Metal and non Metals

Metals are characterized by certain prominent physical properties that are not present in non-metals.

Owing to the presence of less number of electrons in the valence shells of metals and lower ionization potential values, metals lose electrons easily. Therefore, the metal lattices contain free electrons that surround the metal ions (metal kernels). A strong electrostatic force of attraction exists between the metal kernels, which is known as **metallic bond**. The presence of metallic bonds in metals is responsible for the characteristic physical properties of metals.

Metals exist in solid state due to the presence of strong metallic bonds in metal lattices. However, mercury and gallium exist in liquid state unlike other metals. They have high density, high melting point, and boiling point. The metals possessing comparatively weaker metallic bonds have lower density, low boiling points and melting points. Examples in this regard include Na, K, Hg, Ga, etc. Metallic bond being omnidirectional makes the metals highly malleable and ductile. The high thermal conductivity, electrical conductivity and lustre of metals are attributed to the presence of free electrons in the metal lattices.

Non-metals do not lose electrons easily due to more number of electrons in their shells and relatively higher ionization potential values. Therefore, in contrast to metals, non-metals do not possess free electrons.

Only weak intermolecular forces exist in the non-metals. Due to this reason, most of the non-metals exist as gases having lower densities. Few non-metals exist in solid state such as carbon, sulphur, phosphorous, and iodine. Generally, solid non-metals are brittle. Except for few allotropic forms of carbon such as graphite, all other non-metals are bad conductors of electricity.

Info Bytes!

Carbon, a non-metal, has the highest melting and boiling points of all the elements.

Table 6.1 Chemical properties of metals and non-metals

Properties	Metals	Non-metals
Number of electrons in the valence shell	Have 1–3 electrons in the valence shell	Have 4–7 electrons in their valence shell Exceptions: Hydrogen and helium have 1 and 2 electrons, respectively, in their valence shell because the first shell is their valence shell
Formation of ions	Lose electrons from their valence shell to attain a stable structure and form cations	Accept electrons to attain a stable structure and form anions
Formation of oxides	Metals on heating in air/oxygen react to form either basic or amphoteric oxides $4Na + O_2 \rightarrow 2Na_2O$ (basic oxide) $4Al + 3O_2 \rightarrow 2Al_2O_3$ (amphoteric oxide) **Exceptions:** Metals like Au and Pt do not form oxides	Non-metals on heating in air/oxygen form their oxides. The oxides are either acidic or neutral: $S + O_2 \rightarrow SO_2$ (acidic oxide) $2H_2 + O_2 \rightarrow 2H_2O$ (neutral oxide)
Reactions of oxide with water	Metallic oxides give bases on reaction with water: $Na_2O + H_2O \rightarrow 2NaOH$ $K_2O + H_2O \rightarrow 2KOH$ $CaO + H_2O \rightarrow Ca(OH)_2$	Acidic (non-metallic) oxides give acids on reaction with water: $SO_2 + H_2O \rightarrow H_2SO_3$ $CO_2 + H_2O \rightarrow H_2CO_3$
Reactions of oxide with acid (for metallic oxide) **or with base** (for non-metallic oxide)	Metallic oxides react with acids to give their respective salts and water: $Na_2O + H_2SO_4 \rightarrow Na_2SO_4 + H_2O$ $MgO + H_2SO_4 \rightarrow MgSO_4 + H_2O$	Non-metallic (acidic) oxides react with bases to give their respective salts and water: $SO_2 + NaOH \rightarrow Na_2SO_3 + H_2O$ $CO_2 + NaOH \rightarrow Na_2CO_3 + H_2O$
Reaction with acid and water	Metals which are more reactive than hydrogen, replace hydrogen from the acid as well as from water: $Zn + 2HCl \rightarrow ZnCl_2 + H_2$ $Ca + 2H_2O \rightarrow Ca(OH)_2 + H_2$ Copper, tin, and mercury, which are less reactive than hydrogen do not replace hydrogen either from acid or from water	Non-metals do not react with water. The majority of non-metals do not react with acids Since nitric acid is an oxidizing agent, it oxidizes non-metals like sulphur, carbon, iodine, and phosphorus to their respective acids: $S + 6HNO_3 \rightarrow H_2SO_4 + 6NO_2 + 2H_2O$ $C + 4HNO_3 \rightarrow H_2CO_3 + 4NO_2 + H_2O$ $I_2 + 10HNO_3 \rightarrow 2HIO_3 + 10NO_2 + 4H_2O$ $P_4 + 20HNO_3 \rightarrow 4H_3PO_4 + 20NO_2 + 4H_2O$
Displacement reactions	More electropositive metals displace less electropositive metals from their salts: $Fe + CuSO_4 \rightarrow FeSO_4 + Cu$ $Mg + FeSO_4 \rightarrow MgSO_4 + Fe$	More electronegative halogens displace less electronegative ones from their compounds: $2NaBr + Cl_2 \rightarrow 2NaCl + Br_2$ $2NaI + Cl_2 \rightarrow 2NaCl + I_2$

Occurrence of Metals

Generally, most of the metals occur in the combined state in nature. The metals in the combined form are called **minerals**. The most common minerals and ores are in the form of oxides, hydrated oxides, carbonates, sulphides, chlorides, etc., of which a few are listed in the following table.

Table 6.2 Occurrence of metals

Lead	Magnesium	Calcium	Mercury	Sodium	Silver
Lead ochre (PbO)	Magnesite ($MgCO_3$)	Gypsum ($CaSO_4.2H_2O$)	Cinnabar (HgS)	Rock salt ($NaCl$)	Horn silver ($AgCl$)
Galena (PbS)	Dolomite ($CaCO_3.MgCO_3$)	Fluorspar (CaF_2)		Chile saltpeter ($NaNO_3$)	
Anglesite ($PbSO_4$)	Epsom salt ($MgSO_4.7H_2O$) Carnallite ($KCl. MgCl_2.6H_2O$)				

Each metal can exist in the form of various minerals. The mineral from which a metal can be extracted in an easy and cost-effective process is called an **ore**. The extraction of the metal from the ore involves various stages. Though the exact steps involved in the process of the extraction differ from metal to metal, the various stages of general metallurgical process can be broadly categorized into four stages.

General Metallurgical Processes

The metallurgical processes are broadly classified into four steps as listed below:

1. Dressing and concentration of ore
2. Conversion of ore to oxide or desired compound
3. Extraction of metal
4. Refining of metal

Dressing and Concentration of Ore

1. **Dressing of Ore**

   Since ores are obtained in crude form from the earth's crust, they are invariably associated with huge amounts of earthy impurities such as sand, mud, etc. The earthy impurities associated with the ores are called **gangue**. The ores should be freed from gangue before they are subjected to the extraction of metals from them. The process of the removal of gangue from an ore is called the **dressing of ore**.

   (a) **Hand-picking**: During this process, big lumps of rocks are removed by hand. The ore is then subjected to crushing and grinding to make it into smaller pieces.

   (b) **Crushing or Grinding**: The ores are crushed in big jaw crushers to obtain small pieces, which are further hammered in hammer mills to give very small pieces. The small pieces are then pulverized.

   (c) **Pulverization**: In this process, the ore is ground to a fine powder in huge ball mills. In the fine powdered form, the ore is sent for concentration. This process is not mandatory for all the ores. The ore is pulverized only if the fine powdered form of the ore is required for further processes.

2. **Concentration of Ore**

   The removal of gangue from the dressed ore is called **concentration of ore**. Depending upon the type of impurities and of metal, various procedures are employed for the removal of gangue from the ore.

   (a) **Gravity Separation**: This method of separation is applicable to all types of ores except sulphide ores. The method involves the separation of ore and gangue based on the difference in their specific gravities. The pulverized ore is placed on a wide rocking, sloping top table with lateral groove on it and it is treated with a stream of running water. The water carries the ore along with it. The gangue being lighter is washed down the table while the denser ore settles in the grooves of the table. The ore collected in the grooves is thrown sideways by the rocking movement of the table.

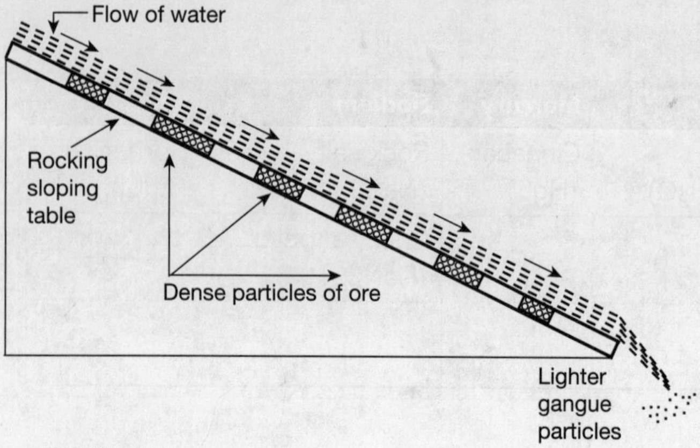

Figure 6.1 Concentration of ore by gravity process

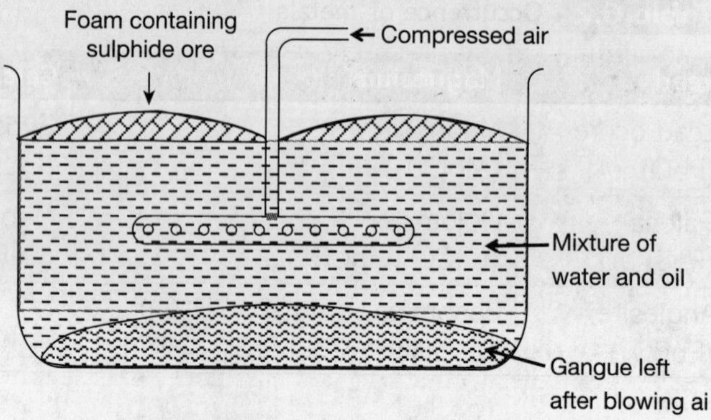

Figure 6.2 Froth floatation process

(b) Froth Flotation: This method is exclusively used for the concentration of sulphide ores. The basic principle involves the differential wetting characteristics of ore and gangue with oil and water, the ore being wet by oil and gangue by water.
The ore is taken in a large tank called the **flotation cell** containing a mixture of pine oil and water. This is then agitated by blowing a current of air into the tank. The oil along with the sulphide ore forms foam that floats on the tank and is removed. The sulphide ore is recovered from this.

(c) Magnetic Separation: This method is employed for the concentration of ores in which either the ore or the gangue is attracted by a magnet and the other is not.
In this, a rubber belt is made to move horizontally over two pulleys of which one is a strong magnet. The powdered ore is made to fall on the moving rubber belt. As the ore is passed over the magnetic pulley, the one (either the ore or the gangue) that is magnetic is attracted towards the pulley and clings to the belt leaving behind the other. As the magnetic component moves away from the magnetic pulley, it falls down as a separate heap. Thus, the ore and gangue are separated based on these magnetic properties.

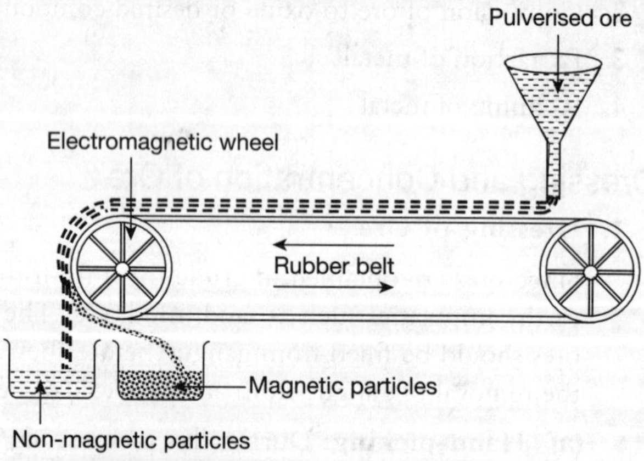

Figure 6.3 Electromagnetic separation

(d) Chemical Separation: This is an exclusive method used for the concentration of aluminium ore (bauxite).
The amphoteric nature of aluminium oxide is the basic principle involved in this method. In this, the ore is treated with the aqueous solution of caustic soda under pressure for a few hours resulting in the formation of sodium meta aluminate:

$$Al_2O_3 + 6NaOH \rightarrow 6NaAlO_2 + 2H_2O$$

Sodium meta aluminate so formed is soluble and, the impurities are removed by filtration. The filtrate is then diluted and aluminium hydroxide precipitates out:

$$3NaAlO_2 + 6H_2O \rightarrow 3Al(OH)_3 + 3NaOH$$

Aluminium hydroxide thus obtained is dried. The dried ore is strongly heated to 110°C till there is no further loss in weight. Aluminium hydroxide decomposes to alumina and water. This method of concentration of ore is called the **Bayer's process**.

Thus, in all the above ways, the gangue is removed and the metal is obtained in the form of its compound.

The metal ores so obtained after having undergone the process of concentration are then converted to their oxide form. The reduction of the oxide form can be carried out further to obtain pure metal.

Conversion of Ore to Oxide

The concentrated ore is converted to its oxide form. The further extraction of the metal from this oxide by reduction is easier than the extraction of metals from other forms. Two methods are used for the conversion of concentrated ore to its oxide form as listed below:

1. Roasting
2. Calcination

Table 6.3 Comparison between roasting and calcination

Roasting	Calcination
During roasting, the ore is strongly heated in the presence of excess air	During calcination, the ore is strongly heated in the absence or limited supply of air
This is mainly performed on sulphide ores, during which sulphur is removed as sulphur dioxide: $4FeS_2 + 11O_2 \rightarrow 2Fe_2O_3 + 8SO_2$	Calcination is mainly performed for carbonate and hydroxide ores where the ores are decomposed to give oxides: $Fe_2O_3.3H_2O \xrightarrow{\Delta} Fe_2O_3 + 3H_2O.$
In addition to converting the ore to its oxide form, this process also results in the removal of moisture and the expulsion of volatile impurities from the ore. Moreover, the resultant ore remains porous	Calcination is also associated with several other advantages like removal of moisture, increasing the porosity of the ore and the expulsion of the volatile impurities. Hydrated ores also get freed from the water of crystallization.

Extraction of Metal from Metal Oxide

The oxide ores obtained by the process of roasting or calcination are subjected to the reduction process. The reduction is, however, carried out by various methods.

The metal thus obtained by the reduction of oxide is not completely pure and is associated with certain impurities like other metals, non-metals, other metal oxides and dissolved gases.

Therefore, the metals extracted are subjected to further purification. This is called the **refining of the metal**.

Table 6.4 Reduction of metal from metal oxide

Reduction by	Applied for the extraction of	Description
Coke	Zinc, iron, lead, copper	The metallic oxide is mixed with coke and heated in a huge furnace. The coke reduces metal oxide to metal: $ZnO + C \xrightarrow{\Delta} Zn + CO$
Carbon monoxide	Iron, lead, copper	Carbon monoxide and hydrogen gases are passed through the oxide at a high temperature. The metal oxide gets reduced to metal. Carbon monoxide gets converted to CO_2: $Fe_2O_3 + 3CO \xrightarrow{\Delta} 2Fe + 3CO_2$
Aluminium powder	Chromium, manganese	A mixture of metal oxide and aluminium powder are ignited. Aluminium, being a very strong reducing agent, reduces the metal oxide to the corresponding metal: $Cr_2O_3 + 2Al \rightarrow Al_2O_3 + 2Cr + heat$
Heating	Mercury, silver	Mercury and silver oxides on heating decompose to give metal and oxygen gas: $2HgO \xrightarrow{\Delta} 2Hg + O_2$
Electrolysis	Sodium, potassium, calcium, magnesium, aluminium	Electricity is passed through fused halides or oxide. The metal ions that are formed move towards the cathode, and get discharged there

Purification or Refining of Metals

Different methods of the refining of metals are available for different metals. The method of refining generally depends upon the type of impurities present with the metal.

Table 6.5 Methods of refining of metals

Processes of purification	Metals to be refined	Processes
Distillation	Iron, mercury	The metal is strongly heated above its boiling point in the absence of air. The metal vaporizes, leaving behind the impurities. The vapors are cooled in earthen retorts, to get the metal in solid or liquid form.
Liquation	Lead, tin (metals with low melting point)	The metal is taken on the upper part of sloping hearth and heated above its melting point. The metal melts, flows down the hearth and is collected at the bottom.
Polling	Copper with cuprous oxide as an impurity	Molten copper is stirred with wooden poles. These poles emit wood gas (CO and H_2) thath reduces copper oxide to copper
Oxidation	Iron with oxidizable impurities	Oxygen is blown through molten metal where the impurities get converted to gaseous oxides and are removed: $C + O_2 \rightarrow CO_2\uparrow$ $S + O_2 \rightarrow SO_2\uparrow$
Electrolytic refining	Aluminium	A block of impure metal is taken as an anode and a thin strip of pure metal is taken as a cathode. The electrolyte is the soluble salt of the metal. On passing the current, the metal ions from the anode dissolve in the electrolyte, go towards the cathode and get discharged there. Electrolysis continues and the cathode becomes a thick block of pure metal.

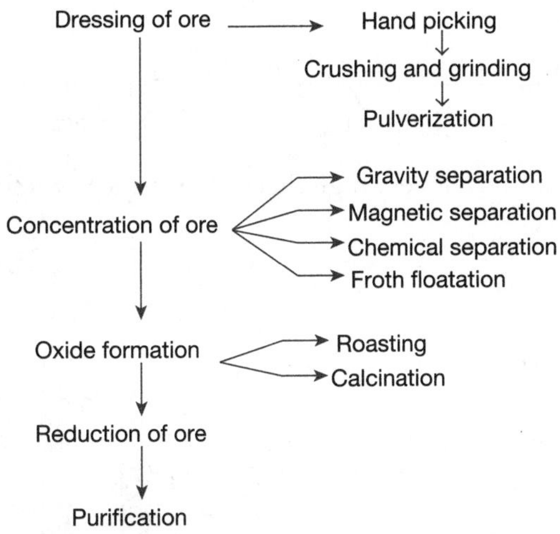

Figure 6.4 Flow chart for common metallurgical processes

Aluminium

Aluminium is a highly reactive metal belonging to the III A group of the periodic table. In nature, aluminium is found in the form of its oxide in its ores.

The important ores of aluminium are as follows:

Bauxite	$Al_2O_3.2H_2O$
Corundum	Al_2O_3
Cryolite	Na_3AlF_6

> **Info Bytes!**
> NALCO (National Aluminium Company Limited) is one of the largest integrated bauxite-alumina-aluminium-power production complexes in India.

Metallurgy of Aluminium

Aluminium is mostly extracted from its bauxite ore.

Dressing of Ore

The ore is crushed and pulverized.

Concentration of Ore

The bauxite ore contains ferric oxide and silica as impurities. It is first concentrated by gravity separation where in silica is removed followed by the removal of ferric oxide impurities by the process of magnetic separation. The ore is then concentrated by chemical process. There are two chemical processes that are generally followed as listed below:

1. **Bayer's Process:** In this process, aluminium ore is treated with concentrated sodium hydroxide. Soluble sodium aluminate is formed, which is filtered off. The filtrate on heating with water gives aluminium hydroxide that gives alumina on strong heating.

2. **Hall's Process:** In this process, bauxite is made to react with sodium carbonate giving soluble sodium aluminate:

$$Al_2O_3{\cdot}2H_2O + Na_2CO_3 \rightarrow 2NaAlO_2 + 2H_2O + CO_2$$

This is dissolved in water and filtered. Carbon dioxide gas is passed through the filtrate, which results in the formation of aluminium hydroxide:

$$2NaAlO_2 + 3H_2O + CO_2 \rightarrow Na_2CO_3 + 2Al(OH)_3$$

Conversion of Ore to Oxide

Aluminium hydroxide obtained by calcination gives alumina:

$$2Al(OH)_3 \xrightarrow{\Delta} Al_2O_3 + 3H_2O$$

Alumina so formed is highly stable and has very high thermal resistance. It is therefore subjected to electrolytic reduction.

Electrolytic Reduction

Electrolysis is carried out in fused state. Since alumina has very high thermal resistance, it does not melt easily. Hence, cryolite and fluorspar are added to alumina to decrease the melting point and increase the electrical conductivity.

The fused electrolyte is taken in an iron tank lined with gas carbon that acts as the cathode. A number of parallel carbon rods dipped in the electrolyte act as the anode. In order to prevent the loss of heat and burning of carbon electrodes, the electrolyte is covered with coke.

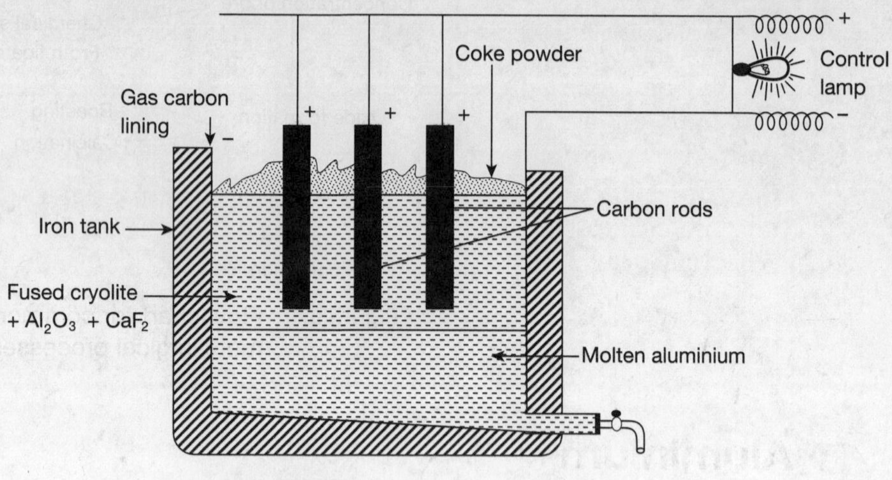

Figure 6.5 Electrolysis of fused alumina

The fused electrolyte contains alumina, cryolite and fluorspar in their ionized states. On passage of current, the ions move towards their respective electrodes:

$$Al_2O_3 \rightarrow 2Al^{3+} + 3O^{2-}$$

$$Na_3AlF_6 \rightarrow 3Na^+ + Al^{3+} + 6F^-$$

$$CaF_2 \rightarrow Ca^{2+} + 2F^-$$

The anions, O^{2-} and F^- move towards the anode. Oxide ion is oxidized to nascent oxygen, which combines with carbon forming carbon dioxide:

At Anode: $O^{2-} - 2e^- \rightarrow [O]$

$C + 2[O] \rightarrow CO_2$

The cations, Al^{3+}, Ca^{2+}, and Na^+, move towards the cathode. Aluminium ion being the least electropositive, gets reduced forming aluminium metal:

At Cathode: $Al^{3+} + 3e^- \rightarrow Al$

The temperature in the tank being higher than the melting point of aluminium, the aluminium formed is in the molten state, and settles at the bottom of the tank from where it is collected from time to time.

As the process of electrolysis continues, concentration of alumina decreases, thereby increasing the resistance of the electrolyte that is indicated by a control lamp. More alumina is added when required.

Konnect

Aluminium extracted by the above process is 99.5% pure and is further refined by electrolytic refining (Hoope's electrolysis).

Electrolytic Refining (Hoopes Electrolysis)

Hoopes method process is also called the **three-layer process** as the cell contains three layers of molten liquids. The cell is an iron tank lined internally with carbon. The electrolyte is composed of aluminium fluoride (36%), cryolite (18%), and calcium fluoride (16%) that forms the middle layer. The lower layer is the impure metal alloyed with copper and serves as the anode.

On passing the current, the aluminium ions from the middle layer go towards the cathode, get discharged there and form the upper layer of pure aluminium while an equivalent amount of aluminium passes into the middle layer from the bottom layer. Pure aluminium is collected from the top layer.

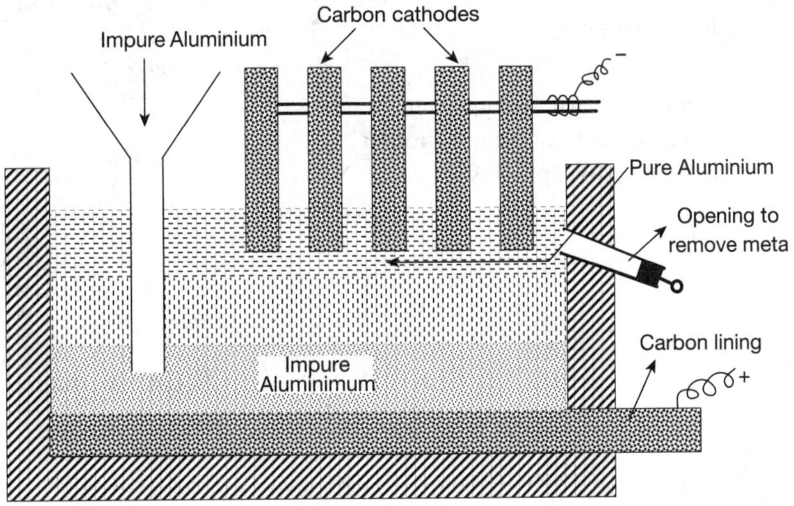

Figure 6.6 Refining of aluminium by Hoopes method

Uses of Aluminium

1. Aluminium being light, is a good conductor of heat, corrosion resistant and cheap, and hence used in making household appliances.
2. It is used in electric transmission as it is a good conductor of electricity.
3. As it can be made into thin sheets and foils, it is used in packing food stuffs.
4. As aluminium is a self-protective metal, when iron is coated with a layer of aluminium it can be prevented from rusting.
5. Aluminium powder along with ammonium nitrate can be used as an explosive.
6. Aluminium being highly electropositive can replace metals like gold and silver from their salts, thus helping in the extraction of these metals.
7. Aluminium being a strong reducing agent, is used in reducing many organic compounds.
8. Aluminium has a great affinity for oxygen. As a result, aluminium can displace metals from the metal oxides provided the metal is less electropositive than aluminium. The reaction being highly exothermic forms the basic principle of thermite welding.

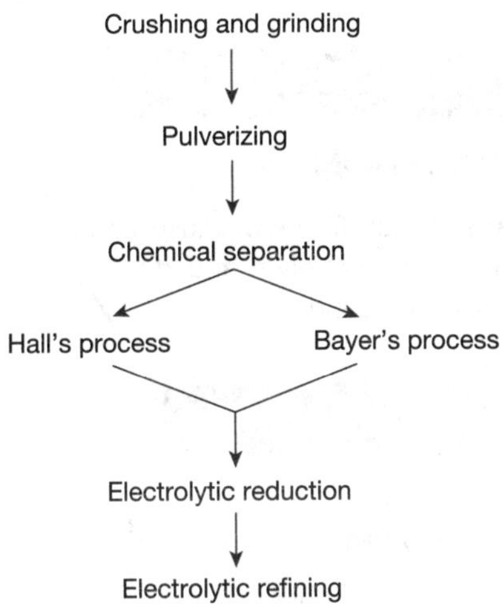

Figure 6.7 Process flow metallurgy of aluminium

Thermite Welding

A mixture of aluminium powder and ferric oxide in 1 : 3 ratio is called **thermite**. Thermite is taken in a funnel-shaped crucible, which is lined inside with magnesite. A mixture of magnesium powder and barium oxide, known as **ignition mixture** is placed on the surface of thermite. A magnesium ribbon is inserted into this mixture.

On lighting the magnesium ribbon, the ignition mixture catches fire. The heat produced by this process makes aluminium react with ferric oxide in which the latter gets reduced to iron. The enormous amount of heat released brings iron into a molten state. The molten iron when allowed to pour over the broken steel pieces solidifies and joins the broken pieces.

The major advantage of this process is that welding can be carried out without disturbing the position of heavy broken parts that would otherwise involve a laborious process.

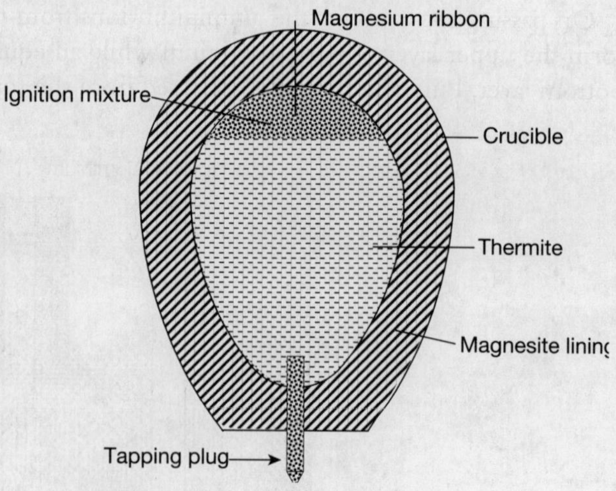

Figure 6.8 Aluminothermic process

EXAMPLE 6.1 Why do ores often undergo roasting prior to metal extraction?

SOLUTION

Roasting is a process in which the ore is heated in the presence of air to convert sulphide ores into oxides. Oxides are generally easier to reduce than sulphides, making subsequent metal extraction more efficient.

EXAMPLE 6.2 In the electrolytic refining process of copper, a thin layer of impurities, often referred to as 'anode mud', settles below the anode. Why does this occur?

SOLUTION

Anode mud forms because certain impurities in the impure copper anode, like gold and silver, are not soluble in the copper sulphate electrolyte and don't get oxidized. Instead, they settle down beneath the anode as they are displaced from the dissolving anode.

EXAMPLE 6.3 Reduction of alumina that is obtained, either by Hall's process or Bayer's process, to aluminium metal is carried out by electrolysis. During this process, cryolite and fluorspar are added to alumina, the entire mixture is covered with coke powder.

(i) Why can alumina not be directly electrolyzed?

(ii) What is the role of addition of cryolite and fluorspar?

(iii) What are the different cathodic and anodic reactions taking place during electrolysis?

SOLUTION

(i) Alumina can be directly electrolyzed because alumina has high thermal stability and hence, very high temperature is required for melting pure alumina.

(ii) Cryolite and fluorspar are added to alumina in order to decrease the melting point of alumina and increase the electrical conductivity of the mixture.

(iii) For the electrolysis of alumina, cryolite and fluorspar are added to it. The mixture undergoes electrolysis in the following way.

$Al_2O_3 \rightarrow 2Al^{3+} + 3O^{2-}$

$Na_3AlF_6 \rightarrow 3Na^+ + Al^{3+} + 6F^-$

$CaF_2 \rightarrow Ca^{2+} + 2F^-$

At anode: $O^{2-} - 2e^- \rightarrow [O]$ $\quad$ $C + 2[O] \rightarrow CO_2$

At cathode: $Al^{3+} + 3e^- \rightarrow Al$

Zinc

Zinc is a transition metal belonging to the II B group of the periodic table. It is highly reactive and found in a combined state in nature.

Important ores of zinc are listed hereunder:

Zinc blend	ZnS
Calamine	$ZnCO_3$
Zincite	ZnO

Info Bytes!

Zinc is an essential trace element in the human body and plays a crucial role in protein synthesis and wound healing.

Metallurgy of Zinc

Zinc is generally extracted from zinc blend (ZnS) or calamine ($ZnCO_3$).

Dressing and Concentration of Ore

The ore is crushed using ball mills and then pulverized. The pulverized ore is concentrated.

The concentration process depends upon the type of ore. Gravity separation process is followed for oxide ore (zincite) and carbonate ore (calamine) and froth flotation process is employed for sulphide ore (zinc blend).

If iron oxide is present as an impurity, it is separated by magnetic separation process.

Conversion of Ore to Oxide

In the case of sulphide ore, it is converted to oxide by roasting:

$$2ZnS + 3O_2 \xrightarrow{\text{heat}} 2ZnO + 2SO_2$$

The carbonate ore is subjected to calcination where it undergoes decomposition to oxide giving out carbon dioxide gas:

$$ZnCO_3 \xrightarrow{\Delta} ZnO + CO_2$$

Reduction of Metal Oxide to Metal Using Coke

Zinc oxide is reduced to zinc by vertical retort process called **smelting**. The retort is a tall cylindrical structure lined internally with clay bricks. An automatic screw conveyer arranged at the bottom acts as an outlet for the waste residue. It is heated internally using producer gas as the fuel.

The powdered zinc oxide is mixed with charcoal and made into small briquettes by pressing. This is taken in the vertical retort where, due to the high temperature, carbon reduces zinc oxide to zinc and itself gets oxidized to carbon monoxide:

$$ZnO + C \xrightarrow{1400°C} Zn + CO$$

The zinc formed in the vapor state escapes out along with carbon monoxide. These vapors are collected in the condenser in which zinc condenses and is collected from time to time while carbon monoxide remains as gas and is used for further heating of the retort.

Info Bytes!

The zinc obtained by this process is 97% pure and is called **zinc spelter**.

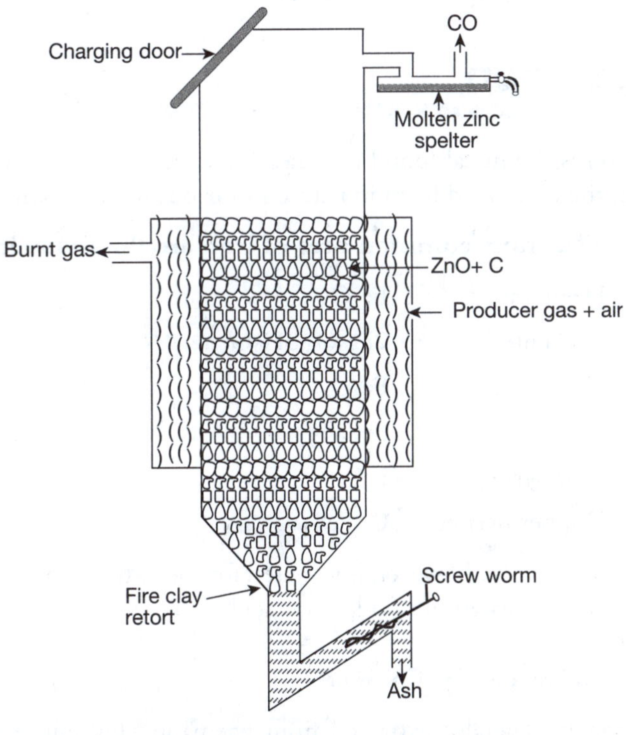

Figure 6.9 Smelting of zinc ore

Refining or Purification

The spelter zinc obtained contains both volatile impurities (Cd and As) and non-volatile impurities (Fe and C) and can be refined by two methods, which we now discuss.

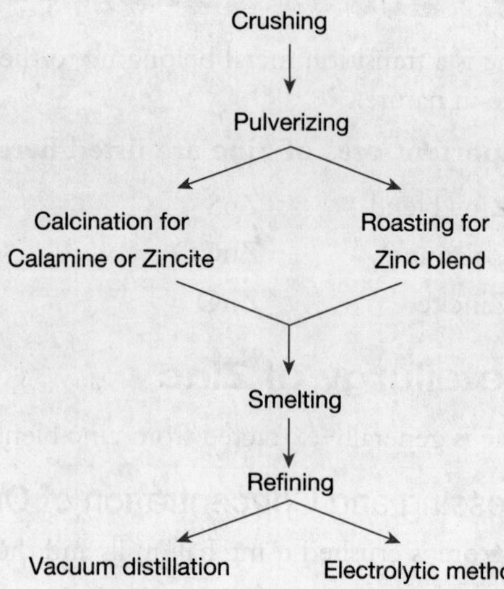

Figure 6.10 Process flow chart for metallurgy of zinc

1. **Distillation Under Low Pressure**
   The spelter is heated at a controlled temperature and the volatile impurities get vaporized. The metal is then strongly heated, when zinc changes to vapors. These vapors are condensed to obtain molten zinc that is poured into earthen moulds in which it is cooled and solidified.
2. **Electrolytic Method**
   A block of impure metal (spelter) is taken as anode and a thin strip of pure metal is taken as cathode. Acidified saturated zinc sulphate solution is taken as the electrolyte. On passing current, zinc from the anode dissolves in the electrolyte in the form of Zn^{2+} ions, goes towards the cathode, gets discharged there and is deposited on the cathode:

   At Anode: $Zn \longrightarrow Zn^{2+} + 2e^-$

   At Cathode: $Zn^{2+} + 2e^- \longrightarrow Zn$

   As electrolysis proceeds, the anode gets thinner and cathode gets (pure metal) thicker.

Uses of Zinc

1. **Galvanization**: Zinc is mainly used for coating iron surfaces to prevent rusting of iron. The process of protecting iron surfaces from rusting by coating it with zinc metal is called galvanization.
2. **In Dry Cells**: Zinc is used to make the cathodes of dry cells.
3. **Reducing Agent**: Because of the ability of zinc to act as a reducing agent, it is used in the extraction of metals.
4. **Alloys**: Used in the preparations of alloys like brass, bronze, etc.

Iron

Iron is the metal found in great abundance in nature. It is highly reactive and is hardly available in free state. Iron exists in the combined form in nature in various minerals among which oxide and sulphide ores are the most significant ones.

The most common ores of iron are the following:

Haematite	Fe_2O_3
Limonite	$2Fe_2O_3.3H_2O$
Magnetite	Fe_3O_4
Siderite	$FeCO_3$
Iron pyrites	FeS_2
Copper pyrites	$CuFeS_2$

Konnect

The core of the Earth is believed to be primarily made of iron and nickel.

Iron pyrite, however, is not used for the extraction and hence is not considered as an ore of iron. It is used as the source for the preparation of sulphuric acid.

Metallurgy of Iron

Iron is generally extracted from haematite, limonite and siderite. Among these hematite and limonite are the most preferred ores.

The manufacturing of pig iron is the first step in the metallurgy of iron. This pig iron is converted to cast iron, which is further used for the manufacture of steel and wrought iron.

Dressing and Concentration of Ore

The ore is crushed to make small pieces from larger chunks.

The crushed ore is concentrated by the process of magnetic separation and further concentration is done by gravity separation process.

Conversion of Ore to Oxide

The concentrated ore is converted to oxide form by the process of roasting that involves heating the ore in the presence of excess air.

On roasting, the carbonate ore decomposes to oxide giving out carbon dioxide. This process is also associated with other advantages like:

1. removal of moisture and other volatile impurities;
2. removal of impurities like sulphur, phosphorous, arsenic, antimony in the form of gaseous oxides;
3. conversion of ferrous oxide to ferric oxide and
4. inducing porosity in the mass, thus rendering easy reduction.

Reduction of Oxide to Metal

The reduction of oxide to metal is carried out with carbon in a blast furnace by the process called **smelting.**

Smelting in Blast Furnace

Blast furnace is a huge chimney-like structure about 30-m high and 8 m in diameter. It is made of iron plates and lined internally with refractory bricks. On the top, it has a double cup and cone arrangement. Below this, there is an outlet for waste gases. A hearth is present at the bottom to collect cast iron and slag, and has separate outlets for each. Hot compressed air is blown into the furnace through pipes called **tuyeres** that are placed above the hearth.

The ore is mixed with coke and limestone approximately in the ratio of 8 : 4 : 1. This mixture is called **charge.**

The charge is lowered into the furnace from the top through the cup and cone arrangement and various reactions take place in the furnace at different levels.

1. **Lower Region (2000–1500°C)**

   Coke combines with the heated air coming from the tuyeres and burns to form carbon dioxide. The reaction, being highly exothermic increases the temperature in this zone to 2000°C:

   $$C + O_2 \rightarrow CO_2 + 97 \text{ kcal}$$

   This region is also called the **combustion zone**.

2. **Middle Region or Fusion Zone (1500–1000°C)**

   The carbon dioxide formed in the lower layer moves to the middle layer where in it is reduced to carbon monoxide:

   $$CO_2 + C \rightarrow 2CO - 39 \text{ kcal}$$

   At such a high temperature, the limestone added decomposes to calcium oxide and carbon dioxide:

   $$CaCO_3 \rightarrow CaO + CO_2 - 43 \text{ kcal}$$

The calcium oxide (quick lime) formed reacts with impurities like sand in the ore and converts them to slag:

$$CaO + SiO_2 \rightarrow CaSiO_3$$

The slag, calcium silicate, goes towards the hearth present at the bottom of the furnace.

As the reactions in the middle region are endothermic, the temperature of this zone decreases.

3. **Upper Region or Reduction Zone (1000–500°C)**

The carbon monoxide formed in the middle region moves to the upper region where in it reduces the iron oxide to iron.

$$FeO + CO \xrightarrow{600-400°C} Fe + CO_2$$

$$Fe_2O_3 + 3CO \rightarrow \xrightarrow{600-400°C} 2Fe + 3CO_2$$

The iron formed here melts due to the high temperature and then due to its high density settles down. Both the slag (calcium silicate) and iron settle down in the hearth. Iron being heavier forms the bottom layer with slag on top. From here, iron and slag are tapped through separate outlets. Iron thus obtained is called **pig iron**. Solid pig iron is re-melted in a vertical furnace known as cupola and thereby gets refined. (Nowadays pig iron is directly poured in a laddle and sent to the converter for steel-making process.

Then it is poured into suitable moulds of required shape. This remelted pig iron is called **cast iron**.

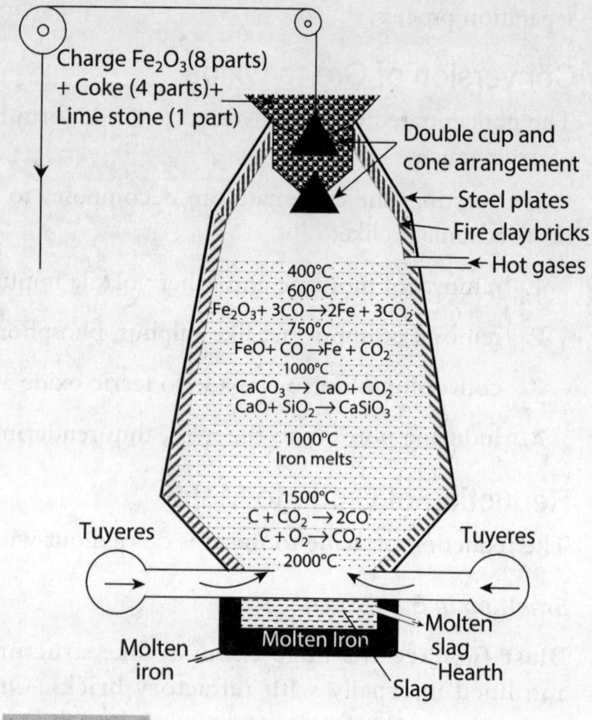

Figure 6.11 Smelting of Iron ore in blast furnace

Table 6.6 Products of blast furnace

	Major products	Byproduct and its composition	Byproduct and its composition
	Pig iron ↓ Cast iron	Slag	Blast furnace gases
Composition	Iron (85%–95%) Carbon (2.5%–5%) Silicon (0.5%–5%) Phosphorus (0.02%–2%)	$CaSiO_3$	Carbon monoxide (30%) Carbon dioxide (10%) Nitrogen (60%)
Uses	• Manufacture of steel • Making drain pipes, manhole cover, gates, machinery, etc.	In the manufacture of cement, slag wool, roadbeds	• Pre-heating the tuyeres • In coke ovens for making coke

Conversion of Cast Iron to Wrought Iron

Wrought iron is the purest form of iron. Apart from iron, it has very small quantities of carbon (0.2%), silicon (0.15%), phosphorous (0.02%), sulphur (0.04%), and manganese (0.05%). It is the refined form of cast iron.

It is prepared by heating cast iron in a reverberatory furnace. The furnace is lined internally with iron oxide. This oxidizes the carbon in the cast iron to gaseous oxides of carbon. The other impurities are slagged off using lime as flux. Heavy rollers are made to roll over the metal obtained, where the slag is squeezed out.

Conversion of Cast Iron to Steel

Cast iron, the impure form of iron, is converted to steel by Bessemer process. Steel is an alloy of iron. Small amounts of carbon and other metals like chromium, manganese, vanadium, and nickel are added to iron to impart special properties required for a variety of uses. The carbon content of steel varies from 0.1 to 1.5% depending on its use. Cast iron is converted to steel by Bessemer process which is carried out in a Bessemer converter.

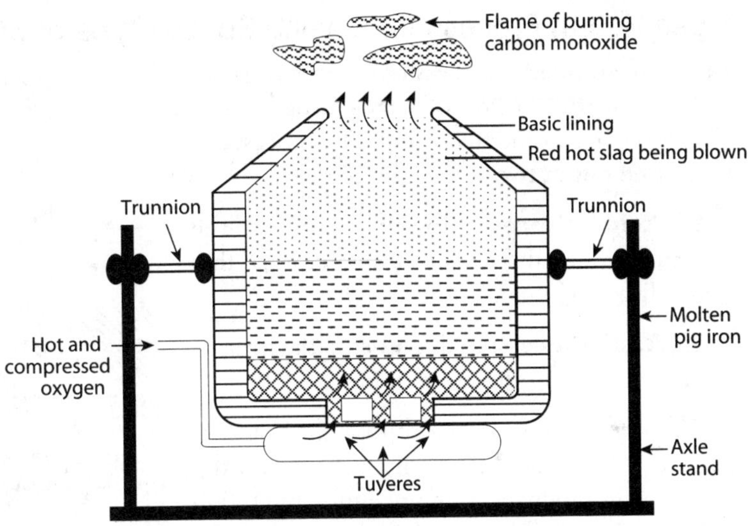

Figure 6.12 Bessemer converter

Structure of the Bessemer Converter

Bessemer converter is a pear-shaped furnace. It is made up of a steel plate lined inside with a refractory material. The lining is made up of silica in case of acidic process and with lime in basic process. Basic process is adopted if the cast iron contains phosphorous as an impurity.

Process of Bessemerisation

At first, the converter is tilted to a horizontal position and the charge of molten cast iron is introduced into it. Then it is brought back to the upright position and a blast of air is passed through the tuyeres present at the bottom of the furnace. Carbon and other impurities present in cast iron combine with oxygen to form their respective oxides:

$$C + O_2 \longrightarrow CO_2$$
$$CO_2 + C \longrightarrow 2CO$$
$$S + O_2 \longrightarrow SO_2$$
$$P_4 + 5O_2 \longrightarrow 2P_2O_5 \text{ (in basic process)}$$
$$2Mn + O_2 \longrightarrow 2MnO$$
$$\left.\begin{array}{l} Si + O_2 \longrightarrow SiO_2 \\ MnO + SiO_2 \longrightarrow MnSiO_3 \end{array}\right\} \text{Slag}$$
$$6CaO + P_4O_{10} \longrightarrow 2Ca_3(PO_4)_2 \text{ (in basic process)}$$

Oxides of manganese and silicon are removed in the form of slag ($MnSiO_3$). In the basic Bessemer process, phosphorus is removed as $Ca_3(PO_4)_2$ in the form of slag.

After the removal of slag and gaseous oxides, CO burns with a bright flame at the mouth of the converter. The disappearance of flame indicates that iron is free from impurities. At this stage, the required amount of spiegeleisen (an alloy of carbon and manganese) is added to the molten iron and the blast of air continues till the alloy melts and mixes with molten iron.

Finally, the molten steel with desired carbon content is formed, which is poured out in moulds and is then cooled.

Open Hearth Process for Making Special Type of Steel

As the name suggests, the shape of the furnace is like a hearth, the top of which is open. The charge is pig iron and steel scrap. The process can be carried out in two ways as listed below:

1. **Acid Process**: In this process, the furnace is lined with acidic refractories, that is, silica brick.
2. **Basic Process**: In this process, the furnace is lined with magnesite or dolomite.

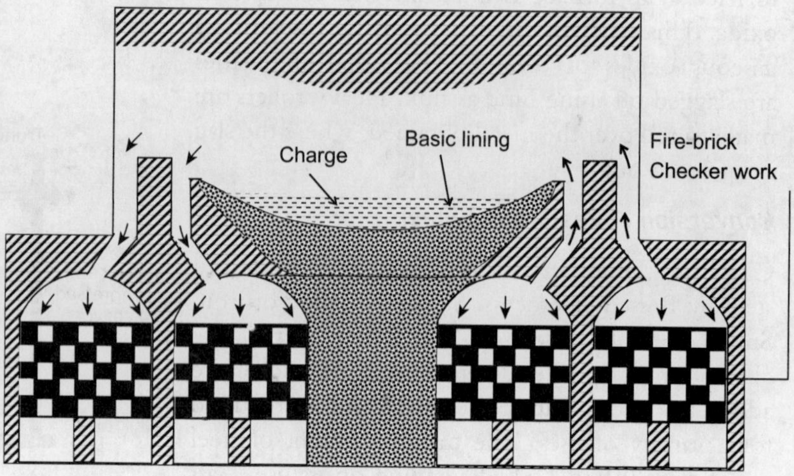

Figure 6.13 An open hearth furnace

The temperature on the top of the hearth is generated by a hot fuel gas that is burns on the hearth and produces a temperature of 1600–1650°C. The final composition of the steel is adjusted by adding ferrosilicon or ferromanganese alloy.

It is a very lengthy process and takes about 5–15 h. Raw materials used in open hearth process have low content of phosphorous and sulphur in them; hence, the steel made by this process is of a better quality

L.D. Process for Making Steel

The latest development in steel making process is the L.D. process. The name of this process is taken from two separate plants situated in Austria, at Linz and Donawitz. It is a very fast process and takes about 20 min to produce steel.

Pure oxygen (99.5%) is lanced from the top of the converter at supersonic speed. This oxygen produces temperature of about 2500–3000°C and oxidizes the impurities present in it and finally steel is produced. The L.D. converter is lined with basic refractory.

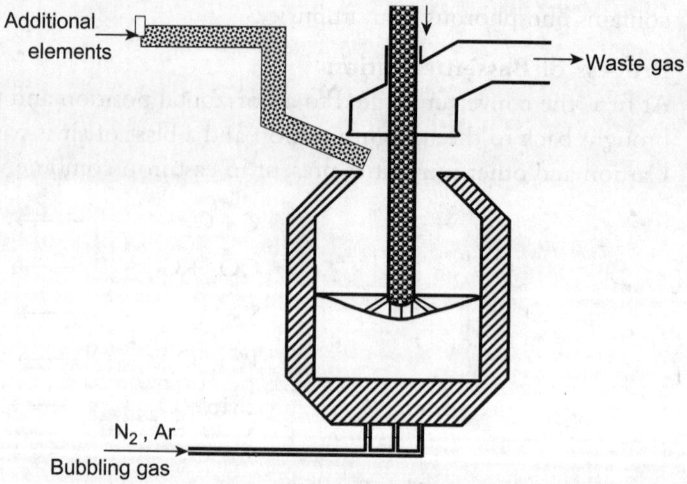

Figure 6.14 Schematic diagram of L–D converter

Varieties of Steel: Many varieties of steel are available. These can be categorized based on the following:

1. the percentage of carbon in steel and
2. the metals (small amounts) present in the alloy.

Table 6.7 Comparative study of mild and hard steel

Mild Steel	Hard Steel
Carbon content in mild steel is less and ranges from 0.15 to 0.5%.	The carbon content here is slightly more ranging from 0.5 to 1.7%.
It is a highly elastic form of steel with greater malleability and ductility.	It is a less elastic form of steel that is tough and has high tensile strength. It is less malleable and ductile.
It is used in making powerful magnets.	It is used in making tools that are used for cutting.

There are five different types of steel based on the other metals present in steel along with iron.

Table 6.8 Different styles of steel and their properties

	Stainless Steel	Manganese Steel	Tungsten Steel	Chrome Steel	Vanadium Steel
Composition	Iron (82% to 84%) Chromium (12% to 14%), Nickel (1% to 2%)	Iron (83% to 84%), Mn (15%), C (0.9% to 1.5%)	Wolfram (1%–20%)	Chromium (1%–4%)	Vanadium (0.2%–1%)
Properties	Resistant to corrosion, mild organic acids, alkalies	Extremely hard	Very hard, tough	Very hard, tough	Very hard, not very brittle
Uses	Utensils, surgical instruments	Safes, army helmets, hammering machines	Swords, armour, ball bearings	Swords, armour, ball bearings	Springs, crank shaft, axles of automobiles

Altering the Properties of Steel by Controlling Temperature

Steel, when heated to high temperature and subsequently cooled in different ways shows different properties.

1. **Hardening of Steel**: The process of heating steel to a temperature of 1000–1250 K and cooling suddenly by plunging it into cold water or oil is called hardening of steel. It is also called **quenching of steel**. Due to hardening, the steel becomes much harder but brittle.
2. **Annealing or Tampering of Steel:** The process of heating hardened steel to 500–610 K followed by slow cooling is called annealing or tempering of steel.

Konnect

The annealed steel is hard and very tough. It has high tensile strength and can withstand a lot of load.

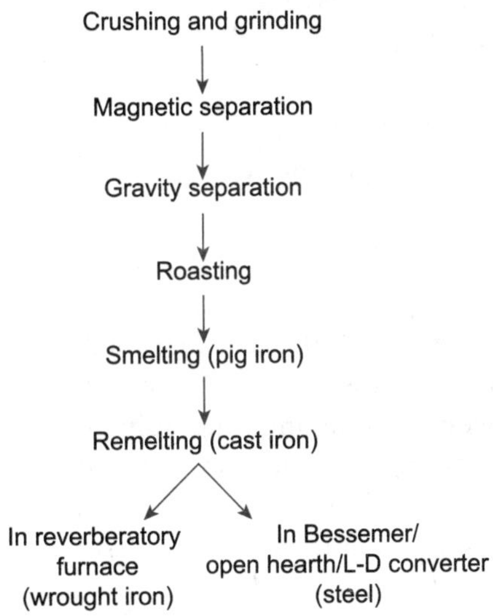

Figure 6.15 Process flow chart for metallurgy if iron

Copper

Copper is a transition metal that belongs to the IB group. It shows variable valencies of +1 and +2. It is highly reactive and found in combined state.

Following are the important ores of Copper:

Cuprite, Cu_2O

Copper pyrites, $CuFeS_2$

Konnect

- The Statue of Liberty contains 81193 Kgs of copper.
- The ancient Indians used copper to make tools, weapons, ornaments, and even utensils.

Metallurgy of Copper

Dressing and Concentration

Dressing of Ore: The ore is crushed in big jaw crushers and then finely powdered in ball mills.

Concentration of Ore: The ore is concentrated by the froth floatation process.

Roasting

The process of roasting is carried out in a reverberatory furnace. The finely powdered ore is heated strongly on the hearth of the furnace in the presence of excess of air. The impurities of sulphur, arsenic, antimony and phosphorous are expelled as volatile impurities. Moisture is also expelled out.

During this process, copper pyrites ore is converted to ferrous sulphide and copper sulphide. During heating, the temperature is maintained below the melting point of the ore:

$$S + O_2 \rightarrow SO_2$$

$$4As + 3O_2 \rightarrow 2As_2O_3$$

$$4Sb + 3O_2 \rightarrow 2Sb_2O_3$$

$$4P + 5O_2 \rightarrow 2P_2O_5$$

$$2CuFeS_2 + O_2 \rightarrow Cu_2S + 2FeS + SO_2$$

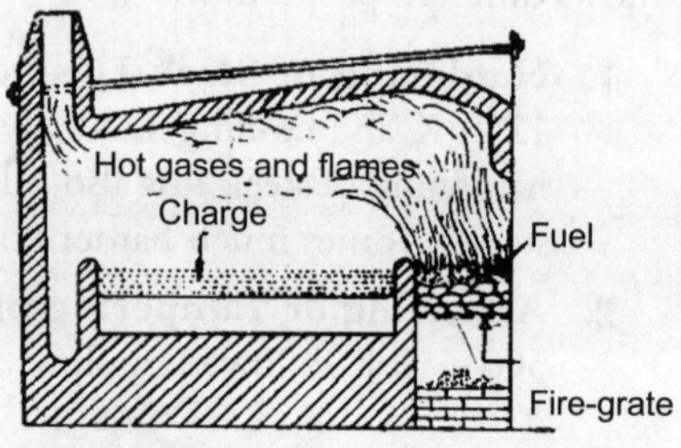

Figure 6.16 Reverberatory furnace

The sulphides partially get oxidized to their corresponding oxides:

$$2Cu_2S + 3O_2 \rightarrow 2Cu_2O + 2SO_2$$

$$2FeS + 3O_2 \rightarrow 2FeO + 2SO_2$$

Smelting

The process of smelting is carried out in a blast furnace. The roasted ore is mixed with sand and coke. A blast of air is sent through the tuyeres at the bottom. In the process of smelting, the sulphides are converted to oxides. The oxides combine with sand to form a fusible slag. Apart from the removal of impurities in the form of slag, conversion of cuprous oxide (formed by partial oxidation in roasting process) to cuprous sulphide also takes place:

$$2FeS + 3O_2 \rightarrow 2FeO + 2SO_2$$

$$\underset{\text{Impurity}}{FeO} + \underset{\text{Flux}}{SiO_2} \rightarrow \underset{\text{Slag}}{FeSiO_3}$$

$$Cu_2O + FeS \rightarrow Cu_2S + FeO$$

Slag is removed and the resultant molten ore containing a little of ferrous sulphide is called matte. This is taken out from the exit at the bottom.

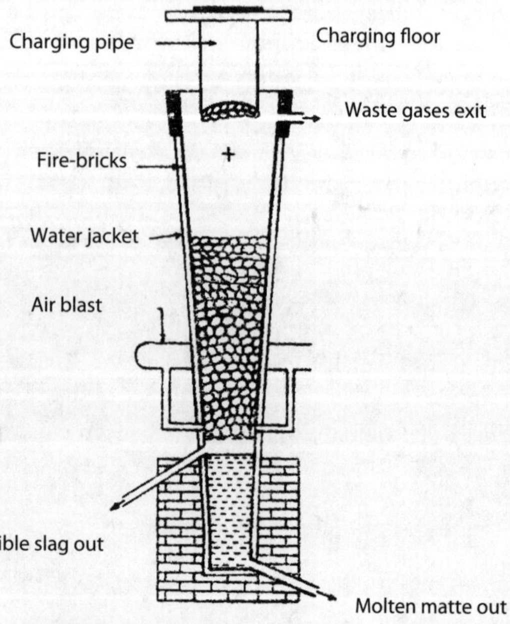

Figure 6.17 Blast furnace for copper

Bessemerization

Bessemer converter is a pear-shaped furnace. It is made up of steel plates and lined by MgO or CaO. It is mounted on trunnions in such a way that it can be tilted in either direction. The matte from the process of smelting is transferred into the Bessemer converter. A blast of sand and air is blown inside. The molten metal drops below the level of tuyeres that escapes from oxidation.

The reaction of roasting and smelting get completed. Entire iron is removed in the form of slag. Cu_2O and Cu_2S react to give copper and SO_2 escapes out:

$$2Cu_2O + Cu_2S \rightarrow 6Cu + SO_2$$

After the completion of the above reactions, the molten copper obtained is poured off. When the molten mass is subjected to solidification, SO_2 gas escapes out. The copper so obtained gets a blister-type appearance and hence is called **blister copper**. Blister copper is purified through electrolytic process.

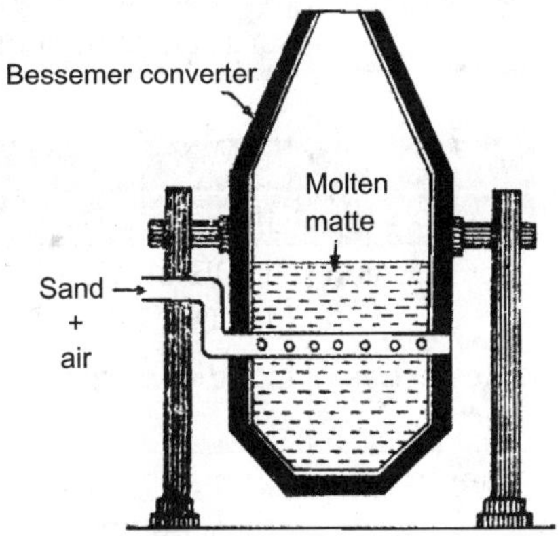

Figure 6.18 Bessemer converter for copper

Electrolytic Purification

The crude copper is subjected to electrolysis by taking the impure copper as anode and a strip of pure copper as cathode. Acidified copper sulphate solution is taken as an electrolyte. Pure copper from anode dissolves and gets deposited at the cathode. The cathode becomes thicker due to the deposition of copper. The impurities are collected in the form of anode mud:

Anode Reaction: $Cu \rightarrow Cu^{2+} + 2e^-$

Cathode Reaction: $Cu^{2+} + 2e^{2-} \rightarrow Cu$

Process Flow Sheet for Metallurgy of Copper

Crushing → Grinding → Froth floatation → Roasting → Smelting → Bessemerization → Electrolytic refining

Figure 6.19 Metallurgy of copper

Table 6.9 Important alloys and their uses

Major component: Copper (Cu)					
Alloy	**Brass**	**Bronze**	**Gun metal**	**German silver**	**Bell metal**
Composition	Cu (60% to 80%), Zn (20% to 40%)	Cu (80%), Zn (10%), Sn (10%)	Cu (88%), Sn (10%), Zn (1%), Pb (1%)	Cu (30% to 60%), Zn (20% to 30%), Ni (15% to 20%)	Cu (80%), Sn (20%)
Properties	Lustrous, more malleable, and ductile than copper	Hard but brittle, resistant to corrosion, takes very high polish	Very hard, gives a very good cast	White like silver, malleable and ductile	Hard and brittle, produces sonorous sound
Uses	For making shells of ammunition utensils, electrical switches, statues	For making shells, statues, coins and utensils	For making barrels of guns, gears and bearings	For making imitation silver jewellery, utensils, etc.	For making bells

(Continued.)

Table 6.9 Continued

Major component: Iron (Fe)				
Alloys	**Stainless steel**	**Manganese steel**	**Tungsten steel**	**Alnico**
Composition	Fe (83%), C (1%), Cr (15%) and Ni (1%)	Fe (84%), Mn (15%) and C (1%)	Fe (79% to 84%), W (20% to 15%) and C (1%)	Fe (50%), Al (20%), Ni (20%) and Co (10%)
Properties	Resists corrosion	Very tough and hard	Very very hard	Highly malleable
Uses	For making utensils and surgical instruments	For making safes, armour and rock cutter	For making high speed tools	For making powerful magnets

Major component: Aluminium (Al)		
Alloy	**Duralumin**	**Magnalium**
Composition	Al (95%), Cu (4%) Mn (0.5%) and Mg (0.5%)	Al (95%) and Mg (5%)
Properties	Light in weight and as strong as steel	Light in weight, strong and resistant to corrosion
Uses	For making aircraft frames, rockets, speed boats, automobiles	For making aeroplane parts, house appliances, mirrors and scientific instruments

Major component: Nickel (Ni)	
Alloy	**Monel metal**
Composition	Cu (28%), Ni (67%) and Fe (5%)
Properties	Resistant to corrosion, malleable, and ductile
Uses	Used for making sinks, doors, and window screws

Major component: Tin	
Alloy	**Solder**
Composition	Sn (50%–60%) Pb (50%–40%)
Properties	Low melting point and resistant to corrosion
Use	Soldering purposes

Major component: Lead	
Alloy	**Type metal**
Composition	Pb (75%) Sn (5%) Sb (20%)
Properties	Hard and expands on cooling
Use	Construction industry

Physical Properties

Table 6.10 Comparative study of properties of copper, iron, zinc, and aluminium

Parameters	Copper	Aluminium	Zinc	Iron
Colour	Reddish orange	Bluish white solid	Bluish white when freshly cut	Light grey
Malleability ductility	High malleability and ductility	High malleability and ductility	Malleable and ductile between 150 and 200°C. Brittle above and below these temperatures.	Tough, malleable and ductile
Conductivity	Very good conductor of heat and electricity	Very good conductor of heat and electricity	Good conductor of heat and electricity	Good conductor of heat and electricity
Melting point	1085°C	720°C	419°C	1535°C
Boiling point	2562°C	2467°C	907°C	2750°C
Density	8.96 g/cm^3	2.7 g/cm^3	7.1 g/cm^3	7.8 g/cm^3
Magnetic property	Does not show magnetic property	Does not show magnetic property	Does not show magnetic property	Highly magnetic. Loses its magnetic property above 770°C

Chemical Properties

Table 6.11 Chemical properties of some metals

Properties	Copper	Aluminium	Zinc	Iron
		Action of air		
Dry air	No reaction with dry air or moist air	No reaction with dry air	No reaction with dry air	No reaction with dry air
Moist air	Formation of superficial coating of green basic carbonate $CuCO_3.Cu(OH)_2$	A thin layer of oxide is formed on the surface: $4Al + 3O_2 \rightarrow 2Al_2O_3$	A layer of oxide is formed that is then converted to carbonate with atmospheric carbon dioxide: $2Zn + O_2 \rightarrow 2ZnO$ $ZnO + CO_2 \rightarrow ZnCO_3$	Formation of a brown powder of hydrated ferric oxide (rust): $4Fe + 3O_2 + xH_2O \rightarrow 2Fe_2O_3.xH_2O$ (rust)
Strong heating	Forms copper oxide. $Cu + O_2 \rightarrow CuO$ $Cu + O_2 \rightarrow Cu_2O$	Burns with bright white light giving a lot of heat	Burns with a bluish white flame	Burns with brilliant white flames: $3Fe + 2O_2 \rightarrow Fe_3O_4$ (triferric tetraoxide)

(Continued.)

Table 6.11 Continued

Properties	Copper	Aluminium	Zinc	Iron
Action with water				
Pure water	Passive to pure water	No reaction due to the formation of protective oxide layer	Passive to pure water	No reaction
With steam	No reaction with steam	Red hot aluminium reacts with steam. The reaction is rapid in the beginning and becomes slow later: $2Al + 3H_2O \rightarrow Al_2O_3 + 3H_2$ (steam)	Hot zinc reacts with steam to form zinc oxide liberating hydrogen gas $Zn + H_2O \rightarrow ZnO + H_2\uparrow$ (steam)	Steam with red hot iron form triferric tetraoxide and hydrogen gas. The reaction is reversible: $3Fe + 4H_2O$ (steam) $\rightarrow Fe_3O_4 + 4H_2$
With non-metals				
Chlorine	Forms chloride on heating with chlorine: $Cu + Cl_2 \rightarrow CuCl_2$	Forms chloride on heating: $2Al + 3Cl_2 \xrightarrow{heat} 2AlCl_3$	Forms chloride on heating: $Zn + Cl_2 \xrightarrow{heat} ZnCl_2$	Forms chlorides when chlorine is passed over red hot iron: $2Fe + 3Cl_2 \rightarrow 2FeCl_3$
With non-metals				
Sulphur	Forms sulphide on heating: $Cu + S \rightarrow CuS$	Forms sulphide on heating: $2Al + 3S \xrightarrow{heat} Al_2S_3$	Forms sulphide on heating: $Zn + S \xrightarrow{\Delta} ZnS$	On strong heating with sulphur, it forms sulphide: $Fe + S \xrightarrow{\Delta} FeS$
Carbon	No reaction with carbon	Aluminium carbide is formed: $4Al + 3C \rightarrow Al_4C_3$	–	–
With acids				
Dilute and concentrated hydrochloric acid and dilute sulphuric acid	No reaction with the liberation of hydrogen gas	Forms respective salts liberating hydrogen gas: $2Al + 6HCl \downarrow 2AlCl_3 + 3H_2$ $2Al + 3H_2SO_4 \downarrow Al_2(SO_4)_3 + 3H_2$	Liberates hydrogen gas forming respective salts: $Zn + 2HCl \downarrow ZnCl_2 + H_2$ $Zn + H_2SO_4 \downarrow ZnSO_4 + H_2$	Forms chloride and sulphate salts, liberating hydrogen gas: $Fe + 2HCl \downarrow FeCl_2 + H_2$ $Fe + H_2SO_4 \downarrow FeSO_4 + H_2$

(Continued.)

Table 6.11 Continued

Properties	Copper	Aluminium	Zinc	Iron
Concentrated sulphuric acid	Copper dissolves with the evolution of SO_2 gas: $Cu + 2H_2SO_4 \downarrow CuSO_4 + SO_2 + 2H_2O$	Forms aluminium sulphate, water and sulphur dioxide gas: $2Al + 6H_2SO_4 \downarrow Al_2(SO_4)_3 + 6H_2O + 3SO_2$	Liberates sulphur dioxide on boiling: $Zn + 2H_2SO_4 \downarrow ZnSO_4 + 2H_2O + SO_2$	Forms ferrous sulphate with the liberation of sulphur dioxide gas: $Fe + 2H_2SO_4 \downarrow FeSO_4 + SO_2 + 2H_2O$
Dilute and concent-rated nitric acid.	$3Cu + 8HNO_3$ (dil.) $\rightarrow 3Cu(NO_3)_2 + 4H_2O + 2NO$ $\therefore Cu + 4HNO_3 \rightarrow Cu(NO_3)_2 + 2H_2O + 2NO_2$ (conc.)	Oxidizes the outer layer to aluminium and renders it passive for further corrosion.	Zinc nitrate and nitric oxide gas with dilute acid $3Zn + 8HNO_3(dil) \downarrow 3Zn(NO_3)_2 + 4H_2O + 2N_2O(g)$ Liberates nitrogen dioxide gas with conc. acid: $Zn + 4HNO_3 \downarrow Zn(NO_3)_2 + 2NO_2 + 2H_2O$	Dilute acid liberates nitric oxide gas: $3Fe + 8HNO_3$ (dil) $\downarrow 3Fe(NO_3)_2 + 4H_2O + 2NO$ Concentrated acid oxidizes the outer layer that makes the metal passive.
With alkalies				
Action with caustic alkalies	No reaction with alkalies	Dissolves in concentrated caustic alkalies forming aluminates: $2Al + 2NaOH + 2H_2O$ (powder) (conc) $\downarrow 2NaAlO_2 + 2H_2$	Forms zincates and hydrogen with concentrated aqueous alkalies: $Zn + 2NaOH(conc) \downarrow Na_2ZnO_2 + H_2$	No reaction with alkalies
With salts of less active metals				
Displacement reactions	Displaces less active metals from their aqueous solutions: $Cu + 2AgNO_3 \rightarrow Cu(NO_3)_2 + 2Ag$	Displaces less active metals from their aqueous salt solutions $3AgNO_3 + Al \downarrow Al(NO_3)_3 + 3Ag$	Displaces the lesser active metals from their aqueous salt $Zn + CuSO_4 \downarrow ZnSO_4 + Cu$	Displaces the less active metal from its aqueous salt solution: $CuSO_4 + Fe \downarrow FeSO_4 + Cu$

Reducing Property:

More active metals can reduce oxides or compounds of less active metals.

Examples:

$Fe_2O_3 + Al \rightarrow Al_2O_3 + 2Fe$

$Zn + CuSO_4 \rightarrow ZnSO_4 + Cu$

$Fe + CuSO_4 \rightarrow FeSO_4 + Cu$

EXAMPLE 6.4 In the L-D converter, why is lime (calcium oxide) added during the steel production process?

SOLUTION

Lime is added for the following reasons:

(i) It acts as a flux, combining with impurities to form slag which can be easily removed.

(ii) Lime neutralizes acidic impurities, ensuring the steel has the desired properties and is not compromised by contaminants.

EXAMPLE 6.5 Steel is more elastic than wrought iron. Give reason.

SOLUTION

Steel is an alloy containing iron and carbon, with the carbon content providing added strength and elasticity. Wrought iron, being almost pure iron, lacks this additional carbon, making it less elastic in comparison to steel.

EXAMPLE 6.6 What is meant by blister copper? What is the reason for the formation of blister copper?

SOLUTION

Copper obtained from Bessemer converter by the process of Bessemerisation gets blister-typeappearance. This is called blister copper. During the process of Bessemerisation, Cu_2O and Cu_2S react to produce copper and SO_2 gas. In this process, copper is obtained in the molten form and then it is solidified. During solidification, SO_2 gas escapes and hence, blister copper is obtained.

POINTS TO REMEMBER

- ✔ A strong electrostatic force of attraction exists between the metal kernels, which is known as metallic bond.
- ✔ The metals in the combined form are called minerals.
- ✔ The mineral from which a metal can be extracted in an easy and cost-effective process is called an ore.
- ✔ The earthy impurities associated with the ores are called gangue.
- ✔ The process of the removal of gangue from an ore is called the dressing of ore.
- ✔ The removal of gangue from the dressed ore is called concentration of ore.
- ✔ Gravity separation involves the separation of ore and gangue based on the difference in their specific gravities.
- ✔ Froth flotation involves the differential wetting characteristics of ore and gangue with oil and water, the ore being wet by oil and gangue by water.
- ✔ Magnetic separation is employed for the concentration of ores in which either the ore or the gangue is attracted by a magnet and the other is not.
- ✔ During roasting, the ore is strongly heated in the presence of excess air.
- ✔ During calcination, the ore is strongly heated in the absence or limited supply of air.
- ✔ The metal obtained by the reduction of oxide is not completely pure and is associated with certain impurities therefore, the metals extracted are subjected to further purification which is called the refining of the metal.
- ✔ A mixture of aluminium powder and ferric oxide in 1 : 3 ratio is called thermite.
- ✔ The zinc obtained by this process is 97% pure and is called zinc spelter.
- ✔ The process of protecting iron surfaces from rusting by coating it with zinc metal is called galvanisation.
- ✔ The ore is mixed with coke and limestone approximately in the ratio of 8 : 4 : 1. This mixture is called charge.

PRACTICE QUESTIONS CLASSROOM WING

Very Short Answer Type Questions

Directions for questions from 1 to 9:
Fill in the blanks.

1. In thermite welding, crucible is lined with__________.
2. The region in the blast furnace where the temperature range is 1500°C to 2000°C is called _________ zone.
3. The charge in the manufacture of special type of steel in open hearth process _________ and _________.
4. Zinc on reaction with steam liberates ______ gas.
5. Polling method is generally employed to ______ with ______ as impurity.
6. Copper on reaction with moist air gives ______.
7. Alnico is an alloy of Al, Ni, Co, and ______.
8. Magnalium is an alloy of ______ and ______.
9. Refining of zinc and mercury is carried out by using _____ process.

Directions for questions from 10 to 26:
Answer the following questions.

10. The below-mentioned chemical reactions involved in the extraction of iron take place in a blast furnace. Arrange them in the following order.
    (i) Formation of iron due to the reaction between roasted haematite and CO.
    (ii) Formation of CO from coke taken as charge.
    (iii) Formation of CO_2 from coke taken as charge.
    (iv) Formation of calcium silicate from silica.
    (v) Decomposition of limestone taken as charge.
11. Which of the zinc ore cannot be extracted through the extraction process represented by the following flow chart:

    Grinding Crushing
    –
    Gravity separation
    –
    Calcination
    –
    Smelting
    –
    Refining
12. If an ore contains an impurity of FeO, identify the flux added to remove it.
13. In which metal exctration hydrogen act as a reducing agent?
14. Which metal oxidation is used as a method of refining?
15. How is alumina melted in the electrolytic extraction process of molten alumina?
16. What is the process called when ZnS is converted to ZnO during the extraction of zinc?
17. How can aluminium be used in the extraction processes of metals?
18. How are slag and molten metal separated from blast furnace?
19. Which is the purest form of iron? How is it useful?
20. What are the major products and by-products of blast furnace in the extraction of iron?
21. What is the slag formed in the basic process of the above conversion?

22. What is the basic process adopted for the conversion of cast iron to steel? What is the difference between acidic and basic process of conversion of cast iron to steel?

23. What type of changes take place in the property of steel if the carbon content is more?

24. What are the products formed when chlorine reacts with
 (i) aluminium
 (ii) zinc
 (iii) iron

25. Which method is employed for the concentration of copper pyrites?

26. What is the basic purpose of roasting and calcination? Compare these two processes.

Short Answer Type Questions

27. A metal 'M' displaces metal 'N' from the solution of its salt and both the metals can liberate hydrogen from acids. Halogen 'X' displaces halogen 'Y' from the corresponding metal halide. Identify the set of metals and halogens from the following options.

28. Identify the possible reactions among the following.
 (A) $2Ag + H_2SO_4 \rightarrow Ag_2SO_4 + H_2$
 (B) $Sn + CuSO_4 \rightarrow SnSO_4 + Cu$
 (C) $2NaBr + I_2 \rightarrow 2NaI + Br_2$
 (D) $2KBr + Cl_2 \rightarrow 2KCl + Br_2$

29. Which of the following metals: Cu, Cr, Mn, Mg cannot be displaced from their solutions by aluminium?

30. State the reactions that take place at the cathode and anode during the process of electrolytic reduction of alumina.

31. (a) Compare the different physical properties of aluminium, iron, and zinc.
 (b) Thermite welding is carried out to join broken pieces of iron. Which of the following statement(s) regarding the above process is/are correct?
 (i) The main chemical reaction that takes place in this process is a displacement and endothermic reaction.
 (ii) The nature of the chemical reaction is highly exothermic and hence iron obtained remains in molten state.
 (iii) Iron can be obtained if iron oxide is made to react with a metal which is more reactive than iron. Hence, aluminium power is used in thermite mixture.
 (iv) Thermite mixture is ignited with the help of coke power.

32. What are the different processes involved in the dressing of ore? Explain.

33. Describe the conversion of cast iron to steel through Bessemerization in brief.

34. Explain froth floatation process for concentrating sulphide ores.

35. How is aluminium refined in Hoope's electrolytic process?

36. What is meant by blister copper? Why is it called so?

37. Describe the reduction of zinc oxide to zinc in brief.

38. Write the reactions of aluminium, iron and zinc with both dilute and concentrated nitric acids.

39. Classify the different types of ores depending on the negative radical present in them. Mention the name of each ore.

Essay Answer Type Questions

40. Describe the processes of conversion of cast iron to wrought iron in brief.

41. Describe smelting of iron in blast furnace. Write all the reactions that take place in different zones of blast furnace.

42. What are the different reducing agents that are used to reduce the metal oxides? Describe how they work with different oxides of metal.

43. Explain the process of roasting and smelting in the extraction of copper from copper pyrites.

44. Describe the different purification processes applied for different metals.

45. Compare the composition, properties, and uses of different alloys of following metals.
 (i) copper
 (ii) aluminium

46. A process flow sheet for the extraction of a metal is given below.

Step 1: Crushing and grinding
↓
Step 2: Pulverization
↓
Step 3: Froth flotation
↓
Step 4: Roasting
↓
Step 5: Reduction by CO

Which of the following ores can be used to extract the respective metal following the steps mentioned above?

(i) Lead ore (ii) Magnesite

(iii) Cinnabar (iv) Galena

(v) Fluorspar

Give reason in support of your answer.

PRACTICE QUESTIONS COMPETITION WING

Level 1: Apply your Concepts

Direction for questions from 1 to 7:
State whether the following statements are true or false.

1. In metallurgy, the concentration of ore is followed by the dressing of ore.
2. In calcination and roasting, volatile impurities are removed.
3. Metals that have low melting point are refined by liquation.
4. In froth flotation process, pine oil is usually added to wet the gangue particles in the ore.
5. Mercuric oxide is reduced by thermal decomposition.
6. Monel metal is an alloy of Cu, Ni, and Fe.
7. In purification of metals, during distillation, metal is strongly heated above its boiling point in the presence of air.

Direction for questions from 8 to 19:
Fill in the blanks.

8. __________is study of extraction of metals.
9. Gold is mostly found in _______ state in nature.
10. The mineral from which a metal can be extracted profitably is called ______.
11. The process of the removal of gangue from the ore is called ______.
12. Grinding of ore to a fine powder in an inert atmosphere is called _________.
13. In the upper region of blast furnace ______ helps in the reduction of iron oxide to iron.
14. In Bessemer converter __________ is removed as phosphate slag.
15. ______ and ___________ are partially oxidized during roasting in the extraction of copper.
16. Iron pyrites are converted to iron oxide by the process of ______.
17. The reaction that is not associated with the middle region of blast furnace during smelting is ________.
18. Chromium and manganese oxides are reduced to metals by using ______.
19. The components in solder are _______.

Direction for question 20:
Match the entries given in Column A with the appropriate ones in Column B.

20. Match the statements of Column A with those of Column B.

Column A (Reaction with Steam)	Column B (Metal)
(i) No reaction	(A) Fe
(ii) Reversible reaction	(B) Mg
(iii) Red hot metal reacts with steam rapidly at the beginning and becomes slow later	(C) Cu
(iv) Liberates hydrogen gas and forms oxide of formula MO where M is the metal	(D) Al
	(E) Zn

Direction for questions from 21 to 39:
For each of the questions, four choices have been provided. Select the correct alternative.

21. **Assertion (A):** Steel obtained from the L-D process is much better than that obtained from the Bessemer process with respect to quality and quantity.

    Reason (R): Pure oxygen (99.5%) is lanced from the top of the converter at supersonic speed.

    (a) Both A and R are true and R is the correct explanation of A.
    (b) Both A and R are true, but R is not the correct explanation of A.
    (c) A is true and R is false.
    (d) A is false and R is true.

22. **Assertion (A):** Metals of moderate reactivity are extracted from their respective oxides by using a suitable reducing agent.

Reason (R): Aluminium due to its very strong affinity towards oxygen acts as a better-reducing agent than CO.

(a) Both A and R are true and R is the correct explanation of A.

(b) Both A and R are true, but R is not the correct explanation of A.

(c) A is true and R is false.

(d) A is false and R is true.

23. **Assertion (A):** Copper pyrites are concentrated by the froth floatation process and then heated strongly in a reverberatory furnace, blast furnace, and Bessemer converter, respectively, for the extraction of copper from it.

Reason (R): Copper pyrites are a sulphide ore of copper and iron and copper is a metal of low reactivity.

(a) Both A and R are true and R is the correct explanation of A.

(b) Both A and R are true, but R is not the correct explanation of A.

(c) A is true and R is false.

(d) A is false and R is true.

24. An ore contains arsenic and antimony as impurities. How are they removed during the process of roasting?

(a) by conversion into As_2O_3 and Sb_2O_3

(b) by conversion into As_2O_5 and Sb_2O_5

(c) by conversion into both trioxides and pentoxides

(d) by conversion into sulphides

25. Aluminium is added in Bessemer process to remove certain impurities, but not in L–D process. This is because:

(a) pure oxygen is passed in Bessemer process

(b) pure oxygen is passed in L–D process

(c) air is passed in L–D process

(d) of addition of spiegel in Bessemer process

26. Which among the following is an oxide ore of lead?

(a) lead ochre

(b) galena

(c) anglesite

(d) dolomite

27. Zinc is refined by:

(a) liquation (or) distillation under reduced pressure

(b) electrolytic method or polling

(c) liquation or electrolytic method

(d) distillation under reduced pressure or electrolytic method

28. Lustre of metal is attributed to:

(a) loosely bound electrons present in the valence shell of the metal atoms

(b) strong electrostatic force of attraction between electrons and metal kernels

(c) omnidirectional nature of metallic bond

(d) none of the above

29. The volatile impurities associated with zinc spelter are:

(a) Cd and Fe

(b) Fe and As

(c) Cd and C

(d) Cd and As

30. Match the entries in Column A with appropriate ones in Column B.

Column A	Column B
(1) German silver	(a) for making printing type
(2) Tungsten steel	(b) soldering
(3) Alloy of Sn and Pb	(c) for making high speed tolls
(4) Alloy of Pb, Sn and Sb	(d) for making jewellery

(a) 1 → b; 2 → c; 3 → d; 4 → a

(b) 1 → c; 2 → d; 3 → a; 4 → b

(c) 1 → d; 2 → c; 3 → b; 4 → a

(d) 1 → d; 2 → a; 3 → b; 4 → c

31. The process employed for the purification of copper with cuprous oxide as the impurity is:

(a) polling (b) liquation

(c) electrolytic process (d) oxidation

32. 'Alclad' is perfectly resistant to corrosion by sea water. The alloy is:

(a) magnalium coated with aluminium

(b) duralumin coated with aluminium

(c) r-alloy duralumin

(d) a mixture of magnalium and duralumin

33. Hardened steel on heating in the range from 220 to 330°C and on slow cooling gives:
   (a) hard steel
   (b) brittle steel
   (c) hard and brittle steel
   (d) hard and tough steel

34. If an ore contains impurity of SiO_2, identify the appropriate flux for the removal of it:
   (a) MnO (b) P_4O_{10}
   (c) O_2 (d) SO_2

35. In the electrolytic reduction of alumina, the electrolyte is covered with coke powder because it:
   (a) prevents oxidation of aluminium formed
   (b) reacts with aluminium forming aluminium carbide
   (c) prevents heat loss from the electrolyte
   (d) none of the above

36. Sequence the following steps involved generally in the extraction of a metal in pure form from its ore.
   (1) The metal obtained from its oxide requires further purification for end use.
   (2) The ore should be converted to its oxide form.
   (3) The ore is beneficial to us if it is hand-picked then metal crushed and ground, and later subjected to pulverization as per the requirement.
   (4) The ore in the form of oxide is required to be reduced.
   (5) Dressed ore is required for it to be concentrated.
   (a) 5 3 2 4 1 (b) 3 5 2 4 1
   (c) 3 5 2 1 4 (d) 3 5 4 2 1

37. Select the steps required for the extraction of aluminium and sequence them.
   (1) froth flotation
   (2) chemical separation
   (3) electrolytic reduction
   (4) smelting
   (5) distillation under low pressure
   (6) electrolytic refining
   (7) pulverization
   (8) conversion of concentrated ore into oxide
   (9) crushing and grinding
   (a) 9 5 7 2 3 8 6 1
   (b) 3 2 1 4 5 6 7 8
   (c) 9 7 2 8 3 6
   (d) 9 7 2 3 8 6

38. The reactions given below represent the processes of reduction to obtain metals from their respective ores. Arrange them in the following order.

   Sodium, aluminium, zinc, chromium, iron, copper, and mercury
   (1) Metal oxide + metal sulphide $\rightarrow$ Metal + SO_2
   (2) Metal oxide + CO $\rightarrow$ Metal + CO_2
   (3) Metal oxide + C $\rightarrow$ Metal + CO
   (4) Metal oxide $\rightarrow$ Metal + O_2
   (5) Metal oxide $\xrightarrow{\Delta}$ Metal + O_2
   (6) Metal oxide + Aluminium $\rightarrow$ Aluminium oxide + Metal
   (7) Metal chloride $\rightarrow$ Metal + Chlorine
   (a) 7 4 3 6 2 1 5 (b) 7 4 3 6 2 5 1
   (c) 1 3 2 4 6 7 5 (d) 7 4 5 2 6 1 5

39. Identify the correct statement(s).
   (a) Magnesium flakes disappear when they are dipped in caustic soda solution.
   (b) During the reaction between copper and dilute nitric acid the oxidation state of nitrogen changes for +5 to +2.
   (c) During the reaction between magnesium and very dilute nitric acid, hydrogen ion gets reduced.
   (d) $AgNO_3$ solution turns blue due to the addition of copper.
   (e) Oxidation state of nitrogen decreases by 3 units during the reaction between Zn and dilute nitric acid.

Level 2: Review Your Concepts

40. If an ore contains an impurity of SiO_2, identify the appropriate flux used for its removal.

41. A common and minor component of alloys bronze, gunmetal and bell metal is also present as one of the components of the other two alloys used for specific purposes. Identify the alloys.

42. What is the role of cryolite and fluorspar during the extraction of aluminium? However, addition of these produces a harmful gas. Explain.

43. 'In the process of reduction of concentrated ore to zinc spelter, ZnO is made into briquettes.' Give reasons.

44. (a) Why are most of the metals hard and have high melting and boiling points?

(b) (i) Identify the reaction that takes place in the middle zone of blast furnace which involves transfer of electrons.

(ii) Identify the combination reaction(s) that take(s) place in the middle region of the blast furnace. What is the significance of this reaction?

(iii) In the middle region of the blast furnace, temperature is less than the lower region. Which reaction(s) is/are responsible for the decrease in temperature?

45. Explain the principle involved in the purification of red bauxite by Bayer's process.

46. Zinc, aluminium, and iron give different products when reacted with sulphuric acid of different strengths (dilute and concentrated), whereas copper reacts only with concentrated sulphuric acid. Justify.

47. Why are aluminium alloys widely used in aircrafts and ships?

48. Why is the iron obtained from the blast furnace not used for making any articles?

49. Metal articles to be electroplated are treated with HCl or H_2SO_4 before electrolysis. Give reasons.

50. Explain the role of aluminium in the extraction of chromium or manganese.

51. Which property of Mn of the alloy spiegel is exploited in the manufacture of steel?

52. What is the effect of Cu on the ZnAl alloys?

53. How are the noble metals containing other metals as impurities purified?

Directions for questions from 54 to 59:
Application-Based Questions

54. One day Dimpy visited an aluminium industry with her father. She found that molten alumina was taken in the fused state for electrolytic reduction process. She asked her father the reason for using fused alumina as an electrolyte instead of the solution of aluminium salt, although the latter can save ample amount of energy. Dimpy's father was pleased with her concern for saving energy, hence he explained to her why nothing could be done about that wastage of energy in that particular instance. What could be his explanation?

55. A, B, C, and D are four metals. Both A and B react with concentrated alkali and also with steam. Reaction of A with steam is rapid in the beginning and becomes slow later. Oxide of C on treatment with A liberates huge amount of heat and C produces brown-coloured flakes on exposure to humid atmosphere. D forms two types of oxides below 1370 K and above 1370 K. Identify A, B, C, and D and write all the balanced chemical equations.

56. Explain the role of coke and sand added during smelting process in the extraction of copper.

57. Auro, a 10th standard student was asked to identify iron, copper, zinc, and aluminium only by observing the effect of action of concentrated nitric acid and caustic soda on each metal. How did he put the reactions of these metals with each of the reagents?

58. Two samples of iron, A and B were given to two students, Rini and Riki, respectively. One of the samples is wrought iron and the other is pig iron. They were asked to observe and study their properties. Rini found that the sample given to her broke easily, whereas Riki's sample was more malleable. Apart from this, it was observed that Rini's sample could be welded at a relatively lower temperature than Riki's sample. Based on the above observations, identify A and B and justify your answer.

59. During metallurgy of iron, its ore, coke and limestone are added to the blast furnace.

(a) What is the role of limestone?

(b) Identify the reducing agent in the extraction of iron during the above process.

(c) Identify slag formed during the above process.

(d) What are the different gases liberated in this process?

Level 3: Assess Your Concepts

60. 'Addition of cryolite and fluorspar to alumina produces a dangerous by-product.' Comment.

61. Why L–D process is preferred to Bessemer process?

62. The alloy alnico finds application in the instruments that requires a very stable temperature. Explain.

63. During the quenching of steel, it is plunged either into a water bath or in an oil bath. Explain why different baths are used.

64. Why is brass preferred to stainless steel for door settings?

Directions for questions from 65 to 70:
Application-Based Questions.

65. In spite of the addition of cryolite and fluorspar to alumina only Al^{3+} and O^{2-} ions are discharged at their respective electrodes. Justify.

66. Explain what happens if bauxite containing iron oxide and silica as impurities is directly subjected to the process of electrolytic reduction without prior purification.

67. The presence of phosphorus is harmful during the manufacture of steel. Give reasons.

68. Steel manufactured using the open hearth process is of better quality compared to steel manufactured by Bessemer process and L–D converter. Give reasons.

69. Ms Joan was teaching metallurgy in a class. She taught her students how an intensely heated steel ingot when plunged into a water bath or an oil bath can acquire different properties. Then she asked the students the reason for using different cooling agents. What would be your answer for making use of different cooling agents?

70. Metal A can be extracted from its ore by strong heating. No reducing agent is required. Metal B can only be extracted by the electrolysis of its molten salt. Metal C can be extracted by using CO or coke. Answer the following questions based on the above information.
(i) Arrange A, B and C based on their reactivity.
(ii) Can all the metals (A, B and C) liberate H_2 on reaction with dilute acid? State reasons for your answer.
(iii) Which of the following reactions is/are valid?
A + compound of B → compound of A + B
B + compound of C → compound of B + C
C + compound of A → compound of C + A
B + compound of A → compound of B + A
(iv) Identify the metal (among A, B and C) having the strongest reducing character.

AT

PRACTICE QUESTIONS JEE-NEET SPECIAL WING

Multiple-Answer Type Questions

Directions for Questions number 1 to 5:

Select one or more correct alternative(s) from the given choices.

1. Choose the processes that are not involved in the purification of metals.
(a) Roasting. (b) Chemical reduction
(c) Distillation. (d) Liquation

2. Which of the following is not an alloy of copper?
(a) Copper pyrites (b) German silver
(c) Cuprite (d) Monel metal

3. 'Galvanization protects iron articles from corrosion, even if the zinc layer is scratched'. Why does this protection persist?
(a) Zinc prevents oxygen from contacting iron, even with a scratch.
(b) Zinc is more reactive than iron
(c) Zinc undergoes oxidation in preference to iron
(d) There is no establishment of an electrochemical cell even after a scratch on the zinc

4. When comparing wrought iron to cast iron, which statement is accurate?
Wrought iron:
(a) Is more susceptible to corrosion
(b) contains lesser carbon content
(c) is less malleable and ductile.
(d) contains fewer impurities.

5. X and Y metals are purified by electrolytic refining. If X has a lower standard reduction potential compared to Y. Predict which of the following pairs could represent X and Y respectively.
(a) Cu, Ag (b) Cu, Zn
(c) Zn, Al (d) Zn, Ag

Comprehension-Based Questions

Directions for Questions number 6 to 11:

Read the following passage and answer the questions given below.

Standard reduction potential of the hypothetical elements A, B, C, D is studied, compared and the details of their comparison are given in the table. Analyse the given details and answer the questions that follow.

Metallic/ Non-metallic elements	Electrodes	Standard reduction potential in Volts
P	P^{2+}/P	-0.2
Q	Q^{2+}/Q	+0.3
R	R^{+}/R	–2.8
S	S^{+}/S	+2.8

6. Predict which of the given elements relatively possess a very high tendency of gaining electrons.
(a) Q (b) S
(c) P (d) R

7. Element with the highest electropositive character is.
(a) S (b) Q
(c) R (d) P

8. Element that can be extracted only by the electrolytic reduction of its molten salt
(a) R (b) Q
(c) P (d) S

9. Which of the ions of P, Q, R is expected to be discharged first at cathode in an electrochemical cell with inert electrodes and a hypothetical electrolyte containing these stable ions in equal concentrations?
(a) Q
(b) P
(c) R
(d) Insufficient data to predict

10. Species of which of the following elements can reduce X^{4+} to X^{2+} [E° = 0.15 V] but will NOT reduce Y^{2+} to Y [E° = –0.236 V]?
(a) P (b) S
(c) Q (d) R

11. Given E1 < E2 < E3 < E4. Match the following

Electrochemical cell (Anode, Cathode)	E_{cell} (Volts)	Spontaneity of the cell reaction. Choose (Y) if spontaneous and (N) if non-spontaneous.
(a) R, P	E3	Y
(b) P, Q	E1	
(c) Q, P	E2	N
(d) S, Hydrogen	E4	

Directions for Questions number 12 to 17:

Read the following passage and answer the questions given below.

The reactions given below represent the processes of reduction to obtain metals from their respective ores.

Metal	Chemical reactions related to the processes of reduction to obtain metals from their respective ores
A	Metal oxide + Aluminium → Aluminium oxide + Metal
B	Metal chloride(l) → Metal + Chlorine (electrolysis)
C	Metal oxide + C → Metal + CO
D	Metal oxide → (heating) Metal + O_2
E	Metal oxide + metal sulphide → Metal + SO_2
F	Metal oxide + CO → Metal + CO_2

12. From the above information, which one of the given metals do you infer as a relatively strong reducing agent
(a) F (b) B
(c) C (d) D

13(i). Choose the statement/s that do not align with the characteristics of metal F.
(a) Its affinity for oxygen is more compared to carbon
(b) Its tendency to get discharge at cathode is greater than that of potassium
(c) Its metal oxides are comparatively more stable than the oxide of metal B
(d) All of the above

13(ii). Which metal is most likely to have a relatively low ion discharge potential.
(a) D (b) F
(c) C (d) A

14. **Assertion(A):** Metal A can displace all other metals given in the above table from their respective salt solutions.

Reason(R): More active metal can displace less active metal from its corresponding salt solution
(a) Both Assertion and Reason are true, and reason is the correct explanation of assertion.
(b) Both Assertion and Reason are true, and reason is not the correct explanation of assertion.
(c) A is true and R is false
(d) A is false and R is true

15. Which of these metals is least likely to react with steam.
(a) D (b) C
(c) F (d) B

16. Pick the odd pair with respect to their relative reduction potentials of one mole of their ions at a given temperature.
(a) B, C (b) F, D
(c) A, E (d) E, C

17. Match the following: Choose all the options that match

List – I Metals	List – II Suitable Examples
A	(i) Zn
B	(ii) Cu
C	(iii) Na
D	(iv) Fe
E	(v) Cr
F	(vi) Hg

ANSWER KEYS

Crossword

Across

3. Duralumin 5. Hardening of steel 6. Combustion 7. Halls process 12. Metalloid
13. Nitrogen dioxide 14. Pulverization

Down

1. Amalgam 2. Magnetic separation 4. Galvanization 8. Gangue
9. Cinnabar 10. Carat 11. Hydrogen

Classroom Wing

Very Short Answer Type Questions

1. Magnesite 2. Combustion zone 3. Pig iron, steel scrap 4. Hydrogen gas
5. Copper, Cuprous oxide 6. $CuCO_3 \cdot Cu(OH)_2$ 7. Fe
8. Magnesium and aluminium 9. Distillation

Competition Wing

Level 1: Apply Your Concepts

1. False 2. True 3. True 4. False 5. True
6. True 7. False 8. Metallurgy 9. free 10. Ore
11. Concentration of ore 12. pulverisation 13. Carbon monoxide 14. Phosphorus
15. Cu_2S, FeS 16. Roasting 17. $C + O_2 \rightarrow CO_2$ 18. Aluminium 19. Sn, Pb
20. (i) - (C), (ii) - (A), (iii) - (D), (iv) - (B),(E) 21. (a) 22. (a)
23. (a) 24. (a) 25. (b) 26. (b) 27. (d)
28. (a) 29. (d) 30. (c) 31. (a) 32. (b)
33. (d) 34. (a) 35. (c) 36. (b) 37. (c)
38. a 39. (b), (c) (d)

JEE-NEET Special Wing

Multiple-Answer Type Questions

1. (a, b) 2. (a, c) 3. (b, c) 4. (b, d) 5. (a, d)

Comprehension-Based Questions

6. (b) 7. (c) 8. (a) 9. (c) 10. (a)
11. ((a) E4–Y, (b) E3–Y, (c) E2–N, (d) E1–N) 12. (b) 13(i). (a, c) 13(ii). (a)
14. (d) 15. (a) 16. (d) 17. A–iv, v, B–iii, C–i, iv, ii, D–vi ii, E–ii, F–iv, ii

Hints and Explanations

Classroom Wing

Very Short Answer Type Questions

1. Magnesite
2. Combustion zone
3. Pig iron, steel scrap
4. Hydrogen gas
5. Copper, Cuprous oxide
6. $CuCO_3 \cdot Cu(OH)_2$
7. Fe
8. Magnesium and aluminium
9. Distillation
10. The order is CBEDA.
    (i) Formation of CO_2 from coke taken as a charge.
    (ii) Formation of CO from coke taken as a charge.
    (iii) Decomposition of limestone taken as a charge.
    (iv) Formation of calcium silicate from silica taken as a charge.
    (v) Formation of iron due to the reaction between roasted haematite and CO.
11. Zinc blend cannot be extracted because it is to be concentrated by the froth floatation process and then roasted before smelting, not calcination.
12. Since the impurity is basic, an acidic flux is required to be added. SiO_2 is the only acidic flux given and reacts with FeO to form $FeSiO_3$.
13. Hydrogen is used to reduce the oxide of tungsten because other reducing agents are ineffective.

    $WO_3 + H_2 \rightarrow W + 3H_2O$
14. Oxidation is used for the refining of iron with oxidizable impurities such as C and S.
15. By the addition of cryolite and fluorspar
16. Roasting
17. Due to its reducing character.
18. Molten metal forms the bottom layer with the slag on top.
19. Wrought iron. Manufacture of steel.
20. Major product $\rightarrow$ Cast iron

    By products $\rightarrow$ Slag ($CaSiO_3$), CO, CO_2 and N_2
21. $MnSiO_3$, $Ca_3(PO_4)_2$
22. Bessemer process

    Acid process $\rightarrow$ Furnace is lined with acidic refractories.

    Basic process $\rightarrow$ Furnace is lined with magnesite/dolomite
23. Brittleness increases
24. (a) $AlCl_3$ (b) $ZnCl_2$ (c) $FeCl_3$
25. Froth flotation process
26. Roasting-Heating of ore below its melting point in presence of air to oxidize the impurities. Calcination-Heating of ore below its melting point in absence of air to remove volatile impurities such as arsenic.

Short Answer Type Questions

27. Both metals 'M' and 'N' are more electropositive than hydrogen. 'M' can displace 'N'. Hence, 'M' should be above 'N' in the reactivity series. Since halogen 'X' displaces 'Y', 'X' should be more reactive than Y. Thus, the correct combination is M -Zn, N - Fe, X - F_2, Y - I_2.
28. $Sn + CuSO_4 \rightarrow SnSO_4 + Cu$

    Tin is more reactive than copper.

    $KBr + Cl_2 \rightarrow KCl + Br_2$

    Chlorine is more reactive than bromine.
29. The metals that are less reactive than aluminium can be displaced by aluminium. Magnesium that is more active than aluminium cannot be displaced by aluminium.
30. At anode: $O^{2-} - 2e^- \rightarrow [O]$

    $C + 2[O] \rightarrow CO_2$

    At cathode: $Al^{3+} + 3e^- \rightarrow Al$

    This process is also called the three-layer process as the cell contains three layers of molten liquids. The cell is an iron tank lined internally with carbon. The electrolyte is composed of aluminium fluoride (36%), cryolite (18%) and calcium fluoride (16%) that forms the middle layer. The lower layer is the impure metal alloyed with copper and serves as the anode.

31. (a) (i) Malleability, ductility
(ii) Conductivity
(iii) Melting, boiling point
(iv) Density, magnetic property

(b) The main chemical reaction is ($Al + Fe_2O_3 \rightarrow Fe + Al_2O_3$) a displacement and exothermic reaction. Hence iron is obtained in molten state. The displacement reaction is carried out with Al since Al is more reactive than iron. Thermite mixture is ignited by magnesium powder and barium peroxide.

(ii) and (iii) are correct.

32. (i) Hand picking
(ii) Crushing and grinding
(iii) Pulverizing

33. (i) Set up
(ii) Raw materials
(iii) Procedure
(iv) Indication for completion.

34. This method is exclusively used for the concentration of sulphide ores. The basic principle involves the differential wetting characteristics of ore and gangue with oil and water, the ore being wet by oil and gangue by water.

The ore is taken in a large tank called the flotation cell containing a mixture of pine oil and water. This is then agitated by blowing a current of air into the tank. The oil along with the sulphide ore forms foam which floats on the tank and is removed. The sulphide ore is recovered from this.

35. On passing the current, the aluminium ions from the middle layer go towards the cathode, get discharged there and form the upper layer of pure aluminium while an equivalent amount of aluminium passes into the middle layer from the bottom layer.

36. Copper obtained from Bessemer converter by the process of Bessemerization gets blister-type appearance. This is called blister copper.

37. Zinc oxide is reduced to zinc by vertical retort process called smelting.

Powdered zinc oxide is mixed with charcoal and made into small briquettes by pressing. This is taken in the vertical retort where, due to the high temperature, carbon reduces zinc oxide to zinc and itself gets oxidized to carbon monoxide:

$$ZnO + C\ (1400°C) \rightarrow Zn + CO$$

Zinc oxide is reduced to zinc by vertical retort process called smelting.

Powdered zinc oxide is mixed with charcoal and made into small briquettes by pressing. This is taken in the vertical retort where, due to the high temperature, carbon reduces zinc oxide to zinc and itself gets oxidized to carbon monoxide:

$$ZnO + C\ (1400°C) \rightarrow Zn + CO$$

38.

Aluminium	Zinc	Iron
Oxidizes the outer layer to aluminium and renders it passive for further corrosion.	Zinc nitrate and nitric oxide gas with dilute acid $3Zn + 8HNO_3(dil) \downarrow 3Zn(NO_3)_2 + 4H_2O + 2N_2O(g)$ Liberates nitrogen dioxide gas with conc. acid: $Zn + 4HNO_3 \downarrow Zn(NO_3)_2 + 2NO_2 + 2H_2O$	Dilute acid liberates nitric oxide gas: $3Fe + 8HNO_3(dil) \downarrow 3Fe(NO_3)_2 + 4H_2O + 2NO$ Concentrated acid oxidizes the outer layer that makes the metal passive.

Essay Answer Type Questions

40. Wrought iron is prepared by heating cast iron in a reverberatory furnace. The furnace is lined internally with iron oxide. This oxidizes the carbon in the cast iron to gaseous oxides of carbon. The other impurities are slagged off using lime as flux.

41. Blast furnace is a huge chimney-like structure about 30-m high and 8 m in diameter. It is made of iron plates and lined internally with refractory bricks. On the top, it has a double cup and cone arrangement. Below this, there is an outlet for waste gases. A hearth is present at the bottom to collect cast iron and slag, and has separate outlets for each. Hot compressed air is blown into the furnace through pipes called tuyeres that are placed above the hearth.

The ore is mixed with coke and limestone approximately in the ratio of 8 : 4 : 1. This mixture is called charge.

Lower region (1500–2000°C)

$$C + O_2 \rightarrow CO_2 + 97 \text{ kcal}$$

Middle region or fusion zone (1500–1000°C)

$$CO_2 + C \rightarrow 2CO - 39 \text{ kcal}$$

$$CaCO_3 \rightarrow CaO + CO_2 - 43 \text{ kcal}$$

$$CaO + SiO_2 \rightarrow CaSiO_3$$

Upper region or reduction zone (1000–500°C)

$$FeO + CO \xrightarrow{600-400°C} Fe + CO_2$$

$$Fe_2O_3 + 3CO \rightarrow \xrightarrow{600-400°C} 2Fe + 3CO_2$$

42.

Reducing agent	Metals reduced	Reactions
Coke	Zinc, iron, lead, copper	$ZnO + C \xrightarrow{\Delta} Zn + CO$
Carbon monoxide	Iron, lead, copper	$Fe_2O_3 + 3CO \xrightarrow{\Delta} 2Fe + 3CO_2$
Aluminium powder	Chromium, manganese	$Cr_2O_3 + 2Al \rightarrow Al_2O_3 + 2Cr + \text{heat}$
Heating	Mercury, silver	$2HgO \xrightarrow{\Delta} 2Hg + O_2$
Electrolysis	Sodium, potassium, calcium, magnesium, aluminium	$Al^{3+} + 3e^- \rightarrow Al$

44.

Processes of purification	Metals to be refined	Processes
Distillation	Iron, mercury	The metal is strongly heated above its boiling point in the absence of air. The metal vaporizes, leaving behind the impurities. The vapors are cooled in earthen retorts, to get the metal in solid or liquid form.
Liquation	Lead, tin (metals with low melting point)	The metal is taken on the upper part of sloping hearth and heated above its melting point.
Polling	Copper with cuprous oxide as an impurity	Molten copper is stirred with wooden poles.
Oxidation	Iron with oxidizable impurities	$C + O_2 \rightarrow CO_2\uparrow$ $S + O_2 \rightarrow SO_2\uparrow$
Electrolytic refining	Aluminium	A block of impure metal is taken as an anode and a thin strip of pure metal is taken as a cathode. The electrolyte is the soluble salt of the metal. On passing the current, the metal ions from the anode dissolve in the electrolyte, go towards the cathode and get discharged there.

46. (i) Lead ore → PbO
(ii) Magnesite → $MgCO_3$
(iii) Cinnabar → HgS
(iv) Galena → PbS
(v) Fluorspar → CaF_2

Fluorspar and magnesite cannot be used for the given flow-sheet because Ca and Mg cannot be extracted by the reduction of the ore with CO.

Since froth flotation is the method for concentration, the ore could be HgS or PbS. In roasting process HgS and PbS both can be converted to their respective oxide. Further heating can convert HgO to Hg. But only by heating Pb cannot be extracted. Reduction by CO is not required for HgS. Hence PbS is the ore.

Competition Wing

Level 1: Apply your Concepts

20. (i) - (C): Cu does not react with steam as it is less reactive than hydrogen.

(ii) - (A): Reaction of Fe with steam is a reversible reaction.

(iii) - (D): Red hot metal that is Al reacts with steam rapidly at the beginning and becomes slow later because of the formation of a coating of Al_2O_3.

(iv) -(B), (E): Zn and Mg react with steam liberating H_2 gas and forms oxide of formula MO where M is the metal.

21. In the L-D process, pure oxygen is used which can remove more number of impurities at a faster rate. In the Bessemer process, the air is used in which 80% is nitrogen that takes away the heat. Hence, the efficiency of this process is less.

Hence, the correct option is (a).

22. Metals of moderate reactivity can be reduced by using reducing agents. However, reducing agents should be selected based on the electro positivity of the metals. Coke and CO are reducing agents. But aluminium is a better-reducing agent.

Hence, the correct option is (b).

23 Since copper pyrite is a sulphide ore, it is concentrated by the froth floatation process. Copper is a metal of medium reactivity and the ore $CuFeS_2$ has to be converted to copper by strong heating. Because of the presence of Fe, some flux is required to be added. Hence, different furnaces are used to carry out a series of reactions required for the extraction of copper from $CuFeS_2$.

Hence, the correct option is (a).

36. 3 The ore is beneficial to us if it is hand-picked and then ore is crushed and grounded, and later subjected to pulverization as per the requirement.

5 Dressed ore is required to be concentrated.

2 Ore is required to be converted to its oxide form.

4 Ore in the form of oxide is required to be reduced.

1 The metal obtained from its oxide requires further purification for end use.

Hence, the correct answer is (b).

37. 9 Crushing and grinding
7 Pulverisation
2 Chemical separation
8 Conversion of concentrated ore into oxide
3 Electrolytic reduction
6 Electrolytic refining

Hence, the correct answer is (c).

38. 7 Metal chloride $\rightarrow$ Metal + chlorine
4 Metal oxide $\rightarrow$ Metal + O_2
3 Metal oxide + C $\rightarrow$ Metal + CO
6 Metal oxide + aluminium $\rightarrow$ aluminium oxide + metal
2 Metal oxide + CO $\rightarrow$ Metal + CO_2
1 Metal oxide + metal sulphide $\rightarrow$ Metal + SO_2
5 Metal oxide $\xrightarrow{\Delta}$ Metal + O_2

Hence, the correct answer is (a).

39. Magnesium does not react with NaOH.

$3Cu + 8HNO_3\ (dil) \rightarrow 3Cu(NO_3)_2 + 2NO + 4H_2O$

In the above reaction oxidation state of nitrogen changes from +5 to +2.

$Mg + HNO_3\ (very\ dil) \rightarrow Mg(NO_3)_2 + H_2$

In the above reactions, H^+ gets reduced to H_2

$2AgNO_3 + Cu \rightarrow Cu(NO_3)_2 + 2Ag$

In the above reaction, $AgNO_3$ solution turns blue since Cu gets oxidized Cu^+

$3Zn + 8HNO_3\ (dil) \rightarrow 3Zn(NO_3)_2 + 2N_2O + 4H_2O$

In the above reaction oxidation state of nitrogen changes from +5 to +1. Hence it decreases by 4 units.

∴ (b), (c), and (d) are correct.

Hence, the correct answer is (b), (c) (d).

Level 2: Review Your Concepts

40. Since SiO_2 is an acidic impurity, a basic flux is required to be added. MnO is the basic flux.

41. The common metal present as a minor component in alloys bronze, gunmetal, and bell metal is tin. Tin is also a common component in other alloys solder and types of metal. Solder is an alloy of lead and tin. Type metal is an alloy of lead, tin, and antimony.

42. (i) Nature and property of an electrolyte.
(ii) Electrolyte used for the extraction of aluminium.
(iii) Thermal stability of the electrolyte.

(iv) Relation between the presence of impurity and melting point of solid.

(v) Effect of addition of cryolite and fluorspar on the melting point of the electrolyte.

(vi) Mechanism of conduction of electricity.

(vii) Effect of addition of cryolite and fluorspar on the conduction of electrolyte.

(viii) Product obtained at the anode during electrolysis.

(ix) Anodic product obtained at the end of the electrolysis.

43. (i) Comparison between briquette and powder form.

(ii) Furnace in which the reduction of concentrated ore takes place.

(iii) Process of reduction.

(iv) Physical state of the raw material in which they react.

(v) Physical state of the product.

44. (a) (i) Nature of metal atoms.

(ii) Type of bond present in metals.

(iii) Relation between the strength of the bond and the properties of metal (melting point, boiling point).

(b) (i) In the middle zone of blast furnace the following reactions take place.

- $CO_2 + C \rightarrow 2CO$
- $CaCO_3 \rightarrow CaO + CO_2$
- $CaO + SiO_2 \rightarrow CaSiO_3$

Only first reaction is an oxidation – reduction reaction.

Hence electron transfer takes place only in this reaction.

(ii) The combination reaction that takes place in the middle zone of the blast furnace is

$CaO + SiO_2 \rightarrow CaSiO_3$

This reaction is responsible for the removal of impurity like silica (SiO_2). Formation of Siag ($CaSiO_3$) takes place in this reaction.

(iii) $CO_2 + C \rightarrow 2CO$ and $CaCO_3 \rightarrow CaO + CO_2$ are endothermic reactions and reduces the temperature of the model zone.

45. (i) Nature of impurity present in red bauxite.

(ii) Chemical composition of the red bauxite and the impurity present in it.

(iii) Comparison of chemical behavior of red bauxite and the impurity with acids and bases.

(iv) Separation technique that can be adopted for removing the impurity based on the above chemical behavior.

46. (i) Comparison of reactivity of Zn, Al, Fe and Cu.

(ii) Comparison of oxidation potentials of zinc, iron, aluminium with hydrogen.

(iii) Type of reaction that takes place when the above metals react with dilute H_2SO_4.

(iv) Change in the property of H_2SO_4 with the increase in concentration.

(v) Change in the product due to the change in the concentration.

(vi) Comparison of oxidation potential of copper with hydrogen.

(vii) Type of reaction that can takes place between copper and concentrated H_2SO_4.

47. (i) Property of aluminium.

(ii) Comparison of properties of metal and its alloy.

48. (i) Gases in the blast furnace.

(ii) Reactions that take place in blast furnace.

(iii) Products obtained and their physical state.

(iv) Effect of the physical state of the product on the iron obtained.

(v) Effect of the impurities on the property of iron.

49. (i) Reactivity of HCl, H_2SO_4 with the impurities present.

(ii) Reactivity of metals.

(iii) Effect of reactivity of metal on its surface.

(iv) Change in composition of the surface of metal.

(v) Reactivity of the substances that are formed on the surface of the metal.

(vi) Reaction between the above substances with HCl or H_2SO_4.

50. (i) Reactivity of aluminium.

(ii) The reaction that the ore should undergo in the extraction of the metal.

(iii) Chemical property of aluminium that is exploited to extract the metal from its ore.

51. (i) Reactivity of Mn with the impurities.

(ii) Kinds of impurities present in iron obtained from the blast furnace.

(iii) Chemical behaviour of manganese.
(iv) Affinity of manganese towards certain impurities.
(v) Formation of slag.
(vi) Type of bond that can be formed between iron and manganese.
(vii) Effect of the formation of the above bonds on the property of steel.

52. (i) Mechanical properties of substance.
(ii) Type of bond present in metal.
(iii) Change in the type of bond during the formation of alloy.
(iv) Effect of change in the type of bond on the physical property of the metal.

53. (i) Reactivity of noble metals.
(ii) Comparison of reactivity of noble metals with other metals.
(iii) Separation technique adopted for the removal of impurities from the noble metal based on the difference in reactivity.

55. Since A and B reacts with concentrated alkali, they are Al and Zn. Reaction of A with steam is rapid in the beginning and becomes slow later and hence A is Al.

$$2H_2O + \underset{(A)}{2Al} + 2NaOH \longrightarrow 2NaAlO_2 + 2H_2 \uparrow$$

$$\underset{(B)}{Zn} + NaOH \longrightarrow Na_2ZnO_2 + H_2 \uparrow$$

$$2Al + 3H_2O \longrightarrow Al_2O_3 + 3H_2$$

$$Zn + H_2O \longrightarrow ZnO + H_2$$

Since oxide of C produces huge amount of heat with A and flakes with humid atmosphere, it is iron.

$$Fe_2O_3 + 2Al \longrightarrow \underset{(C)}{2Fe} + Al_2O_3 + Heat.$$

As D forms two types of oxides above and below 1370 K, it is Cu.

$$\underset{(D)}{Cu} + O_2 \xrightarrow{<1370\,K} Cu_2O$$

$$Cu + O_2 \xrightarrow{>1370\,K} Cu_2O$$

56. Coke is the source of heat in smelting and also it acts as reducing agent, which reduces Cu_2O to Cu:

$Cu_2O + C \rightarrow 2Cu + CO$

SiO_2 combines with the impurities like FeO and is removed as slag:

$FeO + SiO_2 \rightarrow FeSiO_3$

57.

Action concentrated nitric acid	Action of caustic alkali	Inference
No characteristic change	No characteristic change	Iron
Liberates brown colored NO_2 gas	No characteristic change	Copper
Liberates brown colored NO_2 gas	Liberates hydrogen gas	Zinc
No characteristic change	Liberates hydrogen gas	Aluminium

58. In wrought iron, carbon content is much lesser than that in pig iron. Presence of carbon that is a non-metal reduces the malleability of a metal and the metal becomes hard and brittle. Moreover, presence of impurity reduces the melting point of a solid. Hence pig iron, in which carbon content is more, can be welded at a lower temperature. From these two observations, it can be concluded that Rini's sample is pig iron and Riki's sample is wrought iron.

59. (a) Limestone ($CaCO_3$) undergoes thermal decomposition and gives CaO and CO_2. CaO acts as a flux.
(b) Carbon monoxide acts as a reducing agent:
$FeO + CO \rightarrow Fe + CO_2$
$Fe_2O_3 + 3CO \rightarrow 2Fe + 3CO_2$
(c) CaO reacts with the impurity SiO_2 and forms the slag $CaSiO_3$: $CaO + SiO_2 \rightarrow CaSiO_3$
(d) $C + O_2 \rightarrow CO_2(g)$
$CO_2 + C \rightarrow 2CO(g)$
$CaCO_3 \rightarrow CaO + CO_2(g)$
$FeO + CO \rightarrow Fe + CO_2(g)$
$Fe_2O_3 + 3CO \rightarrow 2Fe + 3CO_2(g)$

CO_2 gas is liberated. CO gas is formed, but takes part in the process of reduction of Fe_2O_3 and forms CO_2.

Level 3: Assess Your Concepts

60. (i) Common element present in cryolite and fluorspar.
(ii) Ions present in cryolite and fluorspar.

(iii) Products obtained at the electrodes on complete electrolysis.
(iv) Nature of the products.

61. (i) Comparison of the type of fuel used.
(ii) Comparison of the composition of gases passed through the charge in L–D and Bessemer process.
(iii) Comparison of the process of passing the gases in L–D and Bessemer converter.
(iv) Reactions that takes place in L–D and Bessemer converter.
(v) Change in the rates of reactions due to difference in the above two processes.
(vi) Effect of the presence of the non-reactive component of the gas blasted in Bessemer process on the property of steel.

62. (i) Comparing properties of constituent metals and alloy.
(ii) Composition of alnico.
(iii) Property of alnico.
(iv) Effect of composition on retention of this at higher temperatures.

63. (i) Comparing cooling properties of oil and water.
(ii) Comparison of the property related to rise in temperature of oil and water.
(iii) Effect of property on the rate of cooling of steel.
(iv) Relation between the rate of cooling and the change in the properties of steel.

64. (i) Composition of brass and stainless steel.
(ii) Relation between the composition and the property of the alloy.
(iii) Comparison among the given properties of alloys.
(iv) Requisite for door settings.

65. Cryolite (Na_3AlF_6) and fluorspar (CaF_2) are added to alumina to reduce its melting point. Al^{3+} discharges preferentially over Na^+ and Ca^{2+} at cathode, because of lower discharge potential of Al^{3+} than Na^+ and Ca^+ and at anode, O^{2-} gets discharged due to its lower discharge potential than F^- and is evolved as O_2, which reacts with carbon anode forming CO_2 gas.

66. Crude bauxite contains iron oxide and silica as impurities. If any iron is present in the bauxite, it will get deposited at the cathode in preference to aluminium because iron is less electropositive than aluminium.

67. Phosphorus imparts cold-shortness, that is, high brittleness at normal and especially at room temperature. It increases the tensile strength but at the same time reduces the impact strength due to the formation of iron phosphide.

68. Open hearth process produces better quality steel because:

(i) Open hearth process is a lengthy process due to which the composition of the product can be controlled by checking from time to time.
(ii) As blast of air is not passed in the open hearth process, blow holes are not formed that could make the steel brittle and loss of iron in the form of slag is multified.
(iii) Pure oxygen makes the process of removal of impurities faster and more effective.

69. Different baths are used for quenching steel for different use. Water and oil have different specific heat. Due to the difference in specific heat, dissipation of heat through the bath becomes different. Water has high specific heat. For this reason, dissipation of heat through water is more than that through oil. For decreasing the dissipation of heat through water, hot or boiled water is also used. Sudden cooling makes steel harder, and more brittle. Hence, different baths provide different hardness to the steel and make it useful for different end uses.

70. (i) Since metal A can be extracted from its ore only by strong heating, A is a metal of low reactivity.

Metal B can only be extracted by electrolysis, hence it is the metal of high reactivity. Metal C can be extracted by using CO or coke by a reducing agent. Hence it is a metal of moderate reactivity.

$\therefore$ The order of reactivity is $B > C > A$

(ii) No, since A is less reactive than hydrogen, it cannot liberate H_2 from a dilute acid.

(iii) B + compound of C $\rightarrow$ compound of B + C

C + compound of A $\rightarrow$ compound of C + A

B + compound of A $\rightarrow$ compound of B + A

The above reactions are possible.

A + compound of B $\rightarrow$ No reaction.

(iv) B is the most reactive metal, hence it has the strongest reducing character.

JEE-NEET Special wing

Multiple-Answer Type Questions

1. Distillation, Liquation, electrolysis, electrolytic reduction, polling, oxidation are the processes involved in the purification of metals. Roasting involves heating of sulphide ores in the excess of air to convert them into their corresponding oxides. Chemical reduction involved reduction of metal oxides to metal using suitable reducing agents.

2. Copper pyrites and cuprite are the ores of copper while German silver and Monel metal are the alloys of copper.

3. Even if the zinc layer is scratched, exposing the iron underneath, zinc being more reactive than iron, zinc acts as the anode (where oxidation occurs) while iron acts as cathode (where reduction occurs) in the established electrochemical cell in the presence of moisture in the air. As the metal forming the anode is the one that corrodes first, zinc corrodes instead of iron, thus protecting it by functioning as a sacrificial anode. Typically, a small scratch doesn't disrupt this protective mechanism.

4. Wrought iron has lower carbon content compared to cast iron, and it also tends to have fewer impurities, making it more malleable, ductile, and less prone to brittleness and corrosion compared to cast iron.

5. Standard reduction potential (SRP) is a measure of a substance's tendency to gain electrons and be reduced. Higher reactivity corresponds to a more negative standard reduction potential value. Al, Zn, Cu, Ag are in the increasing order of their SRP values. Given X has lower SRP than Y. So, X and Y can be Cu, Ag or Zn, Ag

Comprehension-Based Questions

6. Elements with positive standard reduction potential values possess a greater tendency to gain electrons i.e., undergo reduction compared to hydrogen. Given element 'S' possess the highest SRP value. Hence it possesses the greatest tendency to undergo reduction compared to the other given elements.

7. Element with negative SRP values have greater tendency to get oxidized compared to hydrogen. Meaning they are more electropositive compared to hydrogen. Among the given elements, element R possess the least SRP value, hence it should possess the highest electropositive character.

8. Elements with least SRP values acts as strong reducing agents. Hence, they cannot be reduced by other reducing agents. Element R possess the least SRP values among all. So, it cannot be reduced by normal reducing agents. Hence can be extracted by the electrolytic reduction of its molten salt.

9. With equal ion concentrations, higher standard reduction potential values favour the discharge of positive ions at the cathode. Among P, Q, and R, R holds the highest positive standard reduction potential, hence likely to be discharged first at the cathode.

10. E° of P^{2+}/P is -0.2V which is greater than -0.236V and less than 0.15V. So, it can reduce X^{4+} to X^{2+} [E° = 0.15 V]

11.
   (a) If R is anode and P is cathode,
   $E_{cell} = E_{cathode} - E_{Anode}$.
   E_{cell} = -0.2-(-2.8) = +2.6 (E4) ⇒ >0
   ⇒ Spontaneous(Y)

   (b) If P is anode and Q is cathode,
   $E_{cell} = E_{cathode} - E_{Anode}$.
   E_{cell} = +0.3-(-0.2) = +0.5 (E3) ⇒ >0
   ⇒ Spontaneous(Y)

   (c) If Q is anode and P is cathode,
   $E_{cell} = E_{cathode} - E_{Anode}$.
   E_{cell} = -0.2-(-0.3) = -0.5 ⇒ <0 (E2)
   ⇒ Non-Spontaneous(N)

   (d) If S is anode and Hydrogen is cathode,
   $E_{cell} = E_{cathode} - E_{Anode}$.
   E_{cell} = +0.00 - (+2.8) = -2.8 (E1) ⇒ <0
   ⇒ Non-Spontaneous(N)

   So, the correct Mach is:
   (a) E4-Y (b) E3-Y
   (c) E2-N (d) E1-N

12. Metals displaying strong reducing properties undergo exclusive reduction to their elemental state through electrolysis of their halide or oxide ores, unlike by conventional heating or using common reducing agents. Among the options provided, it is metal B that is reduced from its chloride ore via electrolysis, while the other metals are reduced by heating or standard reducing agents. Consequently, Metal B can be inferred to be more reactive and a stronger reducing agent among the mentioned metals.

13(i). The chemical reactions involved in the reduction processes for obtaining metals from their ores, specifically for metal B and F, indicate the following:

- Metal B is a more active metal, whereas metal F is moderately active.
- Metal F exhibits a lower affinity for oxygen compared to carbon, evident from its reduction using carbon monoxide (CO).

The stability of metal oxides as well as the discharge potential of the metal ions indeed tends to decrease as the activity of the metal decreases. We know that potassium ranks highest in the metal activity series. Therefore, more active metals like potassium have higher discharge potentials compared to less active metals further down the series. So, metal F should have a greater tendency to get discharge at cathode than that of potassium. Hence, only statements (a) and (c) do not align with the expected characteristics of metal F.

13(ii). As we move down the reactivity series, the discharge potential typically decreases. So, the metals with lower reactivity typically exhibit lower discharge potentials for their ions. Among the metals listed, the oxide of metal D is reduced to its by heating while the oxides of other metals are reduced using reducing agents like C, CO, or aluminium powder. This suggests that metal D is likely to be less reactive compared to the other metals listed in the options.

14. From the given table, chemical reactions related to the processes of reduction to obtain metals from their respective ores for metal A suggests that it is likely to be more active of all the given metals except metal B(as it is extracted by electrolysis). More active metal can displace a less active metal from its corresponding salt solution, Hence A is false, and R is correct.

15. Metals obtained by heating their oxides are typically less reactive. Therefore, they are less likely to react with steam. From the given information, metal D is obtained by heating its metal oxide.

16. Except for option D, the metals in the pairs are arranged in the increasing order based on their reduction potentials.

17. Correct match is: A-iv, v, B-iii, C-i, iv, ii, D-vi ii, E-ii, F-iv, ii

Explanation:

Metal	Chemical reactions related to the processes of reduction to obtain metals from their respective ores	Example with reason
A	Metal oxide + Aluminium → Aluminium oxide + Metal	Metal oxides of Cr, Mn, V, Fe can be reduced using Al powder
B	Metal chloride (l) → Metal + Chlorine (electrolysis)	Halides of more active metals like K, Na, Ca, Mg, Al are reduced to metals by electrolysis.
C	Metal oxide + C → Metal + CO	Oxides of moderately active metals like Zn, Fe, Cu, Ni, Sn, Pb etc can be reduced with coke
D	Metal oxide → (heating) Metal + O_2	Oxides of low activity metals like Cu, Hg, Ag, Au, etc. can be reduced by heating.
E	Metal oxide + metal sulphide → Metal + SO_2	During the extraction of a low active metal like Cu from its sulphide ore, metal is obtained by treating the metal oxide with its sulphide.
F	Metal oxide + CO → Metal + CO_2	Oxides of moderately active metals like Zn, Fe, Cu, Ni, Sn etc can be reduced with carbon monoxide

CHAPTER

7

Industrial Chemistry

Remember

Before beginning this chapter, you should be able to:

- know the classification of matter and concept related to elements.
- describe the industrial applications of derivatives of some elements.

Key Ideas

After completing this chapter, you should be able to:

- understand the preparation, properties, and uses of elements and their compounds.
- explain manufacturing processes and applications of some compounds.
- compare allotropes of elements such as sulphur.
- know methods of preparation, properties and uses of some industrially useful compounds.

Scientific Crypt

A Tribute to Fritz Haber (1868–1934)

Fritz Haber, a German chemist, received Nobel Prize in Chemistry in the year 1918 for his contribution for the preparation of ammonia, an important component of fertilizers and explosives.

Fritz Haber was born on 9 December 1868, in Breslau, Germany. He worked in his father's chemical business after being educated in Berlin, Heidelberg and Zurich. In 1894, he became assistant to Hans Bunte at the University of Karlsruhe.

At Technical University of Karlsruhe, he and his brother-in-law, Carl Bosch, a chemist, have developed the method of catalytic synthesis of ammonia from hydrogen and atmospheric nitrogen under high temperature and pressure. This process of synthesising of ammonia is well known as Haber Bosch process or Haber's process and was a milestone in the progress of Industrial Chemistry, as it ended the dependence on the fast-disappearing natural sources of ammonia located along the coast of Chile.

In 1918, Fritz Haber received the most prestigious award, Nobel Prize for his work on the preparation of ammonia. Apart from this most prestigious award, Haber also received many honours during his lifetime. He has also been regarded as the "father of chemical warfare" for being associated with the usage of chlorine gas and other deadly poisonous gases during World War I.

FUN TIME

CROSSWORD

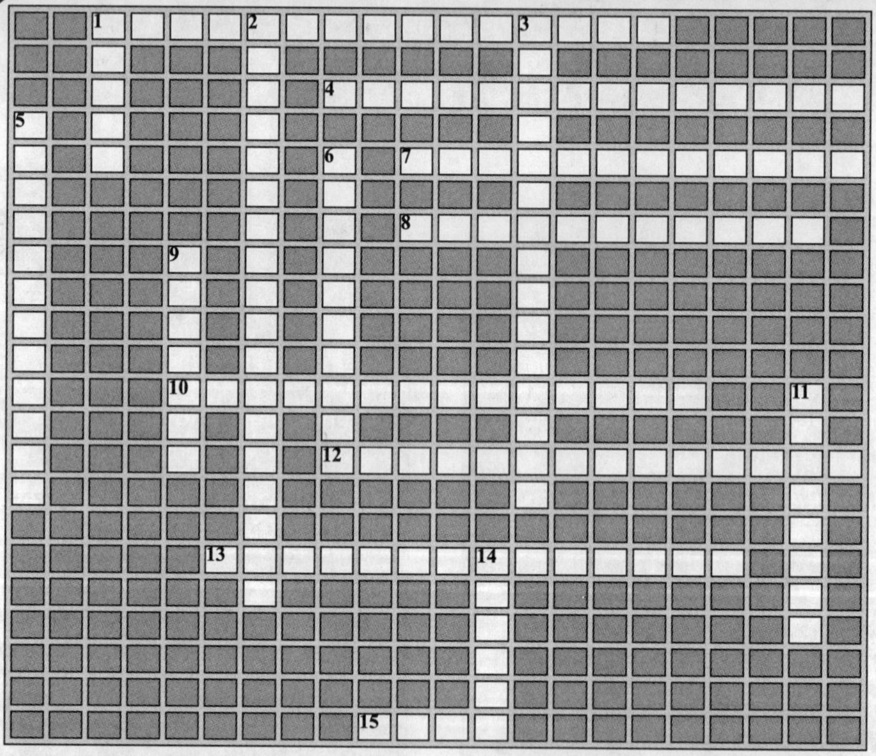

Across

1. Mixed salt made up of calcium chloride and calcium hypochlorite.
4. Allotrope of sulphur which is stable below 95.6°C.
7. $FeSO_4.7H_2O$ is called ______.
8. The common name of sodium carbonate decahydrate.
10. Industrial preparation of nitric acid is done by this process.
12. Copper on reacting with concentrated sulphuric acid evolves this gas.
13. Mixture formed by mixing cement with sand and small pieces of crushed stone.
15. Catalyst used in Haber's process.

Down

1. Finely powdered mixture of sodium carbonate, calcium carbonate and silicon dioxide taken as raw material for the manufacture of glass is called ______.
2. This fertilizer contains two or more macronutrients in a single compound.
3. This allotrope of phosphorus is poisonous in nature.
5. Chemical name of lime
6. The glass which has borax as one of the constituents and used in laboratories.
9. Crystalline allotope of carbon with density 3.5 g/cc.
11. Zinc on reacting with dilute hydrochloric acid evolves this gas.
14. Silicon has high affinity towards this element, as a result silicon does not occur in free state.

INTRODUCTION

Nature is bestowed with a variety of metals and non-metals existing in free state as well as in combined state. These elements like carbon, sulphur, nitrogen, etc., are extracted from the natural resources through different processes. After purification, these elements are either used directly in the elemental state or used as raw materials for the manufacture of a variety of compounds. These compounds have a wide range of applications in various fields. Industrial chemistry deals with the manufacture of these compounds like different acids, ammonia, quick lime, slaked lime, washing soda, etc. Some of the compounds are further used for the manufacture of cement, glass, ceramics, fertilizers, etc., which find applications in the construction of buildings, decorative items, sanitary ware, interiors, telecommunication, spacecraft and various other fields and the study of the manufacture, properties and uses of these materials also come under the scope of industrial chemistry. Some important non-metals are discussed in the following section.

Carbon

Carbon belongs to IV A group of the periodic table. Carbon is one of the most important non-metallic elements as it is invariably present in all animals and plants in the form of various compounds. In addition to this, carbon exists in combined form in the form of many minerals and also in the form of carbon dioxide in the atmospheric air. However, in elemental form, carbon is available in the form of diamond, graphite, etc.

Allotropy

The existence of the same element in different physical forms with similar chemical properties is known as **allotropy**.

Carbon exhibits allotropy and the allotropes of carbon are broadly classified into two main categories, viz., crystalline and amorphous allotropes. Crystalline allotropes are diamond, graphite and fullerene while coke, charcoal, lamp black, gas carbon are amorphous allotropic forms.

Diamond

In diamond, each carbon atom is bonded covalently by single bonds to four other carbon atoms resulting in a single tetrahedral unit of crystal. These tetrahedral crystal units lie in different planes accounting for a rigid three-dimensional structure. The C-C bond length is 1.54 Å and bond angle is 109°28′.

Diamond can be prepared by heating carbon in the form of sugar charcoal in molten iron up to 3800−4000°C which, on subsequent and sudden cooling, crystallises to diamond.

Figure 7.1 Structure of diamond

Physical Properties: Diamond is a hard crystalline substance with a high density (3.5g/cc) and melting point of 3700°C. It also has a very high refractive index of 2.5.

Chemical Properties: Diamond, on heating in the presence of air, catches fire around 800°C to form CO_2:

$$C + O_2 \xrightarrow{800°C} CO_2$$

Uses: Diamond due to its brilliance is used as a precious gem and, due to its sharpness, is used in performing delicate operations.

Graphite

Graphite is another crystalline allotropic form of carbon. Artificially, graphite can be prepared by taking a mixture of sand, coke and ferric oxide in an electric arc furnace. The temperature increases to 3500°C due to the resistance applied by the sand and at this high temperature coke orients itself to form graphite.

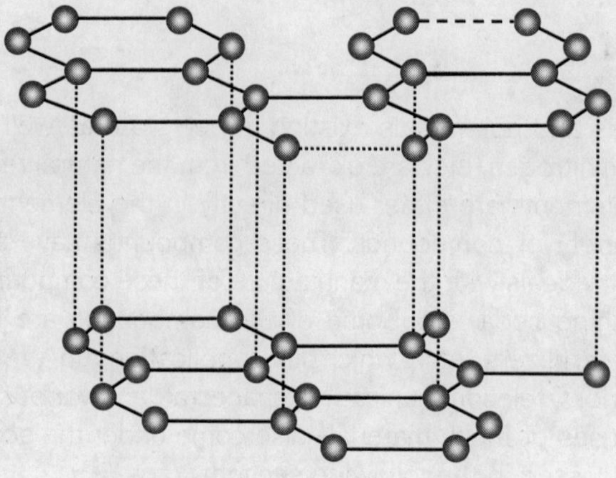

Figure 7.2 Structure of graphite

> **Info Bytes!**
> The carbon allotrope, graphene, is so strong that it's estimated to be 200 times stronger than steel.

In graphite, each carbon atom is bonded to three other atoms resulting in the formation of a layer of hexagonal rings. The remaining unpaired electron in each carbon atom helps to develop weak forces of attraction between different layers. These layers in turn arrange parallel one over the other and are held together by weak forces.

Physical Properties: Graphite, a dark greyish soft lustrous solid has a density of 2.25g/cc and melting point around 3600°C.

Chemical Properties: Graphite, on heating in an atmosphere of pure oxygen, catches fire at 700°C forming a mixture of CO_2 and CO:

$$3C + 2O_2 \xrightarrow{700°C} CO_2 + 2CO + \Delta Q$$

Uses: Graphite is mainly used in making leads of pencil, electrodes, refractory crucibles and as a solid lubricant.

Buckminsterfullerene

Buckminsterfullerene is another crystalline allotropic form of carbon discovered recently. These fullerene molecules are synthesised by subjecting graphite to sublimation using laser radiation. The vapor formed is subsequently cooled in the atmosphere of noble gases. The fullerene molecules mainly consist of C_{60} with smaller amounts of C_{70} and traces of other fullerenes consisting of even number of carbon atoms up to 350.

> **Info Bytes!**
> C_{60} molecule consists of 12 pentagons and 20 hexagons of carbon arranged in 32 rings as a whole. This allotrope of carbon acts as a superconductor on forming compounds with noble gases.

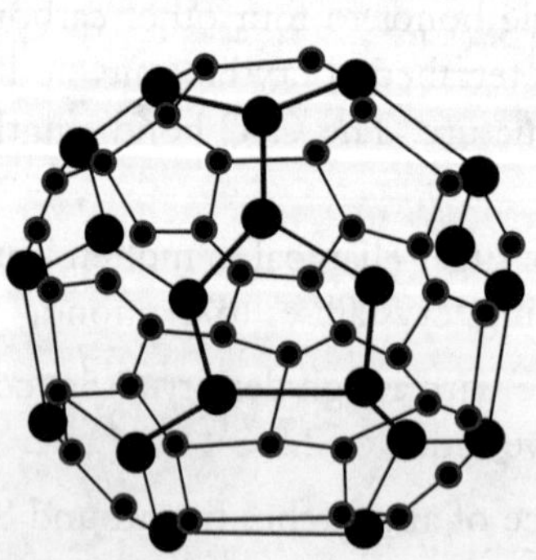

Figure 7.3 Structure of fullerene

Physical Properties: Buckminsterfullerene is a brown-powdered substance with a density of 1.65 g/cc that sublimes at 527°C. It has a refractive index of 2.2.

Compounds of Carbon

Apart from the various organic compounds, carbon occurs in the form of compounds such as oxides, carbides, carbonates, bicarbonates, etc. Carbon can form two oxides, namely carbon monoxide and carbon dioxide.

Carbon Monoxide

Carbon monoxide is not a natural component of atmospheric air. Carbon monoxide is produced by incomplete combustion of automobile fuels or biomass. This is a harmful gas due to its high solubility in the blood. It bonds with hemoglobin forming carboxyhemoglobin that decreases the supply of oxygen to the tissues.

Carbon Dioxide

Carbon dioxide is one of the minor components of atmospheric air. It is added to the atmosphere by means of natural phenomena such as degradation of organic matter, respiration, fermentation, and chemical weathering of rocks. Carbon dioxide is a colorless gas that is soluble in water and is heavier than air. It is consumed by plants during the process of photosynthesis. Carbon dioxide present in the atmosphere should be balanced because excess amount of CO_2 in the atmosphere leads to increase in temperature of the earth that causes global warming.

Silicon

Silicon is the second most abundant element in earth's crust. Just like carbon, silicon is also a non-metal belonging to the IVA group of the periodic table and is present below carbon.

Occurrence

Silicon occurs mostly in the combined state in nature. It exits in the form of oxides, silicates in sand and clay. Aluminium silicate is the most widely distributed silicate in the form of clay. Like carbon, silicon also exhibits allotropy existing in both amorphous and crystalline forms. It is present as a constituent of semi-precious stones like garnet, zircon, opal, etc.

Extraction

Silicon can be extracted from quartz. A mixture of finely powdered quartz with magnesium powder is heated in a fire clay crucible. On heating, magnesium undergoes oxidation while silicon dioxide undergoes reduction leading to the formation of silicon. The product is washed with HCl to dissolve MgO. Unreacted silica is washed away using hydrofluoric acid.

$$SiO_2 + 2Mg \rightarrow 2MgO + Si$$

Silicon can also be prepared by reducing silica with coke, but the silicon obtained in this method has lesser purity:

$$SiO_2 + 2C \rightarrow Si + 2CO$$

Physical Properties

Silicon is a dark brown powder and insoluble in water. Its melting point is 1683 K and boiling point is 2628 K.

Chemical Properties

Table 7.1 Chemical properties of silicon

Properties	Reactions
With oxygen	$Si + O_2 \rightarrow SiO_2$
With steam	$Si + 2H_2O \rightarrow SiO_2 + 2H_2$ (red hot)
With carbon	$Si + Coke \xrightarrow{\text{(at high temperature)}} SiC$

Uses of Silicon

Silicon is widely used in the field of electronics for the manufacture of semiconductor devices. It is also used for the preparation of some alloys like ferrosilicon and silicon bronze. The compounds of silicon have wide range of applications in industry.

Applications of Compounds of Silicon

1. Silica is used for the manufacture of glass, porcelain, building materials and threads of high elasticity.
2. Silicon carbide is used as an abrasive for cutting and grinding glass.
3. Sodium aluminium silicate is used for softening of hard water.

Nitrogen

Nitrogen is the most abundant element in the atmosphere. It is placed in the VA group of the periodic table.

Occurrence

Nitrogen exists in the atmosphere in elemental state. In combined state, nitrogen is present in the form of nucleic acids and amino acids in living systems and ammonium or nitrate salts in soils.

Laboratory Preparation

In the laboratory, nitrogen can be prepared from air.

Procedure

Soda lime is taken in a U-tube and air is slowly pumped through it. The sodium hydroxide present in soda lime reacts with CO_2 present in air forming sodium bicarbonate and the water vapor present in the air reacts with calcium oxide to form calcium hydroxide. Thus, both CO_2 and H_2O are removed.

$$CaO + H_2O \rightarrow Ca(OH)_2$$
$$NaOH + CO_2 \rightarrow NaHCO_3$$

> **Konnect**
>
> Laughing gas or nitrous oxide (N_2O) is a compound of nitrogen and is used in medicine for its anaesthetic and analgesic effects.

The leftover air is passed over red hot copper where the O_2 present in air turns copper to copper oxide. The nitrogen gas present in air, thus, does not undergo chemical reaction and can be collected by the downward displacement of water.

$$2Cu + O_2 \rightarrow 2CuO$$

Compounds of Nitrogen

Ammonia and nitric acid constitute the most important compounds of nitrogen since they are used as raw materials in various industries.

Ammonia

Occurrence

In free state, ammonia is found in traces in air as well as in water.

In combined state, ammonical liquor is obtained by destructive distillation of coal and small deposits of ammonium salts in craters.

Laboratory Preparation

1. Ammonia gas can be prepared by heating ammonium salts with alkalies:

$$2NH_4Cl + Ca(OH)_2 \xrightarrow{\Delta} CaCl_2 + 2H_2O + 2NH_3$$

2. Ammonia gas can be prepared by treating metal nitrides with warm water:

$$Mg_3N_2 + 6H_2O \rightarrow 3Mg(OH)_2 + 2NH_3$$

Industrial Method of Preparation by Haber's process

Ammonia can be synthesised in large scale by Haber's process.

Principle: Ammonia can be synthesised by the reaction of nitrogen and hydrogen in 1 : 3 ratio under high pressure at a moderately high temperature. It is an exothermic reaction.

$$N_2 + 3H_2 \rightarrow 2NH_3 + \text{heat}$$

Conditions Required for the Process

Pressure – 200–900 atm
Temperature – 450–500°C
Catalyst – Iron
Promoter – Molybdenum

Presence of traces of impurities such as carbon dioxide, carbon monoxide, and hydrogen sulphide acts as catalytic poisons and reduces the yield of ammonia. Hence, the removal of these impurities from the raw materials is an essential step in this process.

Table 7.2 Methods of removal of impurities in Haber's process

Impurities	Methods of removal
CO_2	Dissolution in water under pressure
CO	By passing through cuprous formate or cuprous acetate
H_2S	Absorption in KOH solution under pressure

Procedure: Pure and dry H_2 and N_2 are mixed in the ratio of 3 : 1 and the mixture is compressed under high pressure of about 200–900 atm. The compressed gases are led into catalytic chamber containing finely divided iron with molybdenum at 450°C. The product ammonia, unreacted nitrogen, and hydrogen exchange their heat with incoming nitrogen and hydrogen. The outgoing hot mixture contains only 10% NH_3 and condenses at −33°C and 8 atm pressure. The cold mixture is allowed to expand suddenly so that ammonia gets liquefied and when it is passed through water, it dissolves and forms liquid ammonia. The unreacted N_2 and H_2 are recirculated through the plant.

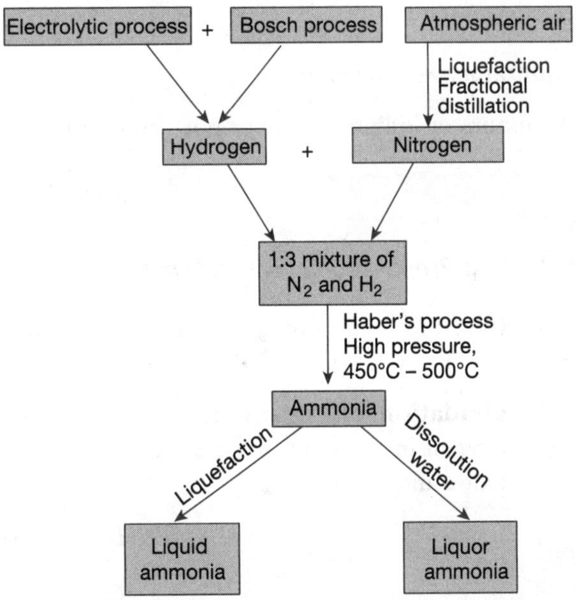

Figure 7.4 Flow chart for the manufacture of ammonia by Haber's process

Physical Properties

Ammonia is a colorless, pungent smelling gas. It has a boiling point of 33°C and a freezing point of −78°C.

Chemical Properties

Table 7.3 Chemical properties of ammonia

Properties	Reactions
Combustion	NH_3 is a non-combustible gas and also does not support combustion.
Oxidation	$4NH_3 + 3O_2 \rightarrow 2N_2 + 6H_2O$ $4NH_3 + 5O_2 \xrightarrow{Pt/900°C} 4NO + 6H_2O$
Reducing agent	$3CuO + 2NH_3 \xrightarrow{\Delta} 3Cu + 3H_2O + N_2$ (reducing agent)
Complex formation	$2NH_3 + H_2SO_4 \rightarrow (NH_4)_2SO_4$ $(NH_4)_2SO_4 + Cu(OH)_2 + 2NH_4OH \rightarrow$ $[Cu(NH_3)_4]SO_4 + 4H_2O$

Uses

Ammonia is used in the manufacture of fertilizers, plastics, industrially useful compounds like HNO_3, baking soda, and washing soda.

Nitric Acid

Nitric acid is a very strong acid that has strong oxidizing properties. Nitric acid is one of the constituents of aqua regia, which can dissolve even noble metals.

Occurrence

Nitric acid occurs in traces in the atmosphere in free state.

In combined state, nitric acid occurs in the form of its mineral nitrates like sodium nitrate, potassium nitrate, and calcium nitrate.

Laboratory Preparation

A mixture of sodium nitrate or potassium nitrate with concentrated sulphuric acid on distillation produces nitric acid.

$$KNO_3 + H_2SO_4 \xrightarrow{<200°C} KHSO_4 + HNO_3$$

Industrial Preparation of Nitric Acid by Oswald's Process

Principle: Preparation of nitric acid in industry involves the catalytic oxidation of ammonia and subsequent dissolution in water. The entire process takes place in three different stages as listed below:

1. **Oxidation of Ammonia into Nitric Oxide in a Catalytic Chamber:** A mixture of ammonia and dry oxygen in the ratio of 1 : 2 when passed over platinum gauze, maintained electrically at 800°C produces nitric oxide and steam:

$$4NH_3 + 5O_2 \xrightarrow{Pt-800°C} 4NO + 6H_2O(steam)$$

2. **Oxidation Chamber:** Nitric oxide gets oxidized to nitrogen dioxide when the mixture of NO, O_2 and steam is allowed to cool to 50°C in the oxidation chamber:

$$2NO + O_2 \xrightarrow{H_2O} 2NO_2$$

3. **Absorption Tower:** Dilute nitric acid is formed when a mixture of nitrogen dioxide and oxygen along with water vapor is passed through water.

Removal of Color

1. By passing dry CO_2 or dry air through colored nitric acid, which drives out nitrogen dioxide gas.
2. By the addition of water drop by drop to nitric acid, the nitrogen dioxide present in it is oxidized to nitric acid:

$$3NO_2 + H_2O \rightarrow 2HNO_3 + NO$$

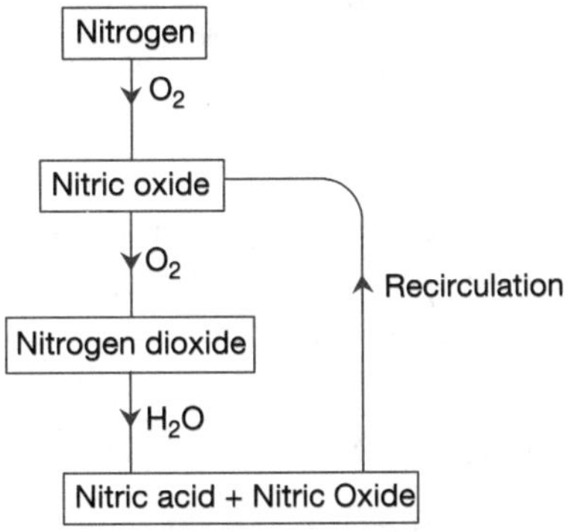

Figure 7.5 Flow chart for the manufacture of nitric acid by Oswald's process

Precautions

1. Impurities should not be present in the gases entering the catalytic chamber to avoid poisoning of the catalyst.
2. Electric heating of the catalyst should be stopped when the reaction speeds up since the reaction is exothermic in nature.
3. The excess oxygen helps to move the reaction forward.
4. Gases must be cooled to 50°C before they are sent into the oxidation chamber.
5. The acid in the absorption tower can be concentrated by evaporation under reduced pressure.

Physical Properties

Nitric acid is colorless acid with suffocating smell and taste. It is highly soluble in water.

Chemical Properties

Table 7.4 Chemical properties of nitric acid

Properties	Reactions
With metal oxide	$K_2O + 2HNO_3(dil) \rightarrow 2KNO_3 + H_2O$
Decomposition	$C + 4HNO_3(conc) \xrightarrow{boiling} CO_2 + 2H_2O + 4NO_2$ $3Cu + 8HNO_3(dil) \rightarrow 3Cu(NO_3)_2 + 4H_2O + 2NO$
With metallic carbonates and bicarbonates	$K_2CO_3 + 2HNO_3(dil) \rightarrow 2KNO_3 + H_2O + CO_2$ $KHCO_3 + HNO_3(dil) \rightarrow KNO_3 + H_2O + CO_2$

Uses

Nitric acid is mainly used in the manufacture of explosives and fertilizers. Due to its oxidizing properties, it is used in purification of gold and as an oxidant in rocket fuel.

Phosphorus

Phosphorus is a non-metal belonging to the VA group in the periodic table and it is known as phosphorus, as it glows in the dark.

Occurrence

Phosphorus cannot exist in the free state, but in the combined state it occurs in the form of phosphates like phosphorite ($Ca_3(PO_4)_2$), chloropatite ($3Ca_3(PO_4)_2.CaCl_2$), and fluorapatite ($3Ca_3(PO_4)_2.CaCF_2$).

Extraction

Phosphorus is mainly extracted from phosphorite ore by heating the mixture of powdered ore along with sand and coke in an electric furnace. The temperature maintained in the furnace is 1400 – 1500°C. At this temperature, calcium phosphate on reaction with sand converts into phosphorus pentoxide. Phosphorus pentoxide so formed reacts with coke to form phosphorus:

$$Ca_3(PO_4)_2 + 3SiO_2 \rightarrow 3CaSiO_3 + P_2O_5$$

$$2P_2O_5 + 10C \rightarrow 10CO + P_4$$

The by-product calcium silicate formed is removed as a slag. The vapors of carbon monoxide and phosphorus are collected from the outlet at the top. These vapors are passed through water, where phosphorus solidifies while CO escapes out. The crude yellow phosphorus is then purified by melting under water, followed by treatment with dilute sulphuric acid and potassium dichromate to remove the impurities by oxidation and redistillation.

Allotropes

Phosphorus exists in two allotropic forms, namely white phosphorus and red phosphorus. We now provide a comparative study of white and red phosphorus.

Table 7.5 Comparative study of white and red phosphorous

White phosphorus	Red phosphorus
A molecule of white phosphorus consists of four atoms that are arranged at four corners of a regular tetrahedron. There exist weak forces between P_4 molecules	Red phosphorus consists of infinite chains of phosphorus atoms that results in a covalent crystal lattice
It is a whitish yellow soft solid with density of 1.8 g/cc	It is a reddish brown solid with density of 2.1 g/cc
It melts at 317 K and has a very low ignition temperature	It sublimes at about 565 K when heated in the absence of air and its ignition temperature is 533 K
It is insoluble in water but readily soluble in non-polar solvents like chloroform, benzene, etc	It is insoluble in water as well as carbon disulphide
It is poisonous in nature	It is non-poisonous in nature

Info Bytes!

Phosphorus has several allotropes including white, red, black, and violet. White phosphorus glows in the dark, a phenomenon known as chemiluminescence.

Chemical Properties

Table 7.6 Chemical properties of phosphorous

Parameters	Reactions
Reaction with air	$P_4 + 5O_2 \rightarrow 2P_2O_5$
Reaction with chlorine	$P_4 + 6Cl_2 \rightarrow 4PCl_3$
	$P_4 + 10Cl_2 \rightarrow 4PCl_5$
With acids	$P + 5HNO_3 \rightarrow H_3PO_4 + 5NO_2 + H_2O$
	$2P + 5H_2SO_4 \rightarrow 2H_3PO_4 + 5SO_2 + 2H_2O$

Uses

Phosphorus is widely used in the match industry due to its low ignition temperature. It is also used in making rat poison, smoke bombs, fireworks, fertilizers, etc.

Konnect

Red phosphorus does not react with any alkali.

Sulphur

Sulphur is a non-metallic element belonging to the VIA group in the periodic table.

Info Bytes!

The word 'sulphur' has been derived from the Sanskrit word 'sulvari' meaning enemy of copper, as it destroys the properties of metals due to its reactivity.

Occurrence

In nature, sulphur occurs both in the free and in the combined states.

Free State

Sulphur, in the free state, is found in the earth's crust (0.03% of the earth's crust is elemental sulphur). In the volcanic regions like Sicily and Japan, it is present near the earth's crust and in the non-volcanic regions of the USA like Texas and Louisiana it is found much below the earth's crust (300–400 m below the earth's crust).

Combined State

Sulphur in the combined state is found in the form of sulphides (in ores), sulphates (in salts) and in organic matter.

Info Bytes!

Organic matter
In insulin, glucosinolates of plants and animals, natural gas, petroleum, crude oil, coal gas and water springs

Table 7.7 Combined states of sulphur

Sulphates		Sulphides	
Salt	Formula	Ores	Formula
Gypsum	$CaSO_4 \cdot 2H_2O$	Cinnabar	HgS
Epsom salt	$MgSO_4 \cdot 7H_2O$	Galena	PbS
Glauber's salt	$Na_2SO_4 \cdot 10H_2O$	Iron pyrites	FeS
		Copper pyrites	CuS
		Zinc blend	ZnS

Extraction

Sulphur has a wide variety of uses in industries. It is extracted from the earth's crust by the following processes:

Sicilian Process

This process is used to extract sulphur, which is near the earth's crust (deposits in Sicily). It is carried out in brick kilns built on sloping hill sides.

Frasch Process

This process is used to extract sulphur, which lie 150–400 m below the earth's crust. This process is also called **Louisiana process** as large deposits of this are found in Louisiana. A direct mining is not possible as sulphur is present in layers of quick sand and gravel.

Process: In this process, three concentric pipes of diameters 25 mm, 76 mm, and 152 mm are drilled through the ground to the sulphur deposits. Superheated steam (170°C) under pressure is sent through the outermost pipe. This melts the sulphur below (m.p. of sulphur = 112°C). Hot compressed air (up to 35 atm) is sent through the innermost pipe, which froths up the molten sulphur below. The sulphur foam formed rises up the middle pipe and is collected.

Advantages: The sulphur extracted in this process is 99.5% pure and does not need further purification.

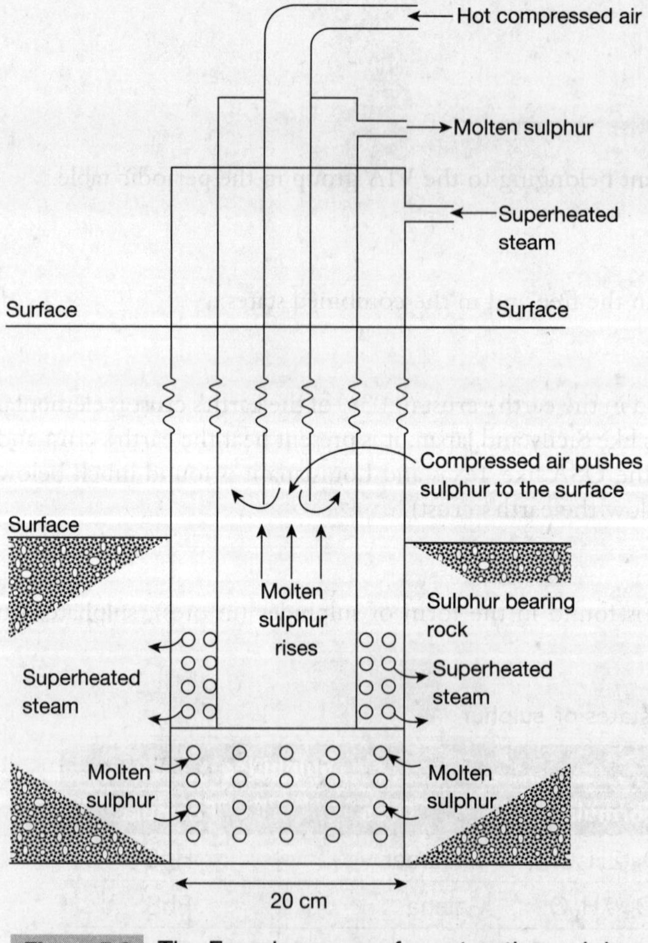

Figure 7.6 The Frasch process for extracting sulphur

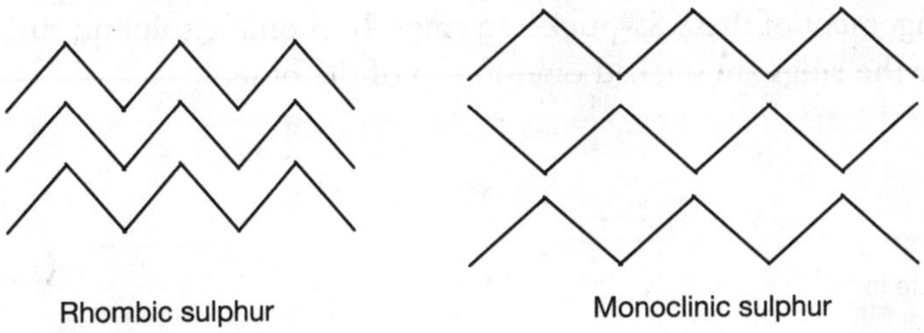

Figure 7.7 Structures of rhombic and monoclinic sulphurs

Allotropes of Sulphur

The phenomenon of existence of an element in more than one physical form is called **allotropy**, and the various forms of the element are called **allotropes**. Sulphur exists in different allotropic forms. Allotropes have same chemical properties but different physical properties.

Konnect

Rhombic and monoclinic are the most common allotropes of sulphur, and they can transform into one another at different temperatures.

The three main allotropic forms of sulphur are the following:

1. rhombic sulphur,
2. monoclinic sulphur and
3. plastic sulphur.

Table 7.8 Comparative study of the allotropic forms of sulphur

Parameters	Rhombic sulphur	Monoclinic sulphur	Plastic sulphur
Other names	Octahedral sulphur, alpha-sulphur	Prismatic sulphur, beta-sulphur	Gamma-sulphur
Preparation	Roll sulphur is dissolved in carbon disulphide. This is allowed to evaporate slowly by slight heating. Rhombic sulphur crystals are left behind	Roll sulphur is heated in an evaporating dish till it melts to pale yellow liquid. This on cooling forms a crust on the surface. Holes are pierced on the crust and the molten sulphur is drained out. Needle-shaped sulphur (monoclinic sulphur) crystals are left behind	Roll sulphur is heated to above 300°C till it turns to dark brown, and this is poured into cold water and the sulphur formed is plastic sulphur
Color	Pale yellow	Amber	Dark brown
Shape/structure	Octahedral 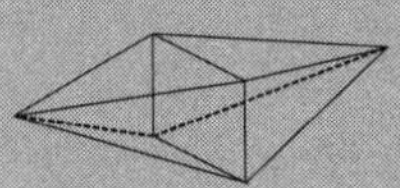	Needle shaped 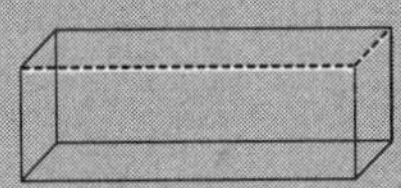	Amorphous
Density	2.08 g/cm^3	1.98 g/cm^3	1.92 g/cm^3
Solubility	Soluble in carbon disulphide	Soluble in carbon disulphide	Insoluble in carbon disulphide
Melting point	112.8°C	119°C	No sharp melting point

Transition Between Rhombic and Monoclinic Sulphur

Rhombic sulphur is stable below 95.6°C and above this temperature it changes to monoclinic sulphur. Conversely, monoclinic sulphur is stable above 95.6°C, but changes to the rhombic variety below this temperature. Hence, 95.6°C is called the transition temperature of these two allotropes of sulphur.

Puckered Ring Structure of Sulphur

Both rhombic and monoclinic sulphur exist in the form of S_8 molecules. These S_8 molecules are in the form of a ring. It forms a crown-shaped molecule with four atoms on the top and four atoms at the bottom.

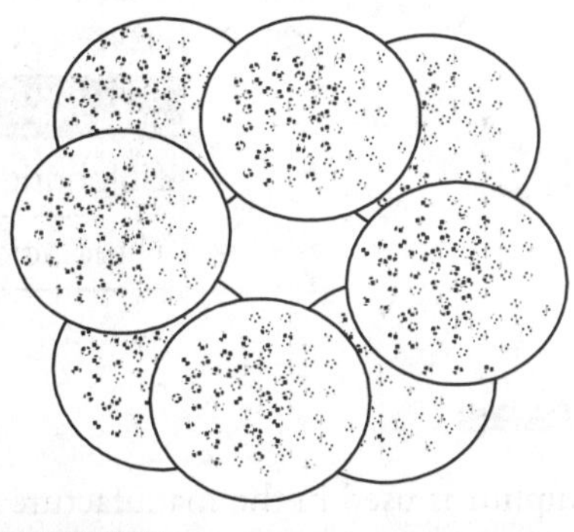

Figure 7.8 Puckered ring structure

The rhombic and the monoclinic forms differ in the arrangement of these S_8-puckered rings. In rhombic sulphur, these rings fit snugly into each other while in monoclinic sulphur the rings are stacked one on top of the other.

Action of Heat on Sulphur

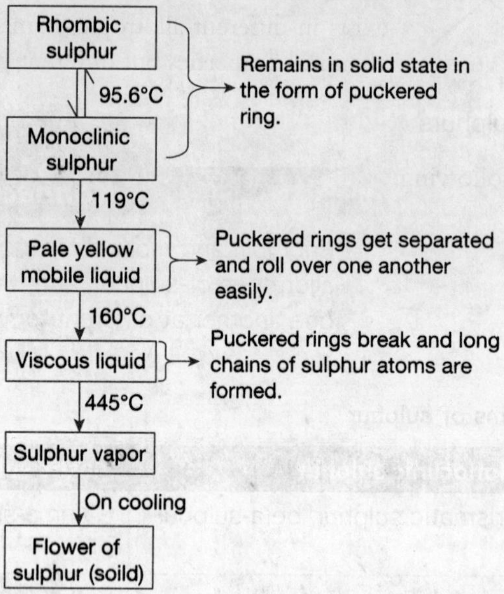

Figure 7.9 Process flow chart for heating of sulphur

Info Bytes!

When melted, sulphur becomes a deep red liquid.

Table 7.9 Chemical properties of sulphur

Parameters	Reactions
With non-metals	
Oxygen	$S + O_2 \xrightarrow{300°C} SO_2$ $2S + 3O_2 \rightarrow 2SO_3$ (trace amounts)
Hydrogen	$S + H_2 \rightarrow H_2S$ (boiling)
Carbon	$C + S \rightarrow CS_2$ (coke)
Chlorine	$2S + Cl_2 \rightarrow S_2Cl_2$
With metals	
Mercury	$Hg + S \rightarrow HgS$
Copper	$2Cu + S \rightarrow CuS$
Iron	$Fe + S \rightarrow FeS$
With acids	
Sulphuric acid	$S + 2H_2SO_4 \rightarrow 3SO_2 + 2H_2O$
Nitric acid	$S + 6HNO_3 \rightarrow H_2SO_4 + 6NO_2 + 2H_2O$

Uses

Sulphur is used in the manufacture of insecticides, gunpowder, and crackers. The most important use of sulphur is in the vulcanization of rubber.

Compounds of Sulphur

Sulphur due to its high reactivity forms a wide variety of compounds. The industrially useful compounds are sulphuric acid, hydrogen sulphide and sulphur dioxide.

Hydrogen Sulphide (H_2S)

Hydrogen sulphide is prepared by the action of dilute hydrochloric acid or dilute sulphuric acid on iron sulphide:

$$FeS + H_2SO_4 \rightarrow FeSO_4 + H_2S$$

$$FeS + 2HCl \rightarrow FeCl_2 + H_2S$$

Physical Properties of H_2S

Hydrogen sulphide is heavier than air and dissolves moderately in water due to partial ionization. It is acidic in nature. It is also known for its characteristic rotten egg smell.

Chemical properties of H_2S

Chemical properties of H_2S are tabulated below:

Table 7.10 Chemical properties of hydrogen sulphide

Parameters	Reactions
Reducing nature	
with oxygen	$2H_2S + O_2 \rightarrow 2S + 2H_2O + CuS$
with metals	$CuSO_4 + H_2S \rightarrow H_2SO_4 + CuS$ (acidified solution of Cu)
with potassium permanganate	$2KMnO_4 + 3H_2SO_4 + 5H_2S \rightarrow K_2SO_4 + 2MnSO_4 + 8H_2O + 5S$
with non-metals	$H_2S + Cl_2 \rightarrow 2HCl + S$

Uses of H_2S

Hydrogen sulphide is used as a laboratory reagent as it gives colored precipitates with metal salts. It is also used as a reducing agent.

Sulphur dioxide (SO_2)

Occurrence of SO_2

Sulphur dioxide exists in trace amounts in the atmosphere in the industrial areas. It is mainly present in atmosphere due to burning of coal and petroleum products.

Preparation of SO_2

Copper on treating with concentrated sulphuric acid evolves SO_2 gas:

$$Cu + 2H_2SO_4 \rightarrow CuSO_4 + 2H_2O + SO_2$$

Physical Properties of SO_2

Sulphur dioxide is a colorless, pungent-smelling gas that is fairly soluble in water. It is heavier than air and boils at −10°C.

Chemical Properties of SO_2

Table 7.11 Chemical properties of sulphur dioxide

Chemical Properties	Reactions involved
Acidic nature (i) With litmus (ii) Reaction with water	Sulphur dioxide changes blue litmus to red. Sulphur dioxide with water forms an unstable sulphurous acid. $H_2O + SO_2 \rightarrow H_2SO_3$
Reducing properties	Sulphur dioxide on reaction with moisture or water, produces nascent hydrogen that helps in the reducing action
Bleaching action	$SO_2\uparrow + H_2O \rightarrow H_2SO_4 + 2[H]$ (reducing agent). The nascent hydrogen produced on being exposed to moisture acts as a bleach.
Addition reactions	$SO_2 + Cl_2 \rightarrow SO_2Cl_2$
Oxidizing property	$2Mg + SO_2 \rightarrow 2MgO + MgS$

Uses of SO_2

Sulphur dioxide is used for the preparation of sulphuric acid and different germicides, insecticides, etc. It is used as a bleaching agent, and antichlor in textile industry.

Sulphuric acid (H_2SO_4)

Sulphuric acid is the most widely used chemical in the industry. The role of sulphuric acid in chemical industry is so significant that it is generally termed as the king of chemicals. It is also known as oil of vitriol as it is being prepared by the distillation of green vitriol ($FeSO_4.7H_2O$).

Occurrence of H_2SO_4

Sulphuric acid mainly occurs in free state in the hot water of sulphur springs. In combined state, it occurs in mineral sulphates, such as Epsom salt ($MgSO_4.7H_2O$). Glauber's salt ($Na_2SO_4.10H_2O$) and green vitriol ($FeSO_4.7H_2O$).

Manufacture of Sulphuric Acid

The large-scale manufacture of sulphuric acid is carried out by the contact process.

Contact Process

In this process, the basic raw material required is SO_2, which is produced by burning sulphur:

$$S + O_2 \rightarrow SO_2$$

Manufacture of sulphuric acid from SO_2 takes place in two steps.

Step I: Sulphur dioxide and oxygen in the ratio of 2 : 1 by volume are passed over vanadium pentoxide, maintained at 450°C under high-pressure conditions. Under these conditions, the sulphur dioxide and oxygen react with each other to form sulphur trioxide. Platinized asbestos can also be used in the place of V_2O_5.

$$2SO_2 + O_2 \rightarrow 2SO_3$$

Step II: Sulphur trioxide thus obtained is dissolved in sulphuric acid to form pyrosulphuric acid or oleum:

$$SO_3 + H_2SO_4 \rightarrow \underset{\text{(Oleum)}}{H_2S_2O_7}$$

The pyrosulphuric acid on treatment with water gives out sulphuric acid:

$$H_2S_2O_7 + H_2O \rightarrow 2H_2SO_4$$

The sulphuric acid prepared by this method is pure and highly concentrated.

Physical Properties of H_2SO_4

Sulphuric acid is a colorless, odourless liquid with density of 1.85 g/cc. It has a boiling point of 338°C.

Chemical Properties of H_2SO_4

Table 7.12 Chemical properties of sulphuric acid

Properties	Reactions
As an oxidizing agent	$2H_2SO_4 \xrightarrow[\text{retort}]{\text{red hot}} 2H_2O + 2SO_2 + O_2$
With metals	$Zn + H_2SO_4 \rightarrow ZnSO_4 + H_2$
With bases	$KOH + H_2SO_4 \rightarrow KHSO_4 + H_2O$ $2KOH + H_2SO_4 \rightarrow K_2SO_4 + 2H_2O$
With non-metals	$C + H_2SO_4 \rightarrow CO_2 + 2H_2O + 2SO_2$
As a dehydrating agent	$C_6H_{12}O_6 \xrightarrow{H_2SO_4} 6C + 6H_2O$

Uses of H_2SO_4

Sulphuric acid is used as a raw material in the manufacture of fertilizers, batteries, rubber, detergents, etc. It is also used as a dehydrating agent.

Sulphuric acid forms some salts like blue vitriol ($CuSO_4.5H_2O$), green vitriol ($FeSO_4.7H_2O$), alum ($K_2SO_4.Al_2(SO_4)_3.24H_2O$) and ammonium sulphate $(NH_4)_2SO_4$, which play a significant role in the industries.

1. **Copper Sulphate ($CuSO_4.5H_2O$):** Copper sulphate is a blue-colored crystalline substance. It loses its crystalline property when heated at 250°C where it loses its five molecules of water and becomes a white amorphous powder.

   In the aqueous state, it can conduct electricity and thus be helpful in electroplating, electrotyping, etc. It is also used as a germicide due to its poisonous nature.

2. **Green Vitriol ($FeSO_4.7H_2O$):** Green vitriol is a light green crystalline solid. It turns to reddish brown color on exposure to air due to aerial oxidation to ferric sulphate. It is used in dyeing and tanning industries.

3. **Alum ($K_2SO_4.Al_2(SO_4)_3.24H_2O$):** Alum is a double salt. It is a white crystalline solid soluble in water. On heating, it loses its water of crystallization above 92°C and forms a swollen mass called **burnt alum**, which is used in medicines. It is mainly used to purify drinking water, as a mordant in dyeing and also in paper and tanning industries.

4. **Ammonium Sulphate $(NH_4)_2SO_4$:** Ammonium sulphate is the most common nitrogenous fertilizer in agriculture. This is prepared by passing ammonia gas and carbon dioxide through a suspension of powdered gypsum in water.

   It is a white crystalline solid that is used for the preparation of alum, ammonium chloride and is also used as a laboratory reagent.

Chlorine

Chlorine is a non-metal belonging to the VIIA group of the periodic table and is called a typical halogen. It is a highly reactive element and generally exists in combined state. The most widely used compound of chlorine is hydrogen chloride. On dissolution in water, it gives out hydrochloric acid.

Hydrogen Chloride and Hydrochloric Acid

Hydrogen chloride was first synthesized by Glauber by heating common salt with concentrated sulphuric acid.

Occurrence of HCl Gas

In free state, hydrogen chloride gas is found in trace amounts in volcanic regions. Hydrochloric acid is secreted as gastric juices in the stomach during digestion.

Laboratory Preparation of HCl Gas

Metallic chloride on treatment with conc. H_2SO_4 liberates HCl. This when passed through water gives out hydrochloric acid:

$$NaCl + H_2SO_4 \xrightarrow{<200°C} NaHSO_4 + HCl$$

Physical Properties of HCl Gas

Hydrogen chloride is a colorless gas with pungent odour and has sour taste. It is extremely soluble in water. Its melting point is −115°C and boiling point is −85°C.

Chemical Properties of HCl Gas

Table 7.13 Chemical properties of HCl gas

Properties	Reactions
With water	$HCl + H_2O \rightarrow H_3O^+ + Cl^-$
With ammonia	$NH_3 + HCl \rightarrow NH_4Cl$

Konnect

Hydrochloric acid is naturally found in our stomachs, aiding in the digestion of food.

Physical Properties of HCl Acid

Hydrogen chloride is a colorless acid with pungent odor and has sour taste. It has a boiling point of 109.8°C and is a corrosive acid.

Chemical Properties of HCl Acid

Table 7.14 Chemical properties of hydrochloric acid

Properties	Reactions
With water	$HCl(dil) + H_2O \rightarrow H_3O^+ + Cl^-$
With metals	$Mg + 2HCl(dil) \rightarrow MgCl_2 + H_2$ $Ca + 2HCl(g) \rightarrow CaCl_2 + H_2$
With base	$K_2O + 2HCl(dil) \rightarrow 2KCl + H_2O$
With metal carbonates	$NH_3 + HCl \rightarrow NH_4Cl$ $K_2CO_3 + 2HCl(dil) \rightarrow 2KCl + H_2O + CO_2$
With metal sulphides	$Na_2S + 2HCl(dil) \rightarrow 2NaCl + H_2S$
Reducing properties	$MnO_2 + 4HCl(Conc) \rightarrow MnCl_2 + 2H_2O + Cl_2$
With metal sulphites	$Na_2SO_3 + 2HCl \rightarrow 2NaCl + H_2O + SO_2$

Uses of HCl Acid

Hydrochloric acid is mainly used in the manufacture of silver chlorides, dyes, drugs, and paints. It is used in the extraction of glue, soldering metals, leather industry, and pickling of metals.

EXAMPLE 7.1

Why is it important to thoroughly grind reactants like sodium carbonate and hydrochloric acid when conducting a chemical reaction in the laboratory?

SOLUTION

Grinding the reactants increases their surface area, which facilitates more effective collisions between particles, leading to a faster and more complete reaction between sodium carbonate and hydrochloric acid.

EXAMPLE 7.2

Why does concentrated sulphuric acid become hot when it is diluted with water?

SOLUTION

The dilution of concentrated sulphuric acid with water is an exothermic process because it involves the formation of strong hydrogen bonds between sulphuric acid molecules and water molecules. These hydrogen bonds release heat energy, making the solution hotter. Additionally, the reaction between sulphuric acid and water is highly exothermic, further contributing to the increase in temperature.

EXAMPLE 7.3

Gold and platinum do not dissolve either in conc HCl or conc HNO_3, but dissolve in the mixture of three parts of conc HCl and 1 part of conc HNO_3. Give reason and write the necessary chemical equations.

SOLUTION

The dissolution of noble metals in aqua regia can be justified as follows:

(i) The concentrated nitric acid oxidizes concentrated hydrochloric acid to liberate nascent chlorine.

$$HNO_{3(conc)} + 3HCl_{(conc)} \rightarrow \underset{\text{Nitrosyl chloride}}{NOCl} + 2H_2O + \underset{\text{Nascent chlorine}}{2[Cl]}$$

(ii) Nascent chlorine reacts with noble metals to form their soluble chlorides that pass into the solution.

$$\underset{\text{Gold}}{Au} + 3[Cl] \rightarrow \underset{\text{Gold[III]chloride}}{AuCl_3}$$

$$\underset{\text{Platinum}}{Pt} + 4[Cl] \rightarrow \underset{\text{Platinum(IV)chloride}}{PtCl_4}$$

EXAMPLE 7.4

(i) Explain an activity to prove that sulphur dioxide is heavier than air.

(ii) Experimentally prove that sulphur dioxide is fairly soluble in water.

SOLUTION

(i) Experiment to prove that sulphur dioxide is heavier than air.

A clean gas jar containing air is taken. Few drops of acidified potassium dichromate is taken in it. A dry glass disc is placed over it. Over this, another gas jar containing sulphur dioxide gas is inverted and then the glass disc is removed. After few minutes, acidified potassium dichromate turns green. This proves that sulphur dioxide is heavier than air.

$$3SO_2 + K_2Cr_2O_7 + H_2SO_4 \rightarrow K_2SO_4 + Cr_2(SO_4)_3 + H_2O$$

(ii) Experiment to prove that sulphur dioxide is fairly soluble in water:

A gas jar containing sulphur dioxide gas is inverted in a trough of water and the initial level of water in the jar is noted. After sometime, it is found that the level of water rises up in the jar. It is because, sulphur dioxide gas dissolves in water and the water rises up.

$$SO_2 + H_2O \rightarrow H_2SO_3$$

EXAMPLE 7.5 Three jars labeled as A, B, and C, filled with SO_2 gas are taken. A burning wooden splinter, burning sodium and burning potassium are introduced into the jars, A, B, and C, respectively. What are the observations? Explain with reason and give the corresponding reactions.

SOLUTION

The burning splinter is put off while sodium and potassium continue to burn.

Reason: The heat produced due to burning of metals dissociates the molecule of sulphur dioxide to sulphur and oxygen. The oxygen so liberated sustains combustion of the metals.

$$4K + 3SO_2 \rightarrow \underset{\text{Potassium sulphite}}{K_2SO_3} + \underset{\text{Potassium thiosulphate}}{K_2S_2O_3}$$

$$4Na + 3SO_2 \rightarrow Na_2SO_3 + Na_2S_2O_3$$

Some Industrially Useful Compounds

Lime

Lime is also called **quick lime**, and the chemical name is calcium oxide.

Manufacture of Lime

Principle: Heating of limestone at 1073–1273 K in lime kiln gives out lime. In this process, the decomposition of calcium carbonate takes place. The process is called **calcination**.

$$CaCO_3 \rightarrow CaO + CO_2$$

Process: The manufacturing process is carried out in a furnace called **lime kiln**. Limestone is introduced into the kiln from the top. It is heated to a temperature of about 1500 K. The complete decomposition of limestone takes place at around 1273 K. Since the reaction is reversible in nature, an outlet is arranged at the top of the furnace through which CO_2 is expelled during the process. Lime formed at the bottom is collected at regular intervals.

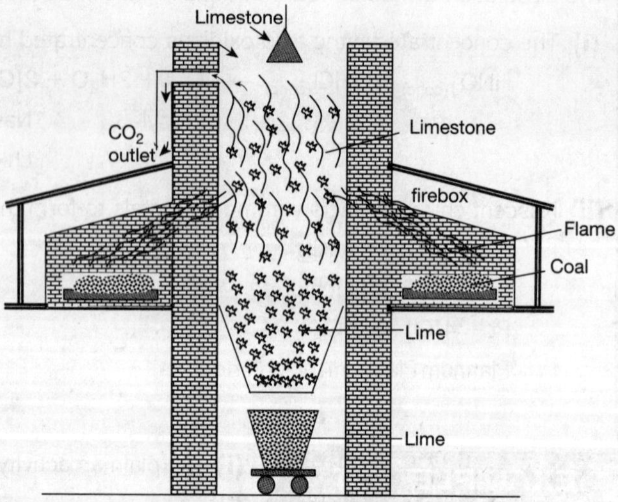

Figure 7.10 A vertical lime kiln

Properties of Lime

1. Calcium oxide is an amorphous white solid.
2. It has a high melting point of 2273 K.
3. Heating it at a very high temperature produces white light.
4. **Reaction with water:** Calcium oxide reacts with water to give out calcium hydroxide or slaked lime. This reaction is highly exothermic. A hissing sound is observed during this reaction. This reaction is called slaking of lime.

$$CaO + H_2O \rightarrow Ca(OH)_2 + \text{Heat}$$

5. **Reaction with acid:** It is a basic oxide and reacts with an acid forming salt and water:

$$CaO + 2HCl \rightarrow CaCl_2 + H_2O$$

Info Bytes!

In India, lime (or 'chuna') is often applied on paan leaves and consumed, believed to aid digestion.

Uses of Lime

1. Used as a drying agent.
2. Used in the manufacture of cement, glass, and calcium chloride.
3. Used in the manufacture of washing soda and bleaching powder.
4. Used as a lining for furnaces.
5. Extensively used for white washing.

Konnect

One of the important reactions of CaO is slaking of lime. During slaking of lime, slaked lime is prepared by the reaction of CaO with water.

Slaked Lime [$Ca(OH)_2$]

Slaked lime is an amorphous white substance. It is sparingly soluble in water and its solubility decreases with temperature. It is used in agriculture, in the manufacture of bleaching powder, caustic soda, glass, etc. and also used for removing temporary hardness of water.

Washing Soda

Washing soda is an important constituent of many detergents. The chemical name of washing soda is sodium carbonate decahydrate with the formula $Na_2CO_3.10H_2O$. The anhydrous form of it is known as soda ash.

Manufacture of Washing Soda using Solvay Process

The process employed for the large-scale preparation of washing soda is ammonia–soda process or Solvay process.

Principle: The basic reaction involved in the process is double decomposition reaction between NaCl and $CaCO_3$:

$$2NaCl + CaCO_3 \rightarrow Na_2CO_3 + CaCl_2$$

But the reaction between NaCl and $CaCO_3$, being reversible, cannot be directly used for the process. Therefore, a process involving other chemical compounds is employed for the manufacture of washing soda.

Raw Materials Used: The raw materials used are sodium chloride, ammonia and limestone.

The entire process takes place in various stages.

Stage 1: Saturation of brine solution with ammonia

Brine solution is taken in a saturation tower of the plant. Ammonia gas containing little amount of CO_2 is passed into it. Ammonia reacts with CO_2 to form ammonium carbonate. This ammonium carbonate renders precipitation of impurities of magnesium, calcium, and iron as carbonates:

$$2NH_3 + H_2O + CO_2 \rightarrow (NH_4)_2CO_3$$

$$(NH_4)_2CO_3 + MgCl_2 \rightarrow MgCO_3\downarrow + 2NH_4Cl$$

The precipitates are removed by filtration. The filtrate is cooled and sent to the next stage.

Info Bytes!

Known as 'soda ash', it's used in India for cleaning purposes and sometimes in traditional cooking.

Stage 2: Carbonation

This process takes place in the carbonation tower. The tower consists of perforated plates arranged one above the other. The ammonical brine from saturation tower is dropped into the carbonation tower and CO_2 gas is forced to bubble up under pressure at the base. The perforated plates help in the mixing up of CO_2 thoroughly with the solution. The pure brine solution in the presence of ammonium hydroxide reacts with CO_2 to form sodium bicarbonate and ammonium chloride:

$$NaCl + NH_4OH + CO_2 \rightarrow NaHCO_3 + NH_4Cl$$

Stage 3: Filtration

The reaction mixture from carbonation tower is subjected to filtration in a rotary vacuum filter. The sodium bicarbonate precipitate is separated. The filtrate contains ammonium salts and is sent into ammonia regeneration tower, where ammonia is regenerated and can be reused.

Stage 4: Calcination

The precipitate of sodium bicarbonate obtained in the third stage is subjected to heating and gives out sodium carbonate. This on recrystallization from water produces hydrated sodium carbonate, that is, washing soda:

$$2NaHCO_3 \rightarrow Na_2CO_3 + H_2O + CO_2$$

$$Na_2CO_3 + 10H_2O \rightarrow Na_2CO_3 \cdot 10H_2O$$

Stage 5: Regeneration of raw materials

The filtrate from the third stage is sent into a regeneration tower. The calcium oxide from lime kiln dissolves in water to give $Ca(OH)_2$. This, on reaction with ammonium salts present in the filtrate, gives out ammonia again. Carbon dioxide gas produced in stage 4 can be recirculated in the first stage.

$$CaO + H_2O \rightarrow Ca(OH)_2$$

$$Ca(OH)_2 + 2NH_4Cl \rightarrow CaCl_2 + 2NH_3 + 2H_2O$$

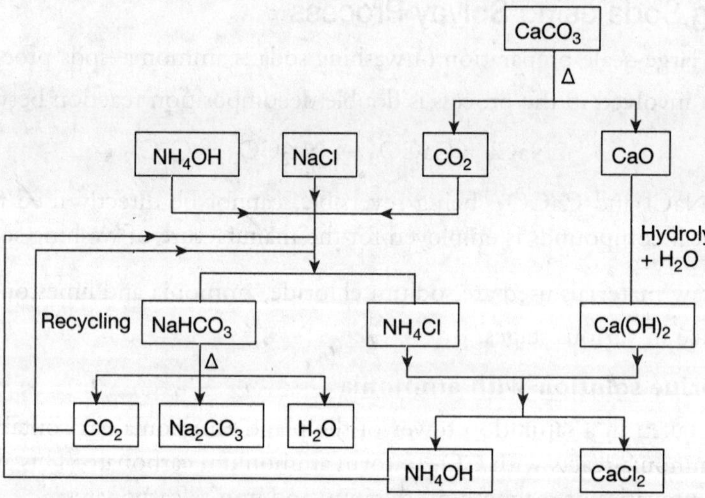

Figure 7.11 Flow chart representing Solvay process for the preparation of washing soda

Advantages of Solvay Process

1. Cheap and abundant raw materials.
2. CO_2 formed in the process is recycled in the process. So it is not required to take fresh $CaCO_3$ each time.
3. $CaCl_2$ is obtained as a by-product.
4. The raw materials are regenerated.

Properties of Washing Soda

1. It is a white crystalline substance that loses water of crystallization on exposure to air and forms a monohydrate. Hence, it is called an efflorescent salt. The loss of water takes place in stages.

$$Na_2CO_3.10H_2O \rightarrow Na_2CO_3.9H_2O \rightarrow Na_2CO_3.H_2O$$

2. **Action of heat:** The hydrated salt loses water of crystallization completely to form an anhydrous salt.

$$Na_2CO_3.10H_2O \rightarrow Na_2CO_3 + 10H_2O$$

Uses of Washing Soda

1. Used in glass industry
2. Used in soap industry
3. Used in softening of hard water
4. Paper and textile industry
5. Metal refining
6. Used in paints and dyes
7. Used in laundry
8. Used in the manufacture of other compounds of sodium

Baking Soda

Baking soda is an important constituent of baking powder and is used for cooking purposes. The chemical name of baking soda is sodium hydrogen carbonate or sodium bicarbonate.

Manufacture of Baking Soda

Solvay process is employed for the preparation of sodium bicarbonate on a large scale. The precipitate obtained in stage 3 of Solvay process being sodium bicarbonate can be dried and used as a commercial sample:

$$NaCl + NH_4OH + CO_2 \rightarrow NaHCO_3 + NH_4Cl$$

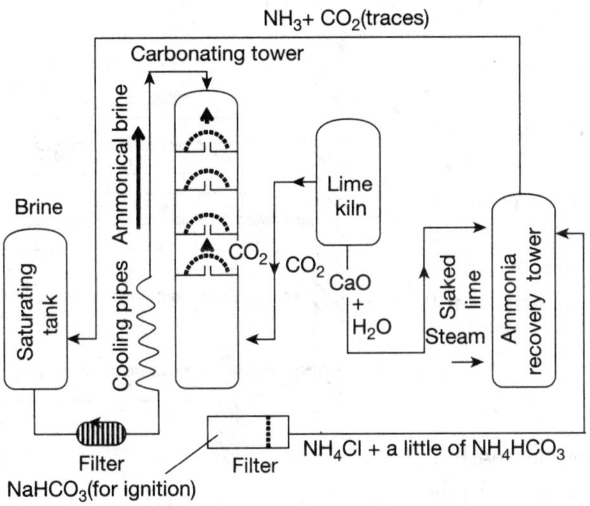

Figure 7.12 Flow diagram of solvay process

Info Bytes!

Commonly used in making traditional Indian sweets and snacks for its leavening properties.

Properties of Baking Soda

1. Baking soda is a white crystalline solid.
2. It is sparingly soluble in water and gives out an alkaline solution.
3. A solution of sodium bicarbonate on heating evolves CO_2 gas forming sodium carbonate:

$$2NaHCO_3 \xrightarrow{\text{Heat}} Na_2CO_3 + H_2O + CO_2$$

Due to this property, it is added to food stuffs to aerate the dough and gives puffy nature to the food material made from the dough.

Uses of Baking Soda

1. It is used as an antacid.
2. A mixture of sodium bicarbonate and tartaric acid is called baking powder. It is an important additive for food and drinks. Sodium bicarbonate, on decomposition, gives out CO_2, which causes bread and cakes to rise. Sodium carbonate produced in the process gets neutralized by tartaric acid present in baking powder.
3. Sodium bicarbonate is taken as one of the constituents in fire extinguishers. A solution of sodium bicarbonate and sulphuric acid is taken in an extinguisher. These are kept separately and they come in contact with each other when the knob is pressed or the extinguisher is inverted. When these two solutions react, CO_2 gas is liberated and it puts out the fire. These are called **soda acid fire extinguishers**.

Bleaching Powder

Bleaching powder is the major constituent of domestic cleaning agents and is also called the **chloride of lime**. The chemical name of bleaching powder is calcium oxychloride and formula is $CaOCl_2$.

Manufacture of Bleaching Powder

Bleaching powder can be prepared on large scale in Hasenclever plant or in Bachmann plant. In both the cases, the principle and process are the same.

Principle: Chlorine reacts with dry slaked lime to form calcium oxychloride:

$$Ca(OH)_2 + Cl_2 \rightarrow CaOCl_2 + H_2O$$

Manufacturing Process in Hasenclever Plant

The plant consists of a number of horizontal cylinders provided with rotating shafts with blades. Slaked lime is dropped into the topmost cylinder. The revolving blades allow the downward movement of slaked lime into the other cylinders. Chlorine gas is introduced into the bottommost cylinder. The counter currents allow a thorough mixing of the raw materials and complete conversion into bleaching powder.

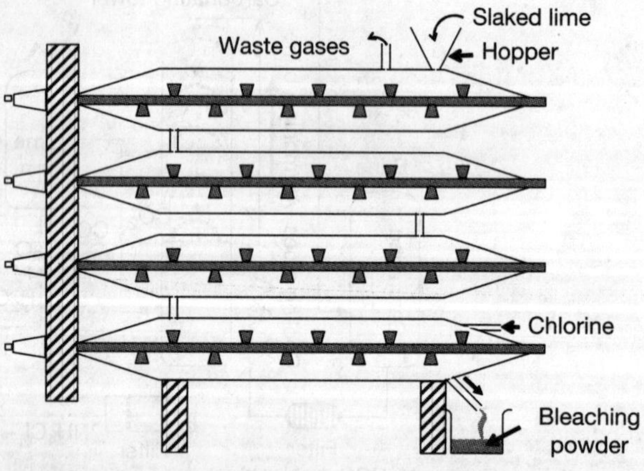

Figure 7.13 Hasenclever plant for the manufacture of bleaching powder

Properties of Bleaching Powder

1. Bleaching powder is a white amorphous powder with a pungent smell of chlorine. It is considered a mixed salt of calcium chloride and calcium hypochlorite [$CaCl_2$ + $Ca(OCl)_2$].
2. **Reaction with Moist Air:** On long standing, bleaching powder undergoes auto-oxidation and loses chlorine:

$$6CaOCl_2 \xrightarrow[\text{air}]{\text{Moist}} 5CaCl_2 + Ca(ClO_3)_2$$

3. **Reaction with Cold Water:** On dissolution in water, bleaching powder dissociates to give chloride and hypochlorite ions:

$$CaOCl_2 + 2H_2O \rightarrow Ca(OH)_2 + HCl + HOCl$$

$$HOCl \rightarrow HCl + [O]$$

hypochlorous acid

$$HCl \rightarrow H^+ + Cl^-$$

chloride

> **Info Bytes!**
> A calcium compound used for disinfecting water and as a bleaching agent. Frequently used to sanitize water in Indian villages and towns.

4. **Reaction with Hot Water:** In hot water, the hypochlorite ion undergoes autoxidation to give chlorate ions and chloride ions:

$$3ClO^- \rightarrow ClO_3^- + 2Cl^-$$

5. **Reaction with Dilute Acids:** On reacting with a small amount of dilute acid, bleaching powder dissociates to give hypochlorous acid that can furnish nascent oxygen. This is the reaction used for determining the quality of bleaching powder.

$$2CaOCl_2 + H_2SO_4 \rightarrow CaCl_2 + CaSO_4 + 2HOCl$$

$$HOCl \rightarrow HCl + [O]$$

6. **Reaction with Excess Dilute Acid:** On reacting with an excess amount of dilute acid, bleaching powder liberates chlorine gas:

$$CaOCl_2 + H_2SO_4 \rightarrow CaSO_4 + H_2O + Cl_2\uparrow$$

7. **Reaction with CO_2:** On passing CO_2 gas along with water through a paste of bleaching powder, chlorine gas is evolved:

$$CaOCl_2 + CO_2 \rightarrow CaCO_3 + Cl_2\uparrow$$

Uses of Bleaching Powder

1. Used for the sterilization of drinking water
2. Used as a bleaching agent for cotton and paper pulp
3. Used in the preparation of chloroform
4. Used as an oxidizing agent and chlorinating agent

Plaster of Paris

Plaster of Paris is an important compound used in the construction work and in orthopedics for joining fractured bones. The chemical name of Plaster of Paris is calcium sulphate hemihydrate with the formula $CaSO_4.½H_2O$.

Manufacture of Plaster of Paris

Principle: Plaster of Paris is manufactured from naturally occurring calcium sulphate dehydrate, which is commonly called **gypsum**. Gypsum is sparingly soluble in water. On heating it carefully at 120–130°C, it loses water of crystallization and becomes $CaSO_4·½H_2O$:

$$CaSO_4.2H_2O \xrightarrow{100°C–130°C} CaSO_4.\tfrac{1}{2}H_2O + 1\tfrac{1}{2}H_2O$$

Properties of Plaster of Pairs

Plaster of Paris is a white amorphous powder. Setting is the most important property of plaster of Paris. On mixing with water, Plaster of Paris becomes a paste. On standing, this paste sets to a hard mass of gypsum. This process is called **setting**.

$$CaSO_4.½H_2O + 1½H_2O \rightarrow CaSO_4.2H_2O$$

Uses of Plaster of Pairs

1. Manufacture of crucibles
2. Making of casts and moulds
3. Dental fillings
4. Surgery for setting fractured bones
5. Preparation of chalks
6. Making false ceilings and giving designs on the walls
7. For sealing the air gaps in laboratory apparatus for making them air tight

Info Bytes!

POP is widely used in India during the festival of Diwali to create idols and decorative items.

Cement

Cement, more popularly known as **Portland cement**, is the most important building material. The name 'Portland cement' originated on the basis of the fact that it resembled a type of natural limestone available in an island named Portland.

Manufacture of Cement

Limestone and clay are the major raw materials used for the manufacture of cement.

Principle: Limestone dissociates at high temperature and provides calcium oxide required for the process. Clay provides SiO_2 and Al_2O_3, which take part in a series of chemical reactions with calcium oxide to produce cement.

Process: The manufacture of cement can be done in two stages. The first stage involves the formation of a homogeneous mixture of the raw materials. This stage can be carried out in two processes, namely, wet process and dry process.

First Stage

1. **Wet process**

   Limestone is crushed to a fine powder. Clay is purified and mixed with fine powder of lime stone in the required proportion. A homogeneous slurry is formed by grinding the above mixture with the required quantity of water.

2. **Dry process**

   Powdered limestone and clay are mixed in proper proportions. The mixture is then subjected to drying and pulverization. The uniform, finely powdered mixture obtained is called **raw meal**.

Second Stage

This second stage of the process is carried out in a rotary kiln. The rotary kiln is made up of steel and consists of a long cylinder 6–10 feet in diameter and 100–250 feet in length. It is lined inside with fire bricks. This cylinder can rotate with a speed of 30–60 turns per hour.

The slurry or raw meal formed in the first stage is called **charge**. The charge is introduced into the rotary kiln through a conveyer arranged at one end. A burner is arranged at the other end of the kiln, and it supplies heat to the kiln. The charge introduced at one end slowly moves towards the hot end of the kiln. As it gets heated up, it loses water and CO_2. Limestone provides calcium oxide. SiO_2 and Al_2O_3 form aluminium silicates. A series of chemical reactions takes place between calcium oxide and aluminium silicates.

A mixture of calcium silicate, aluminium silicate and calcium aluminium silicate is formed. The resultant product formed is in the form of hard agglomerate known as **clinker**. After cooling, the clinker is ground to a fine powder. Further, 2–3% gypsum is added to this and again made into a fine powder. This fine grey powder is called **cement**. It is stored in air-tight bags.

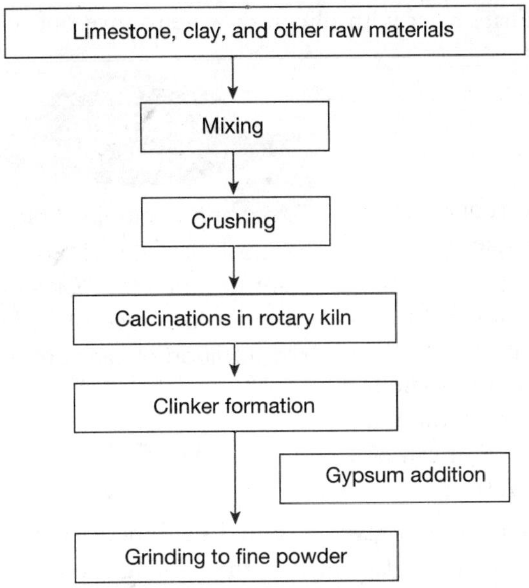

Figure 7.14 Process flow chart for the manufacture of cement

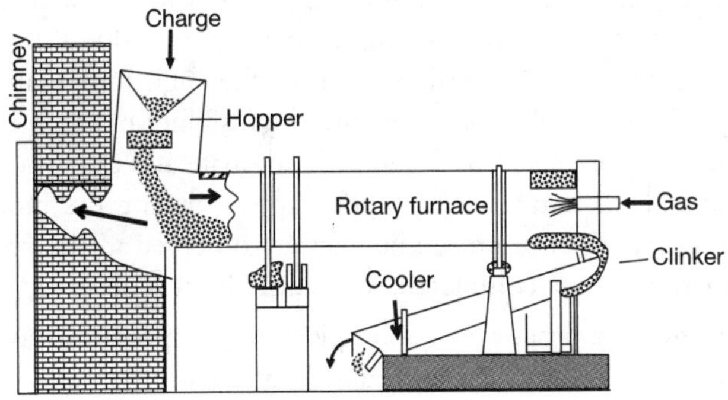

Figure 7.15 Rotary kiln

Applications of Cement

Cement is a homogeneous fine grey powder, which sets after a few hours when mixed with water and then hardens over a period of time into a hard solid. The addition of gypsum to cement decreases the setting time of cement. This property of setting to a hard mass makes cement useful in construction work in various forms such as mortar, concrete, etc.

1. **Mortar:** A mixture of slaked lime, sand and water is known as **mortar** or **lime mortar**. This also has the property of setting to a hard mass due to the evaporation of water coupled with the slow conversion of calcium hydroxide into calcium carbonate by atmospheric carbon dioxide. If cement is added to mortar, it is called **cement mortar**. It is harder than the ordinary mortar and is water proof.

$$Ca(OH)_2 + CO_2 \rightarrow CaCO_3 + H_2O$$

$$Ca(OH)_2 + SiO_2 \rightarrow CaSiO_3 + H_2O$$

2. **Concrete:** For construction purposes, cement is mixed with sand and small pieces of crushed stones. This mixture is known as **cement concrete**. This sets to a hard mass. If steel rods or bars or any other hard material is embedded in the wet concrete, during setting process, the hard mass holds the steel rod or bar thus increasing the strength and the hardness of the resulting structure. Because of reinforcement by steel structure in the concrete, the total system is called **'reinforced concrete cement' (RCC)**.

> **Konnect**
>
> India's first underwater metro in Kolkata passes through a tunnel that is beneath the Hooghly River. The tunnel showcases the modern-day engineering marvels we've achieved with materials like cement and glass.

Glass

Glass is a transparent or translucent material that finds applications in domestic and industrial purposes. Chemically, glass is a homogeneous liquid with very high viscosity made by sodium and calcium silicates with sand. Though these are the major constituents of glass, other compounds are also present in glass depending on the type of glass. Therefore, it has no definite chemical formula.

Manufacture of Glass

The common raw materials used in manufacture of glass are soda ash, limestone, and silica sand.

Principle: At high temperature, sodium carbonate and calcium carbonate react with silicon dioxide to give out sodium silicate and calcium silicate with the liberation of CO_2 gas:

$$Na_2CO_3 + SiO_2 \rightarrow Na_2SiO_3 + CO_2\uparrow$$

$$CaCO_3 + SiO_2 \rightarrow CaSiO_3 + CO_2\uparrow$$

Konnect

Firozabad, a city in Uttar Pradesh, India, is often referred to as the "Glass City of India" because of its age-old tradition of glass making.

Process: A finely powdered mixture of sodium carbonate, calcium carbonate, and silicon dioxide is called **batch**. This batch is mixed with broken glass pieces called **cullet**. This mixture is subjected to heating at 1600−1700 K. The impurities called **glass gall** rise to the surface. Due to the high temperature, the mixture is fused. The addition of cullet also increases the fusibility of the mixture. SiO_2 present in the reaction mixture reacts with sodium carbonate and calcium carbonate to form sodium silicate and calcium silicate. Bubbles appear during the process due to the evolution of CO_2 gas. When no more bubbles are observed in the process, the reaction can be considered to have completed. The entire mass is observed as a clear liquid.

Cooling: The process of cooling is a very important step in the manufacture of glass. It should be done very carefully. Rapid cooling results in brittle and fragile glass. Very slow cooling gives opaque glass. Hence, the cooling should neither be too rapid nor too slow. The process of cooling done at a moderate and uniform rate is called annealing. It results in the formation of good-quality glass. The process of annealing is carried out by passing the liquid glass through a chamber with varying temperature zones on a conveyer belt.

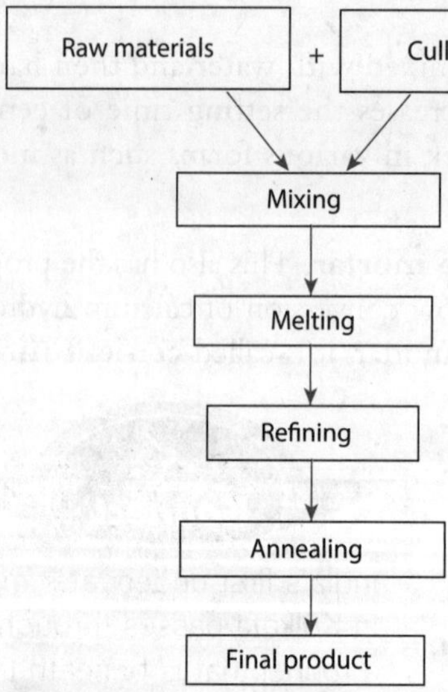

Figure 7.16 Process flow sheet for the manufacture of glass

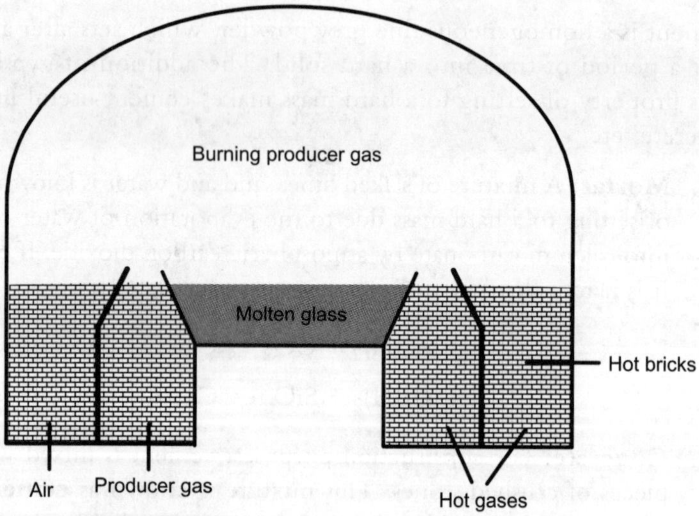

Figure 7.17 Manufacture of glass (tank furnace)

Characteristics of Glass

Glass is a supercooled liquid with very high viscosity. Due to high viscosity, it appears as a solid. Though it is built up of tetrahedral silicate units, the arrangement of these units is not regular in glass. Hence, it has no definite softening point.

Glass Blowing

This is a technique of shaping of glass articles. This is done by melting glass partially and blowing hot air by machine. This can be applied only for heat resistant varieties of glass.

Variety of Glass

Since glass has a wide range of applications in different fields of industry, it is expected to have the required characteristics suitable for different purposes. Different characteristics can be attributed to glass by varying the composition of glass with doping of suitable compounds.

Table 7.15 Types of glasses and their properties

Types of glass	Composition	Properties	Uses
Soda glass or soft glass	Common type Na_2CO_3, $CaCO_3$ and SiO_2	• Fuses at low temperature • Brittle • Cracks easily • ttacked by chemicals • Cheap	Window glass, mirrors, common glassware
Hard glass	K_2CO_3 and $CaCO_3$ and SiO_2	• Hard • Resistant to acids	Hard glass apparatus
Lead crystal glass	K_2CO_3, PbO and SiO_2	• High refractive index • Sparkling	Expensive glass ware, decorative items
Pyrex glass	SiO_2, CaO, borax	• Resistance to chemicals • Thermal resistance	Laboratory apparatus, injection ampules, ovenware
Optical glass and flint glass	$SiO_2 + Pb_3O_4 + K_2CO_3 + CaCO_3$	• More lustre • High refractive index • Soft • Scratches easily	Prisms, lenses, optical devices
Photochromatic glass	$SiO_2 + Na_2CO_3 + CaCO_3 + AgX$	Darkens on exposure to bright light	Sunshield goggles, photogrey spectacles
Safety glass	A layer of transparent plastic between two layers of glass	Not broken easily	Wind screens of aeroplanes, automobiles, bullet proof glasses, etc.
Colored glass	Transition metal oxides (trace amount as dopants are added to impart color)	Different colors	Decorative articles, window panes, artificial gems
Crookes glass	Flint glass + Cerium oxide	Cuts off UV light	Optical lenses

Table 7.16 Colored glasses

Compounds as dopants	Colors of glass
Cr_2O_3	Green
MnO_2	Purple
$AuCl_3$	Ruby
$CuSO_4$	Blue
Cu_2O	Red

Ceramics

Ceramics are materials containing non-metallic oxides, borides, carbides, and nitrides. These are hard and brittle and are resistant to heat and chemicals. They are non-conductors of electricity. Therefore, ceramics are used as good insulators. However, silicon carbide is an excellent conductor of electricity.

Ceramics find applications from very simple pottery to very high technological areas of modern science.

Manufacture of Ceramics

Principle: The way the ceramics is manufactured is called powder metallurgy route. In the process, different raw materials (inorganic oxides like clay, lime stone, feldspar, magnetite, dolomite, synthetic oxides like fused alumina, fused magnesia, etc.) are mixed in a definite proportion depending on the end product. The mixed oxides are calcined and then crushed into different sizes. The different-sized fractions are mixed with binders, pressed into components and sintered at high temperature.

Process of the Manufacture of Specific Ceramic Products

1. **Simple Pottery:** Crushed and finely powdered clay is taken. Water is added to this powder and kneaded to a hard mass. This mass can be moulded into various shapes on a rotating wheel. Then, these articles are dried in air. The dried articles are arranged in a kiln and subjected to heating up to 1373 K. The heating is done in a careful and controlled way. It loses water at 923 K and CO_2 at 1173 K. At this high temperature, SiO_2 and Al_2O_3 react with each other to form aluminium silicate. On heating further to a slightly higher temperature, these silicate units cling together and form interlocking units. Thus, the articles become hard, brittle and porous on heating.
2. **Earthenware and Porcelain Ware:** Raw materials used for this type of ceramics are kaolin, fine sand, and feldspar. The pulverised mixture of raw materials is kneaded with water into a thick mass. This paste is moulded into various shapes and then dried in air chambers. These dried articles are subjected to fixing at much higher temperatures than to what is done in case of simple pottery. The heating of these goes up to 1300 – 1500 K. The articles obtained are porous.

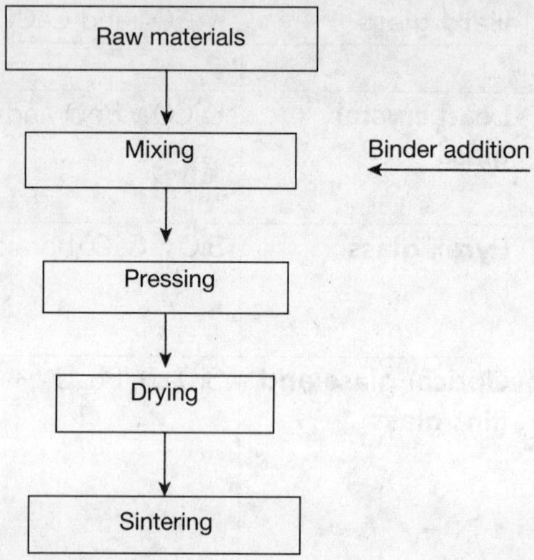

Figure 7.18 Process flow sheet for the manufacture of ceramics

Since feldspar contains some metal oxides in addition to SiO_2 and Al_2O_3, at a high temperature, a mixture of silicates is formed. The earthenware obtained after the process of firing is porous. To make it impervious to liquids, these articles are subjected to a process called glazing. A molten mixture of feldspar, silica, borax, and water is made into a paste by heating. The articles obtained after the process of firing are dipped in this paste and then they are subjected to reheating strongly. Thus, the pottery gets glazy appearance and also loses its porosity.

Areas of application of ceramic materials

1. High temperature applications
   - in refractories
   - heat insulation material
2. Electrical applications
   - Electrical insulator used in electric transmission lines
   - Electrical charge arrestor
   - Magnetic materials used in power applications, telecommunications, microwave applications, etc.
3. Other applications: Abrasive materials, cutting tools, bioceramics like dental implants, artificial bones, etc.

Konnect

Earthenware, porcelain, and brick are examples of ceramic materials. 'Khurja' in Uttar Pradesh is known as the 'Ceramics City' due to its large production of ceramics.

Talcum Powder

Talcum Powder is the most widely used cosmetic containing a mixture of inorganic and organic substances. Basically, the main ingredients are TiO_2, ZnO, MgO, magnesium silicate, salts of stearic acid, calcium or magnesium carbonate, kaolin, and colloidal clay. Perfumes are added in minor amounts that impart pleasant aroma to the face powder.

Common Fertilizers

Plants require around 12 elements for their healthy growth. Among these, the elements required in major amounts are called **macronutrients**. They are nitrogen, phosphorous, and potassium. The elements required in lesser amounts are called **micronutrients**. They are calcium, sodium, sulphur, and magnesium. Apart from these, some other elements like copper, molybdenum, manganese, cobalt, zinc, boron, and iron are also required in trace amounts.

Most of these nutrients are available in the form of their compounds in the soil. Plants absorb these water soluble minerals from soil through roots. In due course of time, the minerals in the soil get exhausted and the soils become deficient of these nutrients. Hence, it becomes essential to replenish the soils with the nutrient elements in order to make them useful for further growth of crops. Those materials added to the soil for this purpose are called **fertilizers**.

Types of Fertilizers

Fertilizers are basically of two types as listed below:

1. **Natural Fertilizers:** They include manures like cow dung and compost. Decayed products of animal wastes and plant wastes also can be used as natural fertilizers.
2. **Synthetic or Chemical Fertilizers:** Depending on the macronutrient available in a particular fertilizer, the fertilizers are classified into three types.

Depending on the mode of use, the fertilizers are again classified into three categories.

1. **Single Fertilizers:** A fertilizer that provides only one macronutrient is called a single fertilizer.

   Example: NH_4Cl, NH_4NO_3, KCl, $Ca(NO_3)_2$
2. **Compound Fertilizers:** A fertilizer that contains two or more macronutrients in a single compound is called a compound fertilizer.

   Example: KNO_3, $(NH_4)_3PO_4$
3. **Mixed Fertilizers:** The mixture of two or more fertilizers in the required proportions can be used according to the requirement of the soil. Such fertilizers are called mixed fertilizers.

   Example: Commercial ones such as Nitrophoska

Konnect

NPK fertilizers, a combination of Nitrogen, Phosphate, and Potassium, are essential for India's Green Revolution. This movement led to record grain outputs in the 1960s and 1970s, transforming India from a food-deficit country to a food-surplus nation.

Nitrogen Fertilizers

Any ammonium salt can be used as a nitrogen fertilizer, since all ammonium salts are water soluble. The most commonly used ones are ammonium nitrate, ammonium chloride, urea, and ammonium sulphate. Among these, urea is the most preferred one due to the easy preparation method and also due to the presence of high percentage of nitrogen in it.

Preparation of Urea

$$CO_2 + 2NH_3 \xrightarrow{200\ \text{atm}} \underset{\text{(ammonium carbamate, an intermediate)}}{NH_2COONH_4}$$

$$NH_2COONH_4 \rightarrow \underset{\text{Urea}}{NH_2CONH_2} + H_2O$$

Apart from these, calcium cyanamide (CaNCN) and calcium ammonium nitrate (CAN) have wider uses as nitrogenous fertilizers. They have an added advantage of providing calcium to the soil in addition to nitrogen.

Info Bytes!

Plants cannot directly take nitrogen from the air, even though it constitutes 78% of the Earth's atmosphere. Nitrogen fertilizers provide this essential nutrient in a form that plants can absorb.

Phosphate Fertilizers

Calcium and ammonium phosphates are the most commonly used ones due to their highly water-soluble nature. Superphosphate of lime, which is a mixture of calcium biphosphate and gypsum in 2 : 3 ratio is used as a phosphate fertilizer.

In recent times, triple superphosphates are prepared and used in preference to superphosphate of lime. Ammoniated phosphates are also superior to others as they provide both nitrogen and phosphorous. Nitrophosphates can also be used for the same purpose.

Preparation of Superphosphate of Lime

Superphosphate of lime can be prepared by the treatment of powdered phosphate rock with conc. H_2SO_4. The mass obtained is hard due to the presence of gypsum. This is crushed to a fine powder and sold as superphosphate of lime.

$$Ca_3(PO_4)_2 + 2H_2SO_4 + 4H_2O \rightarrow Ca(H_2PO_4)_2 + 2CaSO_4.2H_2O$$

Potassium Fertilizers

Most of the potassium salts, being water soluble, can be used as potassium fertilizers. They are KCl, K_2SO_4 and KNO_3. They can also be prepared by easy methods, since they are mostly naturally available in crude form.

Preparation

1. Potassium chloride can be extracted from a mineral carnallite that is naturally available. Its formula is $KCl.MgCl_2.6H_2O$.
2. Potassium sulphate is also present in naturally occurring mineral schonite with the formula $K_2SO_4.MgSO_4.6H_2O$.
3. Potassium nitrate, also known as **nitre** or **Indian saltpetre**, can be prepared from naturally occurring Chile salt petre ($NaNO_3$).

EXAMPLE 7.6 Explain the role of baking soda (sodium bicarbonate) in making cookies rise and become fluffy. How is it different from the role of yeast in bread-making?

SOLUTION

Baking soda (sodium bicarbonate) makes cookies rise and become fluffy by releasing carbon dioxide CO_2 gas when heated. This gas creates bubbles in the cookie dough, causing it to expand and become soft. Unlike yeast in bread-making, which is a living microorganism that ferments and produces CO_2, baking soda is a chemical leavening agent that produces CO_2 through a chemical reaction.

EXAMPLE 7.7 Why is the soda acid fire extinguisher often referred to as a "cartridge-operated" fire extinguisher, and how does its mechanism resemble a science experiment?

SOLUTION

The soda acid fire extinguisher is often referred to as "cartridge-operated" because it employs a mechanism that's reminiscent of a science experiment. When you activate it by pressing a knob or lever, you're essentially conducting a controlled chemical reaction. The extinguisher combines two separate solutions, sodium bicarbonate and sulfuric acid, in a way that rapidly generates carbon dioxide gas—a visually striking outcome, much like a captivating science experiment. So, it's not just a fire safety tool; it's a practical demonstration of how precise chemical reactions can be used in real-life situations.

EXAMPLE 7.8 Why is it essential to carefully control the cooling rate during the annealing process of glass, and how does it impact the properties of the final glass product?

SOLUTION

Careful control of the cooling rate during glass annealing is vital to prevent the formation of internal stresses. Too rapid cooling leads to brittleness, while overly slow cooling results in opacity. Proper annealing ensures that the glass is stress-free, making it strong, clear, and durable.

EXAMPLE 7.9 How is superphosphate of lime manufactured?

SOLUTION

Superphosphate of lime can be prepared by the treatment of powdered phosphate rock with conc.H_2SO_4. The mass obtained is hard due to the presence of gypsum. This is crushed to a fine powder and sold as superphosphate of lime.

$$Ca_3(PO_4)_2 + 2H_2SO_4 + 5H_2O \rightarrow Ca(H_2PO_4)_2.H_2O + 2CaSO_4.2H_2O$$

POINTS TO REMEMBER

- ✔ The existence of the same element in different physical forms with similar chemical properties is known as allotropy.
- ✔ Carbon exhibits allotropy and the allotropes of carbon are broadly classified into two main categories, viz., crystalline and amorphous allotropes.
- ✔ Nitrogen is the most abundant element in the atmosphere. Silicon is the second most abundant element in earth's crust.
- ✔ Ammonia can be synthesised by the reaction of nitrogen and hydrogen in 1 : 3 ratio under high pressure at a moderately high temperature. Ammonia can be synthesised in large scale by Haber's process.
- ✔ Preparation of nitric acid in industry involves the catalytic oxidation of ammonia and subsequent dissolution in water.
- ✔ Nitric acid is mainly used in the manufacture of explosives and fertilizers.
- ✔ Phosphorus is mainly extracted from phosphorite ore by heating the mixture of powdered ore along with sand and coke in an electric furnace.
- ✔ Phosphorus exists in two allotropic forms, namely white phosphorus and red phosphorus.
- ✔ Rhombic sulphur is the most stable form at normal temperature. Monoclinic sulphur and plastic sulphur change to rhombic form on long standing.
- ✔ Rhombic sulphur is stable below 95.6°C and above this temperature it changes to monoclinic sulphur. Both rhombic and monoclinic sulphur exist in the form of S_8 molecules.
- ✔ The manufacturing process of lime is carried out in a furnace called lime kiln.
- ✔ The process employed for the large-scale preparation of washing soda is ammonia–soda process or Solvay process.
- ✔ Plaster of Paris is manufactured from naturally occurring calcium sulphate dehydrate, which is commonly called gypsum.
- ✔ A mixture of slaked lime, sand and water is known as mortar or lime mortar. If cement is added to mortar, it is called cement mortar.
- ✔ Glass is a homogeneous liquid with very high viscosity made by sodium and calcium silicates with sand.
- ✔ A finely powdered mixture of sodium carbonate, calcium carbonate and silicon dioxide is called batch. This batch is mixed with broken glass pieces called cullet.
- ✔ A fertilizer that provides only one macronutrient is called a single fertilizer. A fertilizer that contains two or more macronutrients in a single compound is called a compound fertilizer. The mixture of two or more fertilizers in the required proportions can be used according to the requirement of the soil. Such fertilizers are called mixed fertilizers.

PRACTICE QUESTIONS CLASSROOM WING

Very Short Answer Type Questions

Directions for questions from 1 to 5:
Fill in the blanks.

1. The wide variety of optical properties of optical glass is due to wide range of ________.
2. A mixture of slaked lime, sand and water is known as ________.
3. The powdered mixture of raw materials taken for the manufacture of glass is called ________.
4. ________ are doped during the manufacture of glass to impart color.
5. Mixture of calcium dihydrogen phosphate and gypsum is called ________.

Directions for questions from 6 to 25:
Answer the following questions.

6. What is meant by slaking of lime? Give equation.
7. What is clinker? Why is gypsum added to it?
8. What is RCC? How is it made?
9. What is the chemical name of plaster of Paris? How is it prepared? Give the equation.
10. Which type of glass is used for the manufacture of ornamental glassware, decorative articles, etc.?
11. Addition of water drop by drop removes the colour of nitric acid formed by Ostwald's process. True or false?
12. What happens when dried pots are subjected to firing?
13. What is meant by superphosphate of lime? Give its composition.
14. What is the need of adding fertilizers to soil at regular intervals?
15. What is the reason for the shiny glaze of some ceramic articles?
16. A type of glass darkens on exposure to sunlight. What is it? Why does it show that characteristic property?
17. Give the composition of pyrex glass. Give its uses.
18. What is the composition of the common type of glass?
19. Why is urea the most commonly used nitrogenous fertilizer?
20. Why are potassium fertilizers easily available?
21. How does glass gets its color?
22. Give an example of a compound fertilizer and give its advantage over the single fertilizer.
23. Why is the same process of manufacture employed for both washing soda and baking soda?
24. What is green house effect?
25. Mention one property of each blue vitriol, green vitriol and alum.

Short Answer Type Questions

26. What is the chemical name of bleaching powder? How is it prepared?
27. Two red roses are exposed to two gases 'X' and 'Y' separately. In the case of X, the bleaching action is permanent and that of Y is temporary. Identify X and Y.
28. Observe the diagrams given below of 'X' and 'Y'. What are X and Y? Are they good or bad conductors of heat and electricity?

Carbon atom Covalent bond

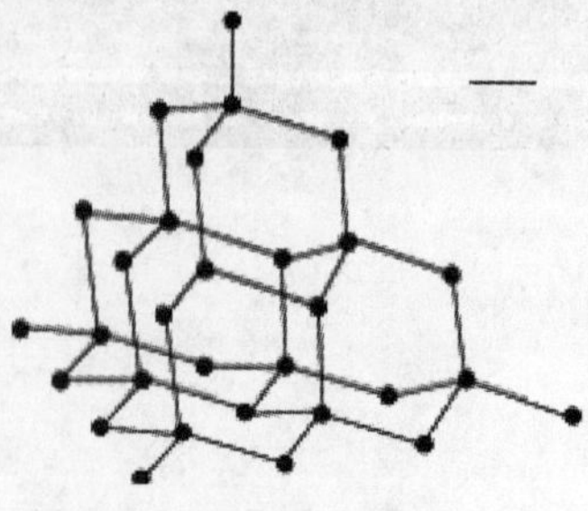

Structure of X

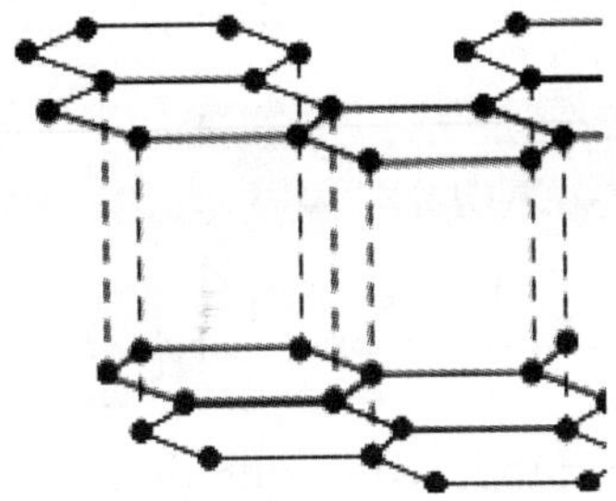

Structure of Y

29. Why is carbon monoxide called a harmful gas?

30. How is ammonia gas prepared in laboratory?

31. Explain the difference in the manufacturing process of simple pottery and porcelain ware.

32. How is urea manufactured? What are the other nitrogenous fertilizers?

33. What is glass blowing? Which type of glass is suitable for that purpose? Why?

34. (a) Give the occurrence of sulphur and phosphorus.
    (b) Flow chart of the manufacture of nitric acid is given.
    (i) Identify A, B and C.
    (ii) Among A, B and C, which is neutral in nature?
    (iii) Give reason for the change in colour (Colourless to light brown) of C on long standing.

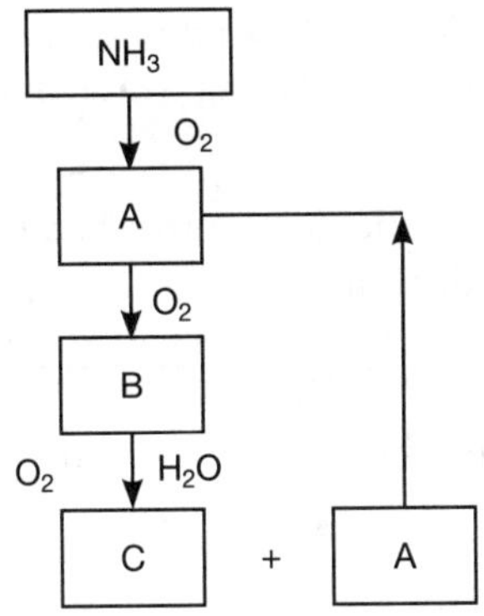

35. How is hydrochloric acid prepared in laboratory?

36. What is the principle involved in the use of bleaching powder for the sterilization of drinking water? Explain.

Essay Answer Type Questions

37. (a) Explain the extraction of phosphorus.
    (b) Determine the change in oxidation state of nitrogen present in ammonia during the oxidation of ammonia in limited and excess supply of O_2 at 900°C and in presence of platinum catalyst.

38. Explain the puckered ring structure of S_8 and the arrangement of these in rhombic and monoclinic sulphur. Also, give the flow chart explaining action of heat on sulphur.

39. Explain the industrial preparation of nitrogen by Haber's process.

40. Give a detailed description of the manufacture of cement.

41. Explain the process of the manufacture of glass. What are its characteristics? Discuss the various types of glass along with their uses.

PRACTICE QUESTIONS COMPETITION WING

Level 1: Apply your Concepts

Direction for questions from 1 to 9:
State whether the following statements are true or false.

1. Fullerene molecules are synthesized by subliming coal using laser radiation.
2. HCl can be used to remove rust from iron.
3. A fire extinguisher contains sodium bicarbonate and acid.
4. Impervious nature of ceramics is the effect of glazing.
5. On long standing, bleaching powder undergoes autooxidation.
6. Setting of mortar is the result of reaction between slaked lime and CO_2 of air.
7. Phosphorous is widely used in match industry due to its low ignition temperature.
8. Diamond is the amorphous allotropic form of carbon.
9. When washing soda is heated, it loses its water of crystallization.

Direction for questions from 10 to 19:
Fill in the blanks.

10. When Mg reacts with HCl, ______ gas is evolved.
11. Lime is ________.
12. When bleaching powder is stored over a long period of time, it undergoes _______.
13. In the preparation of diamonds industrially carbon changes its state from ________ to ________form.
14. The reaction of NaCl and $CaCO_3$ gives sodium carbonate. But this reaction cannot be used for the manufacture of washing soda since it is ______.
15. ________ is the main ingredient used in the preparation of superphosphate of lime.
16. Common name of calcium chloro hypochlorite is ________.
17. ______ and ______ are produced during the combustion of fossil fuels.
18. The clay used for the manufacture of earthenware is ______.
19. The type of glass that consists of a layer of plastic embedded in between two layers of glass is called ___________.

Direction for question 20:
Match the entries given in column A with the appropriate ones in column B.

20. Match the entries of Column A with those of Column B.

Column A (Manufactured Materials)	Column B (Terms Associated with Manufacture)
(i) Glass	(A) Clinker formation
(ii) Bleaching powder	(B) Carbonation
(iii) Pottery	(C) Annealing
(iv) Cement	(D) Counter current mechanism
(v) Baking soda	(E) Sintering

Direction for questions from 21 to 50:
For each of the questions, four choices have been provided. Select the correct alternative.

21. **Assertion (A):** Baking powder is used in preference to baking soda while making cakes.

    Reason (R): Sodium bicarbonate present in baking powder decomposes on heating to give CO_2.

    (a) Both A and R are true and R is the correct explanation of A.

    (b) Both A and R are true, but R is not the correct explanation of A.

    (c) A is true and R is false.

    (d) A is false and R is true.

22. Noble metals get dissolved in aqua regia, the composition of aqua regia is
(a) $3HCl + HNO_3$
(b) $3HNO_3 + H_2SO_4$
(c) $HCl + 3HNO_3$
(d) $HNO_3 + 3H_2SO_4$

23. Which of the following reactions is called slaking of lime?
(a) $CaCO_3 \rightarrow CaO + CO_2$
(b) $CaO + 2HCl \rightarrow CaCl_2 + H_2O$
(c) $CaO + H_2O \rightarrow Ca(OH)_2$ + heat
(d) $CaCO_3 + NaCl \rightarrow Na_2CO_3 + CaCl_2$

24. Identify which contributes for strengthening of lime mortar structures and contributes for weakening of RCC structures.
(a) usage of water containing dissolved salts
(b) addition of lime
(c) absorption of CO_2 from atmospheric air
(d) both (b) and (c)

25. Bleaching powder is effective with cold water, but ineffective with hot water. This is because of
(a) oxidation of chloride radical
(b) reduction of chloride radical
(c) reduction of hypochlorite radical
(d) hydrolysis of hypochlorite radical

26. Which among the following substances is not a component of the mixture used for glazing pottery?
(a) feldspar (b) silica
(c) borax (d) alumina

27. Which of the following substances is a compound fertilizer?
(a) CAN (b) urea
(c) Epsom salt (d) ammonium phosphate

28. The glass containing litharge as an ingredient makes the optical fibres glow because it:
(a) increases the refractive index
(b) has low density
(c) is highly thermally resistant
(d) scatters all the radiations incident on it

29. Which property is imparted to glass by the addition of cerium oxide?
(a) color
(b) resistance to breakage
(c) increase of refractive index
(d) protection from UV light

30. The composition of flint glass is:
(a) $SiO_2 + Na_2CO_3 + CaCO_3$
(b) $SiO_2 + CaCO_3 + CuSO_4$
(c) $SiO_2 + K_2CO_3 + CaCO_3$
(d) $SiO_2 + K_2CO_3 + CaCO_3 + Pb_3O_4$

31. Which of the following statements is true about glass?
(a) Arrangement of silicate units is similar to that of liquid state.
(b) Arrangement of silicate units is similar to that of solid state.
(c) It has low viscosity and hence is not a true solid.
(d) It has high viscosity with sharp melting point and hence is a solid.

32. The broken pieces of glass added to the fused raw materials in the manufacture of glass is called
(a) batch (b) glass gall
(c) cullet (d) none of these

33. When rain water percolates into the cracks of RCC, it further gets weakened due to the:
(a) formation of H_2CO_3
(b) increase in pH value
(c) increase in the percentage of free lime
(d) exothermic hydration process

34. Which of the following is not an ingredient of clinker cement?
(a) calcium silicate
(b) aluminium silicate
(c) calcium aluminium silicate
(d) gypsum

35. Which of the nitrogenous fertilizers can meet the needs for immediate requirement of crop?
(a) potassium nitrate
(b) superphosphate of lime
(c) calcium cyanamide
(d) CAN

36. The steps for the manufacture of nitric acid by Ostwald process are given. Arrange them in sequence.
(1) recirculation of nitric oxide
(2) addition of H_2O to nitrogen dioxide
(3) oxidation of nitric oxide
(4) catalytic oxidation of ammonia

(a) 4 3 2 1 (b) 4 3 1 2
(c) 3 4 2 1 (d) 3 4 1 2

37. For the manufacture of cement various steps are given below. Arrange the steps in a proper sequence.

(1) clinker formation
(2) crushing
(3) addition of gypsum
(4) mixing of raw materials
(5) grinding to fine powder
(6) calcination in rotary kiln

(a) 4 2 6 1 3 5 (b) 2 4 6 3 5 1
(c) 4 3 1 6 5 2 (d) 1 2 3 4 5 6

38. For the manufacture of glass, various steps are given below. Arrange the steps in a proper sequence.

(1) melting of raw materials
(2) adding cullet to raw materials
(3) conversion of raw material to fine powder
(4) annealing
(5) refining

(a) 1 2 3 4 5 (b) 2 1 3 5 4
(c) 3 2 1 5 4 (d) 3 2 1 5 4

39. Which of the following gases with a smell of rotten egg is evolved when sulphuric acid is treated with copper sulphide?

(a) sulphur vapor (b) sulphur dioxide
(c) hydrogen sulphide (d) sulphur trioxide

40. Which of the following reagents is used to test the presence of SO_2 gas?

(a) acidified potassium manganate
(b) alkaline potassium manganate
(c) alkaline potassium dichromate
(d) acidified potassium dichromate

41. Excess of nitrogenous fertilizers is harmful because they:

(a) increase the acidity of the soil
(b) do not get distributed uniformly in the soil
(c) get leached away from the soil easily and pollute the water bodies
(d) produce extra heat that burns plants

42. The ions responsible for the bleaching action of bleaching powder and the ions responsible for loss of bleaching action of bleaching powder due to the storage for long time, respectively, are:

(a) Cl^-, OCl^- (b) OCl^-, Cl^-
(c) OCl^-, ClO_3^- (d) Cl^-, ClO^-

43. In which of the following uses of graphite, is the presence of van der Waal's forces of attraction in graphite not exploited?

(a) pencil lead (b) electrodes
(c) lubricant (d) refractory crucibles

44. Formula of plaster of Paris is:

(a) $CaSO_4.H_2O$ (b) $3CaSO_4.H_2O$
(c) $CaSO_4.2H_2O$ (d) $CaSO_4.½H_2O$

45. Identify the compound that is the final product of Solvay process:

(a) ammonium carbonate
(b) ammonium bicarbonate
(c) sodium carbonate
(d) sodium bicarbonate

46. Manufacture of which of the following does not require limestone as a raw material?

(a) quick lime (b) baking soda
(c) glass (d) plaster of Paris

47. Which among the following is a micronutrient?

(a) potassium (b) phosphorus
(c) nitrogen (d) cobalt

48. Which of the following imparts purple color to glass?

(a) Cr_2O_3 (b) $AuCl_3$
(c) Cu_2O (d) MnO_2

49. Which of the following fertilizers does not replenish nitrogen in the soil?

(a) CAN (b) urea
(c) superphosphate lime (d) ammonium phosphate

50. Which of the following acids is produced by treating KNO_3 with H_2SO_4 under suitable experimental conditions?

(a) HNO_2 (b) H_2SO_3
(c) HNO_3 (d) $H_2S_2O_7$

Level 2: Review Your Concepts

51. 'Observe the following reaction, which includes molecules of sulphur and chlorine. Identify X and Y.

$X + 2H_2O \rightarrow \text{Acid} + 2[H]$

$Y + H_2O \rightarrow \text{Acid} + [O]$

52. Explain why baking powder is used in preference to baking soda in cooking.

53. Explain what the reaction:

$NH_3 + 5O_2$ ¾ $\rightarrow 4NO + 6H_2O$ (with Pt 80°C and H_2O), indicates in Ostwald's process?

54. Sodium and potassium belong to the same group. But potassium carbonate cannot be prepared by Solvay process like sodium carbonate. Explain with appropriate reasons.

55. In many cases, there are cement plants near a steel plant. Explain why.

56. Explain why baking powder containing monocalcium phosphate monohydrate as one of the constituents is preferred to baking soda for baking or as leavening agent.

57. (a) Borosilicate glasses are used as laboratory wares. Give reasons.
(b) Establish glass as a supercooled liquid. What is the role of silver halide in photochromatic glass?

58. Explain the effect of process of cooling on the transparency of glass.

59. The wind screen of a car does not shatter to pieces and scatter when broken. Give reasons.

60. All concrete structures require perfect curing. What purpose does this process serve?

61. How can the glossy, impervious nature of ceramics be obtained? Explain.

62. Older concrete buildings are known to be stronger than newly built concrete structures. How do you account for this?

63. The setting and hardening of cement are the two important stages that take place gradually over a long period of time. Explain the physical and chemical changes associated with them. Justify.

64. In which respect is triple phosphate, as a fertilizer, superior to superphosphate of lime?

65. Inorganic nitrogenous fertilizers are basically of two types—nitrate salts and ammonium salts. Which among these is more preferable? Give reasons in support of your answer.

66. (a) White phosphorus catches fire at room temperature, whereas red phosphorus does not. Explain.
(b) Phosphor bronze is an alloy of copper, tin, and phosphorus. Which properties are imparted to the alloy by adding phosphorus?

67. A divalent metal with atomic number 12 reacts with an acid liberating a gas X. X on treatment with a non-metal Y gives Z, which on dissolution in water produces the same acid.
(a) Identify X, Y and Z and write a balanced chemical equation for the formation of Z from X and Y.
(b) Write the corresponding balanced chemical equations.
(c) The gas Z is collected by upward displacement of air. Justify.

68. Hydrogen is a clean fuel with highest calorific value. However, it cannot be a substitute for petrol or CNG used in automobiles. Explain.

69. 'The air we breathe has 78% nitrogen. But nitrogen is not used to dilute the oxygen in the cylinders carried by scuba divers.' Justify.

70. Why does a substance, which is bleached using sulphur dioxide regain its color on exposure to air while that bleached using chlorine does not?

71. Decomposition of baking soda is the principal reaction in the usage of dry powder fire extinguishers. What characteristics of the reaction are exploited in this process?

72. The superphosphate of lime is always used in combination with ammonium fertilizer. Justify.

73. Pure nitric acid on long standing turns to yellow color. Give a reason.

Level 3: Assess Your Concepts

74. Photoblackening of photochromatic glass doesn't occur when exposed to tube light or any lamp light during night time or in dark. Justify.

75. Urea is not recommended as a fertilizer in very cold places but recommended for highly acidic soils. Explain with appropriate reasons.

76. Usually, salt is sprinkled on pottery at the end of the firing process. Explain the role of salt in this process.

77. How does glass find application in telecommunication industry?

78. Why does glass become opaque on slow cooling?

79. Reinforced concrete cement contains iron in major proportion. However, it does not get rusted and contributes for greater strength and durability of RCC structures. How do you account for this?

80. Phosphorus is chiefly available as phosphate rock. However, it is converted to superphosphate of lime for usage as a fertilizer. Triple phosphate is considered to be superior to superphosphate of lime. Justify with appropriate reasons.

81. Why are fibre optic cables replacing copper cables in telecommunication?

82. Is a good fertilizer expected to be acidic or basic in nature? Justify your answer.

83. Why is ceramic ring (e.g., alumina, silicon nitride, etc.) used as piston ring in internal combustion engines?

84. During the manufacture of cement, 2 – 3%, gypsum is added to it. What role does gypsum play?

AT

PRACTICE QUESTIONS JEE-NEET SPECIAL WING

Multiple-Answer Type Questions

Directions for questions 1 to 5:

Select one or more correct alternative(s) from the given choices.

1. Select the statements that are true with respect to bleaching powder.

   Bleaching powder,

   (a) on long storage, loses its bleaching action due to the formation of OCl_3^- ions.

   (b) can decrease the pH of water when added to it.

   (c) contains two chlorine atoms directly attached to the calcium

   (d) gives nascent oxygen on reacting with excess dilute mineral acids

2. Choose the incorrect set

   (a) Fibre optic cables- Propagates signals by total internal reflection of light.

   (b) RCC- Rainwater when permeates into the cracks of Reinforced Cement Concrete (RCC), deteriorates it by removing calcium hydroxide as calcium carbonate.

   (c) Gypsum- is added to the cement to enhance hydration of calcium silicate

   (d) SO_2 -bleaches by oxidation.

3. Which of the following given minerals are not ores:

   (a) $MgSO_4.7H_2O$
   (b) PbS
   (c) $K_2SO_4.Al_2(SO_4)_3.24H_2O$
   (d) Al_2O_3. $2H_2O$

4. 'X' can dissolve noble metals. Choose the incorrect options with respect to X.

   (a) It is a colourless liquid
   (b) Possess definite set of properties
   (c) Oxidises noble metals when added to it.
   (d) On reacting with gold in the absence of air, it forms a neutral oxide of nitrogen

5. Examine the given table and find the correct match:

Compound	Raw materials required in the manufacturing of the compound
(P) Lime	(i) Ca $(OH)_2$
(Q) Washing soda	(ii) NaCl
(R) Baking soda	(iii) NH_4OH
(S) Glass	(iv) $CaCO_3$
	(v) Na_2CO_3
	(vi) SiO_2

   (a) (P)- (i), (iv)
   (b) (Q)- (ii), (iv).
   (c) (R)- (ii), (iii)
   (d) (S)- (iv), (v), (vi)

Comprehension-Based Questions

Directions for Questions 6 to 11:

Read the following passage and answer the questions given below.

P, when heated carefully at 120–130ºC, loses its water of crystallization partially to form Q and on strong heating loses all its water of crystallization to form R. S is the carbonate salt of calcium.

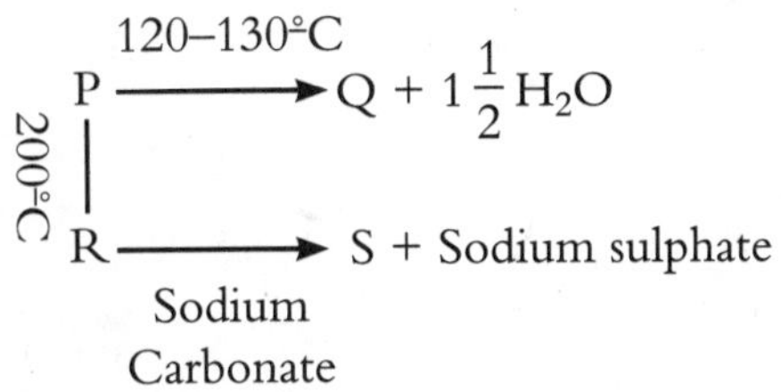

Q serves various purposes in the medicinal field, such as setting fractured bones, creating dental fillings, in construction for false ceilings and wall designs, in making of decorative articles and statues etc. On mixing with water, Q becomes a paste and on standing, this paste sets to a hard mass of P. This process is called setting.

6. Predict the correct chemical formula of Q.

   (a) $2CaSO_4$. H_2O
   (b) $(CaSO_4)_2.H_2O$
   (c) $CaSO_4$. $2H_2O$
   (d) Both (a) and (b)

7. 'Hardening property of 'Q' is exploited in making statues.' 'Q' hardens by,
   (a) the process of dehydration
   (b) the process of hydration
   (c) the process of oxidation with atmospheric oxygen
   (d) the process of combination with atmospheric carbon dioxide

8. The difference in water of crystallization in P and Q is.
   (a) $\frac{3}{2}$ (b) $\frac{1}{2}$
   (c) $\frac{5}{2}$ (d) 1

9. Which of the following given conversions is/are a physical change?
   (a) P to Q (b) R to S
   (c) P to Q (d) None of the above

10. No. of moles of the element present in the highest percentage by weight in one mole of P is
   (a) 5 mol (b) 6 mol
   (c) 2.5 mol (d) 3.25 mol

11. Match the following:

List-1 Compound		List-2 Percentage of metal in the compound	
(A)	P	(i)	6.89*x*
(B)	Q	(ii)	7.35*x*
(C)	R	(iii)	5.8*x*
(D)	S	(iv)	10*x*

Find the correct match.

	(P)	(Q)	(R)	(S)
(a)	(iv)	(ii)	(i)	(iii)
(b)	(i)	(iii)	(iv)	(ii)
(c)	(iii)	(i)	(ii)	(iv)
(d)	(ii)	(iv)	(iii)	(i)

Directions for Questions 12 to 17:

Read the following passage and answer the questions given below.

Powdered rock of A is treated with conc. H_2SO_4 to produce a mixture of calcium compounds B and C. C is a hydrated salt with 2 molecules of water of crystallization. The hard mass so obtained is crushed to a fine powder and sold as fertilizer in the market. The stoichiometric equation related to the reaction mentioned is shown below. Compound A is calcium phosphate

$$A + 2H_2SO_4 + 4H_2O \rightarrow B + 2C$$

12. Predict the anion present in compound B.
   (a) Phosphate (b) Dihydrogen phosphate
   (c) Sulphate (d) Hydrogen sulphate

13. Determine the weight (W) of fertilizer obtained when three moles of A are used in the process.
   (a) 578g (b) 1198 g
   (c) 930g (d) 1734g

14. Find the total weight of water of crystallization in W g of the fertilizer.
   (a) 216g (b) 36g
   (c) 108g (d) 72g

15. **Assertion(A):** The percentage of phosphorous in the Wg of fertilizer is 26.5% .

   Reason (R): The Percentage of an element in a compound changes with the mass of the compound taken.
   (a) Both Assertion and Reason are true, and reason is the correct explanation of assertion.
   (b) Both Assertion and Reason are true, and reason is not the correct explanation of assertion.
   (c) A is true and R is false
   (d) A is false and R is true

16. Which statement accurately describes the effect of above fertilizer on soil pH.
   (a) It makes the soil more acidic
   (b) It makes the soil more basic
   (c) It causes negligible pH alteration in the soil
   (d) Its effect on soil pH varies according to the amount of fertilizer added.

Match the Column

Study the information given in the table and match the entries in list-I with that of list-II.

17.

Compounds of calcium	Uses
P	In the disinfection of water
Q	As an ingredient in the building materials
R	Repair of large bone defects
S	In the preparation of moulds and statues
T	De-icing of roads

List-I		List-II
P	(i)	$CaCl_2$
Q	(ii)	$CaSO_4 . 2H_2O$
R	(iii)	$CaCO_3$
S	(iv)	$CaOCl_2$
T	(v)	$Ca_3(PO_4)_2$
	(iv)	$2CaSO_4 . H_2O$

ANSWER KEYS

Crossword

Across

1. Bleaching powder 4. Rhombic sulphur 7. Green vitriol 8. Washing soda
10. Ostwald process 12. Sulphur dioxide 13. Cement concrete 15. Iron

Down

1. Batch 2. Compound fertilizer 3. White phosphorus
5. Calcium oxide 6. Pyrex glass 9. Diamond 11. Hydrogen 14. Oxygen

Classroom Wing

Very Short Answer Type Questions

1. composition 2. Mortar or lime mortar 3. batch
4. Transition metal oxides 5. super phosphate of lime

Competition Wing

Level 1: Apply your Concepts

1. False 2. True 3. True 4. True 5. True
6. True 7. True 8. False 9. True 10. hydrogen
11. calcium oxide 12. auto-oxidation 13. Amorphous to crystalline
14. Reversible reaction 15. Phosphate rock ($Ca_3(PO_4)_2$) 16. Bleaching powder 17. CO_2, H_2O
18. Kaolin 19. Safety glass 20. (i) → (C); (ii) → (D); (iii) → (E); (iv) → (A); (v) → (B)
21. (d) 22. (a) 23. (c) 24. (c) 25. (c)
26. (b) 27. (d) 28. (a) 29. (d) 30. (d)
31. (a) 32. (c) 33. (a) 34. (d) 35. (a)
36. (a) 37. (a) 38. (a) 39. (c) 40. (d)
41. (c) 42. (c) 43. (d) 44. (d) 45. (c)
46. (d) 47. (d) 48. (d) 49. (c) 50. (c)

JEE-NEET Special Wing

Multiple-Answer Type Questions

1. (a, b) 2. (c, d) 3. (a, c) 4. (a, b) 5. (b; c; d)

Comprehension-Based Questions

6. (d) 7. (b) 8. (a) 9. (d) 10. (b)
11. (c) 12. (b) 13. (d) 14. (a) 15. (c)
16. (d)

Match the Column

17. (P)-(iv); (Q)-(iii), (R)-(v, vi), (S)-(vi), (T)-(i)

Hints and Explanations

Classroom Wing

Very Short Answer Type Questions

1. Optical glass has the widest range of composition with slight variations in the ingredients.
2. Mortar or lime mortar.
3. batch
4. Transition metal oxides
5. super phosphate of lime
6. Calcium oxide reacts vigorously with water to produce slaked lime called slaking of lime. Dissolution of lime in water

   $CaO + H_2O \rightarrow Ca(OH)_2$
7. Mixture of calcium silicate, aluminium silicate, and calcium aluminium silicate. Gypsum plays a very important role in controlling the rate of hardening of the clinker.
8. Steel rods or bars or any other hard material is embedded in the wet concrete. The hard mass holds the steel rod thus increasing the strength and the hardness of the resulting structure reinforcement by steel structure in the concrete, the total system is called 'reinforced concrete cement' (RCC).
9. Calcium sulphate hemihydrates. By heating of calcium sulphate dihydrate.

   $$CaSO_4 \cdot 2HO_2 \rightarrow CaSO_4 \frac{1}{2}H_2O + 1\frac{1}{2}H_2O$$
10. In lead glass, lead oxide is added which increases the optical density of the glass, thereby increasing its refractive index. This type of glass is used for the manufacture of ornamental glassware and decorative articles.
11. Nitric acid formed in Ostwald's process is slightly yellowish in colour due to its self-ionization to produce NO_2 that dissolves in it. This NO_2 can be removed either by passing dry CO_2 through it or by adding water drop by drop to it.
12. Pots become hard, brittle and porous.
13. Superphosphate oflime can be prepared by the treatment of powdered phosphate rock with conc. H_2SO_4. The mass obtained is hard due to the presence of gypsum. This is crushed to a fine powder and sold as superphosphate of lime. Composition is Ca $(H_2Po_4)_2$ $CaSO_4 \cdot 2H_2O$
14. To increase the minerals in the soil.
15. Due to the formation of sodium silicates.
16. Photo chromatic glass. Effect of silver halides.
17. SiO_2, CaO, borax. Laboratory apparatus, oven ware.
18. Sodium (or) calcium silicates
19. Simple method of preparation, high content of nitrogen.
20. They are naturally available in crude form.
21. By doping
22. KNO_3 $(NH_4)_3$ PO_4

    It contains two or more macro nutrients.
23. Because decomposition of baking soda gives washing soda.
24. Increase in temperature of the earth
25. Nature of aqueous solution, aerial oxidation and purification of water respectively.

Short Answer Type Questions

26. (i) calcium oxychloride

    (ii) Bleaching powder can be prepared on large scale in Hasenclever plant or in Bachmann plant. In both the cases, the principle and process are the same.

    $Ca(OH)_2 + Cl_2 \rightarrow CaOCl_2 + H_2O$
27. The bleaching action of Cl_2 is permanent as it bleaches by oxidation. The bleaching action of SO_2 is temporary as it bleaches by reduction. X is Cl_2, Y is SO_2
28. X is diamond and Y is graphite. Diamond is a good conductor of heat and graphite is a good conductor of electricity.
29. Carbon monoxide is harmful because it displaces oxygen in the blood and deprives the heart, brain and other vital organs of oxygen.
30. (i) Ammonia gas can be prepared by heating ammonium salts with alkalies:

    $$2NH_4Cl + Ca(OH)_2 \xrightarrow{\Delta} CaCl_2 + 2H_2O + 2NH_3$$

(ii) Ammonia gas can be prepared by treating metal nitrides with warm water:

$$Mg_3N_2 + 6H_2O \rightarrow 3Mg(OH)_2 + 2NH_3$$

31. (i) Chemicals used

(ii) Reactions involved

32. $CO_2 + 2NH_3 \rightarrow NH_2COONH_4 \rightarrow NH_2CONH_2 + H_2O$

Common fertilizers ammonium nitrate, ammonium chloride, urea, and ammonium sulphate.

33. Glass blowing is a technique of shaping of glass articles. This is done by melting glass partially and blowing hot air by machine.

34. (a) In nature, sulphur occurs both in the free and in the combined states.

Phosphorus cannot exist in the free state, but in the combined state it occurs in the form of phosphates like phosphorite ($Ca_3(PO_4)_2$), chloropatite ($3Ca_3(PO_4)_2.CaCl_2$) and fluorapatite ($3Ca_3(PO_4)_2.CaCF_2$).

(b) (i) A $\rightarrow$ NO

B $\rightarrow$ NO_2

C $\rightarrow$ HNO_3

(ii) A that is, NO is neutral in nature.

(iii) HNO_3 undergoes decomposition to form brown coloured NO_2 gas and hence it turns brown.

35. Blue vitriol loses its crystalline property when heated at 250°C where it loses its five molecules of water and becomes a white amorphous powder. Green vitriol turns to reddish brown color on exposure to air due to aerial oxidation to ferric sulphate.

Alum is a white crystalline solid soluble in water

36. On action with bleaching powder, chlorinated compounds attack the cell membranes of bacteria present in water.

Essay Answer Type Questions

37. (b) $4NH_3 + 3O_2 \rightarrow 2N_2 + 6H_2O$ (Limited supply of O_2)

Oxidation state of nitrogen changes from –3 to 0

$4NH_3 + 5O_2 \xrightarrow{Pt\ 900°C} 4NO + 6H_2O$ (excess supply of O_2)

Oxidation state of NH_3 changes from –3 to +2.

38. These S_8 molecules are in the form of a ring. It forms a crown-shaped molecule with four atoms on the top and four atoms at the bottom.

The rhombic and the monoclinic forms differ in the arrangement of these S_8-puckered rings.

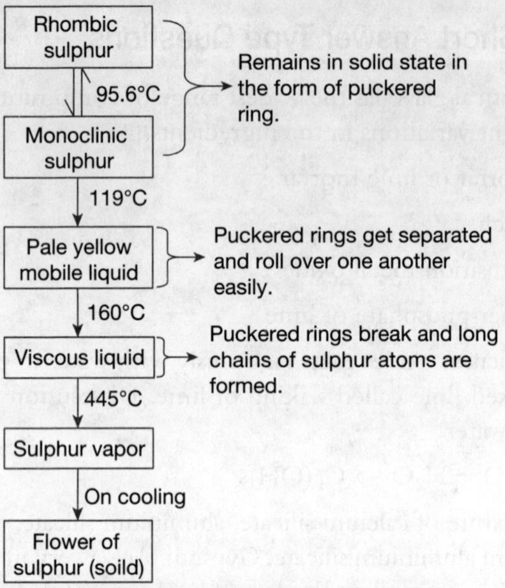

Process flow chart for heating of sulphur

39. (i) Chemicals required

(ii) Reaction set up

(iii) Reactions involved

(iv) Balanced chemical equations

40. The manufacture of cement can be done in two stages. The first stage involves the formation of a homogeneous mixture of the raw materials. This stage can be carried out in two processes, namely, wet process and dry process.

First Stage

1. *Wet process*

Limestone is crushed to a fine powder. Clay is purified and mixed with fine powder of lime stone in the required proportion. A homogeneous slurry is formed by grinding the above mixture with the required quantity of water.

2. *Dry process*

Powdered limestone and clay are mixed in proper proportions. The mixture is then subjected to drying and pulverization. The uniform, finely powdered mixture obtained is called raw meal.

Second Stage

This second stage of the process is carried out in a rotary kiln. The rotary kiln is made up of steel and consists of a long cylinder 6–10 feet in diameter and 100–250 feet in length. It is lined inside with fire bricks. This cylinder can rotate with a speed of 30–60 turns per hour. The slurry or raw meal formed in the first stage is called charge.

The charge is introduced into the rotary kiln through a conveyer arranged at one end. A burner is arranged at the other end of the kiln, and it supplies heat to the kiln. The charge introduced at one end slowly moves towards the hot end of the kiln. As it gets heated up, it loses water and CO_2. Limestone provides calcium oxide. SiO_2 and Al_2O_3 form aluminium silicates. A series of chemical reactions takes place between calcium oxide and aluminium silicates.

A mixture of calcium silicate, aluminium silicate and calcium aluminium silicate is formed. The resultant product formed is in the form of hard agglomerate known as clinker. After cooling, the clinker is ground to a fine powder. Further, 2–3% gypsum is added to this and again made into a fine powder. This fine grey powder is called cement. It is stored in air-tight bags.

41. A finely powdered mixture of sodium carbonate, calcium carbonate and silicon dioxide is called batch. This batch is mixed with broken glass pieces called cullet. This mixture is subjected to heating at 1600–1700 K. The impurities called glass gall rise to the surface. Due to the high temperature, the mixture is fused. The addition of cullet also increases the fusibility of the mixture. SiO_2 present in the reaction mixture reacts with sodium carbonate and calcium carbonate to form sodium silicate and calcium silicate. Bubbles appear during the process due to the evolution of CO_2 gas. When no more bubbles are observed in the process, the reaction can be considered to have completed. The entire mass is observed as a clear liquid.

Cooling

The process of cooling is a very important step in the manufacture of glass. It should be done very carefully. Rapid cooling results in brittle and fragile glass. Very slow cooling gives opaque glass. Hence, the cooling should neither be too rapid nor too slow. The process of cooling done at a moderate and uniform rate is called annealing. It results in the formation of good-quality glass. The process of annealing is carried out by passing the liquid glass through a chamber with varying temperature zones on a conveyer belt.

Competition Wing

Level 1: Apply your Concepts

20. (i) → (C); (ii) → (D);
(iii) → (E); (iv) → (A);
(v) → (B)

21. The yellow colour of nitric acid is due to the dissolution of NO_2 formed by the self-ionization of HNO_3 in it. The yellow colour can be removed by adding water drop by drop to it as NO_2 dissolves in these water drops and gets converted to nitric acid

$3NO_2 + H_2O \rightarrow 2HNO_3 + NO$

Hence, the correct option is (d).

36. 4 Catalytic oxidation of ammonia.
3 Oxidation of nitric oxide.
2 Addition of water to nitrogen dioxide.
1 Recirculation of nitric oxide.

Hence, the correct answer is (a).

37. 4 Mixing of raw materials.
2 Crushing.
6 Calcination in rotary kiln.
1 Clinker formation.
3 Addition of gypsum.
5 Grinding to fine powder.

Hence, the correct answer is (a).

38. 1 Mixing of raw materials.
2 Adding cullet to raw materials.
3 Melting of raw materials.
4 Refining.
5 Annealing.

Hence, the correct answer is (a).

39. Hydrogen sulphide with a smell of rotten eggs is evolved when sulphuric acid is treated with copper sulphide.

Hence, the correct answer is (c).

40. Acidified potassium dichromate is used to test SO_2. SO_2 when passed through acidified $K_2Cr_2O_7$, turns it green.

Hence, the correct answer is (d).

41. Nitrogenous fertilizers leach away from the soil easily due to their high solubility in water and pollute water bodies.

Hence, the correct answer is (c).

42. Bleaching powder contains Ca^{2+}, Cl^- and OCl^- ions. Among these OCl^- ions hydrolyse to give nascent oxygen. Hence these are responsible for the bleaching action. On long standing OCl^- ions get oxidized to ClO_3^- ions that result in loss of bleaching action of bleaching powder.

Hence, the correct answer is (c).

43. Use of graphite as pencil lead, electrodes, and lubricant are due to the presence of free electrons in graphite. Usage in refractory crucibles is due to the high melting point of graphite.

Hence, the correct answer is (d).

44. $CaSO_4 \cdot \frac{1}{2}H_2O$ is the formula of plaster of Paris.

Hence, the correct answer is (d).

45. Sodium carbonate is the final product of Solvay process.

Hence, the correct answer is (c).

46. Limestone is not required as a raw material for the manufacture of plaster of Paris. Gypsum is taken as a raw material for plaster of Paris.

Hence, the correct answer is (d).

47. Cobalt is an example of a micronutrient.

Hence, the correct answer is (d).

48. MnO_2 imparts purple color to glass.

Hence, the correct answer is (d).

49. Superphosphate of lime does not replenish nitrogen in the soil.

Hence, the correct answer is (c).

50. Nitric acid is produced by treating potassium nitrate with sulphuric acid under suitable experimental conditions.

Hence, the correct answer is (c).

Level 2: Review Your Concepts

51. $SO_2 + 2H_2O \rightarrow H_2SO_4 + 2[H]$
(X)
$Cl_2 + H_2O \rightarrow HCl + [O]$
(Y)

52. Baking soda contains only sodium bicarbonate. Although it makes the dough rise and imparts puffiness to the cakes, sodium carbonate imparts a yellowish tinge to the foodstuff. However, baking powder contains tartaric acid that neutralizes the sodium carbonate formed. Therefore, baking powder is used in preference to baking soda in cooking.

53. The reaction:

$NH_3 + 5O_2$ ¾¾ $\rightarrow 4NO + 6H_2O$ (with Pt 80°C and H_2O)

Indicates the removal of the yellow colour of nitric acid prepared by Ostwald's process.

54. (i) The solubility of potassium carbonate is higher than the solubility of sodium carbonate. Hence, when carbon dioxide is passed through a concentrated KCl solution contained ammonia, potassium carbonate is not precipitated.
(ii) Products obtained.
(iii) Identification of the product from which washing soda is prepared.
(iv) Physical property of the product that is exploited for separating the above product from the other.
(v) Comparison of the physical property of the corresponding potassium compound with the above product.

55. (i) Impurities separated during steel manufacturing.
(ii) Raw material used for the manufacture of cement.
(iii) Relation between the raw material and the impurities separated during the extraction of iron in steel plant.

56. (i) Identification of reaction involved.
(ii) Constituent of baking soda.
(iii) Chemical change that baking soda undergoes during the process of baking.
(iv) Products obtained.
(v) Role of the gaseous product.
(vi) Nature of the solid product and its effect on the baked product.
(vii) Reaction between baking soda and monocalcium phosphate.
(viii) Products obtained.
(ix) Role of the product in nullifying the effect in (v).

57. (a) (i) It is chemically and thermally resistance and has good optical clarity.
(ii) Difference between the constituents present in ordinary glass and borosilicate glass.
(iii) Effect of the constituents on the physical properties.
(iv) Constituent that is responsible for the change in physical properties.
(v) Role of this constituent to make the glass suitable for laboratory wares.

(b) Solids have highly organized structures. Constituent particles of glass are haphazardly present. Glass cannot be even considered as amorphous solid due to the following reason.

During the manufacture of glass, it is cooled at a moderate rate. When its temperature drops below the melting point of its constituents, the material remains in a state between liquid and solid. When the material is cooled further, below the glass transition temperature, the movement of the constituent particles slows down and almost ceases.

The structure obtained is organized as a crystal and it does not freeze, but it is more organized than a liquid. Hence it is considered as a supercooled liquid.

Silver halide crystals are embedded in this kind of glass substrate. In the presence of UV rays electrons from the glass convert Ag^+ ions to elemental silver and the glass appears dark. The reaction gets reversed in the shade. The silver return to its original Ag^+(ionic) state and the glass becomes clear.

58. (i) Relation between process of cooling and physical changes that take place in glass.
(ii) Relation between structure and rate of cooling.
(iii) Change in arrangement of constituents of glass during cooling.
(iv) Effect of the change in arrangement of constituents on physical properties of glass.
(v) Relation between the arrangement of constituents and transparency of glass.

59. (i) Windscreen is made up of tempered glass in which the rate of cooling is faster at center than at the surface.
(ii) Reason for scattering of glass when broken.
(iii) Role of additional material used to prevent the scattering of glass.

60. (i) Changes involved during curing.
(ii) Constituents of cement.
(iii) Reaction that takes place between constituents of cement and water.
(iv) Products obtained.

(v) Change in the crystalline structure of the product after the reaction.

(vi) Role of this particular type of crystalline structure for the setting of cement.

61. (a) Simple pottery

Crushed and finely powdered clay is taken. Water is added to this powder and kneaded to a hard mass. This mass can be moulded into various shapes on a rotating wheel. Then, these articles are dried in air. The dried articles are arranged in a kiln and subjected to heating up to 1373 K. The heating is done in a careful and controlled way. It loses water at 923 K and CO_2 at 1173 K. At this high temperature, SiO_2 and Al_2O_3 react with each other to form aluminium silicate. On heating further to a slightly higher temperature, these silicate units cling together and form interlocking units. Thus, the articles become hard, brittle and porous on heating.

(b) Earthenware and Porcelain ware

Raw materials used for this type of ceramics are kaolin, fine sand and feldspar. The pulverised mixture of raw materials is kneaded with water into a thick mass. This paste is moulded into various shapes and then dried in air chambers. These dried articles are subjected to fixing at much higher temperatures than to what is done in case of simple pottery. The heating of these goes up to 1300 – 1500 K. The articles obtained are porous.

Since feldspar contains some metal oxides in addition to SiO_2 and Al_2O_3, at a high temperature, a mixture of silicates is formed. The earthenware obtained after the process of firing is porous. To make it impervious to liquids, these articles are subjected to a process called glazing. A molten mixture of feldspar, silica, borax and water is made into a paste by heating. The articles obtained after the process of firing are dipped in this paste and then they are subjected to reheating strongly. Thus, the pottery gets glazy appearance and also loses its porosity.

62. (i) Process of hardening of concrete.

(ii) Constituents present in cement.

(iii) Changes that the constituent undergo during curing.

(iv) Comparison of time taken by the constituents for the above change.

63. (i) Composition of cement.

(ii) Reaction of water with the major component of cement.

(iii) Phenomenon associated with the above reaction.

(iv) Effect of the above phenomena on the setting of cement.

(v) Type of changes involved in the above phenomena.

(vi) Effect of these changes on the structure of silicates.

64. (i) Properties of the constituents of the given fertilizer.

(ii) Comparison of constituents of triple phosphate and superphosphate of lime.

(iii) Reactions that take place after addition of the respective fertilizer to soil.

(iv) Products obtained

(v) Effect of the product that is not assimilated by the plant on the nature and utility of the soil.

65. (i) The form in which the plant assimilate nitrogen from fertilizer.

(ii) Identification of the salt that cannot be directly assimilated.

(iii) Comparison of time required for the assimilation of the two fertilizers given.

(iv) Relation between usage of fertilizer and requirement of the soil.

66. (a) In white phosphorus the four phosphorus atoms are arranged at the four corners of a regular tetrahedron and exists as isolated P4 units with weak van der Waals forces of attraction between P_4 units. Hence, it is less stable and highly reactive. However, in red phosphorus, all the P_4 units are interlinked with each other to form long chains and hence it is highly stable with lesser reactivity. White phosphorus catches fire immediately on exposure to air since its ignition temperature is low. Red phosphorus does not catch fire at room temperature since it has a higher ignition temperature.

(b) Phosphorus when added to copper forms Cu_3P (copper phosphide) that decreases the malleability and increases hardness of the alloy.

67. (a) $X = H_2$, $Y = Cl_2$, $Z = HCl$

$$\underset{X}{H_2} + \underset{Y}{Cl_2} \rightarrow \underset{(Z)}{2HCl}$$

(b) $Mg + 2HCl \rightarrow MgCl_2 + H_2$

Z in the form of acid reacts with metals like Mg to liberate hydrogen gas along with the formation of the corresponding salt.

$HCl + H_2O \rightarrow HCl$ (acid)

(c) As (Z) HCl gas is heavier than air, it is collected by the upward displacement of air. It is not collected by downward displacement of water as it is highly soluble.

68. Among all fuels, hydrogen has the highest calorific value. Moreover, it is a non-polluting fuel. But it cannot be used as a fuel in automobiles because liquefaction of hydrogen is difficult and it is highly inflammable.

69. Solubility of N_2 in water increases with the increase in external pressure. In deep seas, the percentage of nitrogen that gets dissolved in blood is more than that in case of normal atmospheric pressure. When the scuba diver comes up, the depth of the water becomes less and consequently the pressure decreases. Hence, nitrogen comes out from the blood in the form of bubbles that hinders the flow of blood.

70. SO_2 in the presence of moisture produces nascent hydrogen, which bleaches. Here bleaching takes place due to reduction. On exposure to air, the bleached substance gets oxidized due to atmospheric oxygen and regains its color. Cl_2, however, bleaches due to oxidation and hence the bleaching is permanent.

71. In dry fire extinguishers, baking soda decomposes and it is an endothermic reaction. The CO_2 evolved is much denser than air and serves as a blanket and more over it is a non-supporter of combustion and hence it cuts the contact between air and the combustible substance. Since the decomposition of baking soda is an endothermic process, the temperature of the surrounding area decreases that quickens the process of extinguishing fire.

72. Superphosphate of lime is $Ca(H_2PO_4)_2 + CaSO_4.2H_2O$, calcium sulphate on hydrolysis produces sulphuric acid that is not suitable for the soil. In order to neutralize sulphuric acid, it is used in combination with ammonium fertilizer. Ammonium ions neutralize the H_2SO_4 formed.

73. Pure nitric acid, being unstable, undergoes decomposition and liberates the reddish brown gas NO_2, which turns it yellow.

Level 3: Assess Your Concepts

74. (i) Composition of photogrey lenses/photochromatic glass.
(ii) Nature (microscopic or macroscopic) of components of photochromatic glass.
(iii) Arrangement of components of photochromatic glass.
(iv) Type of chemical change taking place on exposure to sunlight.
(v) Nature of the particles formed.
(vi) Combination of the particles formed.
(vii) Effect of this combination on color.
(viii) Comparison of sunlight and other sources of light.
(ix) Relation between the above required chemical change and the source of light used.

75. (i) Structural formula of urea.
(ii) Identification of the characteristic reaction undergone by urea for usage as a fertilizer.
(iii) Conditions required for the above reaction.
(iv) Nature of the products formed in the above reaction.
(v) Bacterial action on one of the products formed.
(vi) Comparison of basic strength of urea with one of the product formed.
(vii) Nature of the acid required to neutralize the basic character.
(viii) Effect of pH on the characteristic reaction of urea.
(ix) Relation between the temperature of surroundings and the extent of characteristic reaction of urea.

76. (i) Change that takes place during firing of pottery is presence of salt.
(ii) Product obtained due to the reaction between NaCl and a constituent of pottery.
(iii) Physical state of the product at high temperature.
(iv) Effect of the physical state on the surface of the pot.

77. (i) Property of glass required for telecommunication industry.
(ii) Requirements of optical fibre materials used in telecommunications.
(iii) Phenomenon taking place during propagation of signals.
(iv) Property of glass exploited for the above phenomena.

78. (i) Changes that takes place during slow cooling.
(ii) Comparison of arrangement of molecules/ions present in glass during the slow and fast cooling.
(iii) Conditions that make an object opaque.
(iv) Effect of arrangement of molecules/ions on the optical property of glass.

79. Iron is used as a major component in reinforced concrete cement. Though it is in constant contact with moisture and air it does not get rusted. This is because cement slurry is highly alkaline with a pH value of around 12.5. Iron becomes corrosion resistant in a

pH range above 9. Due to this reason, iron does not corrode and contributes for strength and durability of RCC.

80. Phosphate rock ($Ca_3(PO_4)_2$) is insoluble in water, whereas superphosphate of lime is soluble and hence can be assimilated by plants, that is, it provides phosphate (macronutrient) in a water soluble form. But the hydrolysis of superphosphate of lime produces H_2SO_4 that is highly acidic and damages or affects the crop. In combination with the above fertilizer, ammonium fertilizers are added so that these ammonium compounds neutralize the acidity and thus it can be used as an effective fertilizer.

81. In telecommunication a signal is sent through copper cable gets attenuated due to the resistance of the metallic cable. But in fibre optic cables the propagation of signal takes place based on the principle of total internal reflection. Hence, there is negligible loss of signal that makes it most effective cable system in telecommunication.

82. Basic soils are generally preferred for crops. The soils in general are slightly acidic due to the dissolution of CO_2, NO_2 and SO_2 in rain water. Hence, a basic fertilizer is preferable as it neutralizes the acidity of the soil and makes the soil slightly basic.

83. In an internal combustion engine, the piston has to undergo a lot of friction. The heat generated in the internal combustion engine is required for burning fuel. Hence, heat should not be dissipated. Ceramic seal rings are mostly made up of alumina and nowadays silicon nitride is used. They are very hard and excellent thermal resistants. Their thermal conductivity is low that limits the dissipation of heat.

84. When water is added to cement, hydrolysis of calcium silicate takes place. In addition to hydrolysis, the calcium silicate also undergoes hydration and these two processes are responsible for setting of cement in the early stages. Hydration is a physical change while hydrolysis is a chemical change. Hydration of calcium sillicate changes crystal structure to needle like structure (monoclinic) which entangle with each other and provides strength to the cement. Gypsum retards the setting time of cement. If gypsum (2 to 3%) is not mixed, cement gets hardered at a faster rate and cannot impart proper strength to the structure.

JEE-NEET Special Wing

Multiple-Answer Type Questions

1. Structure of Bleaching powder:

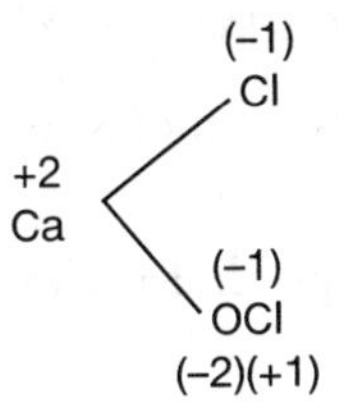

One Cl atom and oxygen atom of OCl group are attached to calcium. On long standing, bleaching powder undergoes auto-oxidation, loses chlorine and forms OCl_3^- ions. :

$$6CaOCl_2 \xrightarrow[\text{air}]{\text{Moist}} 5CaCl_2 + Ca(ClO_3)_2$$

On dissolution in water, bleaching powder dissociates to give chloride and hypochlorite ions thus rendering water acidic. So, the pH value of water decreases. On reacting with an excess amount of dilute acid, bleaching powder liberates chlorine gas:

$$CaOCl_2 + H_2SO_4 \rightarrow CaSO_4 + H_2O + Cl_2\uparrow$$

2. SO_2 bleaches by reduction (removes oxygen from coloured or dirty substances and makes them colourless). Gypsum is added to slow down the setting process of the cement.

3. (a) $MgSO_4.7H_2O$ - commonly known as Epsom salt, and it is not an ore.

   (b) PbS - known as galena, and it is an ore of lead.

   (c) $K_2SO_4.Al_2(SO_4)_3.24H_2O$- Is an alum, not an ore

   (d) Al_2O_3. $2H_2O$- Known as bauxite, an ore of Aluminium

4. Aqua-regia, a mixture of 3:1 ratio of HCl and HNO_3 by volume dissolves noble metals by forming their complexes (it produces anions of metals in +3 oxidation state). It being a mixture, it doesn't possess ant definite set of properties like a pure substance. It is yellow in colour due to the formation of nitrosyl chloride (NOCl) and Cl_2 gas initially and later turns to reddish brown due to the formation of nitrogen oxides (NO and NO_2). On reacting with gold in the absence of air, it forms NO, a neutral oxide of nitrogen.

5.

	Compound	Raw materials required in the manufacturing of the compound
(P)	Lime	$CaCO_3$ (iv)
(Q)	Washing soda	NaCl, $CaCO_3$ (ii, iv)
(R)	Baking soda	NaCl, NH_4OH (ii, iii)
(S)	Glass	$CaCO_3$, Na_2CO_3 SiO_2 (iv, v, vi)

Comprehension-Based Questions

Common solution for 6–11:

$$CaSO_4.\ 2H_2O \xrightarrow{120\text{–}130^\circ C} Q + 1\frac{1}{2}H_2O$$

$$CaSO_4.\ 2H_2O \xrightarrow{200^\circ C} CaSO_4$$

$$CaSO_4 \xrightarrow[\text{Carbonate}]{\text{Sodium}} CaCO_3 + \text{Sodium sulphate}$$

6. Q is Plaster of Paris, Calcium sulphate hemihydrate. So, its chemical formula will be $CaSO_4$. ½ H_2O or $(CaSO_4)_2.H_2O$ or $2CaSO_4$. H_2O

7. Hardening of plaster of Paris (Q) is a hydration reaction, which is the reverse of the dehydration of gypsum (P). Plaster of Paris quickly sets to a hard mass when made into a thin paste with water.

$$2CaSO_4.H_2O \xrightarrow[\text{air}]{\text{Setting}} CaSO_4.2H_2O$$

8. The difference in water of crystallization of P - $CaSO_4$. $2H_2O$ and Q - $CaSO_4$. ½ H_2O is:

$$2\ H_2O - \frac{1}{2}\ H_2O = \frac{3}{2}$$

9. All the given conversions are chemical changes as in each change, an entirely new substance with different set of properties is formed.

10. P is Gypsum. Its chemical formula is $CaSO_4$. $2H_2O$. Molecular weight of Gypsum is 172g

Elements in P-i.e Gypsum	Weight %	No. of moles of the element present in the highest percentage by weight in one mole of P
Ca	$\frac{40}{172} \times = 23.25$	Oxygen is present in the highest percentage by weight in gypsum. Hence, no of moles of oxygen,
S	$\frac{32}{172} \times = 18.6$	$= \frac{\text{Weight of oxygen atoms}}{\text{Atomic weight}}$
O	$\frac{96}{172} \times = 55.81$	$= \frac{96}{16} = 6$ moles
H	$\frac{4}{172} \times = 23.3$	

11.

List – I Compound	List – II Percentage of metal i.e. Calcium
(A) P- Gypsum- $CaSO_4 . 2H_2O$	(i) $\frac{40}{172} \times 100 = 23.25 = 5.8 \times 4 = 5.8x$
(B) Q - Plaster of Paris- $CaSO_4 . 1/2H_2O$	(ii) $\frac{40}{145} \times 100 = 27.586 = 6.89 \times 4 = 6.89x$
(C) R- Calcium sulphate- $CaSO_4$	(iii) $\frac{40}{136} \times 100 = 29.41 = 7.35 \times 4 = 7.35x$
(D) S – Calcium carbonate- $CaCO_3$	(iv) $\frac{40}{100} \times 100 = 40 = 10 \times 4 = 10x$

The correct match is

	(P)	(Q)	(R)	(S)
(c)	(iii)	(i)	(ii)	(iv)

12. Compound A is calcium phosphate, while compound C is a hydrated calcium salt. The resulting fertilizer is identified as superphosphate of lime, a blend comprising calcium hydrogen phosphate and gypsum. Hence, compound B is reasonably calcium dihydrogen phosphate, with the anion being dihydrogen phosphate ($H_2PO_4^-$). This is inferred from the reaction: ($H_2PO_4^-$). $Ca_3(PO_4)_2 + 2H_2SO_4 + 4H_2O \rightarrow Ca(H_2PO_4)_2 + 2CaSO_4.2H_2O$

13. $3Ca_3(PO_4)_2 + 6H_2SO_4 + 12H_2O \rightarrow 3Ca(H_2PO_4)_2 + 6CaSO_4.2H_2O$

Weight of the fertilizer(W)= 3[40+ 2(2 + 31 + 64)] + 6[40 + 32 + 64 + 36]g

= 3(234) + 6(172)= 702+ 1032 = 1734g

14. Wg of fertilizer contains 6 moles of gypsum i.e., $6CaSO_4.2H_2O$.

For every one mole of gypsum 2 moles of water molecules are associated with it

So, 6 moles of gypsum contain 12 moles of water molecules

= 12 × molecular weight=12 × 18 = 216 g

15. Percentage of an element in a compound

$$= \frac{\text{Mass of element in the compound}}{\text{Molar mass of the compound}} \times 100$$

$$= \frac{2 \times 31}{234.} \times 100 = 26.49\% = 26.5\%$$

The percentage composition of elements in a compound is determined by the chemical formula of the compound, representing the ratio of atoms of each element in that compound. This ratio remains consistent regardless of the quantity of the compound taken. Therefore, the percentage of an element in a compound remains constant, irrespective of the mass of the compound taken/obtained.

16. The influence of superphosphate of lime on soil pH depends on the amount of fertilizer added. In smaller quantities, the pH may not appreciably change, but higher quantities can lead to increased soil acidity due to the presence of phosphoric acid. Therefore, the impact on soil pH varies with the quantity of fertilizer applied.

Match the Columns

17.

List – I	Uses	List-II
(P)	In the disinfection of water	(iv) $CaOCl_2$
(Q)	As an ingredient in the building materials	(iii) $CaCO_3$
(R)	Repair of large bone defects	(v) $Ca_3(PO_4)_2$ (vi) $2CaSO_4 . H_2O$
(S)	In the preparation of moulds and statues	(vi) $2CaSO_4 . H_2O$
(T)	De-icing of roads	(i) $CaCl_2$

Unit II

Organic Chemistry

In this Unit

CHAPTER

8

General Organic Chemistry–I

Remember

Before beginning this chapter, you should be able to:

- have knowledge of elements, compounds, and mixtures.
- review the placement of elements in periodic table.

Key Ideas

After completing this chapter, you should be able to:

- study the unique features of carbon.
- understand the classification of organic compounds.
- use the nomenclature rules for organic compounds.
- understand isomerism in organic compounds.
- describe the preparation and properties of simple alkanes, alkenes, and alkynes.
- describe formation of coal and petroleum, isolation of products of distillation of coal and petroleum

Scientific Crypt

A Tribute to Friedrich Wohler (1800–1882)

Friedrich Wohler is regarded as the pioneer of organic chemistry. Synthesis of urea, an organic compound from inorganic compounds by him was a landmark in the history of science which disproved the Vital Force theory which was widely accepted in those times.

Wohler was born in Eschersheim, Prussia in 1800. He studied for a year with Berzelius and while working with him, he developed an interest in inorganic chemistry. Based on the work done by Oersted, Wholer in 1828 extracted aluminium. Wohler also extracted beryllium and went on to produce a variety of aluminium salts. In 1832 Wohler and Von Lie big collaborated to study bitter almonds, the source of cyanide. They proved that pure bitter almond oil does not contain hydrocyanic acid and so is not poisonous. In 1836 Wohler became a professor at the University of Gottingen where he continued his research on cyanides, and aluminium, and became the first to synthesize boron, silicon, silicon nitride, hydride, titanium and many other. Later he served as a professor of Chemistry and Pharmacy at various Universities. He was also appointed as director of laboratories, and inspector general for pharmaceutical companies.

Wohler published 50 papers on various subjects like meteorites and geology. The contributions of Wohler to scientific world were published in the journals every year from 1820 to 1881. In one of the journals it was stated that "for two or three of his researches he deserves the highest honour a scientific man can obtain, but the sum of his work is absolutely overwhelming. Had he never lived, the aspect of Chemistry would have been very different from what it is today".

FUN TIME

CROSSWORD

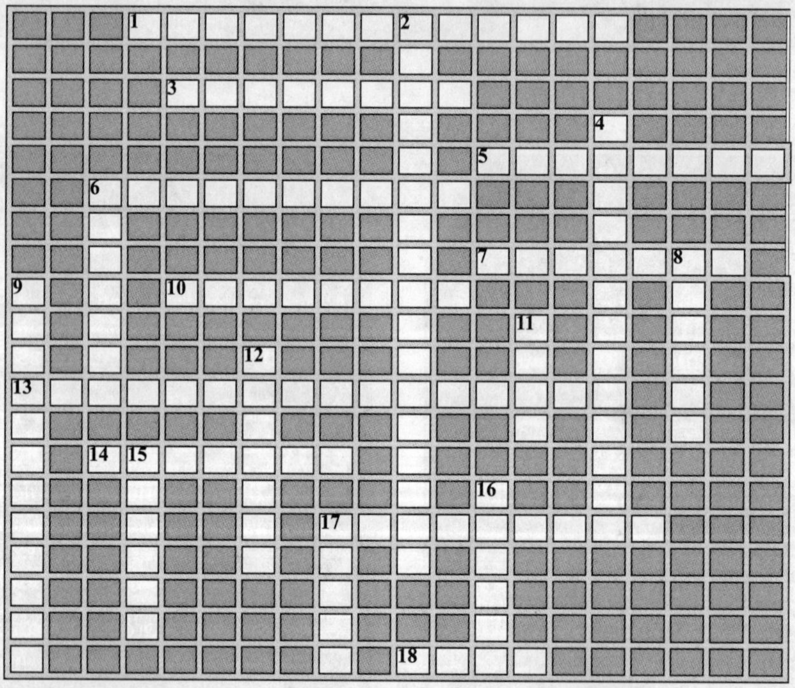

Across

1. The part of name which indicates the extent of saturation or unsaturation in the carbon chain
3. The part of the name which indicates the number of carbon atoms present in the longest carbon chain
5. The reagent used for decarboxylation reaction
6. Type of coal with maximum percentage of carbon
7. Product of ozonolysis of ethyne
10. Trivial name for methane
13. The formula which represents the actual number of atoms of various elements present in one molecule of an organic compound
14. The major component of natural gas
17. Product of polymerisation of ethene
18. Product formed by heating of ammonium cyanate

Down

2. The formula depicting the exact arrangement of atoms present in one molecule of an organic compound
4. The process of heating of coal in the absence of air
6. IUPAC name of aldehyde
8. The class of hydrocarbons in which all the valencies of carbon atoms are satisfied by single bonds
9. Product of ozonolysis of ethene
11. Valency of carbon in the organic compounds
12. IUPAC name of alcohol
15. Product formed by complete hydrogenation of ethyne
16. Hydrocarbon produced by hydrolysis of calcium carbide
17. Residue obtained by the fractional distillation of coal tar

INTRODUCTION

The branch of science which touches almost every aspect of material civilization today is called Organic chemistry. The age old classification of chemical compounds into two broad categories as organic and inorganic compounds originated on the basis of the conception that they basically differ in their source of origin. Inorganic compounds were supposed to take their origin from mineral kingdom whereas organic compounds were believed to have their origin from plant and animal kingdoms. This concept leads to the assumption of vital force theory according to which the synthesis of organic compounds could be carried out only in the presence of a mysterious vital force available in living systems.

Carbon Compounds and its Unique Properties

Organic compounds differ from inorganic compounds in most of the general properties.

1. **Number of Compounds:** The number of organic compounds is much more than that of inorganic compounds. In fact, the organic compounds comprise about 90 per cent of all known compounds.
2. **Composition of Compounds:** Composition of organic compounds is confined to very few elements of the periodic table like carbon, oxygen, hydrogen, nitrogen, halogens, and sulphur. In contrast to these, inorganic compounds are composed of almost all the elements in the periodic table.

All these properties distinguish organic compounds from the inorganic compounds. In view of these characteristics, the study of carbon compounds as a separate branch of organic chemistry is justifiable. These properties of organic compounds are due to some special features possessed by carbon.

1. **Tetravalency:** Carbon atom has electronic arrangement of 2, 4 which represents the presence of 4 electrons in the valence shell. It requires four more electrons to complete its octet. Therefore, carbon exhibits tetravalency.
2. **Catenation:** Carbon has a remarkable property of forming covalent bonds with other carbon atoms, thus, forming long chains. This ability of forming long chains with atoms of the same element is called **catenation**. Among all the elements, carbon shows maximum catenation capacity due to the maximum strength of carbon–carbon bonds. This catenation property of carbon accounts for the formation of innumerable number of compounds.

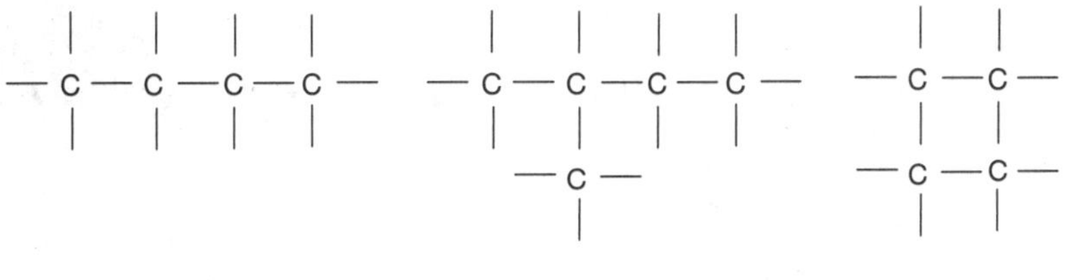

Info Bytes!

Carbon is the backbone of life on Earth. All living organisms have carbon compounds at their core, from the DNA in our cells to the food we eat.

3. **Formation of Multiple Bonds:** Due to its small size, carbon can easily form multiple bonds with carbon, oxygen, nitrogen, etc. This bond multiplicity is also responsible for the formation of a wide variety of carbon compounds.

Examples:

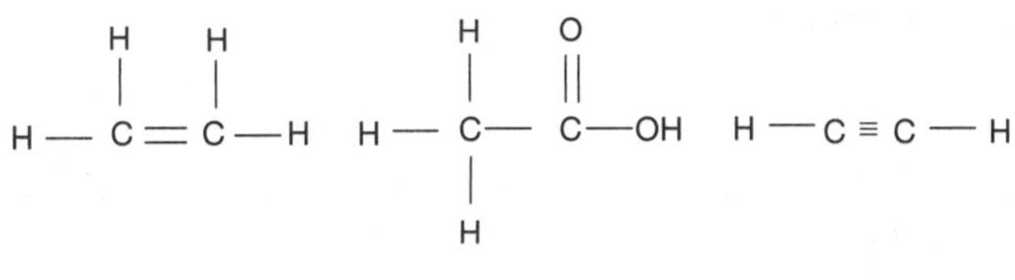

4. **Isomerism:** The molecules of all organic compounds can be represented by two types of formulae. They are discussed in the following:

   (a) Molecular Formula: It indicates the actual number of atoms of various elements present in one molecule of an organic compound. However, it does not give us any idea regarding the type of bonds in the molecule.

   Example: C_2H_6

   In one molecule of ethane, there are two carbon atoms and six hydrogen atoms.

   (b) Structural Formula: It gives the exact arrangement of the atoms of different elements present in the molecule.

   Example:

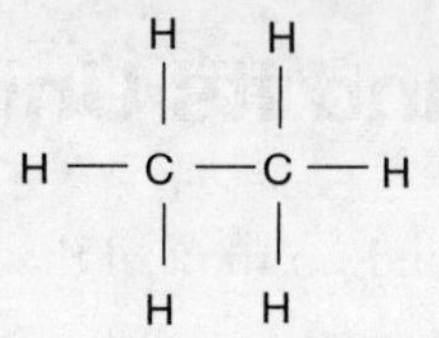

Ethane

In case of organic compounds, it is quite probable that two or more organic molecules may possess the same molecular formulae but different structural formulae. That means the molecules may differ in the structural arrangement of atoms. This phenomenon is called **isomerism.**

Classification of Hydrocarbons

Hydrocarbons are a major class of organic compounds which contain only carbon and hydrogen as the constituent elements.

Hydrocarbons are broadly classified into two categories on the basis of the skeleton of carbon chain.

Aliphatic Hydrocarbons or Open Chain Hydrocarbons

The hydrocarbons which contain straight chain or branched chain of carbons are called **aliphatic hydrocarbons.**

Examples:

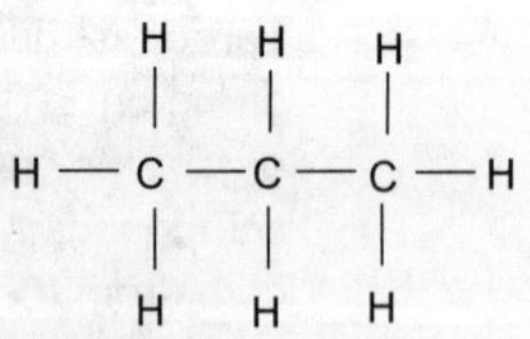

Straight chain hydrocarbon

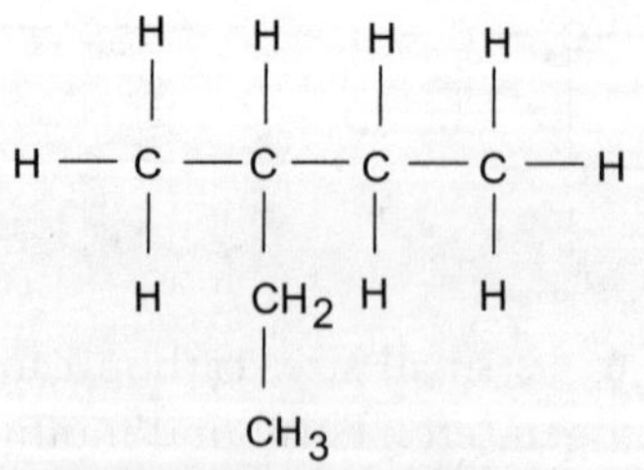

Branched chain hydrocarbon

Konnect

The simplest hydrocarbon, methane (CH_4), is the major component of natural gas and is used as a fuel source around the world.

Aliphatic hydrocarbons are further classified as saturated and unsaturated hydrocarbons based on the nature of carbon–carbon bonds present in the hydrocarbon molecules.

Saturated Hydrocarbons

In the molecules of saturated hydrocarbons, all the valencies of the carbon atoms are satisfied by single bonds. These are called **alkanes**. General formula of this class of compounds is C_nH_{2n+2}.

Examples:

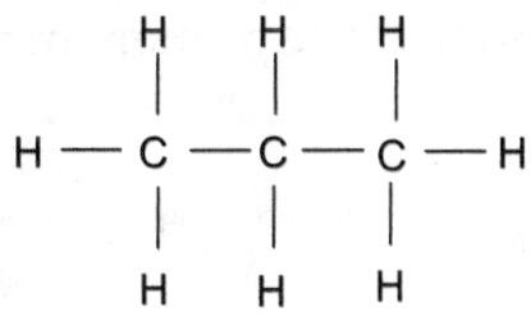

Propane

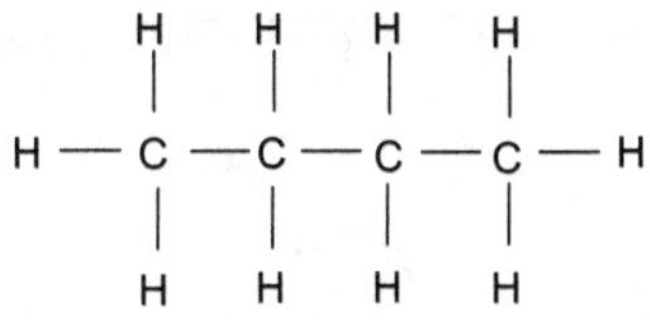

Butane

Unsaturated Hydrocarbons

The molecules of these hydrocarbons contain one or more carbon-carbon multiple bonds. These are called unsaturated hydrocarbons. Based on the type of multiple bond, unsaturated hydrocarbons are further classified into two categories as discussed below.

Alkenes: The unsaturated hydrocarbons which contain a carbon–carbon double bond in their molecules are called alkenes. General formula of alkenes is C_nH_{2n} (assuming that one double bond is present in the molecule).

Examples:

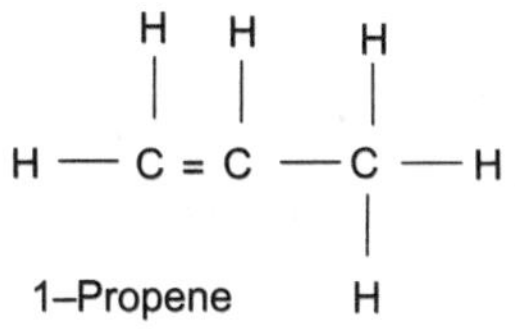

1–Propene

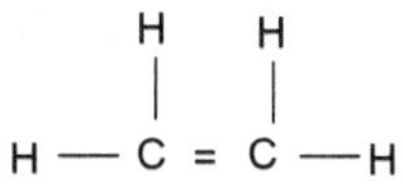

Ethene

> **Info Bytes!**
> Aliphatic hydrocarbons can be saturated (alkanes) or unsaturated (alkenes and alkynes) based on their bonding.

Alkynes: These are unsaturated hydrocarbons which contain a carbon–carbon triple bond in their molecules. General formula of alkynes is C_nH_{2n-2} (assuming that one triple bond is present in the molecule).

Examples:

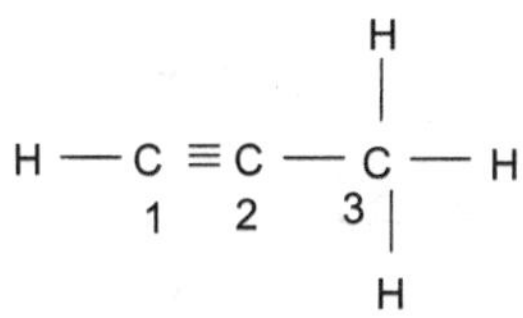

1–Propyne

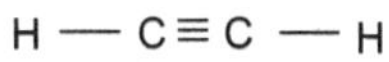

Ethyne

Closed Chain Hydrocarbons

The class of hydrocarbons which possess closed chains of carbon skeleton are called **closed chain hydrocarbons**. On the basis of chemical behavior, they are further classified into two types, i.e., alicyclic and aromatic hydrocarbons.

Alicyclic Hydrocarbons

These compounds resemble aliphatic hydrocarbons in their chemical characteristics. They contain rings of three or more carbon atoms.

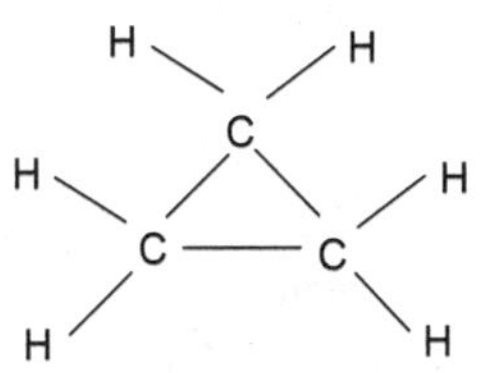

Cyclopropane

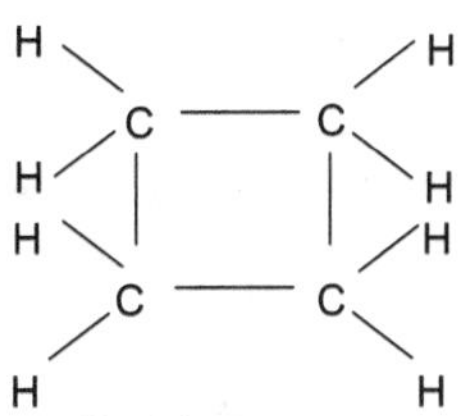

Cyclobutane

> **Info Bytes!**
> Closed chain hydrocarbons, also known as cyclic hydrocarbons, have their carbon atoms connected in a loop or ring structure.

Aromatic Hydrocarbons

This class of compounds also contains rings of carbon atoms but differ widely from aliphatic hydrocarbon analogues in their chemical behavior. They show certain characteristic features which are not shown by aliphatic hydrocarbons.

Benzene is the simplest aromatic hydrocarbon. As a matter of fact, benzene is considered the parent hydrocarbon for the entire class of aromatic compounds since all of them essentially possess one or more benzene rings in their structures.

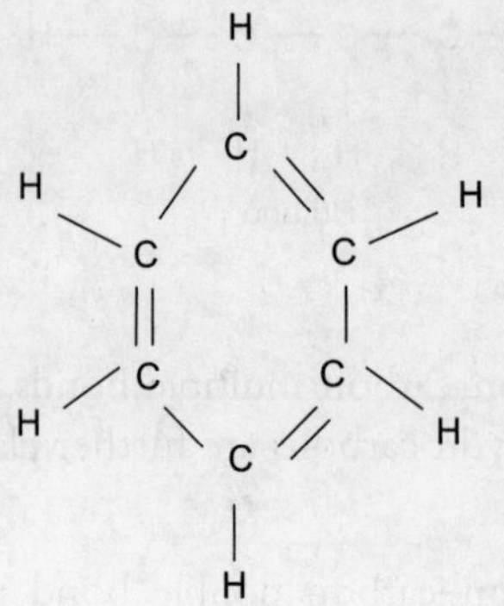

Benzene

Konnect

Benzene, a closed-chain hydrocarbon, was once used in aftershaves and as an industrial solvent until its toxic and carcinogenic properties were discovered.

Nomenclature of Hydrocarbons

Nomenclature implies assigning proper names to various compounds on the basis of certain criteria. In case of organic compounds, two systems of nomenclature are in use which we is discussed below:

Trivial System

In the earlier period when vital force theory was in effect, the names of organic compounds were given on the basis of the source of origin of the compounds. But with the advancement of synthetic organic chemistry and discovery of enormous number of organic compounds, this system of nomenclature lost its significance.

IUPAC System

The need for a more systematic method of naming the organic compounds resulted in framing certain rules for nomenclature of organic compounds by IUPAC.

(a) **Longest Chain Rule**: In the given structural formula, the longest possible carbon chain is selected. This carbon chain is called **parent carbon chain**. Based on the number of carbon atoms in the longest chain, a root word is assigned. The root word for the first four members takes its origin from trivial names. For the other members, Greek numerals are used for giving the root word.

Table 8.1 Root words based on the number of carbon atoms in the longest chain

Number of carbon atoms present in the longest chain	Root word
1	Meth
2	Eth
3	Prop
4	But
5	Pent
6	Hex
7	Hept
8	Oct
9	Non
10	Dec

Example:

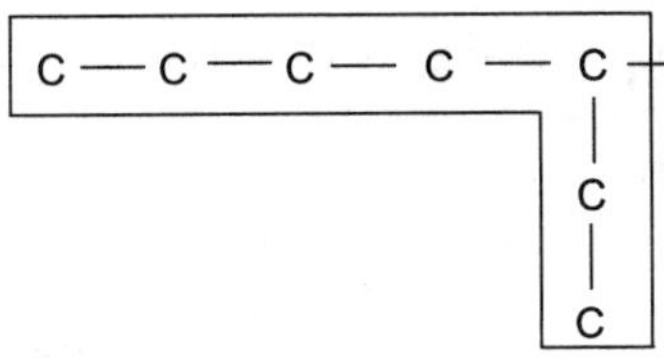

Longest chain with seven carbon atoms.

Root word corresponding to seven carbons—hept.

Konnect

With the systematic naming, it's possible to give a unique name to even very complex organic molecules.

(b) Rule of Primary Suffix: The extent of saturation or unsaturation in the carbon chain is indicated by primary suffix which is added to the root word.

Table 8.2 Primary suffixes based on the nature of compounds

Nature of compounds	Primary suffixes
Saturated (all C–C bonds)	–ane
Doubled bonded	
Unsaturated (one C=C bond)	–ene
Triple bonded	
Unsaturated (one C≡C bond)	–yne

In case of unsaturated hydrocarbons, the parent carbon chain selected should include multiple bonds.

It is also essential to mention the position of a multiple bond in the carbon chain. This is done by numbering the carbon chain from one end to the other. The chain is numbered in that direction in which the multiple bonded carbon gets the least number. The position of multiple bonded carbon is mentioned before the root word.

Examples:

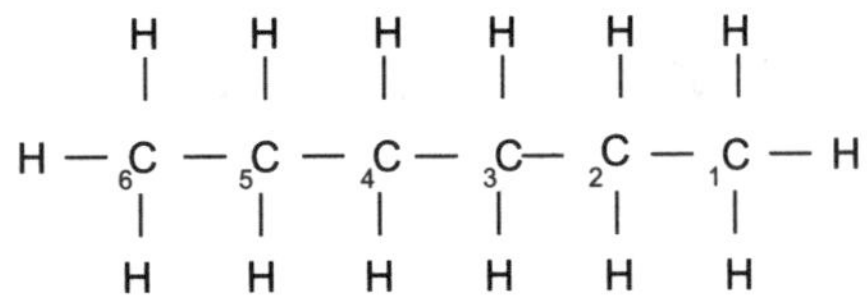

Root Word for 6-carbon Chain: hex

Primary Suffix: ane

Name: Hexane

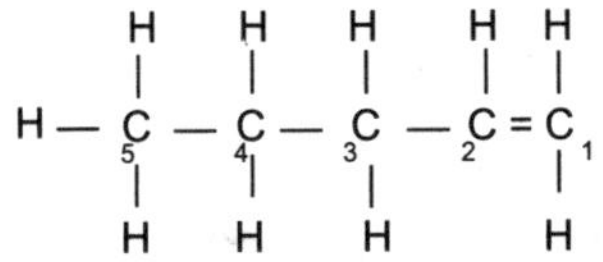

Root Word for Five Carbon Chain: pent

Primary Suffix: ene

Position of Double Bond: 1

Name: 1–Pentene

Info Bytes!

IUPAC uses a combination of prefixes, infixes, and suffixes to denote the length, type, and functional groups of a molecule.

Root Word for Four Carbon Chain: but

Primary Suffix: yne

Position of Triple Bond: 2

Name: 2–Butyne

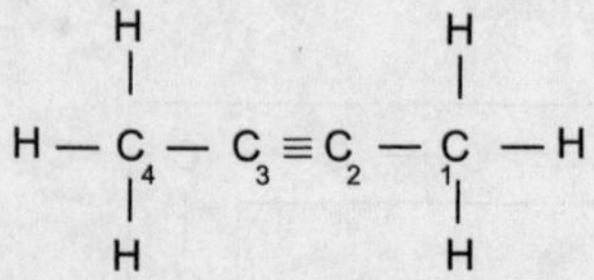

(c) Rules of Substituents: A univalent group formed after the removal of one hydrogen atom from alkane remains attached to the parent carbon chain. This univalent group is called **alkyl group**.

Table 8.3 Alkyl groups based on parent hydrocarbons

Parent hydrocarbons	Alkyl groups (formula)	Alkyl groups (name)
CH_4 (methane)	$-CH_3$	methyl
C_2H_6 (ethane)	$-C_2H_5$	ethyl
C_3H_8 (propane)	$-C_3H_7$	propyl
C_4H_{10} (butane)	$-C_4H_9$	butyl

In case of branched chain hydrocarbon, these alkyl groups which are linked to the parent carbon chain are considered substituents. The prefix corresponding to the alkyl group is added before the root word by mentioning the position number of the carbon in the main chain which it is attached to. The carbon chain is numbered in that direction in which the carbon linked to the substituent gets the least number.

Examples:

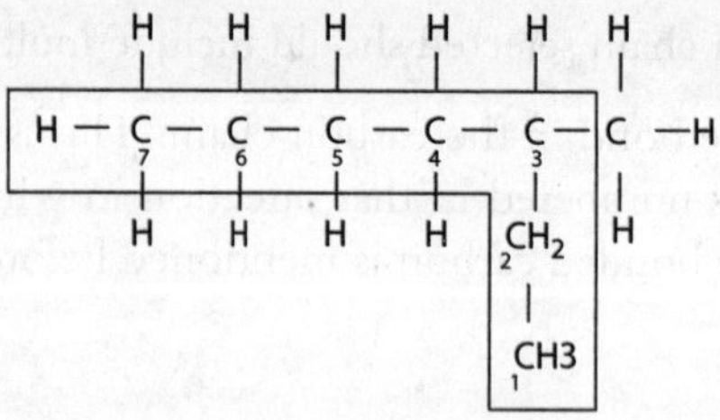

Root Word: hept

Prefix: methyl

Position of the Substituent: 3

Name: 3-methyl heptane

Konnect

IUPAC published the longest chemical name in 2017: the full name for the protein Titin, which has over 189,000 letters.

Isomerism

When two or more substances have the same molecular formulae but differ in the structural arrangement of atoms within the molecule, they are called **isomers** and the phenomenon is called **isomerism.**

Since the isomers differ in the structural arrangement of atoms, the phenomenon is called **structural isomerism.** Depending on the type of variation in carbon chain, the structural isomerism is of different types which we now discuss.

Chain Isomerism in Alkanes

Long chain alkanes differ in the arrangement of carbon atoms in the chain. Two or more molecules may possess the same molecular formula, but they may differ in the arrangement of carbon atoms in the chain. This type of isomerism exhibited by hydrocarbons is known as **chain isomerism** and the molecules are called **chain isomers.** The straight chain isomer is called **n-isomer**. The isomer with a single branch at a carbon atom is called an **iso-isomer**. The isomer with two branches on the same carbon atom is called a **neo-isomer**.

Examples:

1. **Butane**

   Molecular Formula: C_4H_{10}

   Chain isomers of butane

   (a) $H_3C-H_2C-CH_2-CH_3$
   n–butane

   (b) 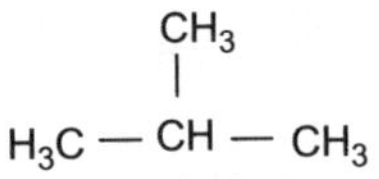
   Isobutane

2. **Pentane**

   Molecular Formula: C_5H_{12}

   Chain isomers of pentane

   (a) $H_3C-CH_2-CH_2-CH_2-CH_3$
   n–pentane

   (b) 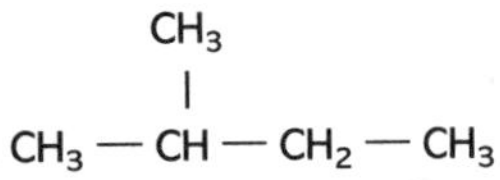
   Isopentane

   (c) 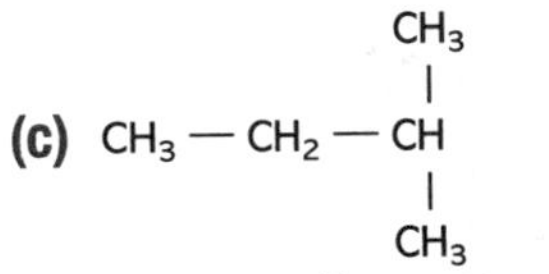
   Neopentane

Info Bytes!

The term 'isomer' comes from the Greek 'isos' meaning 'equal' and 'meros' meaning 'part' due to the equal molecular formulas. Modern Indian research institutions are pushing the boundaries of how isomerism can be applied to drug development.

Position Isomerism

These isomers have same carbon chain with same number of branches but differ in the position of multiple bond or substituent on the carbon chain.

Example:

Pentene

Molecular Formula: C_5H_{10}

$CH_3-CH_2-CH_2-CH=CH_2$
1–Pentane

$CH_3-CH=CH-CH_2-CH_3$
2–Pentane

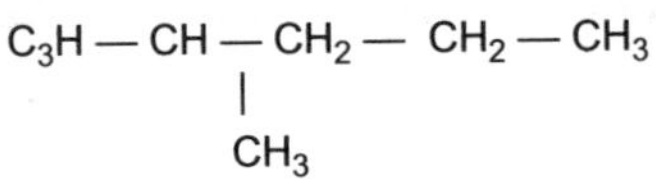
2–Methyl pentane

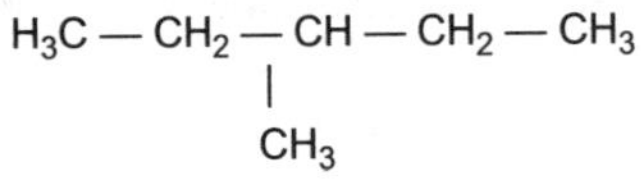
3–Methyl pentane

Thus on rearranging the carbon atoms, different isomers are obtained. These isomers differ largely in physical properties and to some extent in chemical properties. However, the compounds with same constituent elements may possess different molecular formulae but have similar type of bonding and hence show similar chemical properties. These compounds can be arranged into series which gives rise to an idea of homologous series.

Functional Isomerism

Functional isomerism is the type of isomerism in which the isomers differ with respect to the nature of functional group. Since the functional group is responsible for the chemical properties of organic compounds, the compounds with different functional groups possess different chemical properties.

Homologous Series

A series of organic compounds in which each member differs from the next member of the series by a $-CH_2$ unit, when arranged in an increasing order of their molecular weights is called a **homologous series**.

The adjacent members of this series differ by 14u in their molecular weights or $-CH_2$ group, and hence have a general formula. The members show a regular gradation in physical properties and similar chemical properties. Thus, these can be prepared by similar methods.

Table 8.4 Homologous series of alkanes (general formula C_nH_{2n+2})

IUPAC names of the alkane	Molecular formulae	Structural formulae
Methane	CH_4	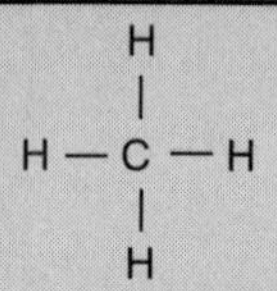
Ethane	C_2H_6	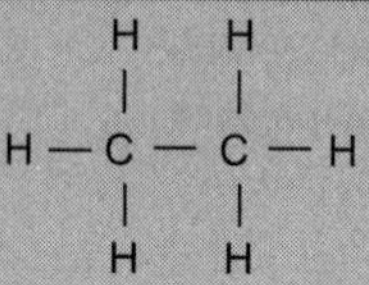
Propane	C_3H_8	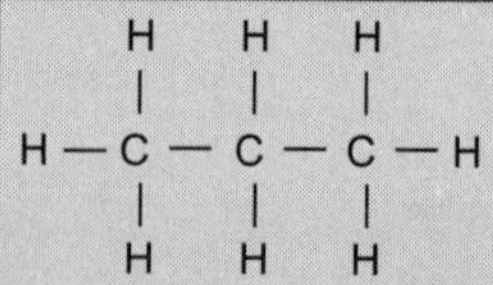
Butane	C_4H_{10}	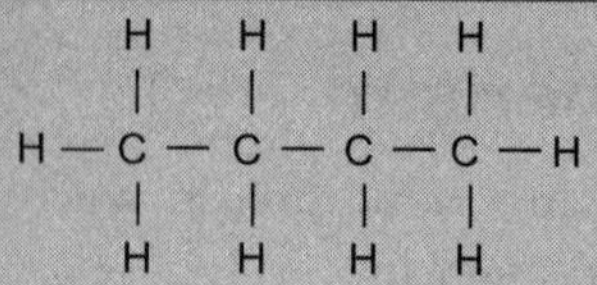
Pentane	C_5H_{12}	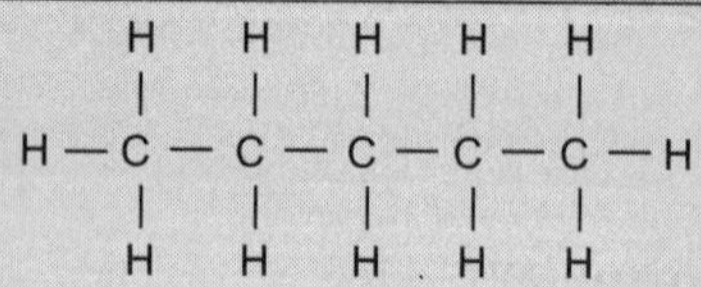

Table 8.5 Homologous series of alkenes (general formula C_nH_{2n})

IUPAC names of the alkene	Molecular formulae	Structural formulae
Ethene	C_2H_4	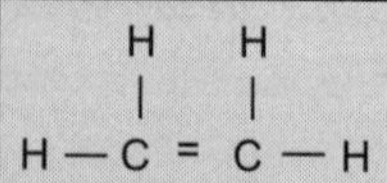
1–Propene	C_3H_6	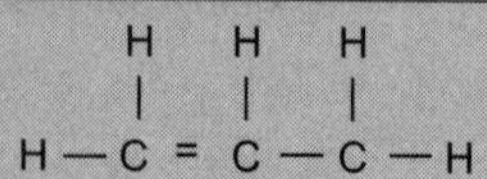
1–Butene	C_4H_8	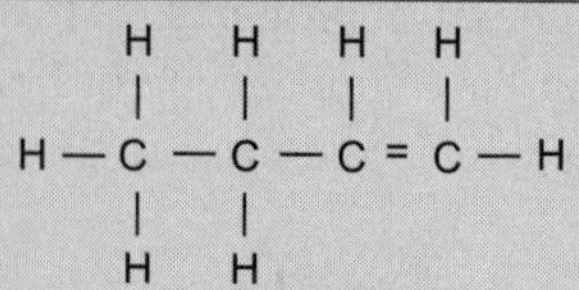
1–Pentene	C_5H_{10}	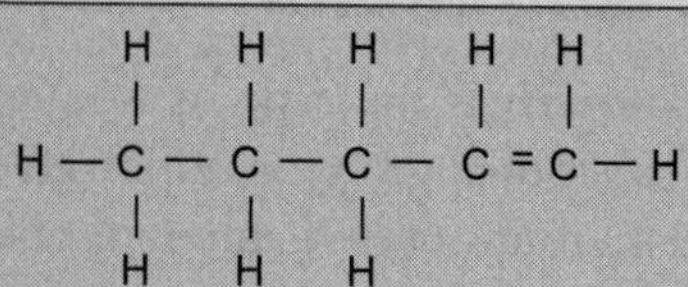

Table 8.6 Homologous series of alkynes (general formula C_nH_{2n-2})

IUPAC names of the alkene	Molecular formulae	Structural formulae
Ethyne	C_2H_2	$H-C\equiv C-H$
1–Propyne	C_3H_4	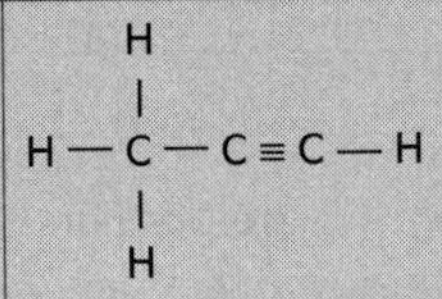
1–Butyne	C_4H_6	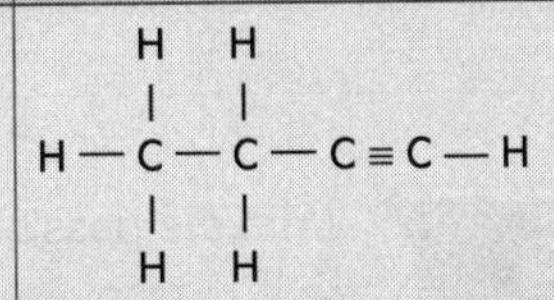
1–Pentyne	C_5H_8	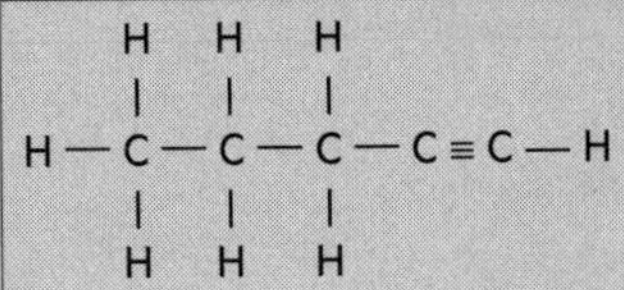

EXAMPLE 8.1

Give IUPAC names for the following:

(i) 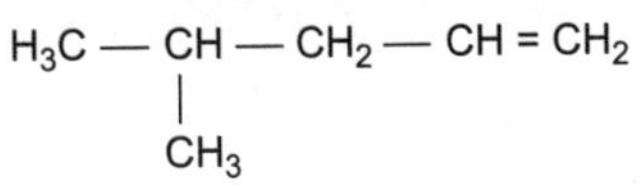

(ii) 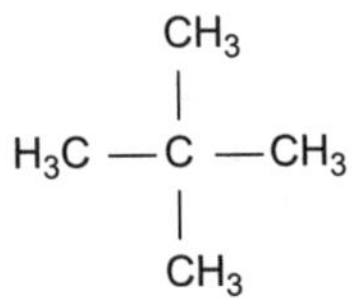

(iii) 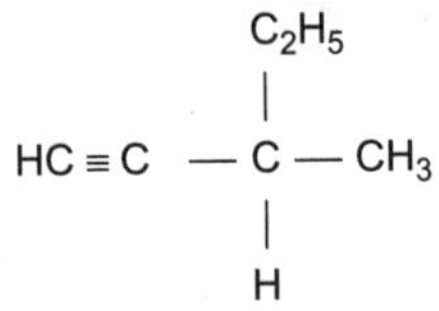

(iv) 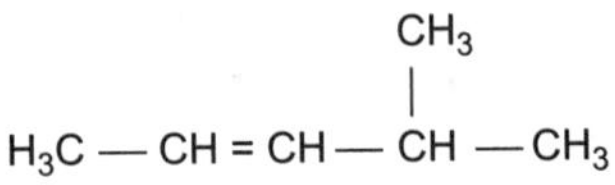

SOLUTION

(i) 4-Methyl-1-pentene

(ii) 2, 2-Dimethyl propane

(iii) 3-Methyl-1-pentyne

(iv) 4-Methyl-2-pentene

EXAMPLE 8.2

Molecular formula of a hydrocarbon is C_5H_{10}. What type of isomerisms are exhibited by it? Give the structural formulae of the isomers.

SOLUTION

Molecular formula C_5H_{10} corresponds to pentene. It can exhibit position isomerism and chain isomerism.

Possible structural formulae are:

(i) $CH_2 = CH - CH_2 - CH_2 - CH_3$

1 – Pentene

(ii) $CH_3 - CH = CH - CH_2 - CH_3$

2 – Pentene

(iii) 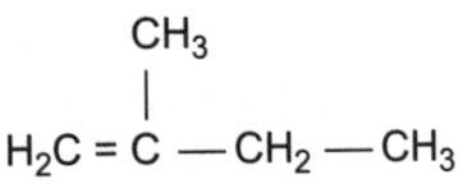

(iv)

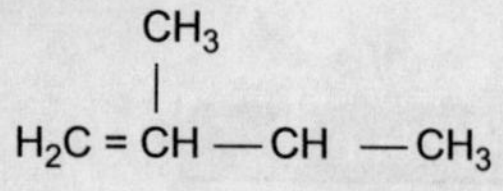

(v)

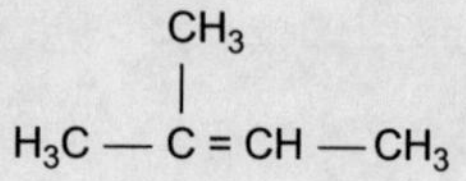

(i), (ii); (iii), (iv); (iii), (v); (iv), (v) are position isomers

(i), (v); (i), (iv); (i), (v); (ii), (iii); (ii), (iv); (ii), (v) are chain isomers

EXAMPLE 8.3

Write the possible isomers for the following molecular formulae.

(a) C_4H_8O **(b)** $C_3H_6O_2$ **(c)** $C_5H_{12}O$

SOLUTION

(a) Molecular formula: C_4H_8O

Possible isomers

(i) $CH_3 - CH_2 - CH_2 - CHO$

Butanal

(ii)

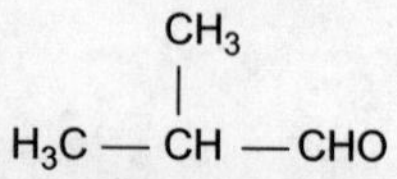

2- Methyl butanal

(iii)

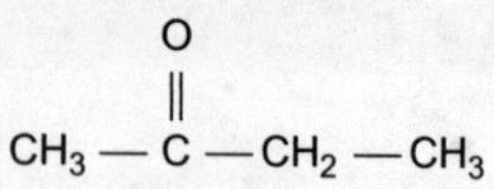

2- Butanone

(i), (iii) functional isomers.

(i), (ii) are chain isomers.

(b) Molecular formula: $C_3H_6O_2$

Possible isomers

(i) $CH_3 - CH_2 - COOH$ Propanoic acid

(ii) $CH_3 - COOCH_3$ Methyl ethanoate

(iii) $HCOOCH_2CH_3$ Ethyl methanoate

(ii), (iii) are metamers while (i), (ii); (i), (iii) are functional isomers.

(c) Molecular formula: $C_5H_{12}O$

Possible isomers:

(i) $H_3C - CH_2 - CH_2 - CH_2 - CH_2OH$

(ii)

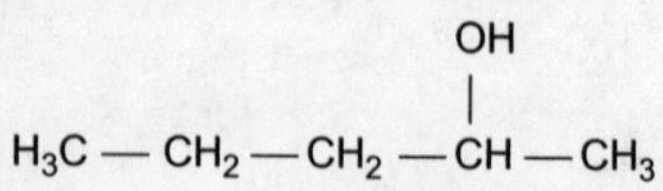

(iii)

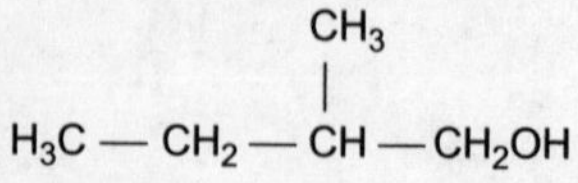

(iv)

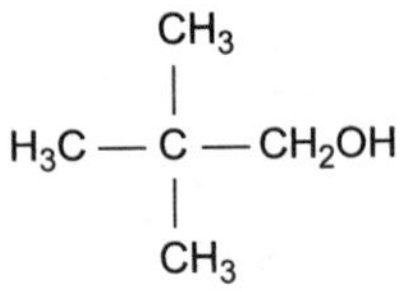

(v)

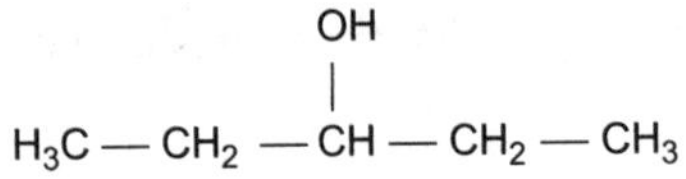

(vi) $H_3C-CH_2-O-CH_2-CH_2-CH_3$

(vii) $H_3C-H_2C-H_2C-H_2C-O-CH_3$

(i), (ii); (i), (iii); (i), (iv) are chain isomers

(i), (ii), (v) are position isomers

(i), (vi); (i), (vii) are functional isomers

Alkanes

Alkanes are aliphatic saturated hydrocarbons represented by the general formula C_nH_{2n+2}, where 'n' is the number of carbon atoms.

Info Bytes!

Alkanes are also known as paraffins or saturated hydrocarbons because they contain only single bonds between carbon atoms.

Methane

Methane is the simplest hydrocarbon of the homologous series of alkanes. The simplest hydrocarbon is an alkane with one carbon attached to four hydrogen molecules. Trivial names for methane are marsh gas and fire damp.

Occurrence

Methane is available in the earth's crust in the form of natural gas as it is the most volatile of all alkanes. Biogas or gobar gas also contains methane a the chief constituent.

Laboratory Preparation of Methane

Principle: In general, all alkanes can be prepared by the decarboxylation of sodium or potassium salts of corresponding carboxylic acids. Carboxylic acids are a class of organic compounds containing –COOH group where the hydrogen is acidic in nature and can be replaced by sodium or potassium. The reagent used for decarboxylation is soda lime (NaOH + CaO).

$$RCOONa + NaOH \xrightarrow{CaO} \underset{\text{(alkane)}}{R-H} + Na_2CO_3$$

Methane can be prepared from the sodium salt of the carboxylic acid containing two carbon atoms. The carboxylic acid containing two carbon atoms is ethanoic acid or acetic acid (CH_3COOH), and its sodium salt is (CH_3COONa), i.e., sodium acetate. This on treatment with soda lime (NaOH + CaO) gives methane.

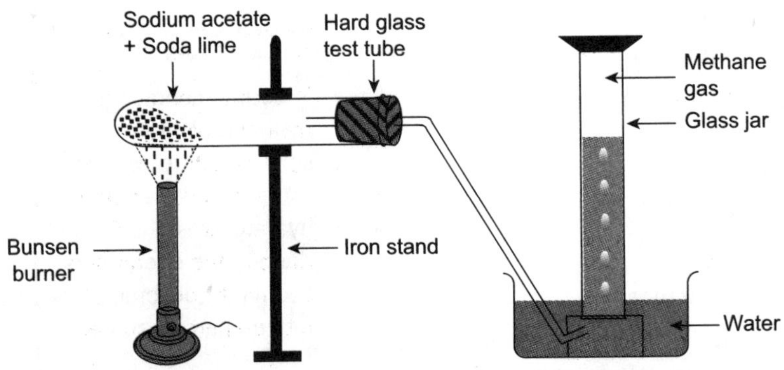

Figure 8.1 Preparation of methane gas

Konnect

Methane is an essential greenhouse gas, trapping heat 25 times more effectively than carbon dioxide over a century.

$$CH_3COOH + NaOH + \rightarrow CH_3COONa + H_2O$$

$$CH_3COONa + NaOH + \xrightarrow{CaO} \underset{\text{(methane)}}{CH_4} + Na_2CO_3$$

Process: The mixture of sodium acetate and soda lime is heated in a hard glass test tube. Methane gas is evolved and is collected by downward displacement of water.

Table 8.7 Physical Properties of Methane

Parameters	Characteristics
Color	Colorless
Odor	No characteristic smell
Taste	Tasteless
Solubility	Insoluble in water and soluble in organic solvents like CCl_4, alcohol
Vapor density	8 (lighter than air)

Chemical Properties of Methane

1. **Combustibility:** Methane burns in excess of oxygen to give carbon dioxide and water. This reaction is called **combustion** and it is an exothermic reaction. It burns with a pale blue flame:

$$CH_4 + 2O_2 \rightarrow CO_2 + 2H_2O$$

In an inadequate supply of oxygen, methane undergoes incomplete combustion to give carbon monoxide and water:

$$2CH_4 + 3O_2 \rightarrow 2CO + 4H_2O$$

2. **Pyrolysis:** On heating methane strongly in the absence of air above 1000°C, methane undergoes decomposition forming carbon and hydrogen.

$$CH_4 \xrightarrow{>1000°C} C + 2H_2\uparrow$$

3. **With Steam:** In the presence of Al_2O_3, methane reacts with steam liberating hydrogen and carbon monoxide.

$$CH_4 + H_2O \xrightarrow[Al_2O_3]{750\ C} CO + 3H_2$$

4. **Substitution Reactions:** Since alkanes are unreactive due to the presence of all C–C single bonds, the characteristic reactions of alkanes are substitution reactions.

Example: **Halogenation of methane**

Methane undergoes substitution reaction with chlorine in presence of sunlight. In this reaction, one or more hydrogens are replaced by chlorine to form the corresponding methylhalides:

$CH_4 + Cl_2 \longrightarrow CH_3Cl + HCl$ (methyl chloride)

$CH_3Cl + Cl_2 \longrightarrow CH_2Cl_2 + HCl$ (methylene dichloride)

$CH_2Cl_2 + Cl_2 \longrightarrow CHCl + HCl$ (chloroform)

$CH\ Cl_3 + Cl_2 \longrightarrow CCl_4 + HCl$ (carbon tetrachloride)

Structure: Methane molecule has four carbon–hydrogen bonds which are arranged tetrahedrally. The shape of the molecule is tetrahedral with a bond angle of 109.5°.

Info Bytes!

In certain conditions, methane can form a solid structure with water called methane hydrate, which is found deep in the ocean floor and might become a future energy source.

Alkenes and Alkynes

Alkenes and alkynes are aliphatic unsaturated hydrocarbons represented by the general formula C_nH_{2n} and C_nH_{2n-2}, respectively, where 'n' is the number of carbon atoms.

Table 8.8 Comparative study of alkenes and alkynes

Parameters	Alkenes	Alkynes
General formula	C_nH_{2n}	C_nH_{2n-2}
Type of carbon–carbon bond	Double bond (C=C)	Triple bond (C ≡ C)
Common name	Olefins	Acetylenes
Simplest compound	Ethene (ehtylene)	Ethyne (acetylene)

Ethene and Ethyne

Ethene and ethyne are the simplest hydrocarbon of homologous series of alkenes and alkynes, respectively.

Table 8.9 Comparative study of ethene and ethyne

Parameters	Ethene	Ethyne
Molecular formula	C_2H_4	C_2H_2
Structural formula	H H H—C=C—C	H—C≡C—H
Trivial name	Ethylene	Acetylene

Konnect

Indian flower markets rely on ethene. When ethene is exposed to unripe fruits and flowers, it speeds up the ripening and blooming process.

Preparation Method of Ethene

Ethene can be prepared by cracking kerosene.

Cracking: Cracking is the process of breaking up of long chain hydrocarbons into smaller chain hydrocarbons by heating at high temperature in the absence of oxygen. Basically, cracking is an important method of preparing simpler alkanes and alkanes from higher alkanes. Cracking is of two types:

1. **Thermal Cracking:** The process involves heating the compound to a high temperature in the absence of a catalyst.
2. **Catalytic Cracking:** The process involves heating the compound in the presence of catalyst.

   Example: Long chain alkane with six carbon atoms, i.e., hexane when subjected to cracking gives butane

$$\underset{\text{(Hexane)}}{CH_3-CH_2-CH_2-CH_2-CH_2-CH_3} \xrightarrow{\text{Heat}} \underset{\text{(Butane)}}{H_3C-CH_2-CH_2-CH_3} + \underset{\text{(Ethene)}}{CH_2=CH_2}$$

Laboratory Preparation of Ethene

In the laboratory, ethene can be prepared by heating ethyl alcohol with excess of concentrated sulphuric acid at 180°C. Apart from ethene, carbon dioxide and sulphur dioxide gases are evolved. These gases are removed by passing the gases over caustic soda. Finally, ethene gas is collected over water by the downward displacement of water.

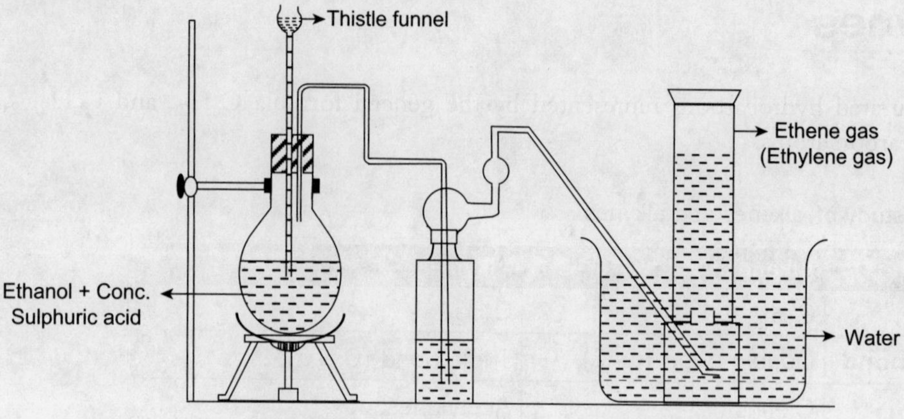

Figure 8.2 Preparation of ethene

$$C_2H_5OH \xrightarrow[180^\circ C]{Con.H_2SO_4} C_2H_4 + H_2O$$

> **Info Bytes!**
>
> Ethene is the world's highest-volume organic compound, primarily used as a building block for various polymers and other organic chemicals.

Laboratory Preparation of Ethyne

Ethyne can be prepared in the laboratory by taking a little amount of calcium carbide in a conical flask to which a few drops of water are added. Ethyne gas is evolved and it is collected by downward displacement of water:

$$CaC_2 + 2H_2O \rightarrow \underset{\text{Ethyne}}{HC \equiv CH} + Ca(OH)_2$$

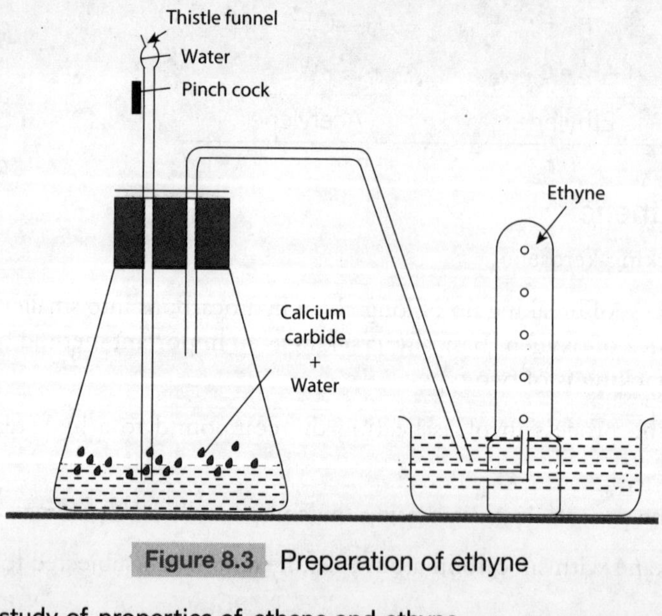

Figure 8.3 Preparation of ethyne

Table 8.10 Comparative study of properties of ethene and ethyne

Physical Properties	
Ethene	**Ethyne**
Colorless, tasteless gas	Colorless, tasteless gas
Peculiar odor	Characteristic garlic odor
Insoluble in water	Insoluble in water
Soluble in non-polar solvents	Soluble in non-polar solvents
Vapor density 14	Vapor density 13
Slightly lighter than air	Slightly lighter than air

(Continued.)

Table 8.10 Continued

Chemical Properties	
Ethene	**Ethyne**
(i) Combustion	
Burns with a pale blue, sooty flame in excess of air $C_2H_4 + 3O_2 \xrightarrow{\text{air}} 2CO_2 + 2H_2O$	Burns in excess of air with evolution of large amounts of CO_2 $2C_2H_2 + 5O_2 \xrightarrow[\text{Air}]{\text{Excess}} 4CO_2 + 2H_2O$
(ii) Hydrogenation	
When equal volumes of ethene gas and hydrogen are passed over heated nickel or platinum at 300°C, one molecule of hydrogen is added 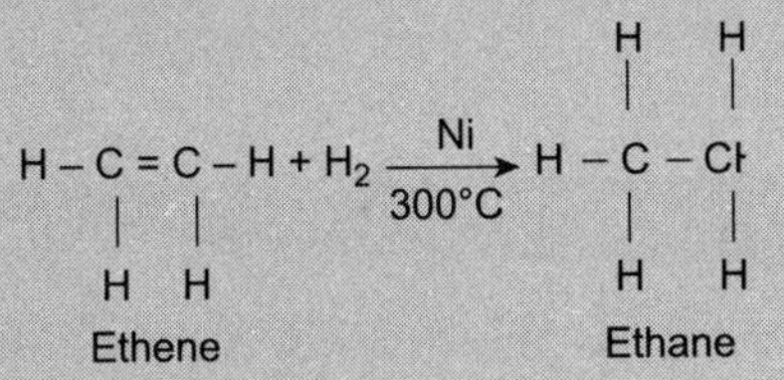	When a mixture of ethyne and hydrogen in 1 : 2 ratio is passed over heated nickel at 300°C, two molecules of hydrogen get added. Product may be ethene or ethane 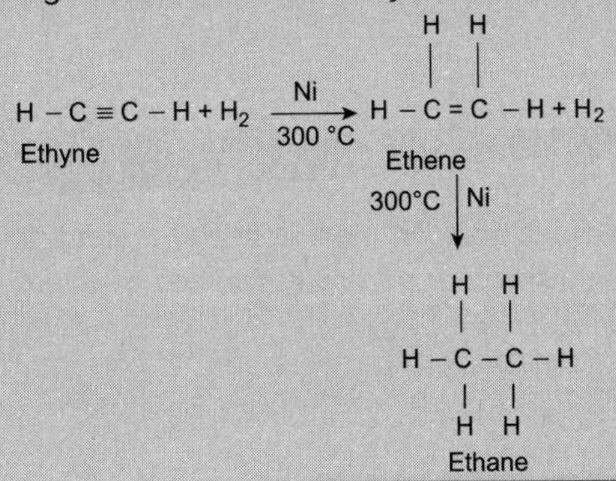
(iii) Addition of bromine	
Decolorization of bromine water takes place when ethene gas is passed through bromine water and one molecule of bromine is added 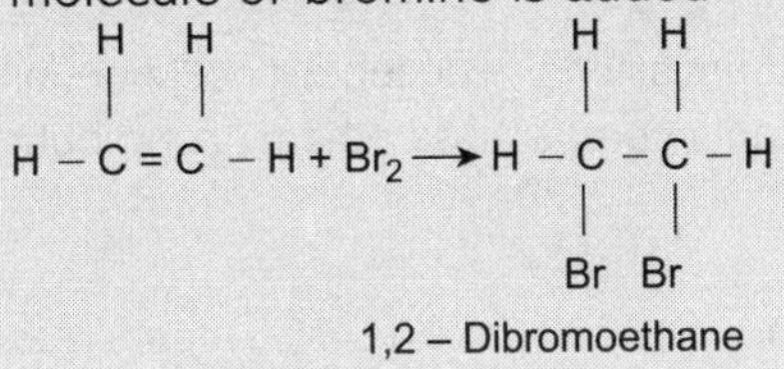	Decolorization of bromine water takes place when ethyne gas is passed through bromine water as two molecules of bromine get added 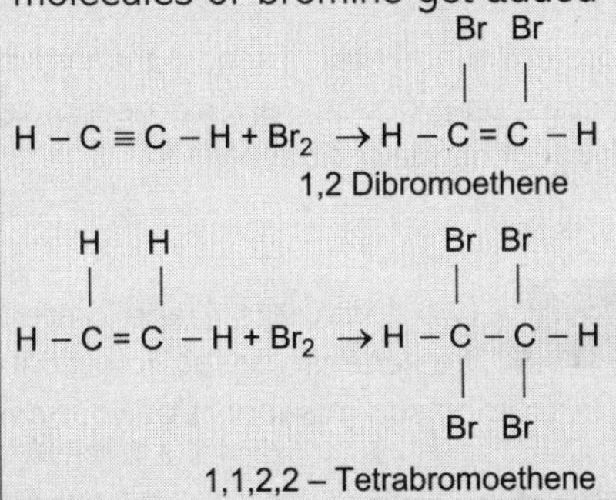
(iv) Polymerization	
A number of ethene molecules add to each other at high temperature forming long chains called polythene $nH_2C = CH_2 \rightarrow (CH_2 - CH_2)_n$	Three molecules of ethyne add to each other forming benzene $3HC \equiv CH \xrightarrow[\text{Red hot Cu tube}]{300°C} C_6H_6$

Applications of Chemical Properties

1. **Hydrogenation of Unsaturated Hydrocarbons:** This reaction is made use of in the hydrogenation of vegetable oils. Some vegetable oils containing unsaturation, when subjected to hydrogenation in the presence of a nickel catalyst at 473 K and 5 atm pressure, get solidified and produce Vanaspathi ghee is formed.

$$\text{Vegetable oils} + H_2 \xrightarrow[473\text{K}, 5\text{atm}]{\text{Ni}} \text{Vanaspathi ghee}$$

Examples: Groundnut oil, mustard oil, cotton seed oil, etc.

2. **Decolorization of Bromine Water**: This reaction is used for testing the unsaturation in organic compounds.

Table 8.11 Uses of hydrocarbons

Compounds	Useful product	Use
Methane	Natural gas Bio gas Derivatives	Automobile fuel, fertilizer synthesis Domestic fuel Synthesis of useful industrial products
Ethene	Polythene Ethene gas	Manufacture of plastics Artificial ripening of fruits, preparation of Thiokol and glycol
Ethyne	Oxy acetylene Acetylene	Welding metals Illumination, ripening of fruits

Konnect

Hydrocarbons, thus, in most cases are useful for the generation of energy. Some of them are available naturally. There are also other natural resources of energy which are widely used.

EXAMPLE 8.4 Explain why methane is considered a more environmentally friendly fuel compared to ethane, highlighting key environmental advantages and any specific environmental concerns associated with each fuel.

SOLUTION

Methane is considered more environmentally friendly than ethane due to its lower carbon emissions, reduced air pollution, and sustainability. Methane combustion produces fewer greenhouse gases and harmful pollutants compared to ethane, contributing to better air quality and climate change mitigation.

EXAMPLE 8.5 Two containers A and B are filled with the same amount of chlorine gas. Limited amount of methane is passed into container 'A' and excess of methane into container 'B'. Identify the products formed in A and B. Give reason in support of your answer.

SOLUTION

If limited amount of methane is passed through the container 'A' methyl chloride is formed first. As the amount of methyl chloride increases, it competes with methane for the available chlorine. Once the concentration of methyl chloride exceeds the concentration of methane, chlorine attacks methyl chloride rather than methane, forming methylene chloride which in similar way gets chlorinated finally forming CCl_4.

The end product is a mixture of methane, methyl chloride, methylene chloride, trichloromethane, and carbon tetrachloride.

$$\underset{\text{Methane + Chlorine}}{CH_4 + Cl_2} \xrightarrow[-HCl]{} \underset{\text{Methyl chloride}}{CH_3Cl} \xrightarrow[-HCl]{Cl_2} \underset{\text{Methylene chloride}}{CH_2Cl_2} \xrightarrow[-HCl]{Cl_2} \underset{\text{Trichloro methane}}{CHCl_3} \xrightarrow[-HCl]{Cl_2} \underset{\text{Carbon tetrachloride}}{CCl_4}$$

In second case if excess of methane is passed, only methyl chloride is formed.

$$\underset{\text{(excess)}}{CH_4} + Cl_2 \rightarrow HCl + \underset{\text{Methyl chloride}}{CH_3Cl}$$

EXAMPLE 8.6 Explain why partially hydrogenated oils are often used in food products like margarine and certain baked goods. What are the advantages of using partially hydrogenated oils in these products over other types of fats and oils?

SOLUTION

Partially hydrogenated oils are used in food products like margarine and baked goods because of their altered chemical structure. During the partial hydrogenation process, some of the unsaturated fatty acids present in oils are converted into saturated or trans fatty acids. Due to the health risks associated with trans fats, many food manufacturers are phasing out the use of partially hydrogenated oils and seeking healthier alternatives such as fully hydrogenated oils or oils low in unsaturated fats. These alternatives provide similar texture and shelf-life benefits without the negative health impacts of trans fats.

Natural Sources of Energy

Energy is the primary requirement for the existence of life on earth. Solar energy, hydel energy, and wind energy are some sources of energy which are inexhaustible. This is because they can be generated continuously and can replace the used up energy from time to time. They are, therefore, called **renewable sources** of energy. On the other hand, there are some energy sources which get exhausted over a period of time as they can not be replenished from time to time so easily. Coal and petroleum are two major **non-renewable sources** of energy. These are organic matter and are formed by the degradation of dead plants and animals.

Millions of years ago, the dead plants and animals were buried beneath the surface of earth. Owing to the high temperature and pressure existing in the bottom most strata of earth's crust, the organic matter in the remains of plants got converted to coal while small marine animals and plants got converted into petroleum. Hence, these are called **fossil fuels**.

Info Bytes!

Coal is a fossil fuel that was formed millions of years ago from the remains of plants and organisms.

Coal and petroleum are complex mixtures of hydrocarbons. Hydrocarbons being combustible, coal, and petroleum also undergo combustion producing large amounts of energy. Therefore, they act as sources of energy. These two are not only the major reservoirs of energy which meet 90 per cent of the energy requirements of the world, but also the main sources for the synthesis of many useful organic chemicals.

Coal

Composition of coal: Coal is mainly composed of carbon and also some hydrocarbons. In addition to these, coal contains some inorganic compounds of nitrogen, oxygen, and sulphur.

Different varieties of coal which differ in the percentage of carbon are available.

Table 8.12 Varieties of coal

Variety of coal	Percentage of carbon
Anthracite	90 per cent
Bituminous	70 per cent
Lignite	40 per cent
Peat	10–15 per cent

Konnect

- India's aromatic attars (perfumes) historically used coal tar derivatives to achieve lasting fragrances.
- The Indian city of Jamnagar boasts the world's largest oil refinery.

Extraction of Coal: The technique used for the extraction of coal from mines depends upon the mode of occurrence of coal in the earth's crust. Coal, when present in the upper layers, is extracted by open cast mining technology. Coal available in the deeper layers of earth's crust can be extracted by using underground mining technology.

Destructive Distillation of Coal: When coal is subjected to heating at high temperatures up to 1300–1700 K in the absence of air, a number of volatile products are obtained along with a non-volatile residue called **coke**. The process of heating of coal in the absence of air is called **destructive distillation** or **carbonization**. The volatile products are mainly composed of three components, namely, coal gas, ammonia, and coal tar.

Isolation of Products: The volatile products are first passed through water. Ammonia gets dissolved in water and is removed. Coal tar being insoluble in water, settles down as an oily liquid. Coal gas which is also insoluble in water escapes out. It consists mainly of methane, carbon monoxide, and hydrogen.

Fractional Distillation of Coal Tar

Coal tar, a black viscous liquid, when subjected to fractional distillation gives different products. These products on further distillation give various aromatic compounds like benzene. These compounds are the parent compounds used in the preparation of various industrially useful products such as dyes, drugs, polymers, pesticides, etc.

Table 8.13 Fractional distillation of coal tarl

Main fraction	Boiling point range (°C)	Composition
Light oil	80–170	Benzene
Middle oil	170–230	Phenol, naphthalene
Heavy oil	230–270	Phenol, naphthalene, anthracene
Green oil	270–400	Anthracene
Residue	Above 400	Pitch

Petroleum

Petroleum is a dark, viscous oily liquid generally known as rock oil or crude oil.

Composition of Petroleum: The precise composition of petroleum cannot be specified since it depends on the place of origin. Nevertheless, petroleum can be considered a complex mixture of hydrocarbons, composed predominantly of alkanes and cycloalkanes. Some petroleum deposits also contain reasonable amounts of aromatic hydrocarbons and alkenes. Trace amounts of oxygen, nitrogen, and sulphur are also present since it is obtained from the remains of dead plants and animals.

Info Bytes!

The world's largest oil refinery is the Jamnagar Refinery in India, processing over 1.2 million barrels per day.

Extraction of Petroleum: Under earth's surface, petroleum deposits are found to be associated with a layer of natural gas. These can be drawn out by drilling deep wells through the various layers of earth till the oil-bearing strata are reached. Due to the process of drilling, pressure is developed in those layers. Consequently, the gases are fizzed out of the solution and the crude oil is gushed out.

As the oil drawn out by this method is only 20 per cent, water or compressed air is pumped through the outer pipe and oil is drawn out through the inner pipe. By this way, it is possible to draw greater proportion of petroleum.

Processing of Petroleum: Since the crude oil is drilled out from earth's crust, it obviously consists of lots of impurities. In addition to this, petroleum being a complex mixture of various hydrocarbons, it

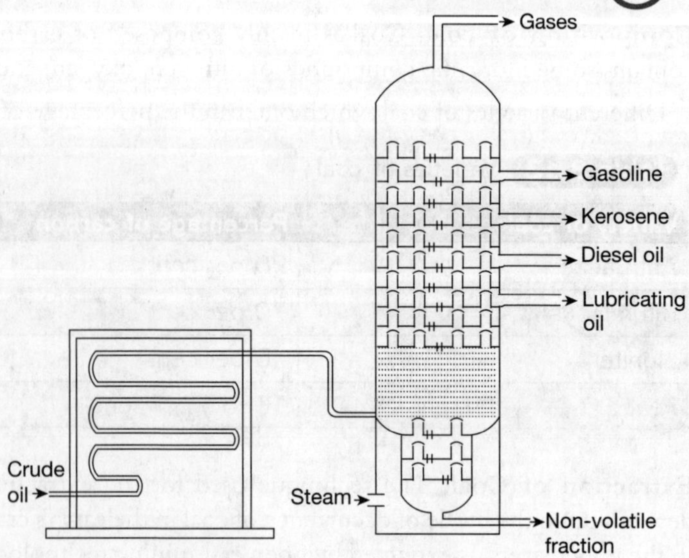

Figure 8.4 Fractionating Tower

is necessary to separate the components. The process of removal of undesirable impurities followed by the separation into different useful fractions is called **refining of petroleum**.

The basic principle involved in refining petroleum is fractional distillation of the crude oil over a specific range of temperature as the different hydrocarbons have different boiling points. The refining is carried out in a fractionating tower. The fractionating tower is a tall cylindrical tower made up of a number of horizontal stainless steel troughs.

The crude oil which is free from impurities is fed at the base of the fractionating tower at 675 K. At this temperature, all the volatile components vaporize and pass through the fractionating tower. As the vapor is passed through this column, they get condensed at different heights of the tower. The components which have higher boiling points get condensed first and the components having lower boiling points are carried to the top. Thus, the various fractions formed by condensation are collected in different trays separately. The non-volatile part of the crude oil remains in the tower in the form of a solid residue called **asphalt**.

Before subjecting crude oil to fractional distillation, it should be freed from inorganic impurities. This is done by passing the raw crude oil between highly charged electrodes which remove all water from the sample. It is, then, treated with copper oxide to remove the sulphur compounds.

Table 8.14 Useful fractions obtained after refining of petroleum

Main fraction	Boiling temperature range	Composition	Uses
Petroleum gas	Below 30°C	C_1–C_4	Fuel, for making carbon black
Crude naphtha	30–150°C	• Petroleum ether (below 90°C) (C_5–C_7) • Petrol (90–120 °C) (C_7–C_9) • Benzene (120°C–150°C) ($C_9 - C_{10}$)	Solvent Motor fuel Dry cleaning
Kerosene oil	150–300°C	C_{10}–C_{16}	Cooking fuel illuminant, oil gas
Fuel oil	300–350°C	C_{16}–C_{20} • Gas oil • Diesel oil • Furnace oil	Motor fuel, cracking stock for petrol
Lubricating oil	350–400°C	C_{20}–C_{24}	Paint oil, lubricants
Paraffin wax	Above 400°C	C_{24} and above	Candles, matches, paints, water proofing, ointments, protective paints.

Important Fuels Obtained from Petroleum

The various components obtained by the process of fractional distillation of petroleum contain mixtures of hydrocarbons having different lengths of carbon chains. These fractions are used as fuels for different purposes after further purification.

> **Konnect**
> Purification makes the fuels devoid of corrosive constituents and unpleasant odors.

1. **Natural Gas:** Since all petroleum deposits are associated with natural gas, extraction of petroleum inevitably involves the collection of natural gas. Natural gas is composed of highly volatile alkanes, predominantly methane. Consequently, it undergoes rapid combustion releasing large amounts of heat.

   Natural gas has a wide range of applications in domestic and industrial activities.

   (a) Compressed natural gas can be used as an automobile fuel, i.e., as a substitute for petrol and diesel. It shows greater fuel efficiency and is available at a lower cost.

(b) Natural gas can also be used as a domestic fuel.

(c) Natural gas can be used as a raw material for the manufacture of carbon black and hydrogen. The hydrogen so obtained can be used in the synthesis of ammonia which is the most important component of nitrogenous fertilizers.

$$CH_4 + H_2O \xrightarrow{1100\,K} CO + 3H_2 + 11.7\,kJ$$

$$N_2 + 3H_2 \xrightarrow[Fe+Mo]{\text{high temperature and pressure}} 2NH_3$$

2. **Petroleum Gas:** This is the most important by-product of petroleum processing. The major proportion of petroleum gas is n-butane, the minor components being ethane and propane.

   Petroleum gas, when subjected to high pressure, can easily pass into liquid state. This easy liquefaction of petroleum gas renders it a very useful domestic fuel in the form of **LPG (liquefied petroleum gas)** it has a high calorific value and burns in air with a blue non-luminous flame. It is associated with very low ignition temperature and can be lighted easily. This, being a colorless and odorless gas, is mixed with small amounts of ethyl mercaptan which imparts a characteristic unpleasant odor to LPG, thus, rendering easy detection of leakages.

3. **Petrol:** The most important product of petroleum processing is petrol or gasoline which is used as a fuel for automobiles. In addition to this, it is also used for dry cleaning of clothes.

Coal and petroleum have wide range of applications both in industry and day-to-day life. All the applications are based on the same principle of combustibility of hydrocarbons. Combustion being a highly exothermic process, the heat energy can be either directly used or can be trapped and converted to another form of energy and used. The domestic fuels like LPG, kerosene, and biogas are important products of petroleum industry. Coal forms the most important fuel for the generation of electricity in thermal power plants.

Some Important Applications of Organic Chemistry

Chemistry has a very important role to play in our daily life and it is more so with organic chemistry. The food we consume, the cosmetics we use, the drugs we use for treating various diseases, etc., are all made up of organic compounds. Therefore, it is not an exaggeration to claim that organic chemistry intrudes into each and every aspect of our day-to-day life.

Use of Organic Compounds as Ingredients of Food

It is a well-known fact that the food is made up of complex organic compounds such as carbohydrates, proteins, oils, fats, vitamins, etc. These are all quite essential for growth and maintenance of our body. In addition to these, there are other ingredients of food which are consumed in relatively lesser proportions. They include food preservatives and food colors. Food preservatives are chemical substances added to packed food items for the purpose of preventing spoilage of food material over a long period of usage.

Table 8.15 Food preservatives and their formulae

Names	Formulae
Acetic acid (vinegar)	CH_3COOH
Sodium benzoate	C_6H_5COONa

Flavoring Agents: These are chemical substances added in minor proportions which enhance the flavor and taste of the food materials.

Examples:

Table 8.16 Flavoring agents and their structures

Names	Structures
Monosodium glutamate (MSG)	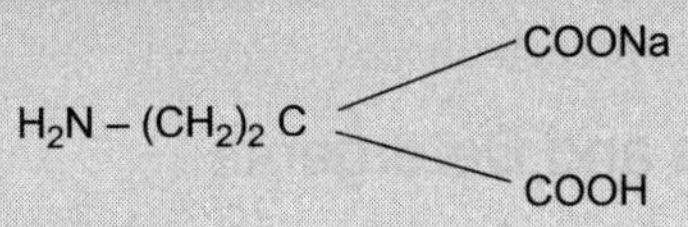
Esters of carboxylic acids	RCOOR[1]
Citric acid or sodium citrate (soft drinks)	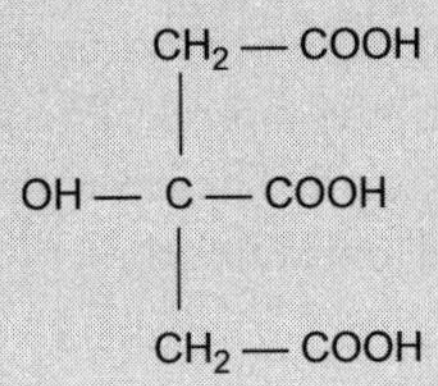

Colouring Agents: Certain chemical substances can be added to food items which impart color to them.

Table 8.17 Examples of food colors

Names	Colors
Tartrazine	Yellow
Erithrocine	Red
Indigo	Carmine (blue)

Apart from all these, certain ingredients like caffeine (alkaloid) are added to chocolates and soft drinks which act as stimulants to central nervous system.

All these ingredients do not constitute essential part of our food. Since these substance have little or no nutritional value and their intake causes more harm to the body, the consumption of these substances should be either avoided or minimized.

Just like in food materials, the role of chemicals in cleaning is also inevitable. Soaps and detergents are the most common commodities used for the purpose of cleaning.

Use of Organic Compounds in Soaps and Detergents

Soap is the sodium or potassium salt of higher fatty acids. Fatty acids are a class of organic compounds, which show characteristic acidic properties. Since fatty acids are the major constituents of vegetable oils, soaps are prepared by the hydrolysis of these oils in presence of an alkali like NaOH or KOH. The most commonly used oils are coconut oil, palm oil, cotton seed oil, ground nut oil, etc.

Detergents are also used for the same purpose and possess similar structure except that detergents are sodium or potassium salts of benzene sulphonic acids. These acids are generally available or made from petroleum products.

Structure and Composition of Soaps and Detergents

Soap molecule is made up of a long chain of hydrocarbons attached to carboxylate group which constitutes anionic part of the molecule and positive part of Na^+ and K^+.

$$C_{17}H_{35}COONa \rightarrow C_{17}H_{35}COO^- + Na^+$$

Sodium salt of stearic acid

Similarly, a detergent molecule is composed of a long chain of hydrocarbons containing benzene ring attached to sulphonate group which constitutes the anionic part.

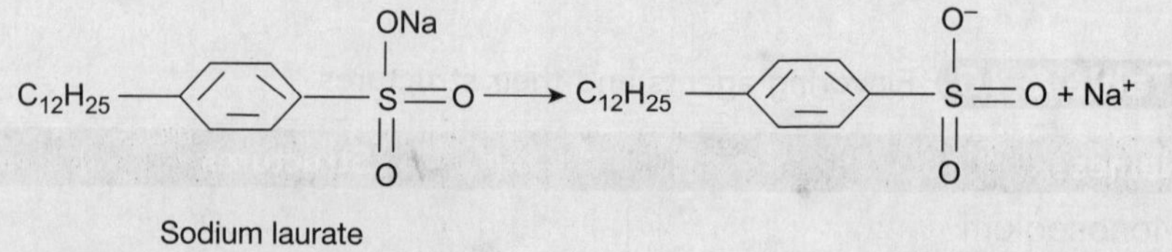

Sodium laurate

Cleansing Action of Soaps and Detergents

Generally, dirt is found to stick to the surface by means of an oily substance. Since oil and water are not miscible with each other, water cannot remove the dirt. When soap is dissolved in water, firstly it reduces the surface tension of water, thereby increasing the area of contact between water and dirt. Secondly, soap gets ionized into an anionic radical such as stearate radical and Na^+ or K^+ as cationic radical. The anionic radical consists of a hydrocarbon chain which is hydrophobic and a hydrophilic carboxylic acid as head. The hydrophilic end dissolves in water and the hydrophobic end mixes with the oil. Thus, soap forms a link between oil and water thereby separating the dirt which forms an emulsion with water and is removed off.

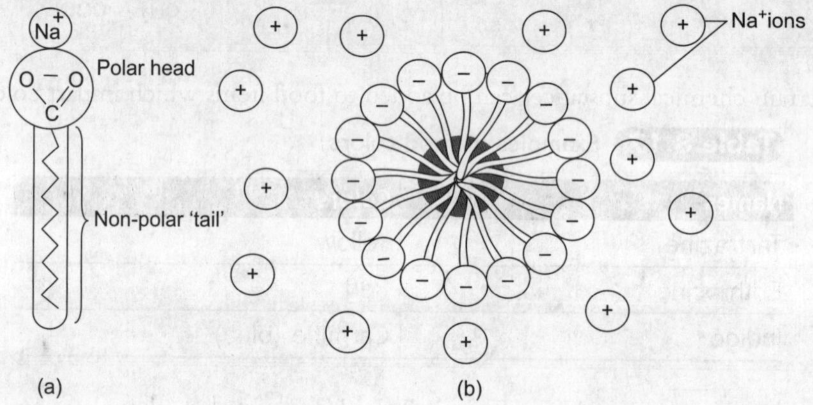

Figure 8.5 (a) A soap molecule and (b) Cross-section of a soap micelle in water

The detergents are also similar in structure and action to soaps. The basic difference between the soap and the detergent is that soap forms insoluble calcium and magnesium stearates on dissolution in hard water. On the other hand, detergents produce soluble calcium and magnesium sulphonates on dissolution in hard water. Therefore, detergents are more efficient with hard water when compared to soaps. However, detergents have a disadvantage of causing environmental pollution over soaps.

Types of Soaps

In addition to the sodium stearate which is the main ingredient, different types of soaps contain different additional ingredients which impart required quality to soaps.

Table 8.18 Types of soaps and their chemical composition

Type of soap	Chemical composition
Washing soap	Washing soda in place of caustic soda
Toilet soap	Caustic soda (for harder soaps) Caustic potash (for soft soaps) Mixture of oils and fats
Baby soap	Olive oil as additional ingredient
Transparent soap	Glycerine and castor oil

With tremendous industrial and technological development of society, hydrocarbons and their derivatives continue to have more and more significant applications. Petroleum is the most important raw material for the manufacture of hydrocarbons. Therefore, it is a high time to realise that the rational and judicious use of exhaustible natural resources can go a long way in achieving sustainable development coupled with conservation of environment.

POINTS TO REMEMBER

- ✔ The ability of forming long chains with atoms of the same element is called catenation. This catenation property of carbon accounts for the formation of innumerable number of compounds.
- ✔ Molecular formula indicates the actual number of atoms of various elements present in one molecule of an organic compound.
- ✔ Structural formula gives the exact arrangement of the atoms of different elements present in the molecule.
- ✔ Hydrocarbons are a major class of organic compounds which contain only carbon and hydrogen as the constituent elements.
- ✔ The hydrocarbons which contain straight chain or branched chain of carbons are called aliphatic hydrocarbons.
- ✔ In the molecules of saturated hydrocarbons, all the valencies of the carbon atoms are satisfied by single bonds.
- ✔ The molecules of these hydrocarbons contain one or more carbon-carbon multiple bonds. These are called unsaturated hydrocarbons.
- ✔ The unsaturated hydrocarbons which contain a carbon–carbon double bond in their molecules are called alkenes.
- ✔ Alkynes are unsaturated hydrocarbons which contain a carbon–carbon triple bond in their molecules.
- ✔ The class of hydrocarbons which possess closed chains of carbon skeleton are called closed chain hydrocarbons.
- ✔ Nomenclature implies assigning proper names to various compounds on the basis of certain criteria.
- ✔ When two or more substances have the same molecular formulae but differ in the structural arrangement of atoms within the molecule, they are called isomers and the phenomenon is called isomerism.
- ✔ Since the isomers differ in the structural arrangement of atoms, the phenomenon is called structural isomerism.
- ✔ Two or more molecules may possess the same molecular formula, but they may differ in the arrangement of carbon atoms in the chain. This is known as chain isomerism and the molecules are called chain isomers.
- ✔ The straight chain isomer is called n-isomer. The isomer with a single branch at a carbon atom is called an iso-isomer. The isomer with two branches on the same carbon atom is called a neo-isomer.
- ✔ Position isomers have same carbon chain with same number of branches but differ in the position of multiple bond or substituent on the carbon chain.
- ✔ Functional isomerism is the type of isomerism in which the isomers differ with respect to the nature of functional group.
- ✔ A series of organic compounds in which each member differs from the next member of the series by a –CH2 unit, when arranged in an increasing order of their molecular weights is called a homologous series.
- ✔ Cracking is the process of breaking up of long chain hydrocarbons into smaller chain hydrocarbons by heating at high temperature in the absence of oxygen.
- ✔ The process of heating of coal in the absence of air is called destructive distillation or carbonization.
- ✔ The process of removal of undesirable impurities followed by the separation into different useful fractions is called refining of petroleum.

PRACTICE QUESTIONS CLASSROOM WING

Very Short Answer Type Questions

Directions for questions from 1 to 6:
Fill in the blanks.

1. Write names for CH_3COCH_3 ________
2. Write names for the functional group – COOH ________
3. Cyclohexane is an example for ________ hydrocarbon.
4. Detergents are sodium salts of ________.
5. ________ is the additive added to soap to make it transparent.
6. ________end of soap dissolves in soft water.

Directions for questions from 7 to 25:
Answer the following questions.

7. What is the purpose of nomenclature in chemistry?
8. What are compounds called that have the same molecular formulae but different structural arrangements?
9. How do chain isomers differ from each other?
10. What differentiates a n-isomer from an iso-isomer and a neo-isomer?
11. How do position isomers differ from each other?
12. What is the principle involved in the refining of crude oil?
13. What are natural gas and petroleum gas?
14. What is meant by destructive distillation? What are the products of destructive distillation of coal?
15. What is meant by decarboxylation? How can methane be prepared by using this reaction?
16. Why is natural gas composed of major proportion of methane?
17. On what basis is coal classified into different varieties?
18. How is ammonia manufactured from natural gas?
19. Give the IUPAC names for the following hydrocarbons.

(a) 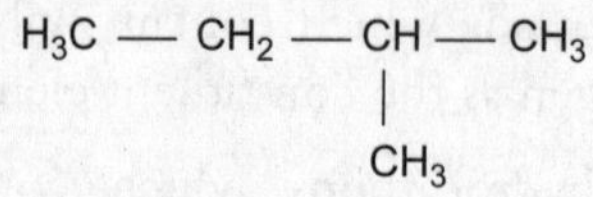

(b) 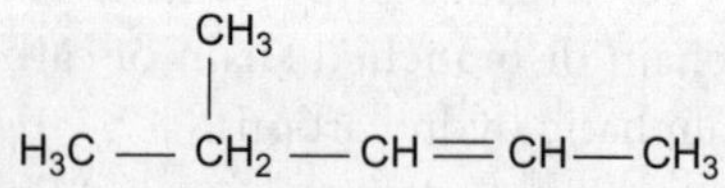

20. Mention some uses of methane.
21. Write the position isomer for butyne.
22. How is acetylene prepared from calcium carbide? Give equation.
23. What is the chemical reaction associated with the hydrogenation of oils?
24. What are soaps? How are detergents different from soaps in chemical composition?
25. What are food preservatives? Give two examples.

Short Answer Type Questions

26. Besides carbon, do other elements exhibit the property of catenation? If so, how does carbon's catenation property stand out?
27. How might two compounds with the same molecular formula differ in their physical and chemical properties?
28. Considering the various types of hydrocarbons – aliphatic, alkenes, alkynes, and closed-chain – how can they be distinguished based on structure and bonding?
29. Why are coal and petroleum considered non-renewable sources of energy?
30. Explain the process of refining crude oil.
31. Explain the composition of petroleum.
32. By giving equations, explain the decolorization of bromine water by unsaturated hydrocarbons.

33. (a) Explain hydrogenation of ethene and ethyne.
    (b) Write chain isomers corresponding to the lowest alkane which shows only two branched chain isomers. Suggest a suitable method of separation for these isomers from a mixture and justify on the basis of their structural features.

34. Give the structural formulae of the first four members of homologous series of alkanes, alkenes, and alkynes.

35. Explain isomerism in alkanes.

36. Explain the laboratory preparation of ethylene.

37. How can CNG be a better alternative to petrol?

38. Explain the advantages of detergents over soaps.

39. Explain the various ingredients added to food items by giving examples.

Essay Answer Type Questions

40. (a) Explain the unique features of carbon.
    (b) In an examination, structures for four organic compounds are given. A student, Jujo, has writ ten the names corresponding to the structures. Identify whether the name is appropriate for the given structure. If not, give reason and suggest the correct name for the structure.

41. Discuss the significance of the catenation property of carbon in the realm of organic chemistry. How does this unique characteristic shape the vast diversity of organic compounds, and why might this property be less prominent in other elements?

42. Contrast the information provided by molecular formulas with that of structural formulas in organic compounds. How can two compounds with the same molecular formula exhibit different properties, and why is the structural formula essential in understanding these differences?

43. Delve into the classification of hydrocarbons based on their structure and bonding patterns. How do aliphatic hydrocarbons differ from closed-chain hydrocarbons, and what is the significance of single, double, and triple bonds in determining the type of hydrocarbon?

44. Explore the concept of isomerism, emphasizing its various forms like chain isomerism, position isomerism, and functional isomerism. Why is understanding isomerism crucial in organic chemistry, and how can it affect the physical and chemical properties of compounds?

45. Identify the fourth homologue of the series with the general formula C_nH_{2n}. Write all the possible structural isomers and their IUPAC names. Explain how these isomers can be distinguished by means of ozonolysis reaction.

PRACTICE QUESTIONS COMPETITION WING

Level 1: Apply your Concepts

Direction for questions from 1 to 9:
State whether the following statements are true or false.

1. Each homologous series is characterized by a general formula.
2. Pentane has three-chain isomers.
3. All saturated hydrocarbons are aliphatic hydrocarbons.
4. Methane can be prepared by the decarboxylation of sodium methanoate.
5. Hydrogenation reaction can be used to detect unsaturation in an organic compound.
6. Ethyne on polymerization gives benzene.
7. Hexyne can decolorise bromine water.
8. Organic chemistry is considered chemistry of carbon compounds.
9. Inorganic chemistry is the chemistry of hydrocarbons and its derivatives.

Direction for questions from 10 to 19:
Fill in the blanks.

10. ________ was the first organic compound synthesized.
11. Unsaturated hydrocarbons give their characteristic ________ reactions.
12. Ability of forming long chains with atoms of the same element is called ________.
13. Closed chain hydrocarbons which do not resemble aliphatic hydrocarbons in their chemical behavior are called ________.
14. IUPAC name of saturated straight chain hydrocarbon with 10 carbon atoms is ______.
15. 1-butene and 2-butene are ________ isomers.
16. Ethane can be prepared by decarboxylation of ______.
17. The method involved in refining of petroleum is ________.
18. Hexane, on cracking, gives ______ and ______.
19. The best quality coal with respect to percentage of carbon is ______.

Direction for question 20:
Match the entries in Column A with the appropriate ones in Column B.

20.

Column A	Column B
A. Natural gas	a. Polymerization of ethene
B. Coke	b. Benzene
C. C_nH_{2n}	c. Methane
D. Kerosene	d. Destructive distillation of coal
E. C_6H_6	e. Refining of petroleum
F. Polythene	f. Alkene

Direction for questions from 21 to 45:
For each of the questions given below, four choices have been provided. Select the correct alternative.

21. Which property of carbon allows it to potentially create a compound with both straight and branched chains as well as a closed-ring structure?
(a) Carbonization (b) Isomerism
(c) Cracking (d) Catenation

22. A hydrocarbon contains only single bonds between carbon atoms. Which statement about this hydrocarbon is correct?
(a) It's an alkyne.
(b) It's an alkene.
(c) It's an aliphatic hydrocarbon, but not necessarily unsaturated.
(d) It's a saturated hydrocarbon.

23. Two organic compounds have the same molecular formula but different structural formulas. Which phenomenon is being described?
(a) Functional isomerism
(b) Chain isomerism
(c) Both A and B
(d) Neither A nor B

24. Which of the following processes might yield shorter hydrocarbon chains from a long hydrocarbon chain?

(a) Catenation
(b) Refining of petroleum
(c) Cracking
(d) Destructive distillation

25. What differentiates an iso-isomer from an n-isomer?

(a) An iso-isomer has a carbon-carbon double bond, while an n-isomer does not.
(b) An iso-isomer has a single branch at a carbon atom, whereas an n-isomer is a straight-chain isomer.
(c) Both iso-isomer and n-isomer are unsaturated hydrocarbons.
(d) An n-isomer has a carbon-carbon triple bond, while an iso-isomer has a double bond.

26. The straight chain isomer of C_4H_{10} is the major component in ________.

(a) biogas (b) petroleum gas
(c) natural gas (d) coal gas

27. The IUPAC name of the following compound is:

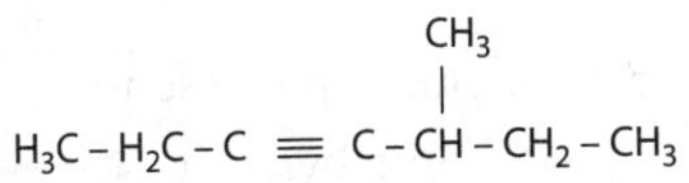

(a) 2-ethyl-3-hexyne
(b) 3-methyl-4-heptyne
(c) 5-methyl-3-heptyne
(d) 5-ethyl-3-hexyne

28. The hydrocarbon obtained on heating calcium oxide with coke in an electric furnace which is followed by hydrolysis is:

(a) C_2H_4 (b) C_2H_6
(c) CH_4 (d) C_2H_2

29. Which of the following can be the best substitute for petrol as an automobile fuel?

(a) petrol (b) biogas
(c) kerosene (d) CNG

30. Structural formula of 3, 4-dimethyl heptane is:

(a) 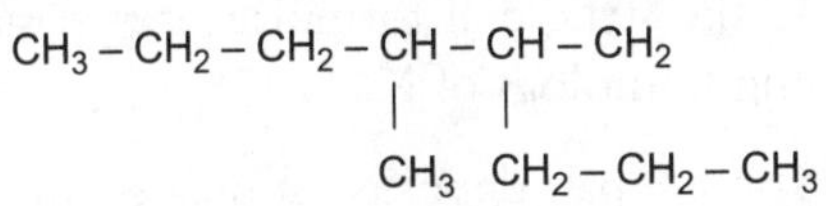

(b) 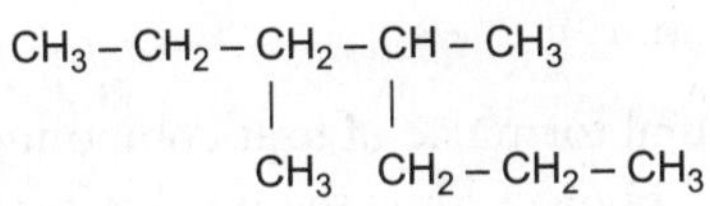

(c) 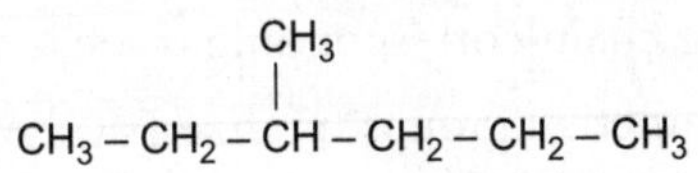

(d) 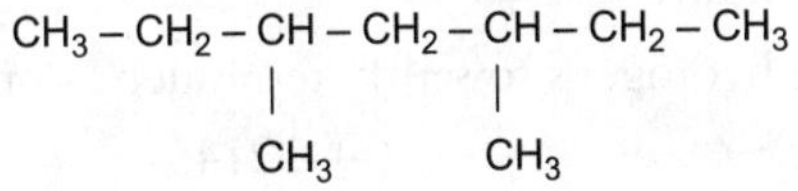

31. The primary suffix for a compound with general formula C_nH_{2n-2} is:

(a) –ane (b) –yne
(c) –ene (d) –enol

32. A compound on hydrogenation yields ethane by consuming 2 molecules of hydrogen. The same compound on being treated with excess of bromine water gives:

(a) CH_2Br_2 (b) $C_2H_4Br_2$
(c) $C_2H_2Br_4$ (d) C_2H_5Br

33. The reagent used for decarboxylation reaction is:

(a) $NaOH + Ca(OH)_2$ (b) only NaOH
(c) NaOH + CaO (d) $NaOH + CaCO_3$

34. Which of the following structures does not correspond to the chain isomer of pentane?

(a) 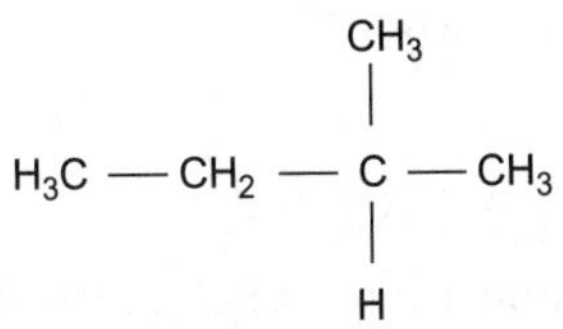

(b) 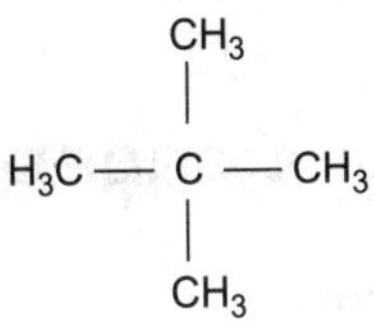

(c) 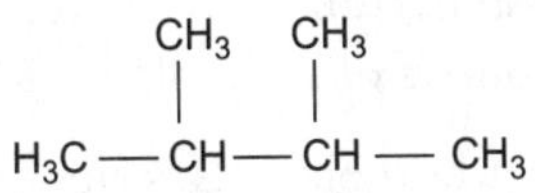

(d) 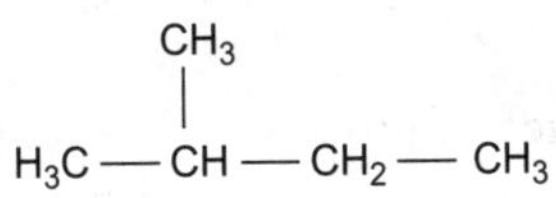

35. Which of the following is not an alkene?

(a) C_4H_8 (b) C_4H_6
(c) C_3H_6 (d) C_5H_{10}

36. IUPAC name of a hydrocarbon is given as 3, 5-Dimethyl-2-hexene. Identify the correct sequence of steps to draw its structural formula.

(1) numbering of carbon chain
(2) locating the position of double bond

(3) writing long chain corresponding to hexane
(4) locating the methyl groups (prefixes) at the respective positions
(5) placing hydrogens to satisfy tetravalency of carbon
(a) 13254 (b) 32145
(c) 13245 (d) 31245

37. Identify the correct sequence of fractions obtained when petroleum is subjected to fractional distillation.
(1) lubricating oil (2) petrol
(3) petroleum ether (4) diesel oil
(a) 2341 (b) 3241
(c) 3214 (d) 2431

38. 1 mole of ethyne on complete combustion gives:
(a) 2 moles of carbon monoxide and half-mole of water
(b) 4 moles of carbon dioxide and 1 mole of water
(c) 2 moles of carbon dioxide and 1 mole of water
(d) 2 moles of carbon dioxide and 2 moles of water

39. Which among the following molecular formulae represents a saturated hydrocarbon?
(a) C_4H_8 (b) C_4H_6
(c) C_3H_4 (d) C_5H_{12}

40. Which among the following pairs belong to the same homologous series?
(a) C_3H_4, C_5H_{10} (b) C_2H_6, C_4H_8
(c) C_2H_4, C_4H_6 (d) C_4H_8, C_5H_{10}

41. The number of bromine molecules required for the decolorization of 1 mole of ethene and ethyne are respectively
(a) one and three (b) two and three
(c) one and two (d) two and four

42. Polymerization of ethyne at 300°C gives:
(a) polyethene (b) polyethyne
(c) benzene (d) polyvinyl chloride

43. The bromination of acetylene gives ________ as the final product.
(a) dibromoethane (b) tetrabromoethane
(c) tetrabromoethene (d) dibromoethene.

44. Which of the following is an identification test for unsaturation in an organic compound?
(a) addition of hydrogen
(b) addition of ozone
(c) addition of bromine
(d) addition of oxygen

45. The hydrocarbon used for welding purpose is:
(a) ethane (b) ethyne
(c) ethene (d) benzene

Level 2: Review Your Concepts

46. Given the concepts of chain isomerism, position isomerism, and functional isomerism, how can one differentiate between two isomers of butanol?

47. Why is the concept of a homologous series crucial in organic chemistry?

48. What is the significance of processes like cracking and refining in the petroleum industry, and how do they affect the end products?

49. (a) Explain the role of natural gas in the preparation of ammonium fertilizers.
(b) An element which belongs to 2nd group and 4th period forms a binary compound X. X on hydrolysis gives Y.
(a) Predict the homologue of Y which gives only two structural isomers.
(b) What happens when the above two isomers are passed through ammonical cuprous chloride solution?
(c) Give justification for the above observations with respect to bonding aspects.

50. How does the destructive distillation of coal differ from its simple burning, and what are the primary products of this process?

51. The percentage composition of a hydrocarbon 'X' is 90 per cent carbon and 10 per cent hydrogen, respectively. Write the structural formulae of two successive and preceding homologs of X.

52. Why are some coal deposits associated with large amounts of sulphur?

53. Give the structural formulae of four compounds of the homologous series succeeding the one having molecular formula C_3H_4. Also give their molecular weights.

54. Compound X can be prepared by passing a gas Y through a metal tube which is at very high temperature. Y on treatment with 2 g of hydrogen gas in presence of nickel gives a compound Z. Z can also be prepared by treating ethyl alcohol with 'ic' acid of sulphur at 170°C. Y can also be prepared by hydrolysis of 'A'. Identify X, Y, Z and A and write all the balanced chemical equations.

55. Two containers A and B are filled with the same amount of chlorine gas. Limited amount of methane is passed into container 'A' and excess of methane into container 'B'. Identify the products formed in A and B. Give a reason in support of your answer.

56. The vapor density of an unsaturated aliphatic hydrocarbon 'X' is 34. Write the structural formula of X and its succeeding homolog Y. Also write the position isomers of X and Y.

57. How does the burning of coal lead to air pollution as well as water pollution?

58. At the end of the process of preparation of soap, common salt is added. Explain the role of common salt in that process.

59. A compound X on hydrolysis produces a gas Y which on hydrogenation produces a gas Z which can decolorise bromine water forming a compound with molecular weight 188 a.m.u. Identify X, Y and Z.

60. Two students Rishi and Kushi were preparing for International Chemistry Olympiad. They had come across a question. In that, a table of boiling points of members of homologous series of alkanes was given and similar trend is followed in other classes of compounds also. Predict the trend observed. What reason can be attributed to the above trend?

61. In an organic chemistry laboratory, a scientist subjected a hydrocarbon to combustion. The products occupied a volume ratio of 4 : 3 under the same conditions of temperature and pressure. The scientist drew the possible structures of the hydrocarbon. She then subjected the compound to ozonolysis to identify the exact structure. Predict the products formed when the compound is treated with bromine water.

62. A research scholar, during his experiment came across an aliphatic hydrocarbon 'X'. In the process of identification of 'X' he passed 'X' through alkaline $KMnO_4$. The solution became colorless. He found out the vapor density of the compound to be 34. Identify X and its succeeding homolog 'Y' and also position isomers of straight chain isomers.

63. The molar ratio of carbon dioxide and water produced by the combustion of one mole of an aliphatic hydrocarbon 'X' is 5 : 4. Write the possible structures of X. What happens when 'X' is passed through bromine water?

64. The government had a proposal for establishing a thermal power plant where coal would be the source of power. A panel has been sent to the site to examine the feasibility of the proposal. The farmers in that area became panicky that their soils may become less fertile and may even become unfit for cultivation. However, the panel members convinced them by giving an assurance that the best quality coal will be used in the plant to minizise the effect. Can you explain the reason why burning of coal makes the soil loses fertility and how quality of coal has a bearing on the above? What other effects does burning of coal have on the environment?

65. CNG is a better automobile fuel when compared to petrol and diesel. Give reasons.

66. Write IUPAC names for the following structures:

(a) 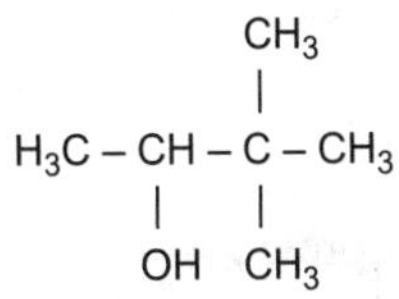

(b) 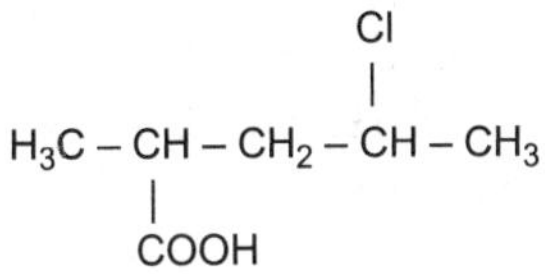

(c) 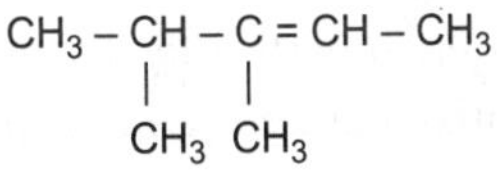

(d) 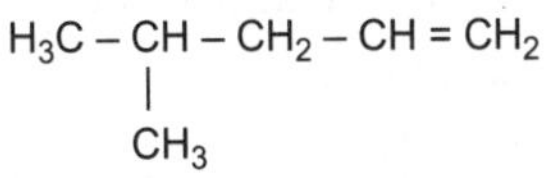

(e) 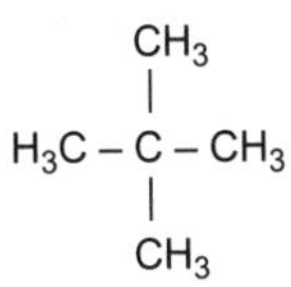

(f) 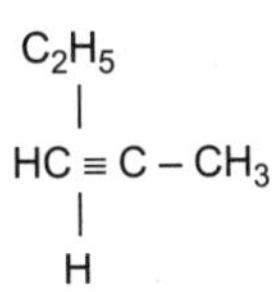

(g) 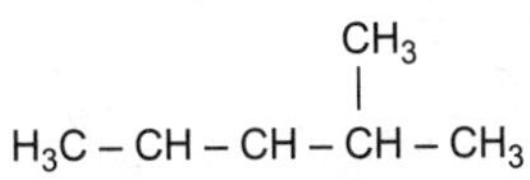

67. 'X' is an alicylic hydrocarbon with the molecular formula C_4H_8. Y is the corresponding aliphatic compound. Give all the possible isomers of Y and their IUPAC names. Identify the products of bromination. When Y is treated with hydrogen what are the products formed? How are these products separated from the mixture?

68. Coke is obtained by the destructive distillation of coal. But, coke is considered to be the purer form of carbon than coal. Give a reason.

69. Give reasons for the following:

(a) Petroleum deposits are always associated with a layer of natural gas

(b) The volatile products obtained by distillation of coal are passed through water.

(c) A mixture of acetylene and oxygen is used for welding metals.

(d) Anthracite coal is of better quality than bituminous coal.

(e) It is possible to prepare an alkane with one carbon atom from a carboxylic acid with two carbon atoms.

Level 3: Assess Your Concepts

70. Catenation and Diversity: If another element, hypothetically, had a higher tendency for catenation than carbon, predict how it might influence the diversity and complexity of compounds formed by that element compared to those formed by carbon.

71. Molecular vs. Structural Analysis: Imagine two compounds with identical molecular formulas but different structural formulas. How might their differences manifest in real-world applications or uses? Propose a scenario or experiment to distinguish between the two based solely on their properties.

72. Hydrocarbon Behaviour: If a previously undiscovered hydrocarbon was found, and it contained both aliphatic and closed-chain structures, hypothesize about its potential properties and reactivity. How might it differ from known hydrocarbons?

73. Isomerism and Drug Design: Isomers can have drastically different effects when ingested by living organisms. Discuss the potential dangers and implications this might have in the pharmaceutical industry when designing new drugs.

74. Homologous Series and Predictability: Based on the trend observed in a homologous series, if you were given the properties of the first few members, how might you predict the properties of subsequent members? Explain the reliability and potential pitfalls of such predictions.

75. Fluorination of methane is explosive. How do you account for this? How can fluorination of methane be carried out?

76. Can kerosene be used as a substitute for petrol in automobiles? Give reasons in support of your answer.

77. Iodination of methane is carried out in the presence of oxidizing agents like iodic acid or HNO_3. How do you account for this?

78. Why are shaving creams and shampoos softer than soap?

79. 'The same coal deposit is found to contain variable composition of coal.' Justify.

80. Detergents are more efficient than soaps, however, with respect to environmental aspects soaps are preferred over detergents. How do you account for this?

AT

PRACTICE QUESTIONS JEE-NEET SPECIAL WING

Multiple-Answer Type Questions

Directions for Questions number 1 to 5:

Select one or more correct alternative(s) from the given choices.

1. Hydrocarbons that cannot show position isomerism.
   (a) C_3H_6 (b) C_4H_8
   (c) C_3H_8 (d) C_5H_8

2. Observe the following figure and identify the correct options with respect to X:

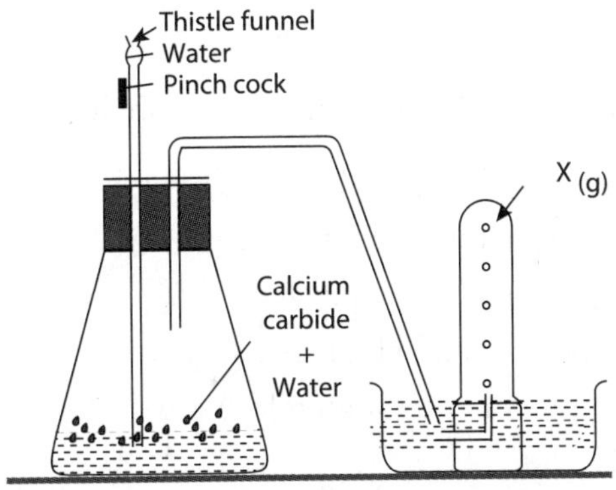

   (a) It is the first homologue of the hydrocarbons with a general formula C_nH_{2n}.
   (b) It is soluble in water.
   (c) It decolourises bromine water
   (d) X when passed through red hot copper at high temperature forms an aromatic compound .

3. The diagram shows a fractionating column used for the separation of crude oil.

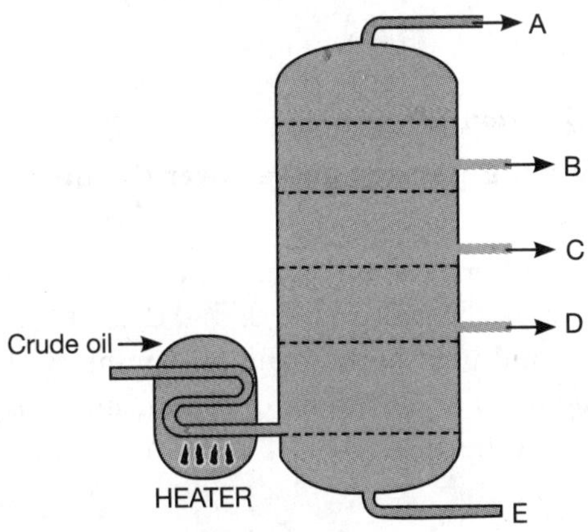

   Observe the figure and choose the true statements.
   (a) C has a higher boiling point than D.
   (b) A has a very less critical temperature compared to other fractions.
   (c) E is comparatively denser than other fractions.
   (d) B < D < E with respect to their viscosity.

4. Incorrect statements regarding the cleaning agents- 'X' and 'Y' for clothes are:

Compound	Description
X	Sodium salt of long chain fatty acid
Y	Sodium salt of sulphonic acid

   (a) Both X and Y contain carboxylate group
   (b) Both X and Y are equally effective when used with distilled water.
   (c) Cleaning with 'Y' is more efficient than 'X' when dealing with hard water.
   (d) 'Y' is the preferred choice for cleaning in all water conditions, mainly because it is more affordable than 'X' in the market.

5. Select the statements that does not correctly describe coal tar.
   (a) It is acquired as one of the fractions in the fractional distillation of petroleum.
   (b) It is produced by the decomposition of coal in the excess supply of air.
   (c) It is a mixture of over 200 hydrocarbons present in fixed proportions.
   (d) It is a thick, liquid substance employed in the construction of tar(or asphalt) roads.

Comprehension-Based Questions

Directions for Questions 6 to 10:

Read the following passage and answer the questions given below.

Aromatic compounds are a fascinating group of organic compounds that exhibit a unique structure and a distinct set of properties. A key characteristic of these compounds is a property known as "aromaticity." For a compound to be considered aromatic, it must be planar (flat; sp^2 hybridised), cyclic (ring-shaped), conjugated (alternate single and double bonds) and obey Huckel's rule. According to Huckel's rule, an aromatic compound must possess ($4n$+2) pi electrons distributed across overlapping *p* orbitals to qualify as aromatic, where '*n*' represents a whole number. In contrast, organic compounds that meet the criteria of being cyclic, planar, and fully conjugated but possess (4n) pi electrons, instead of the ($4n$+2) pi electrons are known as "anti-aromatic" compounds.

Example: Benzene (C_6H_6). Benzene is a ring composed of six carbon atoms, each connected by a pi bond.

No. of pi bonds = 3
No. of pi electrons = 3 x 2 = 6
Huckel's rule:
[4n + 2] pi electrons
[4 x 1 + 2] = 6; n = 1, a whole number, hence this is an aromatic compound

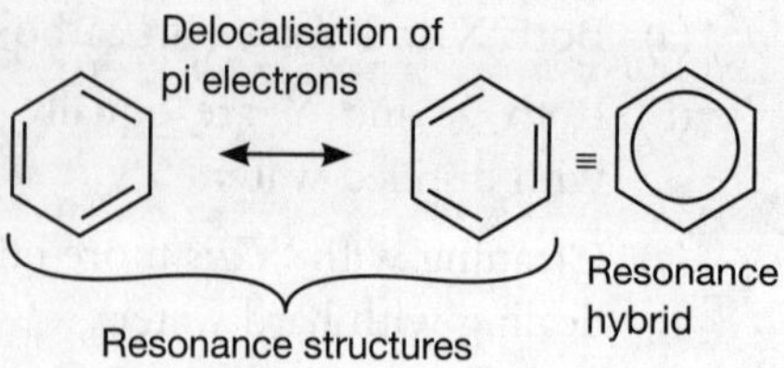

Aromatic compounds are generally more stable than aliphatic compounds due to their aromaticity. Hence, benzene, though unsaturated, its double bonds usually do not undergo addition reactions. Aromatic compounds with two or more fused aromatic benzene rings are called polycyclic aromatic hydrocarbons (PAH) and they have the general formula $C_{4r+2}\ H_{2r+4}$ for rings without substituents, where r = number of rings.

Following are few cyclic organic molecules.

P) 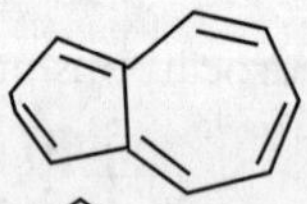 - 10 pi electrons

Q)  _ 4 pi electrons

R) 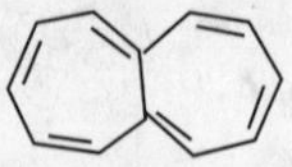 - 12 pi electrons

S) 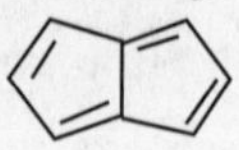 _ 8 pi electrons

6. Find the molecule in the given options that is not conjugated.

(a) R (b) P
(c) Q (d) S

7. Of the given cyclic and planar molecules, choose the molecule(s) that is/are anti-aromatic.

(a) P (b) P,S
(c) R (d) R, S

8. Choose the correct increasing order with respect to their stability.

(a) S, P
(b) P, R
(c) S, P, R
(d) Given data is not sufficient to predict

9. Identify a true statement/s regarding benzene.

(1) It shows the characteristic properties of C = C
(2) Bond angle is 120 degrees
(3) It readily adds chlorine compared to hexene
(4) It is a polymer of acetylene

(a) 1, 2 (b) 2, 4
(c) 1, 4 (d) 1, 2, 3, 4

10. Guess the correct geometrical structure of the aromatic compound with molecular formula $C_{10}\ H_8$.

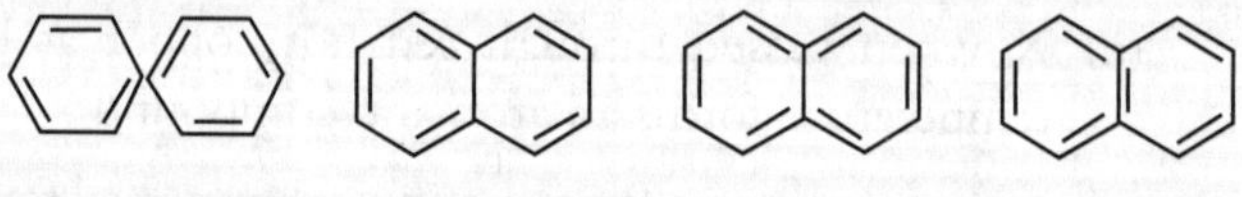

A B C D

(a) A, B (b) C, D
(c) B (d) C

Direction for Question 11:

Read the following passage and answer the questions given below

Aliphatic hydrocarbon 'A' on combustion gives carbon dioxide and water in the molar ratio of 5:4. B and C are the first homologue and next homologue of A respectively. D is also the homologue of A with no of carbon atoms half of that of hydrogen atoms in A.

11. Match the following:

List – I	List – II
(A) A	(i) Used in ripening of fruits
(B) B	(ii) First member of the series to show position isomerism
(C) C	(iii) Possess four -CH_2 groups attached to carbon atom of its functional group
(D) D	(iv) Vapour density is 34

Find the correct match.

	(A)	(B)	(C)	(D)
(a)	(iv)	(i)	(iii)	(ii)
(b)	(iii)	(iv)	(iv)	(ii)
(c)	(iv)	(ii)	(iii)	(i)
(d)	(ii)	(iv)	(iii)	(i)

Directions for Questions 12 to 17:

Read the following passage and answer the questions given below.

Hydrocarbons are the compounds containing only carbon and hydrogen as their constituent elements. The table given below provides the information about different hydrocarbons and their corresponding ratios of carbon to hydrogen.

Hydrocarbon	Ratio of C:H
P	1:4
Q	1:3
R	1:2
S	1:1

Study the information given in the table and answer the questions that follow. (One or more than one options can be correct)

12. Pair of hydrocarbons with the same root word are.

(a) P, Q (b) R, S
(c) P, R (d) Q, S

13. Which of the following hydrocarbon/s possess the most electronegative carbon?

(a) S (b) P
(c) P, Q (d) R, S

14. Identify the hydrocarbon that exhibits position isomerism

(a) R (b) P
(c) Q (d) None

15. Which of the following are the characteristic reactions of Q,

(a) Addition reactions
(b) Substitution reactions
(c) Polymerization reactions
(d) Condensation reactions

16. Choose the correct decreasing order with respect to the hydrogen donating tendency of their carbon atoms.

(a) Q, R, S (b) P, S, R
(c) S, R, Q (d) R, S, Q

17. Substances with higher molecular weights tend to have higher boiling points due to stronger intermolecular forces that need more energy to break and transition into the gas phase. For hydrocarbons of almost same molecular weight, greater the intermolecular forces, higher is the boiling point. The increasing order of strength of intermolecular interactions:

London Dispersion Forces < Dipole-Dipole Interactions < Hydrogen Bonding < Ionic Interactions.

List-I Hydrocarbon	List-II Boiling point in Kelvin scale under the same external conditions.
P	(i) 1.69x
Q	(ii) 1.11x
R	(iii) 1.89x
S	(iv) 1.84x

If x is 100, based on the understanding of above given information, predict the correct match

	(P)	(Q)	(R)	(S)
(a)	(i)	(ii)	(iii)	(iv)
(b)	(ii)	(iii)	(ii)	(i)
(c)	(iii)	(i)	(iv)	(ii)
(d)	(ii)	(iv)	(i)	(iii)

ANSWER KEYS

Crossword

Across

1. Primary suffix 3. Rootword 5. Soda lime 6. Anthracite 7. Glyoxal
10. **Marsh gas** 13. Molecular formula 14. Methane 17. Polythene 18. Urea

Down

2 Structural formula 4. Carbonization 6. Alkanal 8. Alkane 9. Formaldehyde
11. **Four** 12. Alkanol 15. Ethane 16. Ethyne 17. Pitch

Classroom Wing

Very Short Answer Type Questions

1. Propanone 2. Carboxylic acid 3. Saturated cyclic
4. Long chain alkyl benzene sulphonic acids or alkyl sulphate 5. Calcium chloro hypocholrite
6. Hydrophilic

Competition Wing

Level 1: Apply your Concepts

1. True 2. True 3. True 4. False 5. True
6. True 7. True 8. True. 9. False 10. Urea
11. carbon content 12. Catenation 13. Aromatic hydrocarbons 14. Decane
15. Position 16. Sodium propanoate 17. Fractional distillation
18. Ethene, butane 19. Anthracite 20. A : c, B : d, C : f, D : e, E : b, F : a 21. (d)
22. (d) 23. (c) 24. (c) 25. (b) 26. (b)
27. (c) 28. (d) 29. (d) 30. (b) 31. (b)
32. (c) 33. (c) 34. (c) 35. (b) 36. (d)
37. (b) 38. (c) 39. (d) 40. (d) 41. (c)
42. (c) 43. (c) 44. (c) 45. (b)

JEE-NEET Special Wing

Multiple-Answer Type Questions

1. (a, c) 2. (c, d) 3. (b, c, d) 4. (a, b) 5. (a, b, c)

Comprehension-Based Questions

6. (c) 7. (d) 8. (a) 9. (b) 10. (c)
11. (a) 12. (b, d) 13. (a) 14. (d) 15. (b)
16. (c) 17. (d)

Hints and Explanations

Classroom Wing

Very Short Answer Type Questions

1. Propanone
2. Carboxylic acid → COOH
3. Saturated cyclic
4. Long chain alkyl benzene sulphonic acids or alkyl sulphate
5. Calcium chloro hypocholrite
6. Hydrophilic
7. Nomenclature is used to assign proper names to various compounds based on certain criteria.
8. They are called isomers, and the phenomenon is known as isomerism.
9. Chain isomers possess the same molecular formula, but differ in the arrangement of carbon atoms in the chain.
10. An n-isomer is a straight-chain isomer, an iso-isomer has a single branch at a carbon atom, and a neo-isomer has two branches on the same carbon atom.
11. Position isomers have the same carbon chain and number of branches but differ in the position of a multiple bond or substituent on the carbon chain.
12. Fractional distillation.
13. Composed of highly volatile alkanes, predominantly methane; petroleum gas → n-butane, minor components being ethane and propane.
14. Heating of coal at high temperature in the absence of air, non-volatile coke, volatile coalgas, ammonia, and coal tar.
15. Removing of CO_2 from sodium or potassium salts of carboxylic acids.
16. Lighter nature of methane
17. Carbon content
18. Natural gas provides source of hydrogen with which ammonia is prepared by Harbers process

$$N_2 + 3H_2 \xrightarrow[\text{Pressure}]{\text{High temperature}} 2NH_3$$

19. (a) 2-methyl butane (b) 4-methyl 2-pentene
20. Automobile and domestic fuel, fertilizer synthesis, synthesis of industrial products
21. 1-butyne, 2-buyne
22. $CaC_2 + H_2O \rightarrow \underset{\text{Ethyne}}{HC \equiv CH} + Ca(OH)_2$
23. Vegetable oils + H_2 → Vanaspati ghee
24. Soap is the sodium or potassium salt of higher fatty acids. Detergents composed a long chain of hydro carbons containing benzene ring attached to sulphonate group
25. Chemical substances added to packed food items for the purpose of preventing spoilage of food material over a long period of usage. E.g., Acetic acid, sodium benzoate.

Short Answer Type Questions

26. Yes, other elements like silicon exhibit catenation. However, carbon's ability to form stable, long chains and rings due to its small size and tetravalency, especially with atoms of the same element, is unparalleled, leading to a vast number of organic compounds.
27. Two compounds with the same molecular formula can have different structural formulas, meaning they are isomers. Due to their different structures, they might possess distinct physical properties like boiling and melting points and also exhibit varied chemical reactivities.
28. Aliphatic hydrocarbons are either straight or branched chains. Alkenes contain at least one carbon-carbon double bond, alkynes have at least one carbon-carbon triple bond and closed-chain hydrocarbons possess rings of carbon atoms. The type and arrangement of these bonds define each category.
29. Energy sources which get exhausted over a period of time as they can not be replenished from time to time so easily. Coal and petroleum are two major **non-renewable sources** of energy. These are organic mat-

ter and are formed by the degradation of dead plants and animals.

30. Crude oil is refined by passing the raw crude oil between highly charged electrodes which remove all water and impurities from the sample.

31. Petroleum is a complex mixture of hydrocarbons, composed predominantly of alkanes and cycloalkanes. petroleum deposits also contain reasonable amounts of aromatic hydrocarbons and alkenes. Trace amounts of oxygen, nitrogen, and sulphur are also present since it is obtained from the remains of dead plants and animals.

32. Decolorization of bromine water takes place when ethyne gas is passed through bromine water as two molecules of bromine get added.

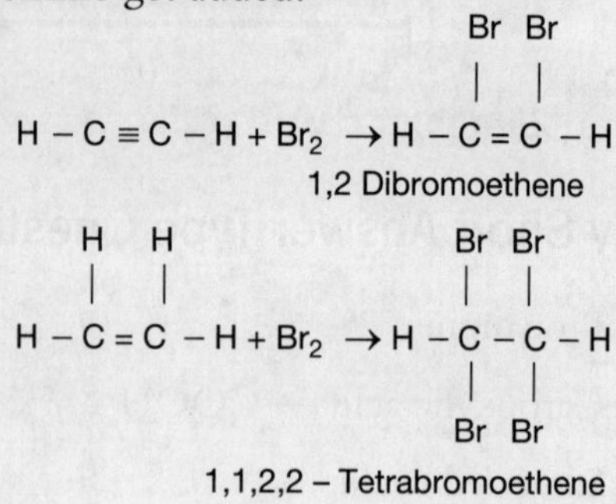

33. (a)

Ethene	Ethyne
Hydrogenation When equal volumes of ethene gas and hydrogen are passed over heated nickel or platinum at 300°C, one molecule of hydrogen is added	When a mixture of ethyne and hydrogen in 1 : 2 ratio is passed over heated nickel at 300°C, two molecules of hydrogen get added. Product may be ethene or ethane
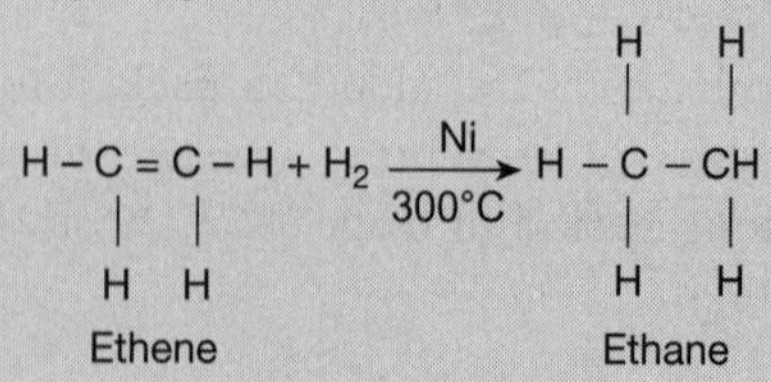	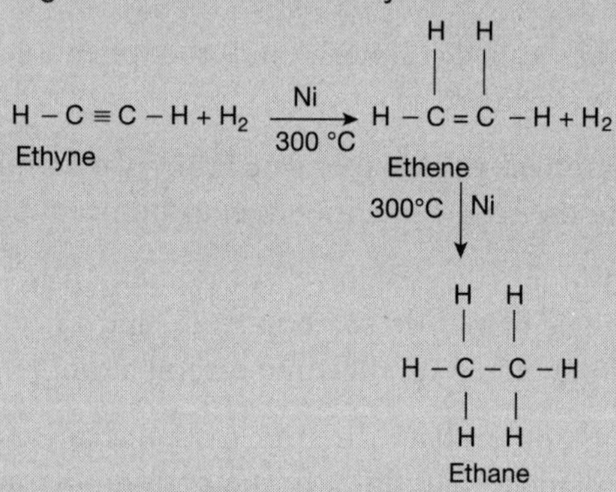

(b) The lowest alkane which shows only two branched chain isomers is pentane. The three isomers are n-pentane, isopentane and neopentane. The structural formulae for these isomers are:

$H_3C – CH_2 - CH_2 - CH_2 – CH_3$ (n – pentane)

```
        CH3
        |
H3C – CH – CH2 – CH3 (isopentane)

        CH3
        |
H3C – C – CH3 (neopentane)
        |
        CH3
```

35. When two or more substances have the same molecular formulae but differ in the structural arrangement of atoms within the molecule, they are called isomers and the phenomenon is called isomerism.

36. In the laboratory, ethene can be prepared by heating ethyl alcohol with excess of concentrated sulphuric acid at 180°C. Apart from ethene, carbon dioxide and sulphur dioxide gases are evolved. These gases are removed by passing the gases over caustic soda. Finally, ethene gas is collected over water by the down ward displacement of water.

(i) Principle with reaction (dehydration of ethyl alcohol)
(ii) Set-up
(iii) Procedure

37. (i) Composition
(ii) Effect on atmosphere
(iii) Calorific value
(iv) Residue on combustion

38. Detergents produce soluble calcium and magnesium sulphonates on dissolution in hard water. Therefore, detergents are more efficient with hard water when compared to soaps.

39. Food preservatives are chemical substances added to packed food items for the purpose of preventing spoilage of food material over a long period of usage.

Flavoring agents: These are chemical substances added in minor proportions which enhance the flavor and taste of the food materials.

Essay Answer Type Questions

40. (a) (i) Catenation
(ii) Isomerism
(iii) Formation of multiple bonds.

(b) (a)

$$\begin{array}{ccccccccc} CH_3 & - & CH & - & CH_2 & - & CH & - & CH_3 \\ & & | & & & & | & & \\ & & CH_3 & & & & OH & & \end{array}$$

2 – Methyl–4–pentanol

(b)

$$\begin{array}{ccccccccc} CH_3 & - & CH_2 & - & CH & - & CH_2 & - & CH_3 \\ & & & & | & & & & \\ & & & & CHO & & & & \end{array}$$

2-Ethyl butanal

(c)

$$\begin{array}{ccccccccccccc} & & C_2H_5 & & & & CH_3 & & COOH & & & & \\ & & | & & & & | & & | & & & & \\ CH_3 & - & CH & - & CH_2 & - & CH & - & CH & - & CH_2 & - & CH_3 \end{array}$$

(d) 4, 6–Dimethyl–3–octanoic acid

$$\begin{array}{ccccccccc} & & Cl & & OH & & CH_3 & & \\ & & | & & | & & | & & \\ CH_3 & - & CH & - & CH & - & C & - & CH_3 \\ & & & & & & | & & \\ & & & & & & CH_3 & & \end{array}$$

4 – Chloro – 2, 2 – dimethyl–3–pentanol

41. Catenation refers to the unique ability of carbon atoms to form long chains with themselves, leading to the vast realm of organic chemistry. This capability stems from carbon's tetravalency and small atomic size, allowing it to form stable covalent bonds with other carbon atoms. Such formations give rise to an array of structures, from straight chains to branched and cyclic compounds. While some elements like silicon exhibit catenation, they don't match the versatility of carbon. This is largely due to the weaker bonds they form, limiting the stability and complexity of their chains. Thus, carbon's catenation property is foundational to the diversity and richness of organic compounds.

42. Molecular formulas represent the count of each type of atom in a compound but don't detail their arrangement. Structural formulas, on the other hand, explicitly illustrate the connections between atoms. Two compounds can share a molecular formula but differ structurally, leading to varied properties. For instance, ethanol and dimethyl ether have the same molecular formula, C_2H_6O, but different structural arrangements. Ethanol has an -OH (alcohol) group, while dimethyl ether has an ether linkage (-O-). Their distinct structures account for their diverse chemical and physical behaviours, emphasizing the critical role of structural formulas in organic chemistry.

43. Hydrocarbons are primarily categorized based on their structure and bond types. Aliphatic hydrocarbons, which can be straight or branched chains, contrast with closed-chain (or cyclic) hydrocarbons that form rings. Further, the presence of single, double, or triple bonds between carbon atoms distinguishes hydrocarbons as saturated (alkanes) or unsaturated (alkenes and alkynes). While alkanes have only single bonds, alkenes and alkynes contain double and triple bonds, respectively. These bond variations not only define the hydrocarbon's classification but also influence its reactivity, with unsaturated hydrocarbons being generally more reactive than their saturated counterparts.

44. Isomerism exemplifies the fascinating diversity of organic compounds, where molecules with identical molecular formulas exhibit different structures. Chain isomerism occurs when carbon atoms rearrange in distinct chain patterns. In position isomerism, the skeletal structure remains consistent, but the position of a functional group or bond changes. Functional isomerism, however, witnesses a shift in the functional group itself, despite an unchanged molecular formula. These structural variations lead to divergent properties. For example, isomers might possess different boiling points, solubilities, or reactivities, underscoring the profound impact of structural nuances on a compound's behaviour.

The detergents are also similar in structure and action to soaps. The basic difference between the soap and the detergent is that soap forms insoluble calcium and magnesium stearates on dissolution in hard water.

45. General formula C_nH_{2n} corresponds to alkene series. The fourth homologue of the series is pentene. Pentene (C_5H_{10}) can have two position isomers 1 – pentene and 2 – pentene.

$$CH_3 - CH_2 - CH_2 - CH = CH_2$$

1 – Pentene

$$CH_3 - CH_2 - CH = CH - CH_3$$
2 – Pentene

Pentene can give a chain isomer which has a position isomers.

$$CH_3 - CH_2 - \underset{\displaystyle CH_3}{\underset{|}{C}} = CH_2$$
2 – methyl – 1 – butene

or

$$CH_3 - \underset{\displaystyle CH_3}{\underset{|}{CH}} - CH = CH_2$$
3 – methyl – 1 – butene

$$H_3C - \underset{\displaystyle H}{\underset{|}{C}} = \underset{\displaystyle CH_3}{\underset{|}{C}} - CH_3$$
2 -Methyl - 2-butene

I. $$\underset{\text{1 – Pentene}}{CH_3 - CH_2 - CH_2 - CH = CH_2} \xrightarrow{\text{Ozonolysis}} \underset{\text{Butanal}}{CH_3 - CH_2 - CH_2 - CHO} + \underset{\text{Methanal}}{HCHO}$$

II. $$CH_3 - CH_2 - CH = CH - CH_2 \xrightarrow{\text{Ozonolysis}} \underset{\text{Propanal}}{CH_3 - CH_2 - CHO} + \underset{\text{Ethanal}}{CH_3 - CHO}$$

III. $$CH_3 - CH_2 - \overset{\displaystyle CH_3}{\overset{|}{C}} = CH_2 \xrightarrow{\text{Ozonolysis}} \underset{\text{Butanone}}{CH_3 - CH_2 - \underset{\displaystyle O}{\underset{||}{C}} - CH_3} + \underset{\text{Methanal}}{HCHO}$$

IV. $$CH_3 - \underset{\displaystyle CH_3}{\underset{|}{CH}} - CH = CH_2 \xrightarrow{\text{Ozonolysis}} \underset{\text{2 – Methyl propanal.}}{CH_3 - \underset{\displaystyle CH_3}{\underset{|}{CH}} - CHO} + \underset{\text{Methanal}}{HCHO}$$

V. $$H_3C - \overset{\displaystyle CH_3}{\overset{|}{C}} = \overset{\displaystyle H}{\overset{|}{C}} - CH_3 \xrightarrow{\text{Ozonolysis}} \underset{\text{acetone}}{H_3C - \underset{\displaystyle O}{\underset{||}{C}} - CH_3} + \underset{\text{acetaldehyde}}{H_3C - \underset{\displaystyle O}{\underset{||}{C}} - H}$$

Competition Wing

Level 1: Apply your Concepts

21. Catenation

Explanation: Catenation is the ability of carbon atoms to link with other carbon atoms to form chains or rings. This unique capability allows for the formation of both straight/branched chains and closed-ring structures in a single compound.

22. It's a saturated hydrocarbon.

Explanation: Saturated hydrocarbons have only single carbon-atom bonds. Alkenes and alkynes are both unsaturated hydrocarbons with double and triple bonds.

23. Both A and B

Explanation: Isomers that have the same molecular formula but differ in their structural arrangement are exhibiting structural isomerism. This can manifest as either chain isomerism, where the carbon chain arrangement differs, or functional isomerism, where the functional group differs.

24. Cracking

Explanation: Cracking is a chemical process where long-chain hydrocarbons are broken down into shorter-chain hydrocarbons, often to produce more useful products like gasoline.

25. An iso-isomer has a single branch at a carbon atom, whereas an n-isomer is a straight-chain isomer.

Explanation: In terms of isomerism, an n-isomer refers to a straight-chain compound, whereas an iso-isomer has a single branch at one of its carbon atoms. The presence or absence of double or triple bonds isn't what differentiates these two.

36. 3 locating the long chains corresponding to hexane
  1 numbering of carbon chain
  2 locating the position of double bond
  4 locating the methyl groups (prefixes) at the respective position
  5 locating hydrogen molecules to satisfy tetravalency of carbon

Hence, the correct answer is (d).

37. 3 petroleum ether
  2 petrol
  4 diesel oil
  1 lubricating oil

Hence, the correct answer is (b).

38. $C_2H_2 + 5O_2 \rightarrow 2CO_2 + H_2O$

When one mole of ethyne is subjected to complete combustion, 2 moles of CO_2 and 1 mole of water are formed

Hence, the correct answer is (c).

39. Saturated hydrocarbons have the general formula C_nH_{2n+2} and C_5H_{12} corresponds to that formula.

Hence, the correct answer is (d).

40. C_4H_8 and C_5H_{10} belong to same homologous series of alkenes as they possess same general formula (C_nH_{2n})

Hence, the correct answer is (d).

41. $H_2C = CH_2 + Br_2 \rightarrow BrH_2C - CH_2Br$

$$HC \equiv CH + 2Br_2 \rightarrow H-\underset{Br}{\overset{Br}{C}}-\underset{Br}{\overset{Br}{C}}-H$$

One mole of ethene requires one mole of bromine and one mole of ethyne requires two moles of bromine for decolorization.

Hence, the correct answer is (c).

42. Polymerization of ethyne at 300°C gives benzene

Hence, the correct answer is (c).

43. The bromination of acetylene gives tetrabromoethane.

Hence, the correct answer is (c).

44. Addition of bromine is used as an identification test for detection of unsaturation in an organic compound as bromine is a reddish brown liquid and loses color due to the addition reaction.

Hence, the correct answer is (c).

45. The hydrocarbon used for welding purposes is acetylene (ethyne) since oxyacetylene flame produces a high temperature of 3800°C.

Hence, the correct answer is (b).

Level 2: Review Your Concepts

46. Two isomers of butanol might differ in the arrangement of carbon atoms (chain isomerism), the position of the -OH group (position isomerism), or the nature of the functional group itself (functional isomerism). By determining these features, one can distinguish the specific type of butanol isomer.

47. The concept of a homologous series is essential because it groups organic compounds with similar properties, structures, and methods of preparation. Each member in the series differs by a consistent unit, which provides a predictable pattern and allows for easier categorization and understanding of organic compounds.

48. Cracking breaks down long-chain hydrocarbons into smaller, more useful ones, increasing the yield of valuable products like gasoline. Refining removes impurities and separates petroleum into fractions based on boiling points, ensuring the purity and functionality of end products such as diesel, kerosene, and lubricants.

49. (a) (i) raw materials for preparation ammonia.
(ii) reaction of chief constituent of natural gas to give the raw material required.
(iii) Haber's process
(iv) role of product of Haber's process in manufacturing ammonium fertilizers

(b) The element which belongs to 2nd group and 4th period is calcium. Calcium carbide is the binary compound of calcium which on hydrolysis gives ethyne (Y).

$$CaC_2 + H_2O \rightarrow Ca(OH)_2 + \underset{\text{Ethyne}}{C_2H_2}$$

(a) Since ethyne belongs to alkyne series, its homologue which gives two structural isomers should be butyne (C_4H_6)

$$\underset{1-\text{butyne}}{HC \equiv C - CH_2 - CH_3} \qquad \underset{2-\text{butyne}}{H_3C - C \equiv C - CH_3}$$

(b) When 1 – butyne is passed through ammonical cuprous chloride solution, a reddish brown precipitate is formed.

$$HC \equiv C - CH_2 - CH_3 + CuCl_2 + NH_4OH \rightarrow Cu - C \equiv C - CH_2 - CH_3 + Cu(OH)_2$$

2 – butyne does not give the above reaction

(c) In 1-butyne, a hydrogen atom is attached to sp hybridized carbon. With increase in 's' character of hybrid orbital, the electronegatively of carbon increases. As a result, the hydrogens attached to sp hybrid carbon become acidic and hence leave as H^+ ions. Therefore, 1-butyne forms acetylides and 2-butyne does not form acetylides as it has no hydrogens attached to sp hybrid carbons.

50. Destructive distillation is the heating of coal in the absence of air, preventing combustion. Instead of just producing heat and light as in burning, it yields a variety of products like coal tar, coal gas, and coke, each with distinct industrial applications.

51. (i) identification of atomic ratio
(ii) calculation of simple atomic ratio from atomic ratio
(iii) calculation of integral ratio and molecular formula from simple atomic ratio
(iv) prediction of succeeding and preceding homologs of above hydrocarbon

52. Coal contains sulphur due to impurities accumulated by the surroundings.

53. characteristics of homologous series

54. (i) identification of Z
(ii) identification of Y from Z
(iii) identification of X from given reaction of Y
(iv) identification of A from Y

55. (i) effect of amount of methane on product formation
(ii) the initial product formed in container A
(iii) comparison of amounts of methane and product present is container A with time
(iv) comparison of reactivity of methane and product with chlorine
(v) final products formed in container A
(vi) product formed in container B based on availability of reactants

56. (i) calculation of molecular weight of X
(ii) calculation of molecular formula of hydrocarbon from molecular weight
(iii) identification of type of hydrocarbon based on formula
(iv) identification of possible ways the atoms can be arranged
(v) identification of succeeding homolog of the above hydrocarbon
(vi) number of position isomers of succeeding homologue based on number of carbon atoms

57. When coal burns, the chemical bonds holding its carbon atoms in place are broken, releasing energy and other harmful gases and substances such has NO_2, SO_2, mercury, etc.

58. Common salt is added to precipitate out all the soap from the aqueous solution. Adding of common salt to soap solution decreases the solubility of soap due to which all the soap precipitates out from the solution in the solid form.

59. (i) identification of Z
(ii) nature of 'Z'
(iii) identification of 'Y,' based on its hydrogenation reaction

60. The van der Waal's forces which hold the non-alkane molecules are weak and have a very short range. The larger the molecule, the stronger are the intermolecular forces. Since boiling point depends upon the intermolecular forces, the boiling points of alkanes increase with increase in chain length. Also as the molecular weight increases, the velocity of the molecule decreases at a particular temperature. Thus, alkanes tend to be in a liquid or a solid state.

61. General combustion equation is

$$C_xH_y + \left(x + \frac{y}{4}\right) O_2 \rightarrow x.CO_2 + \frac{y}{2} H_2C$$

As the molar ratio of CO_2 and H_2O is 4 : 3,

$$x = 4 \text{ and } \frac{y}{2} = 3 \Rightarrow y = 6$$

$$\therefore X = C_4H_6$$

Since it reacts with bromine water and its formula indicates that X is butyne

∴ X may be 1-Butyne or 2-Butyne

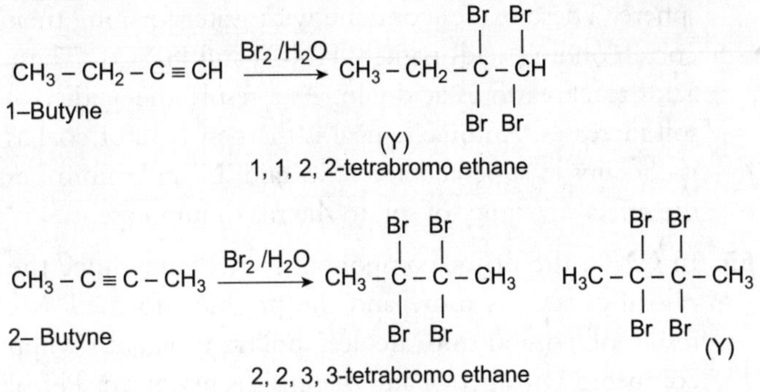

62. Molecular mass of X is 68. It may be alkene or alkyne.

Alkene	Alkyne
$\therefore C_nH_{2n}$	$C_nH_{2n} - 2$
$12n + 2n = 68$	$12n + 2n - 2 = 68$
$14n = 68$	$\Rightarrow n = 5$
$n = \frac{68}{14}$	$\therefore X \text{ is } C_5H_8$

But it is impossible.

Succeeding homogolue 'Y' is C_6H_8 (hexyne) Position isomers of X are 1-Pentyne, 2-Pentyne. Position isomers of Y are 1-Hexyne, 2-Hexyne and 3-Hexyne.

63. The molecular formula of hydrocarbon giving CO_2 and H_2O in 5 : 4 ratio can be C_5H_8.

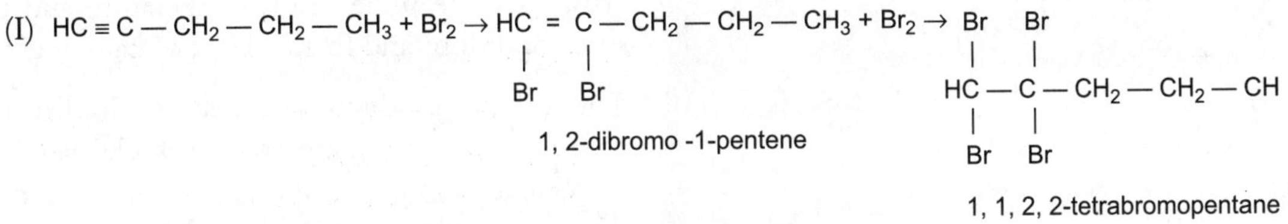

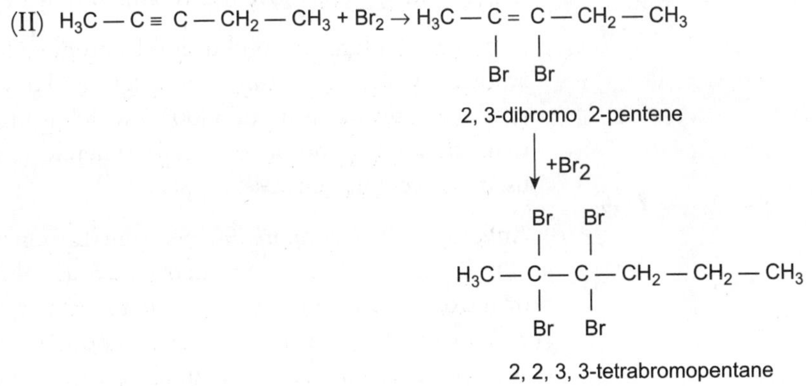

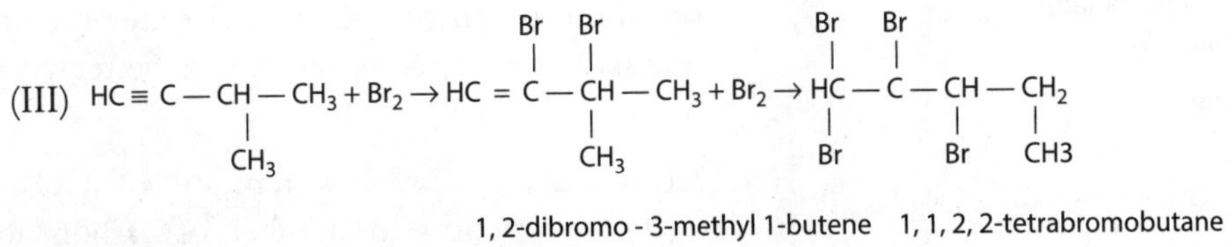

64. Coal is formed from various organic compounds. In coal along with carbon, nitrogen and sulphur are also present in varying amounts. When the coal is burnt the N and S form corresponding oxides which escape into the atmosphere. These oxides combine with water forming their corresponding acids namely HNO_3 and H_2SO_4. These acids reach earth as acid rain. As a result, the acidity of soil increases. Anthracite coal is the best type of coal as it contains least percentage of `S' and `N' and minimises the effect of acidity of soil to the maximum extent.

65. In CNG, the major component is methane. Since the calorific value is more and the products formed as a result of combustion are less polluting agents when compared with petrol and diesel, it is preferred. Petrol and diesel are mixtures of hydrocarbons where incomplete combustion takes place forming carbon monoxide which cases air pollution. Moreover in petrol and diesel sulphur and nitrogen are present which form corresponding oxides. These oxides cause air pollution. Further CNG undergo rapid combustion due to its low ignition temperature.

66. (a) 3, 3-Dimethyl-2-butanol
(b) 4-Chloro-2–methyl pentanoic acid
(c) 3, 4-Dimethyl-2-pentene
(d) 4-Methyl-1-pentene
(e) 2, 2-Dimethyl propane
(f) 3-Methyl-1-pentyne
(g) 4-Methyl-2-pentene

67. X is cyclobutane
Y is butane
Isomers of Y are

(a) $CH_3—CH=CH—CH_3$,
2 – Butene

(b) $CH_3—CH_2=CH=CH_2$
1 – Butene

(c) 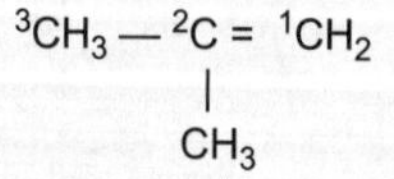
2 – Methyl – 1 – Propene

(a), (b) are position isomers. (a) and (c) as well as (b) and (c) are chain isomers.

(a)

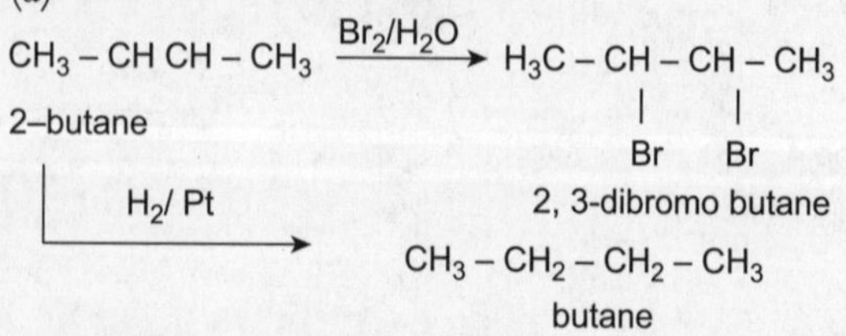

(b)

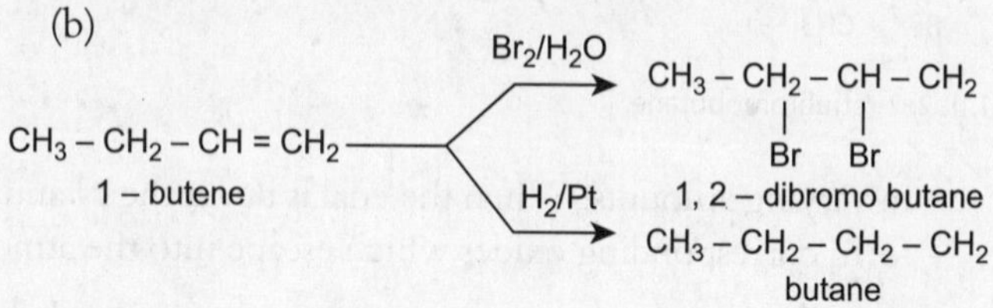

(c)

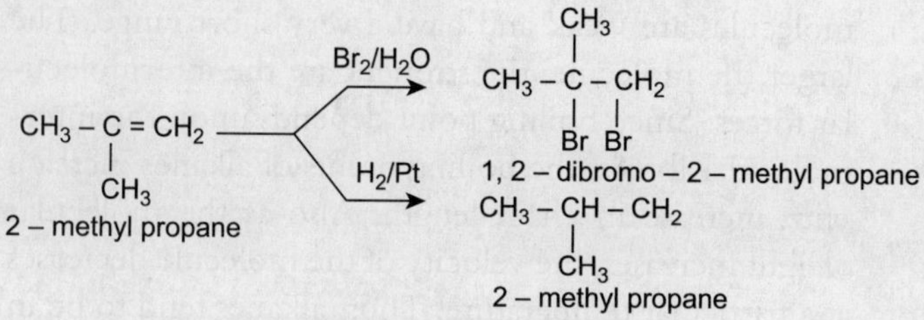

Therefore, the hydrogenated products are n-butane C in case (a), (b) and isobutene in case if (c). Among these two n-butane is having high boiling point than isobutane. The boiling point is proportional to surface area of the molecule, more is the surface area more are the intermolecular forces of attraction between the molecules. So, its boiling point increases. Between n-butane and isobutene n-butane is having high surface area; so, boiling point is more when compared to isobutene. Hence, these two can be separated by fractional distillation.

68. Coal contains appreciable proportion of sulphur and nitrogen as it is formed by the degradation of dead organic matter. During destructive distillation of coal, sulphur and nitrogen are removed and coke is obtained which is a purer form of carbon.

69. (a) The most volatile hydrocarbons under the earth's crust vaporize under high temperature and pressure conditions and form a layer of natural gas.

(b) The volatile products obtained by distillation of coal may contain some water-soluble gases such as NH_3 as impurities. Therefore, they are passed through water to remove the volatile impurities.

(c) Acetylene undergoes combustion to produce large amount of heat. A mixture of acetylene and oxygen produces a temperature of 3800°C which is higher than the melting points of metals. Therefore, it is used for welding purpose.

(d) Anthracite coal contains 90 per cent carbon and 10per cent of other components such as sulphur or nitrogen. Bituminous coal contains 70 per cent carbon and 30 per cent of other components such as sulphur and nitrogen. As sulphur and nitrogen contribute much to the air and water pollution, anthracite coal is considered as a better type of coal.

(e) Decarboxylation involves removal of CO_2 and resultant reduction in number of carbon atoms from the parent carboxylic acid. Hence, alkane with one carbon atom is prepared from carboxylic acid with two carbon atoms.

Level 3: Assess Your Concepts

70. The unique ability of an atom to bond with atoms of its own kind is called catenation. Carbon is the poster child for this property, allowing it to form a wide array of structures, from simple chains to complex networks. Were another element to have an even stronger ability to catenate, the number and variety of compounds it could form might be staggering. Such a robust catenation ability could potentially lead to compounds with multifaceted structures, each imparting its own set of properties and functionalities, opening doors to potentially ground-breaking applications in science and technology.

71. At its core, the molecular formula is like a grocery list, telling you what you need but not how to cook the dish. On the other hand, the structural formula is the detailed recipe. Two compounds might have the same list of ingredients (atoms) but assembled in different ways, resulting in different dishes (compounds) with unique tastes (properties). Thus, their real-world applications can be distinct. For instance, one might be used as a sweetener, while the other, due to its different structure, might be bitter.

72. Hydrocarbons are compounds of carbon and hydrogen. A hybrid hydrocarbon with features of both aliphatic (chains) and cyclic (rings) structures would be a molecular marvel. This type of hydrocarbon would almost certainly have properties from both worlds. It may have intermediate levels of reactivity and distinct physical properties, such as a distinct boiling point, making it a valuable compound in certain chemical processes or applications.

73. Isomers are like molecular twins with different careers. While they might look similar or even identical at a glance, their behaviour, especially in a biological context, can be starkly different. In the world of medicine, this is crucial. A drug's efficacy and safety are determined by its structure. An isomer of a beneficial drug might be inactive or even harmful, which is why pharmaceutical companies invest heavily in ensuring the correct structural formation of their drugs.

74. A homologous series is akin to a set of Russian nesting dolls, where each doll, although similar in appearance, is distinct in size. With each step in the series, the molecule grows by a predictable unit. By understanding this pattern and studying the properties of the earlier members, we can make educated predictions about the properties of later members. However, nature often throws curveballs, and while general trends might hold, specifics can deviate due to various molecular interactions.

75. Attack of fluorine on methane is highly exothermic reaction with very less activation energy. The high amounts of energy released in this step make the fluorine molecules to dissociate in greater number leading to a greater increase in the rate of reaction, which ultimately makes the reaction explosive. Hence, the mixture of CH_4 and F_2 when diluted with inert gas like He or Ne or N_2, the rate of the reaction can be decreased. And also when the reaction is carried in a copper vessel copper being good conductor of heat, absorbs excess heat and thus makes the reaction to be moderate.

76. No, kerosene cannot be used as a substitute for petrol as an automobile fuel. Pasoline has lower ignition temperature and the hydrocarbons have carbon chain length ranging from C_5–C_{10}. Kerosene has higher ignition temperature and the hydrocarbons have carbon chain length ranging from C_{10} to C_{18}. Due to higher ignition temperature, kerosene cannot be ignited by spark plug. Because of longer carbon chain, it produces very high knocking which makes it unsuitable for use as an automobile fuel.

77. Chlorination of methane gives methyl chloride and hydrochloric acid, which are stable, where as iodination of methane gives methyl iodide and hydrogen iodide which is a strong reducing agent and hence reduces CH_3–I to CH_4.

So, iodination is reversible:

$$CH_4 + I_2 \rightleftharpoons CH_3I + HI$$

As a result iodination is carried out in the presence of oxidizing agent like HIO_3 which oxidizes HI to I_2 and thus prevents the reversibility of the reaction.

$$5HI + HIO_3 \rightarrow I_2 + H_2O$$

$$CH_4 + I_2 \xrightarrow{HIO_3} CH_3I + I_2 + H_2O$$

78. Soaps are prepared by subjecting oils or fats to hydrolysis with sodium hydroxide. That means, soaps are sodium salts of higher fatty acids. Shampoos and shaving creams are prepared by subjecting oils or fats to hydrolysis with potassium hydroxide. That means they are potassium salts of higher fatty acids. Potassium salts are more soluble than sodium salts. Hence shampoos and shaving creams are softer than soaps.

79. Coal is formed when wood and plant remains decompose in the absence of air. They contain carbon, hydrogen, and oxygen. The process of gradual decomposition results in the increase of carbon content by the removal of hydrogen and oxygen in the form of water. As they become richer in carbon, the quality of coal goes on increasing from the stage of peat to the stage of anthracite. This is the reason why the same coal deposit may contain coal of different compositions.

80. Detergents are salts of alkyl sulphonates while soaps are sodium or potassium stearates. When used with hard water, the calcium and magnesium stearates formed being insoluble in water result in wastage of soap. However, the calcium and magnesium sulphonates formed with detergents are soluble in water and hence do not result in wastage of detergent. That means, when used with hard water, detergents are more efficient than soaps. But, detergents are not as easily biodegradable as soap. So, detergents cause greater pollution than soaps.

JEE-NEET Special wing

Multiple-Answer Type Questions

1. Hydrocarbons with a minimum of four carbons can exhibit position isomerism.

   Hence, C_3H_6 and C_3H_8 cannot exhibit position isomerism

2. Calcium carbides on hydrolysis gives ethyne (gas) and calcium hydroxide. It is the first homologue of the hydrocarbons with a general formula C_nH_{2n-2}. It is non-polar so is soluble in non-polar solvent but not a polar solvent like water. As it is an unsaturated compound, it decolourises bromine water and undergoes polymerization to form benzene, an aromatic compound.

3. Higher is the molecular weight, more will be its density, boiling point, critical temperature, and viscosity. During fractional distillation of crude oil, the component with higher molecular weight gets condensed first and the components with lower boiling points are carried to the top.

   So, A < B < C < D < E is the correct order with respect to their molecular weight, density, boiling point, critical temperature, and viscosity.

4. 'Y' is a detergent and 'X' is a soap. 'X' contains carboxylate group ($RCOO^-$) while Y contains sulphonate group (RSO_3^-). Detergents are more effective in cleaning clothes compared to soaps as they do not form insoluble salts like soaps with calcium and magnesium present in water if any . Formation of insoluble salts by soaps leads to the wastage of soap and inefficient cleaning. Hence 'X' and 'Y' are equally effective when used with distilled water as it does not contain any dissolved salts in it. But cleaning with 'Y' is more efficient than 'X' when dealing with hard water or potable water, as it contains dissolved salts of calcium and magnesium it.

5. Coar tar, is a thick viscous liquid obtained by the decomposition of coal in the limited supply of air, i.e., destructive distillation of coal. It is a thick, viscous substance and is employed in the construction of tar roads. It is a mixture of over 200 hydrocarbons present in an indefinite proportions.

Comprehension-Based Questions

6. All the given molecules contain alternate single and double bonds except Q. Hence it is not conjugated.(Also not planar as one of the carbons in it is sp^3 hybridised).

7. Organic compounds that meet the criteria of being cyclic, planar, and fully conjugated but possess ($4n$) pi electrons, instead of the ($4n + 2$) pi electrons are known as "anti-aromatic" compounds.

   For Molecule:

   R: No of pi electrons $=12 \Rightarrow 4(3) \Rightarrow$ possess $4n$ pi electrons $\Rightarrow$ Anti-aromatic

   S: No of pi electrons $=8 \Rightarrow 4(2) \Rightarrow$ possess $4n$ pi electrons $\Rightarrow$ Anti-aromatic

   P: No of pi electrons $=10 \Rightarrow [4(2) + 2] \Rightarrow$ possess $4n + 2$ pi electrons $\Rightarrow$ Aromatic

   Hence molecules R and S are anti-aromatic.

8. Aromatic compounds are more stable than anti-aromatic compounds. As only molecule P among the given ones is aromatic, that is supposed to have highest stability compared to the other compounds. (a) is the only choice ending with P. Hence, it should be the correct option.

9. Acetylene on catalytic polymerization gives benzene. All 'C' atoms in benzene are sp^2 hybridised and hence the bond angle is 120 degrees. Though it contains C = C carbons, it being an aromatic compound with aromaticity, is highly stable compared to aliphatic compound hexene. It shows substitution reactions like C - C but not the characteristics properties of C = C. Hexene (aliphatic) is less stable compared to benzene. So, it readily cannot add chlorine compared to hexene.

10. Because it is an aromatic compound, all carbon atoms should be sp^2 hybridised and should possess alternate single and pi bonds. Also, if no of pi bonds are 6, pi electrons = 12. According to Huckel's rule, $4n + 2 = 12$, means n is not a whole number. Only in molecule B, each carbon is sp^2 hybridised and possess alternate single and pi bonds, and n=2. So, molecule in option B should be the correct geometrical structure of the aromatic compound with molecular formula $C_{10}H_8$.

11. Aliphatic hydrocarbon 'A' on combustion gives carbon dioxide and water in the molar ratio of 5:4.

   $$C_xH_y + \left(\frac{x+y}{4}\right) O_2 \rightarrow xCO_2 + \left(\frac{y}{2}\right) H_2O$$

   Given x =5 and y =4.

   $\Rightarrow$ no of Carbon = 5 and Hydrogens = $\frac{y}{2} = 4 \Rightarrow y = 8$

   $\Rightarrow$ Hydrocarbon A is C_5H_8

   As B and C are the first homologue and next homologue of A

   B is C_2H_2 and C is C_6H_{10}

$$\text{Vapour density} = \frac{\text{Molecular weight}}{2}$$

Acetylene is used in the ripening of fruits.

C_6H_{10} - condensed formula

$(CH_2)_4\text{-}C \equiv CH$

D is also the homologue of A with no of carbon atoms half of that of hydrogen atoms in A.⇒ D= C_4H_6, which is the first member of the series to show position isomerism

Correct match is

	(A)	(B)	(C)	(D)
(a)	(iv)	(i)	(iii)	(ii)

Common solution for 12–17:

Hydrocarbon	Name of the hydrocarbon	Ratio of C:H
P- CH_4	Methane	1:4
Q- C_2H_6	Ethane	1:3
R- C_2H_4	Ethene	1:2
S- C_2H_2	Ethyne	1:1

12. Root word of Q, R and S is 'Eth'.

13. Electronegativity is proportional to the percentage of '*s*' character of hybridised orbitals (because these orbitals are closer to the nucleus). Higher is the "*s*" character of the hybridised orbitals of carbon, higher will be its electronegativity. '*sp*' hybridised carbons in alkynes possess the highest percentage of "*s*" character (50%) compared to that of alkenes (33.3% in sp^2) and alkanes (25% in sp^3). So, the triple bonded carbon atoms in alkynes exhibit high electronegativity. (Hence, H^+ ions can be donated easily).

14. Hydrocarbons with a minimum of four carbon atoms can exhibit position isomerism.

15. Substitution reactions are the characteristic reactions of alkanes.

16. Hydrocarbons with more electronegative carbon atoms tend to create a higher positive charge on their hydrogen atoms, increasing their acidity. The level of electronegativity directly relates to the "*s*" character in hybridized orbitals, with '*sp*' orbitals being more electronegative than sp^2 or sp^3. Consequently, the hydrogen donating tendency, representing the acidic strength of hydrocarbons, aligns with this order. Therefore, in terms of hydrogen donating tendency, the correct decreasing sequence would be Ethyne > Ethene > Ethane.

17. The molecular weight of methane (P) is the smallest among the given hydrocarbons, suggesting it should have the lowest boiling point. Ethane (Q), Ethene (R), and Ethyne (S) possess similar molecular weights (30g, 28g, 26g respectively). However, the carbon atoms in Ethyne exhibit greater electronegativity, inducing polarity through dipole formation. This leads to stronger dipole-dipole interactions in ethyne compared to the van der Waals forces in ethene and ethane. Although both alkane and alkyne possess van der Waals forces, the size of alkene is shorter due to sp2 hybridization and shorter bond lengths. Since van der Waals forces increase with size, alkanes have higher boiling points than alkenes. Consequently, the correct order of increasing boiling points among these hydrocarbons will be P < R < Q < S. So, the correct match is:

	(P)	(Q)	(R)	(S)
(d)	(ii)	(iv)	(i)	(iii)

CHAPTER

9

General Organic Chemistry–II

Remember

Before beginning this chapter, you should be able to:

- understand the preparation and properties of alcohols, carbonyl compounds, and carboxylic acids.
- describe carbohydrates, proteins, nucleic acids, oils, fats, and hormones.
- explain the importance of organic chemistry in polymers cosmetics, dyes, drugs, soaps, detergents, etc

Key Ideas

After completing this chapter, you should be able to:

- remember the primary classification of organic compounds.
- name organic compounds.
- recall the preparation and properties of simple alkanes, alkenes, and alkynes.

Scientific Crypt

A Tribute to Emil Fischer (1852-1919)

Emil Fischer's name immediately comes to mind when we think of people who have changed the way we understand the intricate world of biology at its most basic level. Nobody could predict the monumental impact this young man would have on science when his birth in 1852 in the quiet town of Euskirchen in Germany. Fischer's extraordinary journey into the realm of organic chemistry began at the prestigious University of Strasbourg. Fischer demonstrated an uncanny knack for decoding biomolecules at a time when many mysteries about them remained unsolved.

Fischer's efforts resulted in the creation of the Fischer projection, a clever way of representing the 3D structure of sugars on paper. Consider trying to explain how a complex toy is manufactured by using only a drawing—essentially what Fischer achieved for sugars!

But sugar wasn't his only passion. Proteins, the building blocks of life, captivated Fischer as well. He studied how amino acids, the smaller units that makeup proteins, connect together. This was revolutionary because it paved the way for modern protein research.

Fischer received the Nobel Prize in Chemistry in 1902 for his outstanding contributions. While this award is significant, Fischer's true legacy lies in how his work continues to influence and inspire scientists today. Every time we read about biomolecules in our textbooks, we are reminded of the incredible scientist who laid the groundwork.

FUN TIME

CROSSWORD

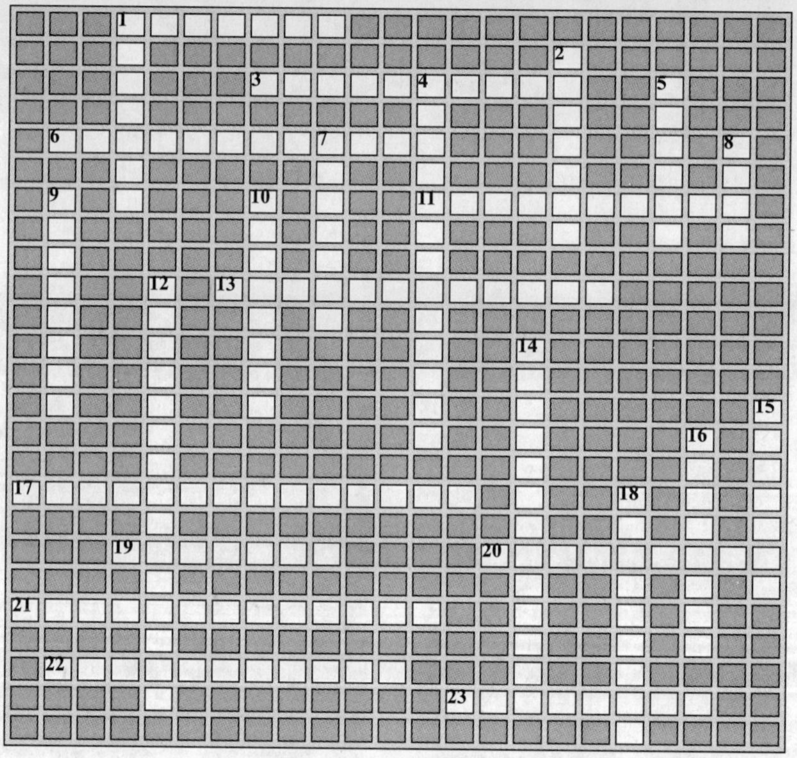

Across

1. Common name of alkenes
3. The part of an organic molecule that binds dye to the fabric
6. The common name of vitamin C
11. Addition of ozone to unsaturated hydrocarbon followed by hydrolysis in the presence of zinc
13. Addition of halogen to unsaturated hydrocarbon
17. Ammoniacal silver nitrate solution is
19. IUPAC name of aldehyde
20. The enzyme that converts sucrose into two monosaccharides
21. Oxidation followed by subsequent hydrolysis in the presence of an oxidizing agent
22. The part of an organic molecule that imparts colour to the fabric
23. Condensation polymer of phenol with formaldehyde

Down

1. Secondary suffix for carboxylic acid
2. The common name of vitamin A
4. Addition of hydrogen to unsaturated hydrocarbon in the presence of a catalyst
5. The enzyme that converts glucose into ethyl alcohol
7. IUPAC name of alcohol
8. The name given to the fermented liquor
9. The number of carbon atoms in the parent carbon chain is indicated by _______
10. IUPAC name of ketone
12. 100 per cent pure ethyl alcohol
14. Common name of alkynes
15. The basic unit of polymer
16. The aqueous solution of methanal is called _______
18. Thermal decomposition of hydrocarbons at very high temperature

INTRODUCTION

Organic chemistry profoundly influences the human society. This is because it plays a major role in all walks of our lives. Carbon forms millions of compounds though it combines only with few elements like hydrogen, oxygen, nitrogen, halogens, and sulphur. The compounds containing only carbon and hydrogen are called hydrocarbons. The compounds which possess other elements in addition to carbon and hydrogen are called organic compounds with heteroatoms. The atom or group of atoms present in a molecule of an organic compound which is responsible for the characteristic properties of the compound is called functional group. The organic compounds containing each type of heteroatoms can be further classified on the basis of the nature of the functional group.

Our daily needs of life such as food, clothing, soaps and detergents, medicines, etc., owe their origin from organic compounds. Some of them are very essential for sustenance of life while some others tremendously contribute to improve the quality of life. The special significance of organic chemistry owes not only to the uniqueness of carbon to form innumerable compounds, more astonishingly, with a limited number of elements but also to the immense industrial importance associated with the organic compounds.

Nomenclature of Organic Compounds

According to the IUPAC system, which follows the same pattern for all families of organic compounds, the name of an organic compound can be divided into three major parts, namely:

1. Root word
2. Primary suffix
3. Secondary suffix

Thus, for the organic compounds with functional groups, corresponding secondary suffix is added along with root word and primary suffix.

Secondary suffix is the part of the name which follows the primary suffix. It represents the functional group attached to the carbon chain. 'e' of the primary suffix is replaced by the corresponding secondary suffix.

Konnect

- The International Union of Pure and Applied Chemistry (IUPAC) sets the rules for organic compound naming to ensure that chemists around the world can communicate clearly and effectively.

Table 9.1 General naming features of different functional groups

Functional groups	Classes of the compound	Secondary suffixes	IUPAC names
–OH (hydroxyl)	Alcohol	–ol	Alkanol
–CHO	Aldehyde	–al	Alkanal
$>C=O$	Ketone	–one	Alkanone
–COOH	Carboxylic acid	–oic acid	Alkanoic acid

Rules for IUPAC Nomenclature of Organic Compounds

1. At first, the longest continuous carbon chain which includes the 'functional group' is selected. Then the carbon chain is numbered from the end nearer to the functional group. The carbon bearing the functional group should get the least number.

   Example:

$$\overset{3}{H_3C}-\overset{2}{CH_2}-\overset{1}{CH_2}-OH$$

1 – Propanol

2. If both the functional group and the alkyl substituent are present in an organic compound, the numbering of the parent carbon chain is given from the end nearer to functional group (the carbon atom bearing functional group should get the least number in preference to the substituent).

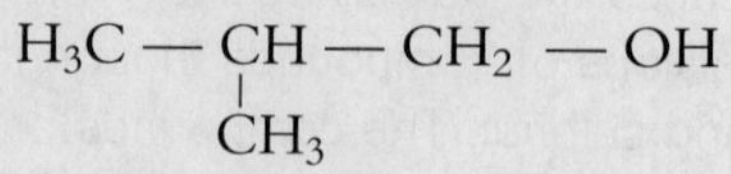

3. If both the alkyl substituent and the halogen group are present in an organic compound, then the carbon chain is numbered from the end nearer to halogen group (the carbon bearing the halogen group should get the least number).

The prefixes (of both alkyl and halogen group) are to be arranged in alphabetical order while writing the name of the compound.

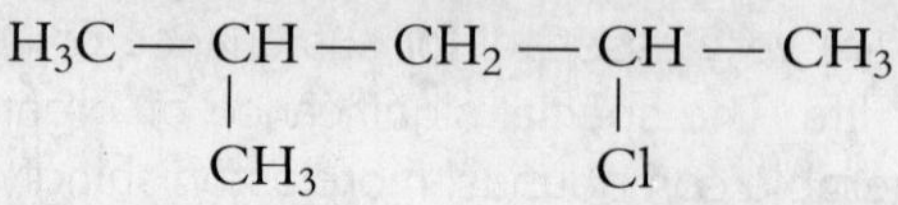

2 – Chloro – 4 – methyl pentane

When the substituent like alkyl group is present in an organic compound, the corresponding prefix 'alkyl' is used and when the heteroatom like halogen is present, the corresponding prefix 'halo' (like chloro, bromo, iodo, etc.) is used and the corresponding IUPAC name is 'haloalkane.'

4. When more than one alkyl substituent is present on the parent carbon chain, then the numbering is given in such a way that the 'sum of the locants' is the least.

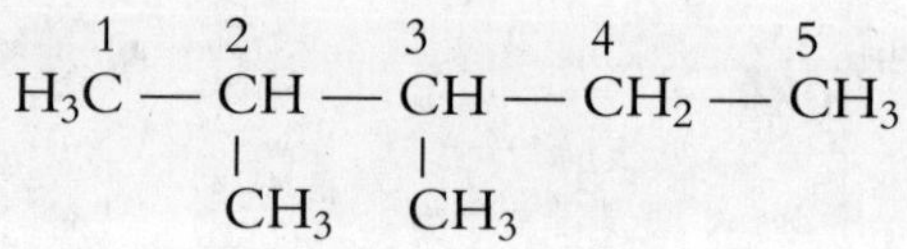

2, 3 – Dimethyl pentane

5. If 'sum of the locants' is equal, then the numbering of carbon chain starts from the end nearer to the smaller alkyl group.

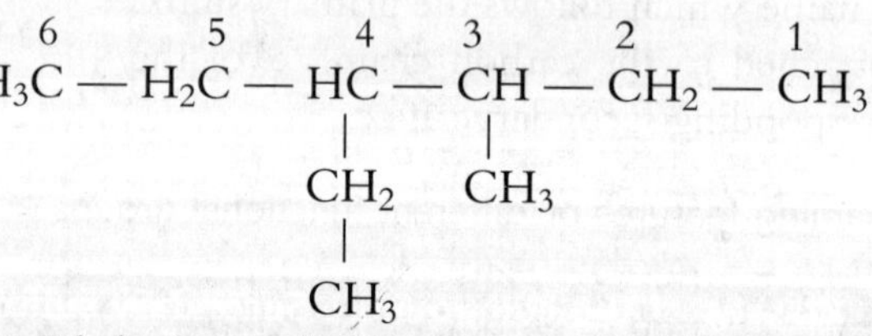

4 – Ethyl – 3 – methylhexane

IUPAC Nomenclature for Esters and Ethers

The IUPAC names of majority of the organic compounds with different functional groups are given by following the above rules. But the IUPAC nomenclature of some functional groups such as ethers and esters follows a slightly different trend.

Ethers

Ethers are a class of compounds that contain an oxygen atom bonded to two alkyl groups.

General molecular formula: $C_nH_{2n+2}O$.

Functional group: — O —

General formula: $R^1 — O — R$ (R, R^1 — same or different alkyl groups)

Nomenclature of Ethers

The first name is given 'alkoxy' for the smaller alkyl group ('R') attached to 'O' and is followed by a second name 'alkane,' for the larger alkyl group (R^1) attached to 'O.'

Thus, the general IUPAC name for ethers is 'alkoxy alkane.'

Examples:

$H_3C-O-CH_3$	Methoxy methane
$H_3C-O-CH_2-CH_3$	Methoxy ethane

Esters

These are derivatives of carboxylic acids where carboxylate group is attached to two alkyl groups.

General molecular formula: $C_nH_{2n}O_2$

Functional group: $-\overset{\overset{\displaystyle O}{\|}}{C}-O-$

General Formula: $R^1-\overset{\overset{\displaystyle O}{\|}}{C}-O-R$

(R^1— H or alkyl group R — alkyl group)

> **Konnect**
>
> Esters are functional derivatives of carboxylic acids, since they contain the common 'acyloxy' group namely '$R-\overset{\overset{\displaystyle O}{\|}}{C}-O-$'

Nomenclature of Esters

The 'R' group attached to 'O' ($R^1-\overset{\overset{\displaystyle O}{\|}}{C}-O-R$) is given the first name as corresponding 'alkyl' and the remaining structure is given the second name 'alkanoate.'

Thus, the IUPAC name for esters is 'alkyl alkanoate.'

Examples:

$H-\overset{\overset{\displaystyle O}{\|}}{C}-O-CH_3$	Methyl methanoate
$H_3C-\overset{\overset{\displaystyle O}{\|}}{C}-O-CH_3$	Methyl ethanoate

Isomerism

Just like hydrocarbons, organic compounds with any functional group can exhibit chain isomerism. Position isomerism in these compounds arises due to the difference in the position of functional group on the carbon chain. In addition to these two types, some of these compounds also exhibit other types of isomerism namely functional isomerism and metamerism.

1. **Functional Isomerism:** Compounds with the same molecular formula but different functional groups are called **functional isomers** and this phenomenon is called **functional isomerism.**

   Examples:

   Two functional isomers are possible with the molecular formulae C_2H_6O.

   One isomer with an alcoholic functional group (R—OH) and the other with an ether linkage or functional group (R—O—R)

(a) Molecular formula: C_2H_6O

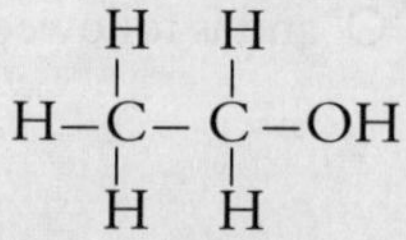

Common Name: Ethyl aclohol
IUPAC: Ethanol

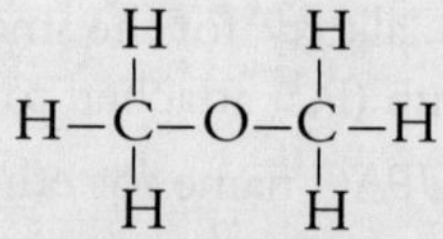

Common Name: Dimethyl ether
IUPAC: Methoxy methane

(b) Molecular formula: C_3H_6O

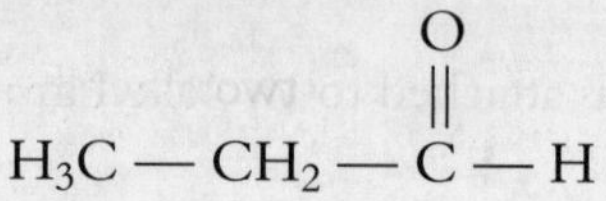

Common Name: Propanaldehyde
IUPAC: Propanal

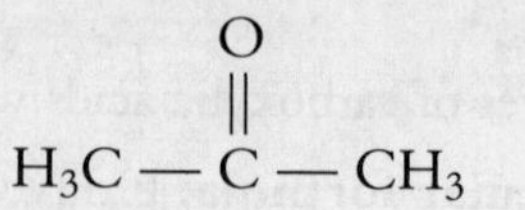

Common Name: Acetone
IUPAC: Propanone

Two functional isomers namely propionaldehyde and acetone are possible for the molecular formula.

C_3H_6O, one with aldehydic functional group ($R-\overset{\overset{\large O}{\|}}{C}-H$) and the other with the ketone functional group ($R-\overset{\overset{\large O}{\|}}{C}-H$).

2. **Metamerism:** The isomers in which there is an unequal distribution of carbon chain or atoms on either side of the functional group are called **metamers** and this phenomenon is termed as **'metamerism.'** Thus, metamers differ in the size of an alkyl group or chain on either side of the functional group.

Konnect

Metamerism is exhibited by compounds having divalent functional groups.

Example:

Molecular formula: $C_4H_{10}O$

$H_3C-CH_2-O-CH_2-CH_3$

Common Name: Diethyl ether
IUPAC: Ethoxyethane

$H_3C-O-CH_2-CH_2-CH_3$

Common Name: Methyl propyl ether
IUPAC: Methoxypropane

Functional Groups Containing Oxygen

Alcohols

The class of compounds where the alkyl chain is attached to –OH group is called **alcohols**. They are represented as R-OH, where 'R' stands for alkyl group. The general formula of alcohols is $C_nH_{2n+1}OH$. The common names for alcohols are given by using the name of the alkyl radical. The IUPAC name of alcohols is alkanols.

Example:

H_3C-CH_2-OH

Common name: ethyl alcohol

IUPAC name: eth + ane + ol — ethanol

Info Bytes!

- Alcohols can act both as acids and bases in chemical reactions, making them versatile reagents in the lab.

Table 9.2 Homologous series of alcohols

Alkanes	Formulae of alkane	Formulae of alcohol	Common names	IUPAC names
Methane	CH_4	$CH_3–OH$	Methyl alcohol	Methanol
Ethane	$H_3C–CH_3$	$H_3C–CH_2–OH$	Ethyl alcohol	Ethanol
Propane	$H_3C–CH_2–CH_3$	$H_3C–CH_2–CH_2–OH$	Propyl alcohol	1-Propanol
Butane	$H_3C–CH_2–CH_2–CH_3$	$H_3C–CH_2–CH_2–CH_2–OH$	n-butyl alcohol	1-Butanol

Preparation of Methyl Alcohol and Ethyl Alcohol

Table 9.3 Methods of preparation

Methyl alcohol	Ethyl alcohol
Hydrolysis of alkyl halides	
Boiling methyl halides with aqueous sodium hydroxide or aqueous potassium hydroxide	Boiling ethyl halides with aqueous sodium hydroxide or aqueous potassium hydroxide
$CH_3Cl + NaOH\ (aq) \rightarrow CH_3OH + NaCl$	$C_2H_5Cl + NaOH\ (aq) \rightarrow C_2H_5OH + NaCl$
Industrial methods	
From water gas: Water gas when mixed with hydrogen and passed over heated catalyst like chromic oxide or zinc oxide at 350°C gives methyl alcohol: $[CO_2 + H_2] + H_2 \xrightarrow[350°C]{Cr_2O_3/ZnO} CH_3OH$	**From ethene:** Ethene on reaction with conc. H_2SO_4 at very high pressure and at 80°C gives ethyl hydrogen sulphate which on boiling with water gives ethyl alcohol: $H_2C = CH_2 + H_2SO_4 \rightarrow CH_3 - CH_2 - HSO_4$ $CH_3 \cdot CH_2 \cdot HSO_4 + H_2O \xrightarrow{70–80°C} H_3C - CH_2 - OH + H_2SO_4$

On a large scale, ethyl alcohol can be manufactured by fermentation of molasses or starch.

Fermentation of Molasses

Fermentation is the process of decomposition of a complex organic compound into simpler compounds by means of microorganisms. **Molasses** is the mother liquor left after the crystallization of cane sugar from sugar cane juice.

Principle: Dilute solution of molasses which contains sucrose on standing for few days after the addition of yeast cells undergoes decomposition to form ethyl alcohol. This is due to the presence of enzymes such as invertase and zymase in the yeast cells.

$$\underset{\text{Sucrose}}{C_{12}H_{22}O_{11}} + H_2O \xrightarrow[30°C]{\text{Invertase}} \underset{\text{Glucose}}{C_6H_{12}O_6} + \underset{\text{Fructose}}{C_6H_{12}O}$$

$$\underset{\text{Ethyl alcohol}}{2C_2H_5OH + 2CO_2} \leftarrow \text{Glucose}$$

Process: Molasses contains 30–40% uncrystallized sugar. This is diluted by adding water and the percentage of sugar is brought down to 10%. Sulphuric acid is then added to maintain the pH of the solution at 4. Salts like ammonium sulphate or ammonium phosphate are added to this solution. These salts act as food for the yeast cells.

Yeast is added to the solution and the solution is allowed to stand as such for 24–72 h. The temperature is maintained at 30°C. The fermented liquor is known as **wash**. It contains 15–20% ethyl alcohol. When this is subjected to fractional distillation, 93–95% ethyl alcohol is obtained. This is called **rectified spirit**. However, 100% ethyl alcohol can be obtained by adding anhydrous CaO to the rectified spirit. Further, 100% ethyl alcohol is known as **absolute alcohol**. For industrial use, 5% methyl alcohol is added to ethyl alcohol. This is called **denatured spirit**.

Fermentation of Starch

Instead of molasses, starch can also be taken as the starting material for the manufacture of ethyl alcohol. Starch is warmed with freshly germinated barley called **malt** at 50°C for 1 h. Malt contains diastase enzyme. Starch is converted to maltose sugar by hydrolysis in the presence of diastase. The remaining process continues in the same manner as in molasses, except that the enzyme maltase carries out the fermentation process of sugar which is in the form of maltose:

$$\underset{\text{Starch}}{(C_6H_{10}O_5)_n} + \frac{n}{2}H_2O \xrightarrow{\text{Diastase}} \frac{n}{2}\underset{\text{Maltose}}{C_{12}H_{22}O_{11}}$$

$$C_{12}H_{22}O_{11} + H_2O \xrightarrow{\text{Maltase}} 2\underset{\text{Glucose}}{C_6H_{12}O_6}$$

$$C_6H_{12}O_6 + H_2O \xrightarrow{\text{Zymase}} 2C_2H_5OH + 2CO_2$$

Uses of Ethyl Alcohol

1. **Industrial Solvent:** Since a wide range of organic compounds are soluble in ethyl alcohol, it is the most common industrial solvent. To discourage its misuse as beverage, 5% methyl alcohol is added to this, thus making it unfit for drinking. This is called denatured spirit.
2. **In Medicines:** Many medicines contain alcohol as one of the constituents in small quantities.
3. **As Beverage:** Different brands of alcoholic beverages contain different percentages of alcohol.

Table 9.4 Percentage of alcohol in different alcoholic beverages

Alcoholic beverages	Percentage of alcohol
Beer	3–5
Cider	2–4
Wine	8–10
Gin, brandy, whisky, and rum	35–40

Info Bytes!

- The world's oldest known bottle of wine, containing ethanol, dates back to around 325 AD.

Spurious Alcohol

Manufactured ethyl alcohol is available cheaply. But heavy excise duty and taxes are imposed on the alcohol in order to discourage people from getting addicted to drinking alcohol. The industrial alcohol is not taxed heavily. Since this is available at cheaper rates, this is diluted and sold as alcohol for drinking purpose. As this contains toxic substances like methyl alcohol, pyridine, or copper sulphate, etc., the alcohol also becomes toxic. This is called **spurious alcohol**. Spurious alcohol can also be made by subjecting jaggery to fermentation. During this process, methyl alcohol and acetaldehyde are also formed. These impurities impart toxic effect to ethyl alcohol.

Table 9.5 Physical properties of alcohol

Methyl alcohol	Ethyl alcohol
Colorless liquid	Colorless liquid
Strong odor	Sweet smell
Inflammable	Inflammable
Highly toxic	Less toxic with a burning taste
Soluble in water and organic solvents	Soluble in water and organic solvents
Boiling point 64.5°C	Boiling point 78.1°C
Consumption can cause blindness and even death.	Consumption for long period can cause damage of liver, kidneys, etc.

Table 9.6 Chemical properties of alcohols

Methyl alcohol	Ethyl alcohol
Reaction with active metals	
With sodium, products are sodium methoxide and hydrogen: $2CH_3OH + 2Na \rightarrow \underset{\text{Sodium methoxide}}{2CH_3ONa} + H_2$	With sodium, products are sodium ethoxide and hydrogen: $2C_2H_5OH + 2Na \rightarrow \underset{\text{Sodium ethoxide}}{2C_2H_5ONa} + H_2$
Reaction with PCl	
Products are methyl chloride and phosphorous acid. $3CH_3OH + PCl_3 \rightarrow \underset{\text{Chloromethane}}{3CH_3Cl} + H_3PO_3$	Products are ethyl chloride and phosphorous acid. $3C_2H_5OH + PCl_3 \rightarrow \underset{\text{Chloroethane}}{3C_2H_5Cl} + H_3PO_3$
Reaction with acetic acid (esterification)	
Product formed is methyl acetate: $CH_3OH + CH_3COOH \rightarrow \underset{\text{Methylacetate}}{CH_3COOCH_3} + H_2O$	Product formed is ethyl acetate: $C_2H_5OH + CH_3COOH \rightarrow \underset{\text{Ethyl acetate}}{CH_3COOC_2H_5} + H_2O$
Reaction with conc. H_2SO_4 (dehydration)	
Product is dimethyl ether obtained at 140°C: $2CH_3OH \xrightarrow[140°C]{\text{conc. } H_2SO_4} CH_3OCH_3 + H_2O$	Product depends upon the temperature. At 140°C, diethyl ether is obtained and at 170°C ethane is obtained: $2C_2H_5OH \xrightarrow[140°C]{\text{conc. } H_2SO_4} \underset{\text{Diethyl ether}}{C_2H_5OC_2H_5} + H_2O$ $C_2H_5OH \xrightarrow[170°C]{\text{conc. } H_2SO_4} \underset{\text{Ethene}}{H_2C = CH_2} + H_2O$

(Continued.)

Table 9.6 Continued

Methyl alcohol	Ethyl alcohol
Oxidation	
Passing methyl alcohol vapor over hot copper gives formaldehyde or methanal: $CH_3OH \xrightarrow[300°C]{Cu} HCHO + H_2$ Methanal	On passing ethyl alcohol vapors over hot copper catalyst at 300°C gives acetaldehyde or ethanal: $C_2H_5OH \xrightarrow[300°C]{Cu} CH_3CHO + H_2$ Ethanal
On treating with alkaline $KMnO_4$, the product formed is formic acid: $CH_3OH + [O] \xrightarrow[\text{or acidified } K_2Cr_2O_7]{alk.KMnO_4} HCOOH$	On treating with alkaline $KMnO_4$, the product obtained is acetic acid or ethanoic acid: $C_2H_5OH + [O] \xrightarrow[\text{or acidified } K_2Cr_2O_7]{alk.KMnO_4} CH_3COOH$

Table 9.7 Uses of alcohols

Methyl alcohol	Ethyl alcohol
Used as a solvent	Used as a solvent for many organic compounds
Used in paints and varnishes	Pure and dilute alcohol is used as a beverage
In manufacturing other industrially useful organic compounds *Examples:* (i) Formic acid – antiseptic and tanning of leather (ii) Formaldehyde – preservative for biological specimens, for making industrial alcohol	In manufacturing many organic compounds including dyes, synthetic rubber, varnishes, paints, perfumes, antiseptics, etc.

Isomerism in Alcohols

Alcohols exhibit three types of isomerism as listed below:

1. **Chain Isomerism**: These isomers differ in the arrangement of carbon atoms in the chain.
   Example: n-butyl alcohol and isobutyl alcohol
   Molecular formula: $C_4H_{10}O$
   Structural formulae:

$$CH_3 - CH_2 - CH_2 - CH_2OH$$

1 – Butanol

$$\begin{array}{c} CH_3 - CH - CH_2OH \\ \quad | \quad\quad\quad \\ \quad CH_3 \quad\quad\quad \end{array}$$

2-Methyl-1-proponal

2. **Position Isomerism:** The isomers differ in the position of functional group (–'OH' group) on the carbon chain.
   Example: 1-Propanol and 2-Propanol
   Molecular formula: C_3H_8O

Structural formulae:

$$CH_3 - CH_2 - CH_2OH$$

1 – Propanol

$$\begin{array}{c} CH_3 - CH - CH_3 \\ | \\ OH \end{array}$$

2 – Propanol

3. **Functional isomerism**: These are the isomers which differ in the nature of functional groups.

Example: C_2H_6O

	$H_3C - CH_2 - OH$	$H_3C - O - CH_3$
Common name:	Ethanol	Methoxy methane
IUPAC name:	Ethyl alcohol	Dimethyl ether

Aldehydes and Ketones

The classes of compounds in which there is a $>C = O$ group are called **carbonyl compounds**. The general formula of the carbonyl compounds is $C_nH_{2n}O$. If the carbonyl compound contains $>C = O$ group linked to hydrogen on one side and alkyl group on the other side, that class of compounds is called **aldehydes**. If the carbonyl group is linked to two same or different alkyl groups on either side, the class of compounds is called **ketones**.

Aldehydes are represented by a general formula, $\begin{array}{l} H \diagdown \\ \quad\; C = O \\ R \diagup \end{array}$

Ketones are represented by a general formula, $\begin{array}{l} R \diagdown \\ \quad\; C = O \\ R' \diagup \end{array}$

Konnect

- Aldehydes and ketones are essential in the flavour and fragrance industry. Vanilla, for example, mainly comprises the aldehyde vanillin.

The IUPAC names of aldehydes are 'alkanals' and those of ketones are 'alkanones.'

Examples:

	CH_3CHO	H_3CCOCH_3
Common name:	Acetaldehyde	Acetone
IUPAC name:	Ethanal	Propanone

Table 9.8 Homologous series of aldehydes/ketones

Formulae of aldehyde/ketone	Common names	IUPAC names
HCHO	Formaldehyde	Methanol
CH_3CHO	Acetaldehyde	Ethanol
CH_3CH_2CHO	Propanaldehyde	Propanol
CH_3COCH_3	Acetone (dimethyl ketone)	Propanone
$CH_3CH_2COCH_3$	Ethyl methyl ketone	Butanone

Formaldehyde/Methanal

Preparation

Methyl alcohol on controlled oxidation in the presence of a catalyst gives formaldehyde:

$$2CH_3OH \xrightarrow[900K]{Cu} HCHO + 2H_2O$$

Info Bytes!

- Formaldehyde, a simple aldehyde, is used in embalming fluids.

Physical Properties

Table 9.9 Physical properties of methanal

Parameters	Characteristics
Color	Colorless
State	Gas
Odor	Strong smell
Boiling point	252 K
Solubility	Highly soluble in water

Chemical Properties

1. **Oxidation:** Methanal on oxidation in presence of oxidizing agents such as HNO_3 or acidified $K_2Cr_2O_7$ or acidified $KMnO_4$ gives formic acid (methanoic acid):

$$HCHO + [O] \rightarrow HCOOH$$

2. **Oxidation in Presence of Tollen's Reagent (ammonical silver nitrate solution):** Formaldehyde on heating with Tollen's reagent gets oxidized to formic acid. Ag^+ ions get reduced to metallic silver. As a result of this, a shining silver mirror is formed along the inner walls of the test tube.

$$HCHO + AgNO_3 \xrightarrow[[O]]{NH_4OH} HCOOH + NH_4NO_3 + NH_3 + Ag + H_2O$$

3. **Oxidation in Presence of Fehling's Reagent:** Fehling's reagent is an alkaline cupric salt solution dissolved in sodium potassium tartarate (Rochelle salt). Formaldehyde on heating with Fehling's reagent in hot water gives a red precipitate of cuprous oxide. Methanal gets oxidized to methanoic acid.

$$HCHO + 2Cu(OH)_2 + NaOH \xrightarrow{\Delta} HCOONa + Cu_2O + 3H_2$$

4. **Reduction:** Methanal on reduction in the presence of palladium gives methyl alcohol:

$$HCHO + H \xrightarrow[[H]]{Pd} CH_3OH$$

5. **Addition of HCN:** A double bond is present between carbon and oxygen in formaldehyde. The π-bond can be broken during addition of another molecule. On the addition of HCN to the double bond, hydrogen is added to oxygen and cyanide is added to carbon thereby giving an additional compound cyanohydrin.

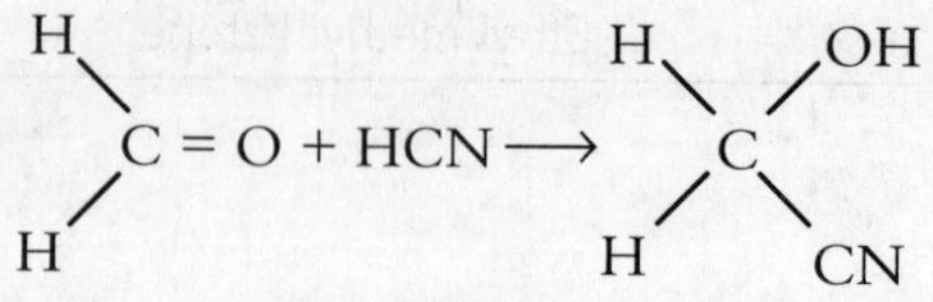

Methanal cyanohydrin

Uses of Methanal

1. The aqueous solution of methanal is called formalin. It acts as a disinfectant. Hence, it is used for the preservation of biological specimens.
2. Methanal is used manufacturing a plastic called bakelite, which is used for making electric switches.
3. Methanal is also taken as a raw material for the manufacture of dyes, medicines, etc.

Acetone or Propanone

Preparation

An aromatic hydrocarbon, cumene on reaction with oxygen gives an intermediate product which on reaction with acid gives propanone along with phenol:

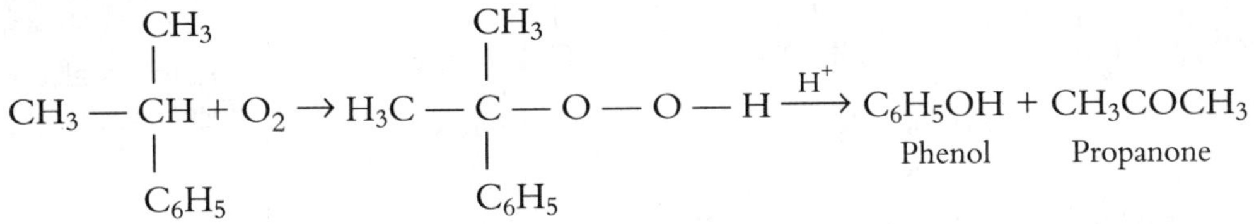

Cumene

Physical Properties

Table 9.10 Physical properties of acetonel

Parameters	Characteristics
Color	Colorless
Nature	Volatile liquid
Boiling point	329 K
Solubility	Soluble in water

Chemical Properties

1. **Reduction:** Propanone on reduction with $LiAlH_4$ or $NaBH_4$ gives 2-Propanol.

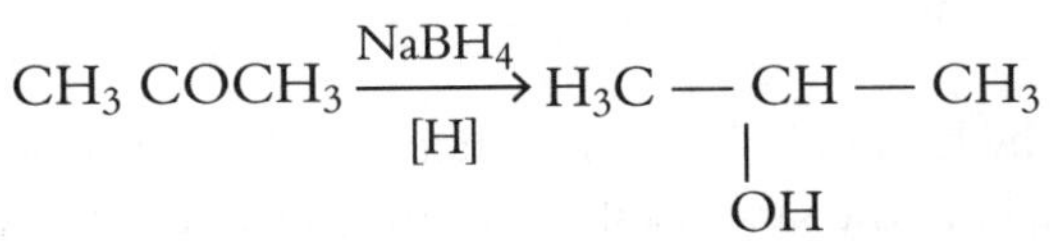

2 - Propanol

2. **Oxidation:** Propanone on oxidation with potassium permanganate in acidic medium gives ethanoic acid:

$$CH_3COCH_3 \xrightarrow[{[O]}]{KMnO_4/H^+} CH_3COOH$$

Ethanoic acid

3. **Addition of HCN:** When HCN is added to the > C = O bond in propanone, hydrogen is added to oxygen and cyanide is added to carbon. This gives propanone cyanohydrin.

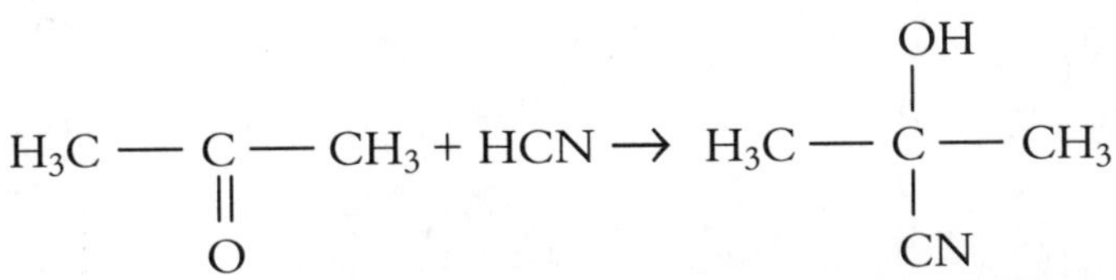

Propanone cyanohydrin

Uses of Acetone

1. An important solvent for organic compounds
2. Used in the manufacture of nail polish remover
3. Making artificial leather and synthetic resin

Isomerism in Aldehydes and Ketones

1. **Chain Isomerism:** Aldehydes exhibit chain isomerism due to the variation in the length of the carbon chain.

   Examples: n-Butyraldehyde and isobutyraldehyde

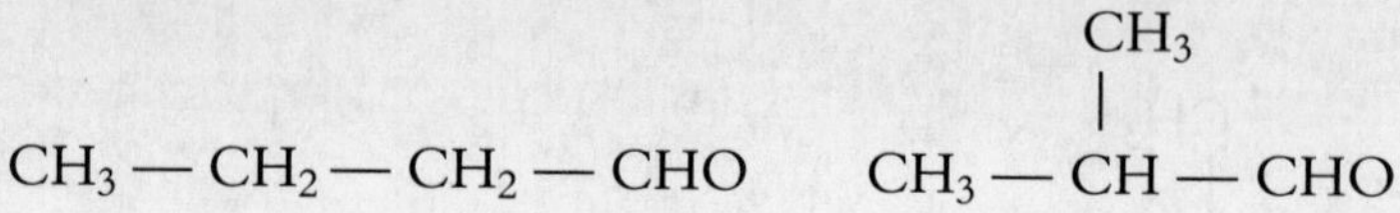

n – Butyraldehyde   Isobutyraldehyde

> **Konnect**
>
> Ketones also exhibit chain isomerism.

Examples: Diethyl ketone and Isopropyl methyl ketone

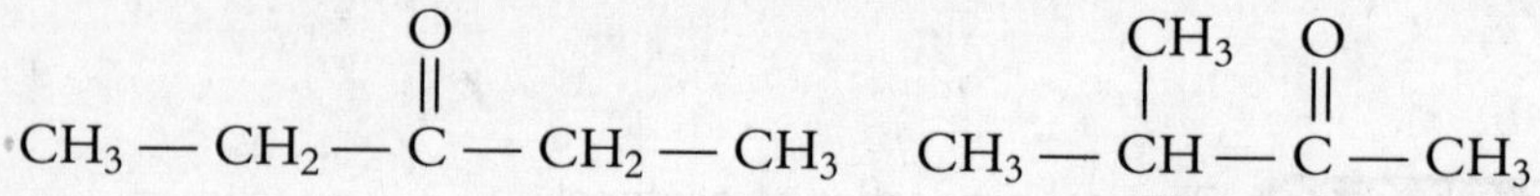

Diethyl ketone   Isopropyl methyl ketone

2. **Position Isomerism:** Aldehydes cannot exhibit position isomerism. This is because –CHO group is a chain-terminating group and it should always be placed in the first position. Ketones exhibit position isomerism due to the location of carbonyl group in different positions.

   Examples: 3-Pentanone and 2-Pentanone

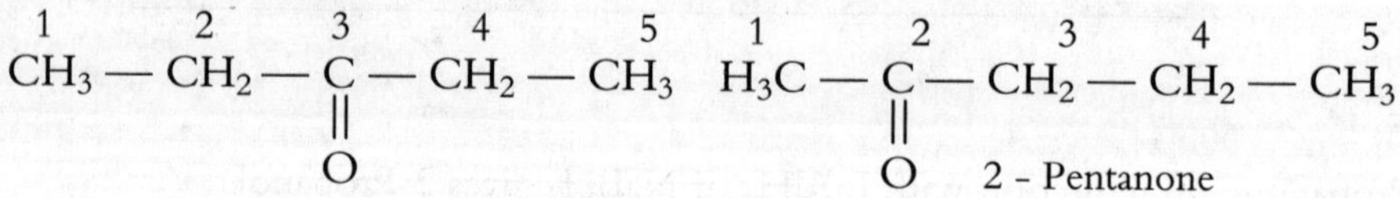

2 - Pentanone

3-Pentanone

3. **Functional Isomerism:** Aldehydes and ketones are functional isomers to each other. Functional isomerism arises when two or more compounds have the same molecular formula but different functional groups.

   Examples: Propanal and propanone

   Molecular formula: C_3H_6O

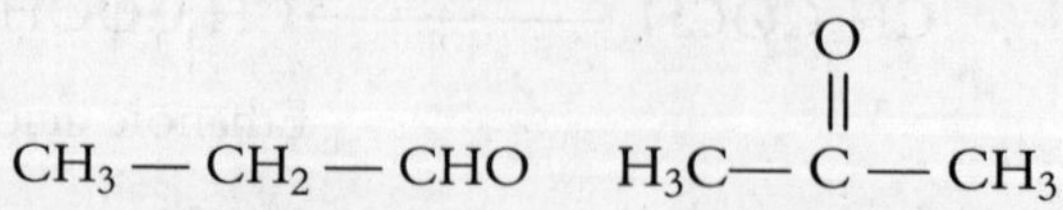

Propanal   Propanone

Carboxylic Acids

The organic compounds which contain $-\overset{O}{\overset{\|}{C}}-OH$ (carboxyl group) as a functional group are known as **carboxylic acids**, since this group is a combination of carbonyl group (>C = O) and hydroxyl group (–OH). The general molecular formula of carboxylic acids is '$C_nH_{2n}O_2$.' Since they show significant acidity, they are called acids.

The common names of these acids are mostly derived from the source of their origin.

Examples:

Formic acid (Formica – ants)

Acetic acid (Acetum – vinegar)

According to the IUPAC system, these compounds are named by adding a secondary suffix 'oic acid' to the corresponding 'alkane.' These are named as alkanoic acids.

Table 9.11 Homologous series of carboxylic acids

Formulae	Common names	IUPAC names
HCOOH	Formic acid	Methanoic acid
CH_3COOH	Acetic acid	Ethanoic acid
CH_3CH_2COOH	Propionic acid	Propanoic acid
$CH_3CH_2CH_2COOH$	Butyric acid	Butanoic acid

Konnect

- Acetic acid, which gives vinegar its pungent smell and sour taste, is a carboxylic acid.
- Some ants spray formic acid, another carboxylic acid, as a defense mechanism.

Acetic Acid (Ethanoic Acid)

Acetic acid is the most important fatty acid which, as a dilute solution, is used as a preservative for foods such as pickles, vegetable sauce, etc.

Methods of Preparation

1. Ethyl alcohol on oxidation by air in the presence of a bacteria of the genus *Acetobacter*, gives acetic acid:

$$CH_3CH_2OH + [O] \xrightarrow{\textit{Acetobacter}} CH_3COOH + H_2O$$

2. **Commercial Preparation:** Acetic acid can be obtained by the reaction between methyl alcohol and carbon monoxide in presence of iodine and rhodium as catalysts:

$$CH_3OH + CO \xrightarrow{I_2-Rh} CH_3COOH$$

Physical Properties

Table 9.12 Physical properties of acetic acid

Parameters	Characteristics
Color	Colorless liquid
Odor	Pungent smell
Boiling point	391 K
Solubility	Soluble in water

Chemical Properties

1. **Acidic Character:** When acetic acid reacts with metals/alkalies, the corresponding salt is formed.

   Examples:

$$2CH_3COOH + 2Na \longrightarrow 2CH_3COONa + H_2$$

$$CH_3COOH + NaOH \longrightarrow CH_3COONa + H_2O$$

$$CH_3COOH + Na_2CO_3 \longrightarrow CH_3COONa + CO_2 + H_2O$$

2. **Reaction with Alcohols:** Acetic acid reacts with alcohols to give the corresponding ester. This reaction is known as **esterification**.

   Examples:

$$CH_3COOH + CH_3OH \longrightarrow \underset{\text{Methyl acetate}}{CH_3COOCH_3} + H_2O$$

$$CH_3COOH + C_2H_5OH \longrightarrow \underset{\text{Ethyl acetate}}{CH_3COOC_2H_5} + H_2O$$

3. **Decarboxylation:** Sodium or potassium salt of acetic acid on reaction with soda lime gives methane due to the removal of CO_2 from the carboxylic acid:

$$CH_3COONa + NaOH \xrightarrow{CaO} CH_4 + Na_2CO_3$$

Uses of Acetic Acid

1. As a reagent in laboratory
2. In the preparation of synthetic vinegar
3. For the preparation of white lead

Isomerism in Carboxylic Acids

1. **Chain Isomerism:** Just as other compounds, carboxylic acids also exhibit chain isomerism due to the variation in the nature of carbon chain.

   Examples: n-butryic acid and isobutryic acid

$$\underset{\text{n-Butyric acid}}{CH_3-CH_2-CH_2-COOH} \qquad \underset{\text{Isobutyric acid}}{CH_3-\overset{\overset{CH_3}{|}}{CH}-COOH}$$

2. **Position Isomerism:** Carboxylic acids do not exhibit position isomerism like aldehydes due to the fact that –COOH group is the chain-terminating group.
3. **Functional Isomerism:** Carboxylic acids show functional isomerism with esters.

   Examples: Propanoic acid and Methylacetate

$$\underset{\text{Propanoic acid}}{CH_3CH_2COOH} \qquad \underset{\text{Methyl acetate}}{CH_3COOCH_3}$$

EXAMPLE 9.1 Two compounds A and B are functional isomers. A has fruity smell and undergoes hydrolysis in presence of acid or base to give C and D, C has same functional group as B. C and B are simultaneously treated with sodium hydroxide. The compounds obtained are treated with soda lime to give two successive homologs E and F which are the first two members of the series. Identify A, B, C, D, E, and F.

SOLUTION

$\underset{(A)}{CH_3COOCH_3}$ and $\underset{(B)}{CH_3CH_2COOH}$ → functional isomers

$$\underset{(A)}{CH_3COOCH_3} + H_2O \xrightarrow[HCl]{NaOH\ or} \underset{(C)}{CH_3COOH} + \underset{(D)}{CH_3OH}$$

'C' has same functional group as 'B'

$$\underset{(C)}{CH_3COOH} + NaOH \rightarrow CH_3COONa + H_2O$$

$$\underset{(B)}{CH_3CH_2COOH} + NaOH \rightarrow CH_3CH_2COONa + H_2O$$

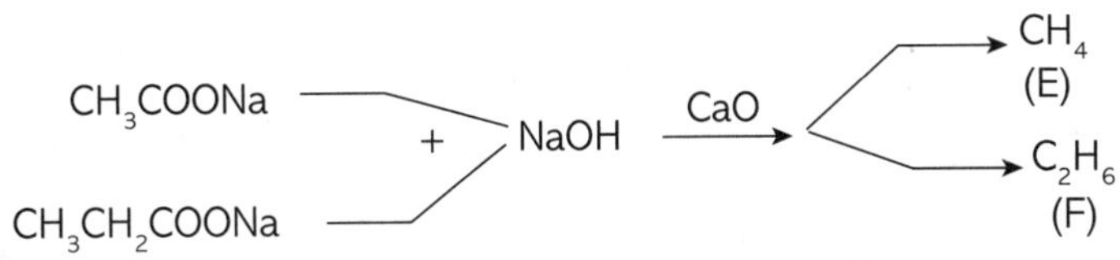

CH_4 and C_2H_6 are first two members of alkanes.

EXAMPLE 9.2 The first homolog of the series with general formula C_nH_{2n} on oxidation with alkaline $KMnO_4$ gives a compound which is added to water used as a coolant in automobiles. Identify the compound and explain the purpose of its addition to water.

SOLUTION

The first homolog of the series with general formula C_nH_{2n} is ethene.

$$H_2C = CH_2 + [O] \xrightarrow{KMnO_4} \underset{\text{Ethene glycol}}{\begin{array}{c} CH_2OH \\ | \\ CH_2OH \end{array}}$$

Water is used as a coolant in automobiles because it can absorb large amount of heat from the engine due to high specific heat. However, in cold countries, the water may freeze to ice due to very low temperature. Similarly in summer season water may tend to boil as it absorbs heat. Ethylene glycol is added to water, which can prevent freezing as well as boiling. This is because addition of ethylene glycol to water leads to depression in freezing point as well as elevation in boiling point. As a result, water can maintain liquid range over a wide range of temperature.

EXAMPLE 9.3 Identify A, B, C, D in the following conversions given and write their structural formulae.

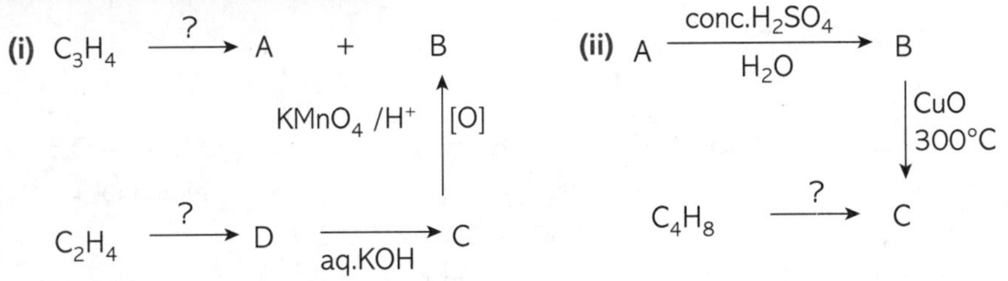

SOLUTION

(i)

$$H_3C-C\equiv CH \xrightarrow[Zn/H_2O]{O_3} \underset{\text{(A)}}{CHO-CHO} + \underset{\text{(B)}}{H_3C-COOH}$$

$$\underset{\text{(C)}}{H_3C-CH_2-OH} \xrightarrow{KMnO_4/H^+} \underset{\text{(B)}}{H_3C-COOH}$$

$$H_2C=CH_2 \xrightarrow{HCl} \underset{\text{(D)}}{H_3C-CH_2-Cl} \xrightarrow{aq\ KOH} \underset{\text{(C)}}{H_3C-CH_2-OH}$$

(ii)

$$\underset{\text{(A)}}{CH_2=CH_2} \xrightarrow[H_2O]{conc.H_2SO_4} \underset{\text{(B)}}{C_2H_5-OH}$$

$$\underset{\text{(B)}}{C_2H_5-OH} \xrightarrow{CuO,\ 300^\circ C} \underset{\text{(C)}}{CH_3-CHO}$$

$$CH_3-CH=CH-CH_3 \xrightarrow[H_2O]{O_3/Zn} \underset{\text{(C)}}{CH_3-CHO} + CH_3CHO$$

EXAMPLE 9.4

In the oxidation of methanol (methyl alcohol), which reagent is commonly used, and what are the products formed? Explain the significance of this reaction in industry.

SOLUTION

In the oxidation of methanol (methyl alcohol), the common reagent used is oxygen (O2), often with the assistance of a catalyst like copper (Cu) at elevated temperatures. The products formed are carbon dioxide (CO_2) and water (H_2O).

$$2CH_3OH + O_2 \rightarrow 2CO_2 + 4H_2O$$

In the oxidation of methanol (methyl alcohol), the common reagent used is oxygen (O_2), often with a catalyst like copper (Cu) at elevated temperatures. This reaction produces carbon dioxide (CO_2) and water (H_2O). It's significant in industry for formaldehyde production, energy generation, Methanol-to-Olefins (MTO) processes, and its relatively lower environmental impact compared to other hydrocarbon combustion reactions. (Note: Methanol-to-Olefins (MTO) is like a magical transformation that turns a special liquid called methanol into very useful building blocks called olefins. These olefins serve as essential building blocks for the production of a wide range of products, including plastics and various industrial materials.)

EXAMPLE 9.5

Complete the following reactions.

(i) $CH_3-CH_2-CH_2-COONa + NaOH$

(ii) $CH_3-I + H_2$

(iii) $C_2H_5Br + KOH$

(iv) $CO + H_2 + H_2$

(v) $CaC_2 + H_2O$

SOLUTION

(i) $\underset{\text{Sodium salt of butanoic acid}}{CH_2-CH_2-CH_2-COONa} + NaOH \rightarrow \underset{\text{Propane}}{CH_3-CH_2-CH_3} + Na_2CO_3$

(ii) $\underset{\text{Iodomethane}}{CH_3-I} + H_2 \rightarrow \underset{\text{Methane}}{CH_4} + HI$

(iii) $\underset{\text{Bromoethane}}{C_2H_5Br} + KOH \xrightarrow{\Delta} \underset{\text{Ethanol}}{C_2H_5\text{–}OH} + KBr$

(iv) $\underset{\text{Water gas}}{[CO + H_2]} + H_2 \xrightarrow[300^\circ C \text{ under pressure}]{Cr_2O_3-ZnO} \underset{\text{Methanol}}{CH_3 - OH}$

(v) $CaC_2 + H_2O \rightarrow \underset{\text{Ethyne}}{CH\equiv CH} + Ca(OH)_2$

EXAMPLE 9.6

How do you bring about the following conversions?

(i) Methane to methyl alcohol.
(ii) Ethyl chloride to methane
(iii) Ethane to benzene

SOLUTION

(i) Step 1: Methane on chlorination in the presence of sunlight produces methyl chloride.

$$CH_4 + Cl_2 \xrightarrow{\text{Sunlight}} CH_3Cl + HCl$$

Step 2: Methyl chloride on reaction with aqueous potassium hydroxide gives methyl alcohol.

$$CH_3Cl + KOH\ (aq) \rightarrow \underset{\text{Methanol}}{CH_3OH} + KCl$$

(ii) Ethyl chloride to methane

$$C_2H_5Cl + NaOH\ (aq) \rightarrow C_2H_5OH + NaCl$$

$$C_2H_5OH + [O] \rightarrow CH_3COOH$$

$$CH_3COOH + NaOH \rightarrow CH_3COONa + H_2O$$

$$CH_3COONa + 2NaOH \rightarrow CH_4 + Na_2CO_3 + H_2O$$

(iii) (a)

$$H_3C-CH_3 + 2Br_2 \xrightarrow{\text{Sunlight}} \begin{array}{ccc} Br & & Br \\ | & & | \\ HC & - & CH \\ | & & | \\ Br & & Br \end{array}$$

Tetrabromoethane

(b)

$$\begin{array}{ccc} Br & & Br \\ | & & | \\ HC & - & CH \\ | & & | \\ Br & & Br \end{array} + 2Zn \longrightarrow HC \equiv CH.$$

(c) $HC \equiv CH \xrightarrow[\text{300°C}]{\text{red hot 'Cu' tube}}$

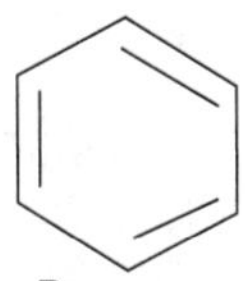

Benzene

EXAMPLE 9.7

Write the equations for the following laboratory preparations.

(i) Ethanol from iodoethane
(ii) Ethene from chloroethane
(iii) Ethane from sodium salt of propanoic acid
(iv) Acetic acid from ethanol.

SOLUTION

(i) Ethanol from iodoethane can be prepared by treating with aqueous KOH.

$$C_2H_5-I + KOH(aq) \rightarrow C_2H_5-OH + KI$$

(ii) Chloroethane on treatment with alcoholic KOH gives ethene.

$$C_2H_5-Cl + KOH(alk) \rightarrow C_2H_4 + KCl + H_2O$$

(iii) Sodium salt of propanoic acid on treatment with NaOH gives ethane.

$$CH_3-CH_2-COONa + NaOH \rightarrow CH_3-CH_3 + Na_2CO_3$$

(iv) Ethanol on oxidation in presence of $H^+/K_2Cr_2O_7$, gives acetic acid.

$$C_2H_5-OH + H^+/K_2Cr_2O_7 \rightarrow CH_3-COOH$$

It is quite obvious that the various organic compounds associated with various functional groups are the essential components of biomolecules. However, the biomolecules generally possess high molecular weight organic compounds. This is because they may contain long chains of hydrocarbons as in the case of oils and fats or they may be formed by the polymerization of simpler organic molecules as in the case of carbohydrates and proteins. Hence, the study of biomolecules is closely associated with the study of organic chemistry.

Biomolecules

Carbohydrates

Carbohydrates are the ultimate source of most of our food materials. Apart from this, they are mostly present in cotton and wood in the form of cellulose. Therefore, carbohydrates provide us with all basic necessities of life like food, clothing and shelter. Since carbohydrates are produced during the process of photosynthesis and consumed by animals as a source of energy, the study of carbohydrates, in addition to giving an understanding of the commodities of daily use, also gives scope for understanding the various biochemical processes involving their formation and usage.

These are an important class of organic molecules containing carbon, hydrogen and oxygen and defined as polyhydroxyaldehydes, polydroxyketones or compounds which produce these on hydrolysis. They are so named since they were considered to be hydrates of carbon with the general formula $C_x(H_2O)_y$. They are also called **saccharides** due to the similarity in taste to sugar which is known as **Saccharin**.

Classification

Carbohydrates are broadly classified on the basis of the products formed on hydrolysis. The three main categories of carbohydrates are listed below:

Monosaccharides

The class of carbohydrates which cannot be hydrolyzed into simpler saccharide units are called **monosaccharides.** They may contain chains of 3–10 carbon atoms and can be represented by a general formula $(CH_2O)_n$. Since they contain one carbonyl group and remaining are hydroxyl groups, they are termed as polyhydroxy aldehydes or ketones. Monosaccharides are further classified into 'aldoses' and 'ketoses,' which contain 'aldehyde' and 'ketone' functional groups, respectively.

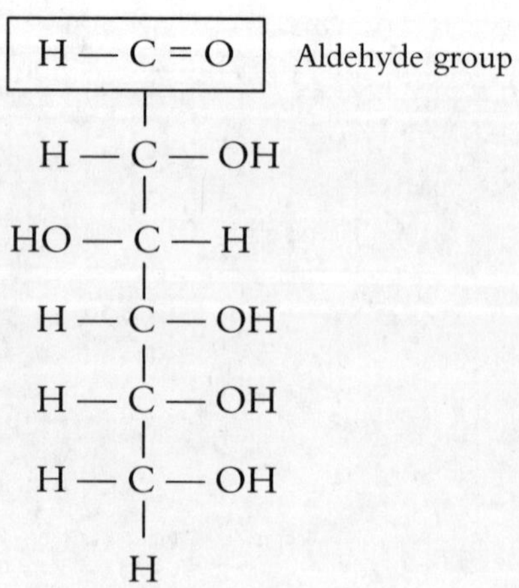

Glucose (aldose)

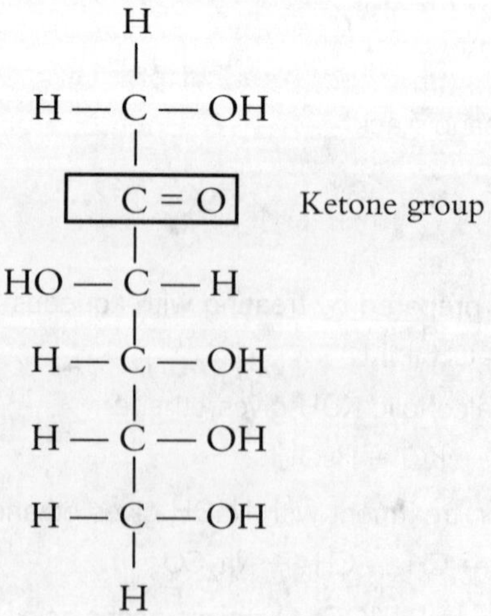

Frutose (ketose)

Info Bytes!

- The word "carbohydrate" means "hydrated carbon," reflecting their chemical composition.
- They are the body's primary energy source, especially for the brain and muscles during physical activity.

Depending on the number of carbon atoms in the chain, they are further classified into various types as shown below:

Table 9.13 Classification of monosaccharides

Number of carbon atoms	Classes	Examples
3	Trioses	Glyceraldehyde
4	Tetroses	Erythrose
5	Pentoses	Arabinose, ribulose, etc.
6	Hexoses	Glucose, fructose, galactose, mannose, etc.

Oligosaccharides

The class of carbohydrates, which on hydrolysis, gives 2–9 monosaccharide units are called **oligosaccharides**. Most common oligosaccharides give two or three or four monosaccharide units on hydrolysis and are named as disaccharides, trisaccharides and tetrasaccharides, respectively.

In the case of oligosaccharides, the different monosaccharide units are joined by means of glycoside linkage. A **glycoside linkage** is a bond formed by the loss of one water molecule between the carbonyl group and hydroxyl group of the monosaccharide units.

Table 9.14 Examples and features of oligosaccharides

Classes	Examples	Formulae	Products of hydrolysis
Disaccharide	Sucrose	$C_{12}H_{22}O_{11}$	Glucose, fructose
Disaccharide	Maltose	$C_{12}H_{22}O_{11}$	Glucose, glucose
Disaccharide	Lactose	$C_{12}H_{22}O_{11}$	Glucose, galactose
Trisaccharide	Raffinose	$C_{18}H_{32}O_{16}$	Glucose, fructose, galactose
Tetrasaccharide	Stachyose	$C_{24}H_{42}O_{21}$	Glucose, fructose and two moles of galactose

Polysaccharides

Polysaccharides represent the class of carbohydrates which can be hydrolyzed into a number of monosaccharide units. The number of units can range from hundreds to thousands also. They can be further classified on the basis of the kind of monosaccharide units formed by hydrolysis. They are represented by a general formula $C_n(H_2O)_{n-1}$ or $(C_6H_{10}O_5)_n$.

In contrast to monosaccharides and disaccharides, which are called **sugars**, polysaccharides are called **non-sugars** due to their bland taste.

Sweetness of a carbohydrate results from the interaction of the hydroxyl groups with the taste receptors on the tongue. The various carbohydrates differ in their relative sweetness for which sucrose is taken as the standard.

Konnect

The polysaccharides, which on hydrolysis, give only one kind of monosaccharides are called **homopolysaccharides** and those, which give different kinds of monosaccharides are called **heteropolysaccharides**.

Table 9.15 Comparative study of various simple carbohydrates

Classes	Examples	Formulae	Functional groups or types of bond	Sources	Characteristic properties	Relative sweetness
Monosaccharides	Glucose (grape sugar)	$C_6H_{12}O_6$	–CHO group (aldehyde)	Honey, ripe grapes, some fruits, blood and urine of mammals	Soluble in water, give reactions of aldehydes and are called reducing sugars	74
	Fructose (fruit sugar)	$C_6H_{12}O_6$	$R_2C=O$ group (R, R: keto group)	Fruits, honey	Soluble in water, non-reducing sugars	173 (maximum)
Disaccharides	Sucrose (table sugar) or (cane sugar)	$C_{12}H_{22}O_{11}$	Glycoside bond between one glucose unit and one fructose unit	Sugar cane and beet root	Soluble in water, non-reducing sugars	100
	Maltose	$C_{12}H_{22}O_{11}$	Glycoside bonds between two glucose units	Germinating cereals	Soluble in water, reducing sugars	32
	Lactose	$C_{12}H_{22}O_{11}$	Glycoside bond between one glucose unit and one galactose unit	Milk	Soluble in water, non-reducing sugar	16

Identification Tests for Some Carbohydrates

Carbohydrates that reduce Tollen's, Fehling's, and Benedict's reagent are called **reducing sugars**. All monosaccharides (aldose or ketose) are reducing sugars.

Info Bytes!

All monosaccharides (aldose or ketose) are reducing sugars.

Both glucose and fructose (monosaccharides) give positive result for Tollen's, Benedict's, and Fehling's test.

1. **Tollen's Test:** A little amount of glucose or fructose is dissolved in water and the solution is taken in a clean dry test tube. In another test tube, a little amount of silver nitrate is dissolved in 5% NaOH solution. A grey precipitate of silver hydroxide is formed. The precipitates are dissolved by adding a few drops of ammonium hydroxide.

   Ammonical silver nitrate solution so obtained is called **Tollen's reagent**. Addition of this reagent to glucose or fructose solution followed by heating in water bath lead to the formation of shining silver mirror on the walls of the test tube due to the reduction of Ag^+ ions to Ag.

2. **Benedict's Test:** Measured proportions of sodium citrate and sodium carbonate are dissolved in water. In this solution, copper sulphate is dissolved. The resulting solution is called Benedict's reagent. Addition of Benedict's reagent to glucose or fructose solution followed by heating in water bath results in the formation of a red precipitate. This is due to the reduction of Cu^{2+} to Cu^+.

3. **Fehling's Test:** Fehling's reagent is an alkaline solution of cupric ion complexed with sodium or potassium tartarate ions. When this reagent is added to glucose or fructose solution, followed by heating in water bath, results in the formation of a red precipitate due to the formation of cuprous oxide (reduction of Cu^{2+} to Cu^+).

Sucrose, a disaccharide, does not give positive result to Tollen's or Benedict's or Fehling's test. Hence, it is called a **non-reducing sugar**.

The addition of a few drops of concentrated HCl to the sucrose solution results in the hydrolysis of sucrose to glucose and fructose. Glucose and fructose being reducing sugars gives Tollen's test, Benedict's test, and Fehling's test.

Starch, a polysaccharide is insoluble in water. A thick paste can be made with hot water. Further addition of hot water gives a clear solution of starch.

Test for starch: Addition of 1% iodine solution in alcohol or KI solution to starch solution gives blue color.

Manufacture of Sucrose

The main sources of sucrose being sugarcane and beetroot, sucrose can be manufactured from both the sources. However, sugarcane is the most common source for the manufacture of sucrose.

Principle: Sugarcane contains 10%–15% of sucrose by weight. Sugarcane juice on purification followed by concentration and crystallisation results in the formation of colorless crystals of sugar.

To account for this, lime and $Ca(OH)_2$ are added, which is studied under three different headings.

Process: The process of manufacture of sucrose is carried out in four different steps.

1. **Extraction of Juice from Sugarcane:** Sugarcane is subjected to washing and then when put in cutting machines gets chopped into small pieces. These pieces are then sent into roll crushers where crushing takes place to extract juice from sugarcane. Addition of water in this stage enhances the efficiency of extraction. This process results in the extraction of 93% of the juice. The remaining cane left after extraction is called **bagasse**. It is considered as a by-product of sucrose manufacture as it can be used as a fuel in some industries for the manufacture of paper, cardboards, and generation of electricity.

2. **Purification of Sugarcane Juice:** The sugarcane juice is slightly acidic in nature and contains some impurities and suspended particles. Acidity should be removed from sugarcane juice before subjecting it to further process. This is because if the juice is acidic, during the process of concentration, some amount of sugar is lost due to hydrolysis.

   (a) **Defecation:** This process involves the addition of calcium hydroxide which neutralizes the juice and also removes the suspended impurities in the form of precipitates.

   (b) **Carbonation:** This step involves the passage of carbon dioxide gas through the juice obtained from the first step. In this process, excess lime is removed as carbonates and some coloring matter and some inorganic salts are removed and settled as mud. The juice is then filtered.

   (c) **Sulphitation:** The juice obtained after filtration in the above step is subjected to treatment with sulphur dioxide. It being a good bleaching agent decolorizes the juice. This also serves to neutralize excess of lime carried from the first step. Calcium sulphite so formed is removed by filtration.

   The precipitate obtained in the last step is called **press mud** and is used as a fertilizer.

3. **Concentration and Crystallization of Juice:** The juice obtained at the end of second stage is called 'clarified juice' which contains 85% of water. When it is subjected to evaporation, the percentage of water is reduced to almost half. Further, concentration of juice is carried out initially at low pressure and later in vacuum. The concentrated juice is taken in vacuum pans and concentrated till a supersaturated solution is obtained.

4. **Isolation and Drying of Crystals:** The juice remaining at the end of the third stage contains 10% of water. Since it is a supersaturated solution, sucrose crystals are separated out by a process called centrifugation. The sugar crystals obtained are then exposed to hot air to remove the minor traces of water.

Konnect

The mother liquor left after the crystallisation of sucrose from sugarcane juice is called **molasses**. This is a very important by-product of sugar industry.

Proteins

Among all biomolecules, proteins are the most important ones. The diverse functions performed by proteins in the biological system make them the most vital substances of life. The name 'proteins' has been originated from the Greek word '*proteios*', which means 'of prime importance' as all living cells invariably contain them. **Proteins** are the most abundant organic molecules to be found in living cells and 50% of their total dry mass is protein.

Due to the diversity of the structure, proteins have a wide range of structural and metabolic activities in the biological systems of various living organisms.

Examples:

1. Proteins in hair–Keratin
2. Insulin in pancreas
3. Enzymes like cellulase, amylase, etc.
4. Blood contains a red pigment called haemoglobin which is also proteinic in nature

> **Konnect**
>
> - There are 20 different amino acids that can be combined in various ways to make a protein.
> - The human body can produce 11 amino acids, but the remaining 9 - termed 'essential' - must be obtained from food.

Structure of Protein

Proteins are high polymers or polyamides, (of high molecular mass) where a single protein molecule consists of hundreds to thousands of amino acid units. These units consist of 20 odd amino acids combined in different ways, thus forming a large number of protein molecules. Therefore, **amino acids** are considered as the basic units of protein molecules.

Basically, there are 25 different amino acids commonly found in proteins. All these amino acids can be synthesized by plants from the basic raw materials like CO_2, water and other inorganic compounds of nitrogen. Animals do not have the ability to synthesize these amino acids on their own. Hence, they depend on plants for these amino acids. Thus, they obtain 10 amino acids directly from the food they consume. These amino acids are termed as **essential amino acids**. By making use of these amino acids, the other amino acids can be synthesized and such amino acids are termed as **non-essential amino acids**.

This classification of amino acids as essential and non-essential amino acids does not actually reflect their relative significance. Instead, the classification implies the ability of the living systems to synthesize a particular amino acid within the system.

Nomenclature of Amino Acids

The general formula of the amino acid can be given as $R - \underset{\displaystyle NH_2}{\underset{|}{CH}} - COOH$ where 'R' is an alkyl group.

Amino acids are named as amino carboxylic acids according to the IUPAC system. Their trivial names have generally originated from their sources. They are preferably indicated by a three-letter symbol. While writing genetic code, they are represented by one-letter code. The various amino acids differ in the characteristic feature of the nature of alkyl side chain.

Structure of Amino Acids

Every amino acid molecule has a central carbon atom to which one acidic carboxyl group (COOH) and one basic amino group ($—NH_2$) are attached. Apart from these two functional groups, the other two valencies of carbon are satisfied by an alkyl group and a hydrogen atom. The uniqueness and specificity of each amino acid can be attributed to the nature of the alkyl group attached.

Table 9.16 Some simple essential amino acids

Nature of alkyl chains	Trivial names	Symbols	Codes
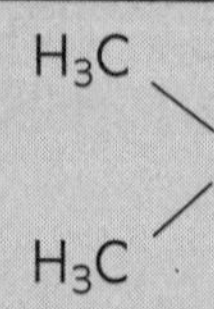	Valine	Val	V
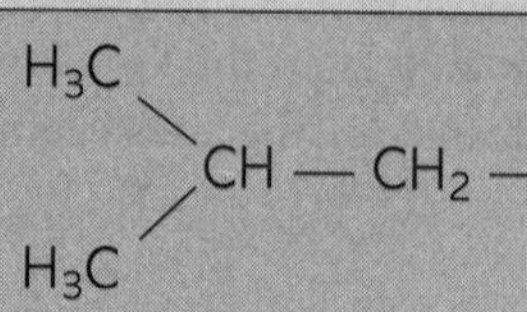	Leucine	Leu	L

(Continued.)

Table 9.16 Continued

Nature of alkyl chains	Trivial names	Symbols	Codes
$H_3C - CH_2 - \underset{CH_3}{\underset{\vert}{CH}} -$	Isoleucine	Ile	I
$HN = \underset{NH_2}{\underset{\vert}{C}} - NH - (CH_2)_3 -$	Arginine	Arg	R
$H_2N-(CH_2)_4-$	Lysine	Lys	K
$H_3C-CHOH-$	Threonine	Thr	T
$C_6H_5-CH_2-$	Phenylalanine	Phe	F

Table 9.17 Some simple non-essential amino acids

Nature of alkyl chains	Trivial names	Symbols	Codes
$-H$	Glycine	Gly	G
$-CH_3$	Alanine	Ala	A
$H_2N - \overset{O}{\overset{\Vert}{C}} - CH_2 - CH_2$	Glutamine	Gln	Q
$HOOC-CH_2-CH_2-$	Glutamic acid	Glu	E
$H_2N - \overset{O}{\overset{\Vert}{C}} - CH_2 -$	Asparagine	Asn	N
$HO-CH_2-$	Serine	Ser	S
$HS-CH_2-$	Cysteine	Cys	C
$HO-C_6H_4-CH_2-$	Tyrosine	Tyr	Y

Properties of Amino Acids

1. Amino acids are polar covalent compounds.
2. They are crystalline substances which are soluble in water.
3. They have high melting points.
4. Since each molecule of the amino acid contains an acidic —COOH group and a basic $-NH_2$ parts, they exhibit amphoteric nature. The amino acid has the tendency to transfer the H^+ ion from the —COOH group to the $-NH_2$ group. As a result of this, the molecule carries a negative charge on one end and positive charge on the other end. It is this charge separation which makes the molecule dipolar and the dipolar ions thus formed are called **zwitter ions**.

   Examples:

$$\underset{\text{Amino acid}}{H_3C - \overset{H}{\overset{|}{\underset{NH_2}{\underset{|}{C}}}} - COOH} \longleftrightarrow \underset{\text{Zwitter ion}}{H_3C - \overset{H}{\overset{|}{\underset{NH_3^+}{\underset{|}{C}}}} - COO^-}$$

5. Peptide bond formation is the characteristic property of amino acids. Since amino acids have two functional groups, two similar or dissimilar amino acids can combine together by the elimination of a water molecule. The bond hence formed is called a **peptide bond**. A number of amino acids can join together by means of a number of peptide bonds and the resultant molecule is called a **polypeptide**.

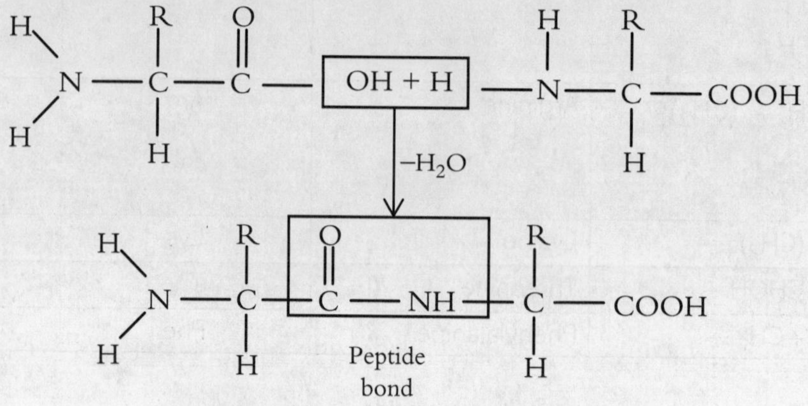

Figure 9.1 Formation of the Peptide Bond

Synthesis of Proteins from Amino Acids

Innumerable number of proteins is formed from the 20 odd amino acids available. This is possible because the sequence in which amino acids are linked with each other changes from one protein to the other. The proteins differ in number and sequence of the amino acids. Due to this, the proteins perform different functions in the biological systems. A slight variation in the number or sequence of amino acids in a protein makes the protein ineffective for carrying out the respective function.

Blood contains an important protein called **hemoglobin**. This protein performs the function of absorbing oxygen to form oxyhaemoglobin which performs important metabolic process. Hemoglobin is made up of 574 amino acids in a specific sequence. Variation of even one amino acid in the sequence makes hemoglobin ineffective for carrying oxygen in the blood. This leads to a disease called 'sickle cell anaemia.'

A part of normal sequence of hemoglobin: –Val–His–Leu–Thr–Pro–Glu–Glu–Lys

A part of sickle cell anaemia sequence of hemoglobin: –Val–His–Leu–Thr–Pro–Val–Glu–Lys

Significance of Carbohydrates and Proteins

The chemistry of biomolecules is closely associated with the sources of energy in plants and animals. These sources of energy being carbohydrates, the energy cycle involves the various steps associated with the production and consumption of these nutrients.

Solar energy is the primary source of energy for all natural processes. Green plants trap the solar energy and carry out the process of photosynthesis which is highly endoergic process of conversion of carbon dioxide and water vapor to glucose and oxygen. The oxygen so liberated during the process of photosynthesis is taken up by the animals by means of respiration. Carbohydrates which are consumed by the animals are subjected to

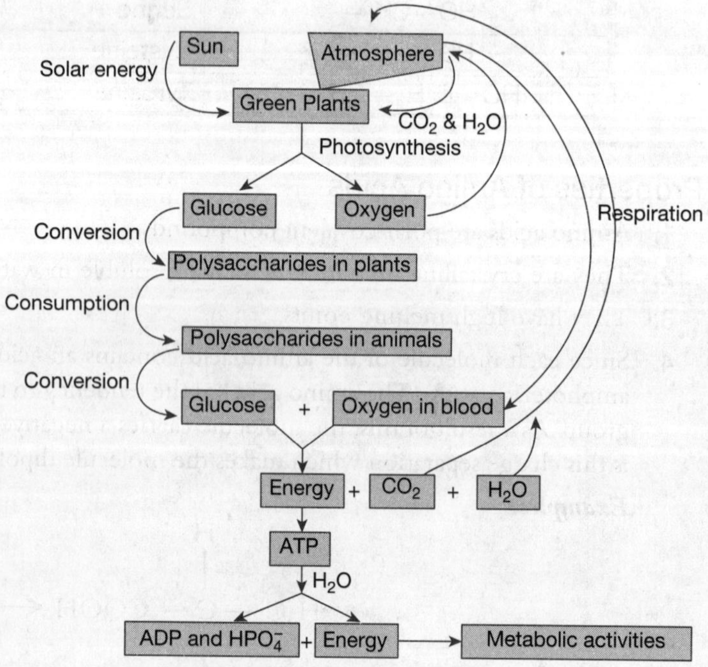

Figure 9.2 Energy cycle

oxidation in the living cells with the help of oxygen present in blood. The energy liberated during the above process is stored in living cells in adenosine triphosphate (ATP) molecules. Each ATP molecule hydrolyzes to give adenosine diphosphate and HPO_4^- with the liberation of 36 kcal of energy. This energy is utilized for various metabolic activities.

$$ATP + H_2O \longrightarrow ADP + HPO_4^- + energy$$

Each ATP molecule can store 36 kcal of energy. In the absence of metabolic activities in the living system, the energy remains stored in the ATP molecules. During the process of metabolism, these ATP molecules undergo hydrolysis, thereby, releasing the required amount of energy.

All these processes involve the role of enzymes which are biocatalysts. Enzymes as well as ATP molecules are constituted by proteins.

Food containing high content of Carbohydrates and Proteins

The various food materials contain varying amounts of carbohydrates and proteins. The amount of energy released in kilocalories by the combustion of one gram of the food is called **calorific value**. Depending on the amount of carbohydrates present in various food stuffs, they differ in their calorific values. For example, the calorific value of glucose is 3.81 cal/g. The nutritive value of the food material ultimately depends on its calorific value. The calorific value of the same food item also varies for the cooked and the uncooked state of food.

Table 9.18 Calorific values of cooked and uncooked food items

Cooked food items	Calorific values	Uncooked food items	Calorific values
Rice	110	Egg	173
Paratha	360	Milk	85
Green vegetables	130	Butter	730
Bread	245	Oil/ghee	900
Pulses	345	Chocolate bar	545

The amount of energy so released is utilized for doing various anabolic activities. Just as the various stuffs have different calorific values, the various anabolic activities also require variable amounts of calories. The quantity and the quality of the food material to be consumed depend not only on the nutritive values of the food stuffs but also on the regular activities performed by the individuals.

Table 9.19 Calories required for some activities

Activities	Calories required
Walking	228
Golf	300
Bicycling	414
Swimming	420
Tennis	426
Running	870

Oils and Fats

In addition to carbohydrates and proteins, oils, and fats form another important class of nutrients. Carbohydrates are considered as immediate sources of energy and proteins are responsible for structural and metabolic activities, whereas oils and fats act as the most important reservoirs of energy. In addition to being rich in nutritive value, oils and fats serve as important raw materials for the manufacture of soaps, vanaspathi ghee, paints, and varnishes. Seeds of plants are the sources of vegetable oils, rich sources of essential fatty acids. Animal sources of fats are milk, ghee, eggs, fish, and meat.

Structure and Chemical Composition of Oils and Fats

With respect to chemical composition, oils, and fats are known as triesters of glycerol or triacylglyerol associated with long chains of fatty acids.

Glycerols are trihydric alcohols where the three carbon atoms can be attached to three –OH groups. Fatty acids are carboxylic acids with long carbon chains ranging from 14 to 22 carbon atoms. If the fatty acid molecule contains one or more double bonds, it is called an **unsaturated fatty acid**. Glycerol, which undergoes condensation with three molecules of fatty acids, loses three molecules of water to form corresponding triesters, known as **triglyceride** or **triacylglycerol**.

Examples:

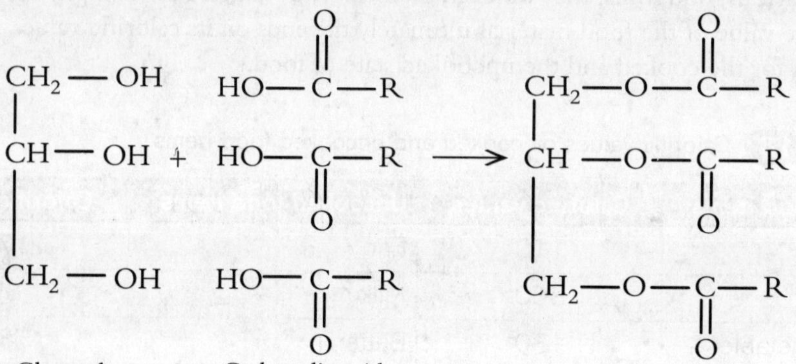

Glycerol Carboxylic acid Triglyceride

R, R′, and R″ are alkyl groups

Classification of Oils and Fats

The triglycerides which are solids at room temperature are called **fats** and the triglycerides which are liquids at room temperature are called **oils**.

This difference in phase in triglycerides depends on the extent of unsaturation present in the fatty acid part of the triglycerides. In the case of fats, the extent of unsaturation is less and hence they exist as solids. In the case of oils, the extent of unsaturation is more and hence they exist as oils.

Saturated oils or fats are glycerides of lauric acid ($C_{11}H_{23}COOH$) and stearic acid ($C_{17}H_{35}COOH$) which are saturated fatty acids.

Examples: Coconut oil, butter – lauric acid

Animal fat – stearic acid

Unsaturated oils are glycerides of unsaturated fatty acids like oleic acid ($C_{17}H_{33}COOH$) or linoleic acid ($C_{17}H_{33}COOH$).

Examples: Cotton seed oil, animal fat – oleic acid

Linseed oil – linoleic acid

They can be solidified by converting the unsaturated fatty acid into the corresponding saturated fatty acids. This can be done by subjecting the oils to a process called **hydrogenation**.

Hydrogenation of Oils

The process involves the passage of hydrogen gas through the unsaturated oil at 200°C temperature and 5 atm pressure in the presence of nickel catalyst. The carbon–carbon double bonds in the fatty acids are broken due to the addition of hydrogen to these bonds. Therefore, the unsaturated oils get converted to saturated fats, thereby leading to solidification. The solidified fat thus formed has a higher melting point. Hence, this process is also called **hardening of oils**. The process of hydrogenation carried out is generally partial since complete hydrogenation gives very hard fats unsuitable for cooking purposes. Fats so obtained are more resistant to spoilage in addition to having a better taste and odor.

> **Info Bytes!**
> Generally, the term 'oils' can be applicable to both unsaturated oils and saturated oils. However, the term 'fats' is confined to saturated oils only.

$$\underset{\text{(Unsaturated)}}{\text{Oil}} + H_2 \xrightarrow[\substack{200^\circ C \\ 5\ \text{atm}}]{\text{Ni}} \underset{\text{(saturated)}}{\text{Fat}}$$

Physical Properties

1. Generally odorless and tasteless
2. Immiscible with water and lighter than water
3. Highly soluble in organic solvents

Uses

1. Various vegetable oils such as groundnut oil, coconut oil, sunflower oil, etc., are used for cooking.
2. The hydrogenated oils such as dalda, vanaspathi, ghee, etc., are also used for cooking purposes.
3. Some oils like coconut oil, mustard oil, olive oil, etc., are used for cosmetic purposes.
4. Cod liver oil and eucalyptus oil have medicinal value.
5. Oils and fats find industrial applications in the manufacture of soaps, paints, varnishes, detergents, etc.

EXAMPLE 9.8 Explain why starch is used as a thickening agent in cooking and food preparation. How does it work at the molecular level to thicken sauces, gravies, and other dishes?

SOLUTION

Starch is used as a thickening agent in cooking because its molecular structure allows it to form a gel-like network when heated in the presence of water. This network traps water molecules, thickening sauces and gravies as it cools. Starch consists of amylose and amylopectin, with amylose being water-soluble and playing a key role in thickening due to its ability to form hydrogen bonds with water.

EXAMPLE 9.9 A patient's blood sample is tested for glucose concentration using Benedict's reagent. After the reaction with the reagent, the solution turns from blue to orange. If the patient's blood sample initially contained 10 grams of glucose, how much glucose is estimated to be present in the blood sample based on the colour change?

SOLUTION

The colour change in the reaction with Benedict's reagent is indicative of the concentration of glucose in the blood sample. The extent of colour change can be used to estimate the glucose concentration. In this case, based on the orange colour change observed with Benedict's reagent, the estimated glucose concentration in the blood sample is approximately 10 grams per litter (g/L).

Important Applications of Organic Chemistry

Polymers

There are many organic compounds which are useful for various purposes in our daily life. They include plastics, rubber, synthetic fibres, dyes, medicines, cosmetics, petroleum products, etc. Among these, plastics and synthetic fibres are made up of synthetic polymers which are obtained from simple organic molecules. **'Polymers'** as the name itself suggests are giant organic molecules made up of many simpler units which may be identical or not. The simple compounds which join together to give polymers are called **monomers**. Polymers are otherwise called **macromolecules**. The process of formation of polymers from the corresponding simple monomer molecules is called **polymerization**. Polymers can be naturally occurring or they may be man-made.

Synthetic Polymers

Some of the natural polymers such as starch, proteins, nucleic acids, rubber, silk, etc., are available in living systems, whereas many polymers can be prepared in a laboratory from simple organic compounds. These are called **synthetic polymers** in order to distinguish them from natural polymers.

There are two types of polymerizations as listed below:

1. **Addition Polymerization:** This reaction involves joining the individual organic molecules by breaking of π-bonds and adding the molecules together.

   The macromolecules formed are called **addition polymers**.

Examples:

$$2H_2C = CH_2 \xrightarrow[\text{or HCl}]{H_2SO_4} -CH_2-CH_2-CH_2-CH_2-$$

$$\underset{\text{ethylene or ethene}}{nCH_2 = CH_2} \xrightarrow{H_2SO_4} \underset{\text{polyethylene or polythene}}{(CH_2-CH_2)_n}$$

Konnect

- Natural rubber is a polymer, and its discovery predates synthetic polymers by thousands of years.
- The name "polymer" derives from the Greek words "poly" meaning many and "meros" meaning part.

Table 9.20 Some examples of addition polymers

Name of monomers	Formulae	Names of polymer	Formulae	Uses
Ethene	$H_2C=CH_2$	Polyethene	$(CH_2-CH_2)_n$	Toys, pipes, bags, containers
Vinyl chloride	$CH_2=CH-Cl$	PVC (polyvinyl chloride)	$(CH_2-CH)_n$	Floor tiles, toys, rain coats
Tetrafluoroethene	$CF_2=CF_2$	Teflon	$(CF_2-CF_2)_n$	Non-stick cookware coating
Propene	$CH_2-CH=CH_2$	Polyprene	$(CH_2-CH(Cl))_n$	Fibres for carpets, fishing nets
Isoprene	$H_2C=C(CH_3)-CH=CH_2$	Natural rubber	$(CH_2-C(CH_3)=CH-CH_2)_n$	Water proof materials sheets, balls, tyres, shoes
1, 3-Butadiene	$H_2C=CHCH=CH_2$	Synthetic rubber, Buna-S	$(CH_2-CH=CH-CH_2)_n$	Same as natural rubber
Chloroprene	$H_2C=C(Cl)-CH=CH_2$	Neoprene	$(CH_2-C(Cl)=CH-CH_2)_n$	Insulating material, conveyor belts in mines, synthetic fibre

2. **Condensation Polymerization:** A reaction in which the joining of monomer molecules involves a loss of simple molecules such as water or ammonia is called **condensation polymerization**. The resulting products are called **condensation polymers**.

   This type of polymerization is possible only between the molecules having two reactive sites or functional groups. The classes of organic compounds which involve in this process are generally alcohols, carboxylic acids, amines, and amides.

   The basic reactions involve the formation of ester group or amide group.

   Example:

$$RCOOH + HOR^1 \xrightarrow{H_2SO_4} RCOOR^1 + H_2O$$

$$RCOOH + \begin{matrix}H\\ \\ H\end{matrix}\!\!>N - R^1 \rightarrow RCONHR^1 + H_2O$$

   (R & $R^1 \rightarrow$ alkyl groups)

Table 9.21 Some Examples of Condensation Polymers

Names of monomers	Formulae of monomers	Names of the polymer	Uses
Ethylene glycol + Dimethyl terephthalate	CH_2OH–CH_2OH + $C_4H_4(COOCH_3)_2$	Terylene (or) (polyester) Dacron	Manufacture of synthetic fabric
Hexamethylene diamine + adipic acid	$H_2N(CH_2)_6NH_2$ + $HOOC—(CH_2)_4—COOH$	Nylon – 6, 6 (polyamide)	Manufacture of synthetic fabric

Classification of Polymers

Polymers can be classified into three types depending on the structure and physical properties. They are listed below:

1. **Elastomers/Rubber:** Elastomers are polymers which exhibit the unique property of high elasticity. They can be stretched to 5–10 times their original length under tension and their original dimension can be reversed back on the release of the load. Thus, elasticity is the characteristic property.

   Elastomer/rubber is an addition polymer. Naturally available rubber can be formed from latex of rubber trees. The basic monomer units in rubber are isoprene units. This polymer is highly elastic in nature. This natural rubber is subjected to a process called vulcanization which makes the rubber temperature resistant. **Vulcanization** is the process of heating of natural rubber with sulphur which improves the elasticity as well as reduces the sticky nature of rubber. During this process, different isoprene units are joined together by C–S–S–C bonds. Synthetic rubbers are also addition polymers.

   Examples: Buna–S, thiokol rubber, etc.

   Elastomers can be of two types—natural and synthetic elastomers.

   Natural rubber is the example of natural elastomer and examples of synthetic elastomers are Buna-S rubber and neoprene. Following are the characteristics of rubber:

   (a) The material is soft.

   (b) It can withstand very high strain.

2. **Fibres:** Fibres are polymers which have the characteristic property of high tensile strength and can be elongated into long thin threads.

   Cellulose is a natural polymer, a main constituent, present in natural fibres such as cotton, wool, and silk. Synthetic fibres are nylon, polyester, terylene, orlon, rayon, etc. Following are the characteristics of fibres:

   (a) High tensile strength

   (b) Ability to withstand pressure and temperature (sunlight and ironing)

   (c) Resistance to chemical reactions with alkalies and solvents of dry cleaning

   (d) Resistance to aerial oxidation

   Preparation of Synthetic Fibre: From a polymeric material, the synthetic fibre can be obtained by spinning. Spinning of fibre can be of various types as discussed below.

   (a) Melt Spinning: The molten polymer when pumped through a porous spinneret jet followed by cooling gives fibre.

   Examples: Nylon and dacron

   (b) Dry Spinning: The polymer is made to dissolve in an organic solvent that has a low boiling point. It is pumped through the spinneret. The solvent is evaporated by sending hot air around the spinneret. Thus, a fibre is obtained.

   Examples: Cellulose acetate and Orlon

3. **Plastics:** The polymers which can be extended as sheets or pipes or which when dissolved in suitable solvents form paints and emulsions or which can be molded into various shapes are called plastics. For making various types of plastics, small amounts of other compounds are added to the polymeric organic compound. These compounds which are added are called fillers, plasticizers, and lubricants.

Table 9.22 Uses of plastics

Monomers	Polymers	Uses
Styrene	Polystyrene	Insulating materials, packing, TV, refrigerator lining
Vinyl chloride	Polyvinyl chloride (PVC)	Pipes, floor coverings, gramophone records

Following are the characteristics of plastics:

1. Tough and hard materials.
2. High resistance to chemical reactions with water, heat and pressure, atmosphere.
3. Ease of fabrication.
4. Ease of color mixing.
5. Resistance to corrosion.

Adhesives

The substance which is used for attaching materials at their surfaces is called an **adhesive**.

1. **Natural Adhesives:** Natural adhesives are made from bones of animals and fish, milk protein casein, vegetable protein, egg albumin, blood albumin, starch, etc.

   Examples: Gum-Arabica, shellac, glue, etc.

2. **Synthetic Adhesives:** Synthetic adhesives can be obtained from derivatives of cellulose. The additional materials such as wetting agents, fillers and preservatives are added to adhesives.

   Examples: Epoxy resins, silicones, phenol–urea formaldehyde resin, polyvinyls, polystyrenes, polyamides, etc.

Characteristics of Adhesives

1. It should be capable of holding the material together by surface attachment.
2. It should dry at a faster rate.
3. The solvents should not react with the material to which the adhesive is applied.

Info Bytes!

- Ancient Egyptians used adhesives made from animal products to bind things together over 3,000 years ago.

Cosmetics

Cosmetics is a class of materials used for cleaning or beautification of a person. They include creams, talcum powders, cleaning lotions, nail polishes, etc.

1. **Cold Creams:** They are emulsions of oil in water used to protect skin from external effects. Following are the characteristics of cold creams:
   - **(a)** Should melt at body temperature.
   - **(b)** Should easily spread over the skin.
   - **(c)** Should not be sticky and greasy.
   - **(d)** Should act as a shield to hot sun, cold weather and wind.

   Ingredients of a cold cream: Almond oil, bees wax, rose water, butter, olive oil, borax, and paraffin wax.
2. **Nail Polish:** It is a polymeric resin applied on nails for cosmetic purpose. Following are the characteristics of nail polish:
   - **(a)** Non-toxic in nature.
   - **(b)** Faster evaporation of solvents and faster drying.
   - **(c)** Water insoluble in nature.
   - **(d)** Should be available in attractive colors.

   Ingredients of nail polish: Organic polymer, a plasticizer, coloring pigments, perfume, low boiling solvent. The polymeric resin may be a derivative of nitrocellulose. Plasticizer can be castor oil. The low boiling solvents can be alcohols, benzene, etc.

Konnect

Ancient Egyptians used cosmetics not just for aesthetic reasons but also for health and protection. The eyeliner they famously wore, made from kohl, helped protect their eyes from the desert sun.

Dyes

These substances are organic coloring materials which can impart colors to various fibres. Following are the characteristics of dyes:

1. Resistance to sunlight.
2. Resistance to soaps and detergents.
3. Ability to spread uniformly over the fabric.
4. Resistance to water.
5. Resistance to heat and temperature.
6. Ability of easy drying.

Structural Aspects of the Ingredients of Dyes

All dyes are basically aromatic organic compounds. The unsaturated group of the organic molecule which imparts color to the fabric is called **chromophores**.

Example: $-NO_2$, $-NO$, $-N=N-$, $>C=O$, $>C=S$ groups.

The other part of the molecule intensifies the color of the dye. In addition to this, it is this part which forms bonds with the fibre. These are called **auxochromes**.

Example: $-COOH$, $-OH$, $-SO_3H$, $-NH_2$, $-NHR$ groups

Classification of Dyes

On the basis of the nature of chromophore present in the dye, the dyes are classified into various types. Some of these types of dyes are discussed below:

Table 9.23 Classification of dyes on the basis of chromophore

Chromophores	Types of dye	Examples
$-NO_2$	Nitro dye	Martius yellow
$-NO$	Nitroso dye	Naphthol green
$-N{\equiv}N$	Azo dye	Methyl orange, Bismarck brown
$-C{=}O$	Quinone dye	Indigo

Dyes can be classified into various types on the basis of the method of application as discussed below:

1. **Acid Dyes**

   These are water soluble anionic dyes that are applied to fibre such as silk, wool, and nylon. Attachment to the fibre is attributed to salt formation between anionic groups in the dye and cationic group of the fibre.

2. **Basic Dyes**

   Basic dyes are water soluble cationic dyes. Those are mainly applied to acrylic fibres, but find some use for wool and silk also. Basic dyes are also used for the coloration of paper.

3. **Direct Dyes**

   The dying with direct dyes is normally carried out in neutral or slightly alkaline dye bath at or near boiling point, with the addition of NaCl or Na_2SO_4. Direct dyes are used for cotton, paper, leather, wool, silk and nylon. They are also used as pH indicators.

4. **Mordant Dyes**

   These dyes cannot dye the fabric directly. When some substances called mordants are added to these dyes, they can produce wash-fast colors. The mordants include salts of some metals like aluminium, iron, and chromium. Acidic dyes require basic mordants and basic dyes require acidic mordants.

   Example: Alizarin

5. **Vat Dyes**

   These are a kind of developed dyes. The actual dye is colorless. On application to the fabric, it gets oxidized and converted to the colored form. The colorless form is called **leuco form**.

   Example: Indigo

Table 9.24 Classification of dyes on the basis of method of application

Types of dye	(Method of application) Media required	Examples
Acid dye	Acid medium	Orange I
Basic dye	Basic medium	Malachite green
Direct dye	Neutral medium	Martius yellow
Mordant dye	Insoluble and applied along with soluble dye	Alizarin
Vat dyes	Reduced form	Indigo

Drugs

The word 'drug' is derived from the French word 'drogue' which means a dry herb. This is because, in ancient times, drugs were extracted from various plant parts.

A **drug** can be defined as a substance which is used for prevention, diagnosis, treatment, or cure of a disease in human beings or animals.

Characteristics of an Ideal Drug

1. Localized site of action.
2. Efficient in action.
3. Should have negligible side effects.
4. Should not cause any damage to host tissues.
5. Should not acquire tolerance on prolonged usage.

Therapeutic Action of Drugs

It is the effect of a particular drug on localized site to produce a desired action on the desired physiological process. Based on the physiological action or therapeutic action, drugs are classified into four types as listed below:

1. **Drugs Acting on Central Nervous System:** These drugs work either to stimulate or depress the action of brain and spinal cord. These are also called **tranquilizers**.

   Examples: Meprobamate, Amytal (barbiturates), etc.

2. **Drugs Acting on Peripheral Nervous System:** These drugs act to stimulate or block temporarily the action of body nerves. These are also called **analgesics**.

   Examples: Aspirin, Paracetamol, Benadryl, etc.

3. **Cardiovascular Drugs:** These drugs act on the blood vessels and on the functioning of heart. That means, they may be cardiotonic, anti-hypertensive and hypocholestemics. Some drugs also act on renal system and they are called diuretics.

   Examples: Aspirin, naproxen, etc.

4. **Chemotherapeutic Drugs:** Treating the disease by chemical substances is called **chemotherapy**. Chemotherapy is the use of drugs to kill an invading microorganism present in the body cells without causing any damage to the host cells. These are further classified into various types based on their action on the type of microorganism.

Chemotherapeutic drug	Examples
Anti-malarial drugs	Chloroquine
Antiseptics	Dettol, boric acid, etc.
Anti-fungals	Sulphadiazine
Anti-biotics	Erythromycin, tetracycline, chloramphenicol, penicillin, etc.
Anti-viral drugs	Aureomycin
Anti-tuberculosis drugs	Rifampicin, cycloserine, etc.

Vitamins

These are the compounds which are required by animals in small quantities for their metabolic activities and for the maintenance of normal health. They form part of the food materials consumed. However, their deficiency causes various diseases. Hence, the supplementation of vitamins to the body in the form of drugs is essential in times of need.

Table 9.25 Chemical names and deficiencies of vitamins

Vitamins	Chemical names	Deficiency disorders
A	Retinol	Night blindness
B_1	Thiamine	Beriberi
B_2	Riboflavin	Tongue sores and sores at mouth corner

(Continued.)

Table 9.25 Continued

Vitamins	Chemical names	Deficiency disorders
B_3	Nicotinic acid	Pellagra
B_5	Pantothenic acid	No deficiency symptoms reported
B_6	Pyridoxine	Convulsions
B_{12}	Cyanocobalamin	Anaemia
C	Ascorbic acid	Scurvy
D	Calciferol	Rickets
E	Tocoferol	Infertility
K	Phylloquinone	Bleeding or haemorrhage

Hormones

These are chemical substances produced by endocrine glands inside the human or animal body. They control the metabolic rate, and hence act as metabolic catalysts. For example, insulin secreted by pancreas controls the glucose levels in blood. But deficiency of these hormones in the body results in physiological disorders or disease. In order to cure these disorders, the hormones should be given externally as a drug. These drugs also form the part of anti-fertility drugs and are known as **contraceptives**.

Pharmaceutical Formulations

Pharmaceutical formulations are the various forms in which drugs are given to the patients. A drug cannot be directly consumed by a patient due to its unpleasant taste, smell, and appearance. Above all, the drug when passing through the system may show harmful effects on various parts of the body. It has to be released at its site of action in required amounts at regular intervals.

Due to these reasons, a drug is mixed with other ingredients and modified into various forms like tablets, capsules, syrups, tonics, ointments, injections, powders, etc.

1. **Tablets:** To the powdered drug, suitable gum is added, dose is determined and then molded into solid form called 'tablets.'

   Mode of Preparation

   (a) **Dry Method:** All ingredients are granulated and screened through a mesh sieve. The dry granules are compressed and packed.

   (b) **Wet Method:** The granulated drug and other ingredients are dispersed in a binder excipient uniformly and screened through a mesh sieve. The granules are dried on trays in hot air ovens and compressed to get tablets and the tablets are packed.

2. **Capsules:** When the drug is bitter or when it causes harm to the intestinal walls or when the drug is to be absorbed slowly, it is made into a capsule form. These are also prepared in the same manner as the drug in the form of powder or granules is filled in an outer covering.

3. **Syrups and Tonics:** The drug is dissolved in a suitable solvent and made into a colloid or suspension. Flavouring agents and colors are also added to these to give them good taste, odor, and appearance. Most of the pediatric drugs are in these formulations.

4. **Injections:** When the drug action is required immediately, drug formulations are introduced directly into the body fluids such as injections.

   The drug is made to dissolve in a suitable solvent to form a solution. These are the formulations where the drug is directly injected into the muscles or nerves.

Soaps

Soap is the sodium or potassium salt of a long chain of fatty acids.

Hydrolysis of triglycerides in the presence of alkali gives salts of the corresponding fatty acids and glycerol. This reaction is known as **saponification of ester**.

$$\underset{\text{Triglyceride}}{RCOOR^1} + NaOH \xrightarrow{H_2O} \underset{\text{Soap}}{RCOONa} + \underset{\text{Glycerol}}{R^1OH}$$

Process: The process of manufacturing of a soap is carried out in three steps as discussed below:

1. **Hydrolysis:** This step is carried out in a stainless steel tower. Coconut oil or cotton seed oil or animal fat is taken in the tower. Superheated steam is passed through the oil at 240–250°C under a pressure of 4.1 mega pascals for 2–3 h in presence of zinc oxide or calcium oxide catalyst. The oil gets hydrolyzed to give a mixture of fatty acids and glycerol. Glycerol, being highly soluble in water, is separated by distillation, leaving behind fatty acids.
2. **Separation:** The fatty acids obtained are used further for the preparation of the soap. In this step, the mixture of fatty acids is separated and required fatty acid is used for further process. The mixture is dried and separated by fractional distillation. The fatty acids required are chosen, mixed in required ratios (this dictates the quality of soap) and sent for neutralization.
3. **Neutralization:** The fatty acids are neutralized by using bases. The type of base used depends on the type of soap to be manufactured. Different salts of fatty acids have different uses in soaps.

$$\underset{\text{glyceride}}{\begin{array}{l} CH_2{-}O{-}COC_{17}H_{33} \\ | \\ CH_2{-}O{-}COC_{17}H_{33} \\ | \\ CH_2{-}O{-}COC_{17}H_{33} \end{array}} + 3NaOH \longrightarrow \underset{\text{glycerol}}{\begin{array}{l} CH_2OH \\ | \\ CHOH \\ | \\ CH_2OH \end{array}} + \underset{\text{soap}}{3C_{17}H_{35}COONa}$$

Table 9.26 Types of soaps

Types of soap	Bases used for neutralization
Toilet soap	KOH
Laundry soap	NaOH
Water proof texture	$Ca(OH)_2$, $Al(OH)_3$
Dry cleaning	Triethanol ammonium hydroxide

Certain other additives are also added to the soap to give them certain extra features.

Table 9.27 Examples of additives

Soap/Features	Additives added
Deodorant soap	3, 4, 5-Tribromosalicylanilide
Shaving soap/Slow drying lather	Stearic acid
Transparent soap	Glycerine
All soaps	Perfumes, soda ash, sodium bicarbonate

A large variety of soaps is available in the market for various purposes. The best quality soap is the one which gives maximum lather with water. Soap, however, does not form lather with hard water.

Detergents

Detergents are sodium salts of alkyl benzene sulphonate or fatty alcohol sulphates.

Manufacture of Detergents

Manufacture of detergents also involves three stages as discussed below:

1. Treating alkyl benzene or fatty alcohol with oleum, $(H_2SO_4 + SO_3)$ gives alkyl benzene sulphonate or fatty alcohol sulphate, respectively.
2. Alkyl benzene sulphonate and fatty alcohol sulphate are acids and are treated with sodium hydroxide. Sodium salt of alkyl benzene sulphonate and fatty alcohol sulphate are formed.
3. In this step, builders like salt, soda ash, and sodium bicarbonate are added to the sodium salt of alkyl benzene sulphonate or fatty alcohol sulphate to give detergents.

$$\underset{\text{Lauryl alcohol}}{nC_{11}H_{33}CH_2OH} \xrightarrow{H_2SO_4} nC_{11}H_{23}CH_2OSO_3H \xrightarrow{NaOH} \underset{\text{Sodium laurylsulphate}}{nC_{11}H_{23}CH_2OSO_3^-Na^+}$$

A wide variety of detergents is manufactured and hence available with different trade names in the market.

Cleansing Action of Soaps and Detergents

The basic principle behind the working of soaps and detergents is the same. Soap, being a sodium or potassium salt of stearic acid, can be ionized into stearate ions and Na^+ or K^+ ions. The stearate ion is hydrophobic in nature which consists of long chain of hydrocarbon which forms the tail part and carboxylic acid which is hydrophilic in nature and forms the head part.

$$\underset{\text{Soap}}{CH_3(CH_2)_{15}CH_2COONa} \xrightarrow{H_2O} \underset{\text{Stearate ion}}{CH_3(CH_2)_{15}CH_2COO^-} + Na^+$$

$$CH_3(CH_2)_{15}CH_2COO^-$$

$$\Rightarrow CH_3(CH_2)_{15}CH_2 \text{ hydrophobic tail; } COO^- \text{ hydrophilic head}$$

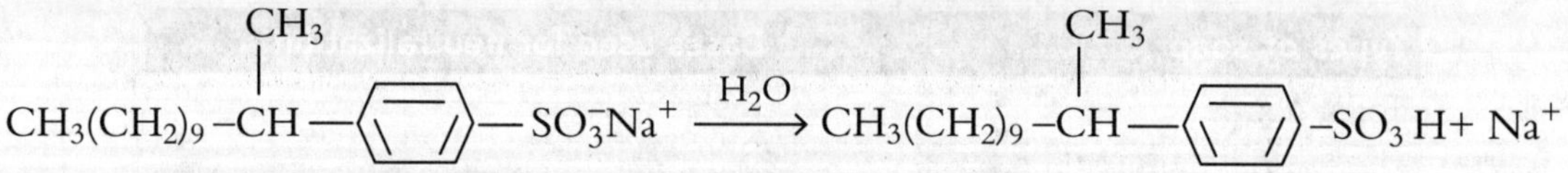

Sodium salt of alkyl benzene sulphonic acid
(detergent)

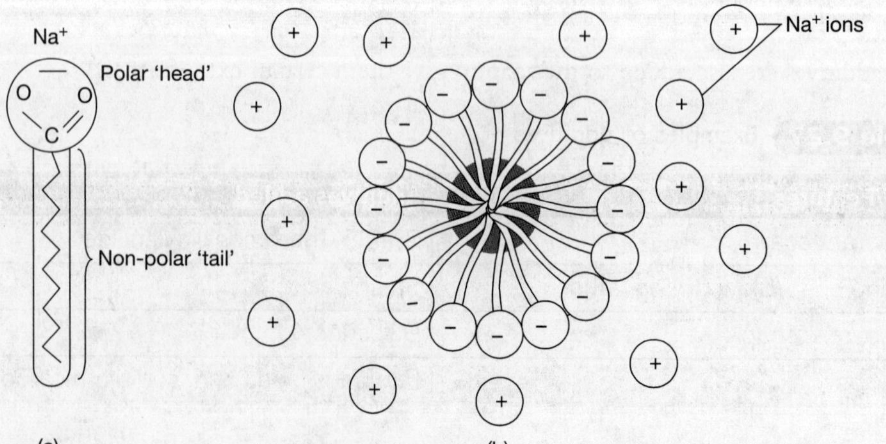

Figure 9.3 (a) A soap molecule (b) Cross section of a soap micelle in water

Advantage of Detergents Over Soap

Detergents are sodium or potassium salts of alkyl sulphonic acids. The hydrocarbon tail part remains the same as is soap, whereas the head part contains $-SO_3^-$ end instead of COO^- end. Cleansing action of detergents is the same as that of a soap.

$$\underset{\text{(Hard water)}}{2RCOO^-Na^+ + MgSO_4} \rightarrow (RCOO)_2^- Mg^{+2} + Na_2SO_4$$

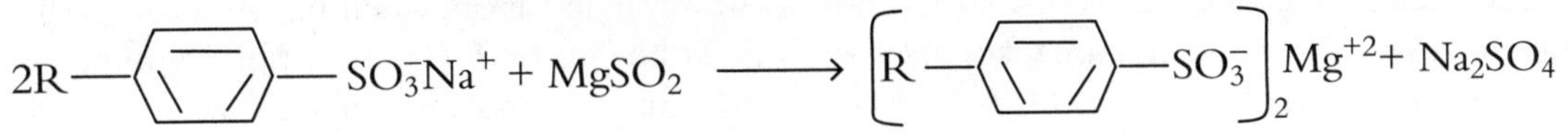

Soaps are efficient in action only when they are used with soft water. But when they are used with hard water, they cannot work efficiently. Hard water contains Ca^{+2} and Mg^{+2} ions. When soap dissolves in hard water, these ions form insoluble salts with stearate ions of soap. Thus, the stearate ion concentration available for micelle formation gets reduced.

Detergents are more efficient than soaps since the calcium or magnesium salts of sulphonic acid formed are soluble in hard water and, therefore, do not cause any precipitation.

Disadvantages of Using Detergents

Though detergents are more efficient than soaps, they are disadvantageous as they add to water pollution. This is because of the fact that the branched chain of hydrocarbon parts of detergent molecules is resistant to degradation and persist for a longer time in the environment.

This difficulty could be overcome by reducing the extent of branching to minimum thus rendering faster degradation of detergent molecules. These are termed as biodegradable detergents.

Petroleum and Petrochemicals

Petroleum is a dark viscous oily liquid with unpleasant odor, which originates at depths of thousands of feet below the earth's surface. It is also called rock oil (Petra means rock and oleum means oil) or crude oil.

Composition: Petroleum mainly consists of a complex mixture of hydrocarbons, predominantly alkanes (straight and branched chain $-C_1$ to C_{40}) and cycloalkanes. Further, aromatic hydrocarbons are present in considerable amounts in the same petroleum deposits. In addition to these, compounds of oxygen, nitrogen and sulphur are also found in petroleum in minor proportions. However, the composition of petroleum is variable depending upon the place of its origin.

Extraction of Petroleum: All crude oil deposits contain a gaseous mixture of lower alkanes called natural gas. Methane is the major constituent of natural gas. Petroleum is found floating on the layer of salt. Petroleum can be obtained by drilling a deep well through the various layers under the earth's surface till the oil-bearing strata are reached. During the process of drilling, pressure created in the underground reservoir allows the gases to fizz out of solution pushing crude oil to the surface. Pipes are introduced up to the oil level through which the crude oil can be drawn out. But by this method only 20% of the crude oil gushes out. To draw more petroleum out, either water or compressed air is pumped through the outer pipe and oil is drawn out through the inner pipe.

Processing of Petroleum

The crude oil extracted from the earth's crust contains a lot of impurities. It has to be first processed in oil refineries. The petroleum drawn out by the process of drilling is transported through pipes to the oil refineries and distilled. This oil is of two kinds. One is heavy oil or lubricating oil which is used as such. The second one is light oil which must be subjected to a series of operations for purification and separation.

Purification of Crude Oil

The purification of crude oil involves two major steps:

1st Step: Removal of impurities: Since crude oil is present with a layer of salt beneath earth's surface, it contains salt water as the major impurity. This water can be removed by passing the crude oil sample between two highly charged electrodes. Water droplets are attracted towards the electrodes and separated out. The oil so obtained is devoid of water and is subjected to treatment with copper oxide. The sulphur compounds present in the oil react with copper oxide forming copper sulphide which is removed by filtration.

2nd Step: Fractional distillation: After the removal of impurities, the crude oil obtained is a pure mixture of hydrocarbons. This method involves heating of the mixture over a specific range of temperature in a fractionating column with a long tube. This allows separation of various components of the mixture according to their boiling points.

The crude oil is taken in an iron retort and heated up to 350–400°C. The various components in the oil evaporate at this temperature. The vapors so obtained are passed through a fractionating column. The fractionating column consists of a number of horizontal stainless steel trays in a tall cylindrical tower. The vapors when passed through this column cool down and get condensed. The condensation takes place at different heights of the fractionating column. The high boiling components get condensed first leaving behind the low boiling components. The liquids formed by condensation are collected in different trays and are collected separately. At the end of the fractional distillation, a cake like solid residue remains in the retort. This is called **'asphalt'**.(crude oil rich in naphthalene).

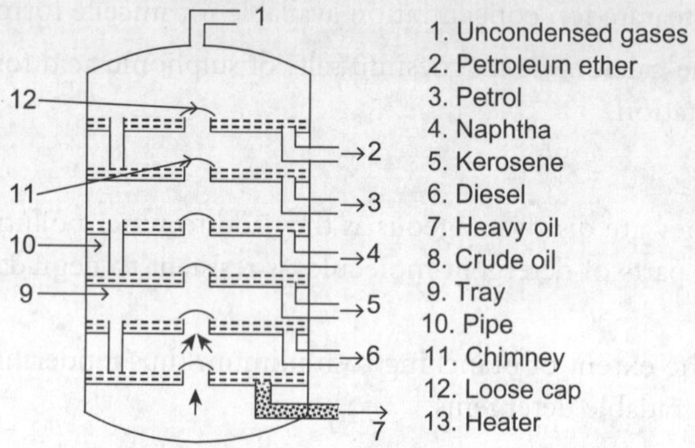

Figure 9.4 Purification of crude oil

Info Bytes!

- The word 'petroleum' is derived from Latin: 'petra' (rock) + 'oleum' (oil), meaning 'rock oil'.
- Petrochemicals serve as the backbone for products as diverse as plastics, fertilizers, clothing, cosmetics, etc.

The various components obtained at various stages can be used for different purposes. These products which are derived from crude oil by this refining process are used as fuels. Depending on the actual composition of fraction and the purpose for which it is used, these fractions are subjected to further purification. As a result, these products get free from corrosive constituents and also from unpleasant odors.

Table 9.28 Main fractions obtained after processing of petroleum

Main fractions	Boiling temp. ranges	Composition alkanes	Uses
Petroleum gas	Below 30°C	C_1 to C_4	Fuel, for making carbon black
Crude naphtha	30–150°C	• Petroleum ether (below 90°C) (C_5–C_7) • Gasoline or petrol (90–120°C) (C_7–C_9) • Benzene (120°C–150°C) (C_9–C_{10})	Solvent Motor fuel Dry cleaning
Kerosene oil	150–300°C	C_{10}–C_{16}	Cooking fuel, illuminant oil gas
Fuel oil	300–350°C	C_{16}–C_{20} • Gas oil • Diesel oil • Furnace oil	Motor fuel, cracking stock for gasoline
Lubricating oil	350–400°C	C_{20}–C_{24}	Paint oil, lubricants
Paraffin wax	Above 400°C	C_{24} and above	Candles, matches, paints, water proofing, ointments, protective paints

Petrol or Gasoline

It is the most important product of petroleum. It is mainly used as a fuel for automobiles. This is also used as a solvent for the dry-cleaning of clothes. The petrol which is directly obtained by fractional distillation of crude oil is called straight-run petrol.

Petrol can also be manufactured by a process of cracking of heavier petroleum products.

Cracking

Cracking is decomposition of long chain hydrocarbons into simple hydrocarbons at high temperature and pressure in presence of catalysts. The petrol so obtained is more efficient than the straight-run petrol.

Cooking Gas/Domestic Gas

Cooking gas is technically called liquefied petroleum gas (LPG). It is a mixture of propane, propene, and butane with little amount of ethane. This gaseous mixture when subjected to high pressure gets liquefied. This liquefied mixture is kept in cylinders at high pressure and is used as the cooking fuel and also as motor fuel.

Petrochemicals

Petroleum is an important raw material for the manufacture of industrial chemicals. These products obtained from crude petroleum are called petrochemicals. Petrochemicals find extensive applications in the manufacture of plastics, synthetic fibres, synthetic rubber, pesticides, detergents, dyes, drugs, etc.

Thus petroleum forms the most important raw material for the manufacture of various fuels. Nevertheless, the significance of petroleum is being shifted to the manufacture of petrochemicals which form the backbone of organic chemical industry. Therefore, researches are going on for development of alternative sources of energy in place of petroleum for a rational and judicious use of this exhaustible natural resource.

EXAMPLE 9.10 Why is it recommended for individuals at risk of cardiovascular disease to limit their intake of trans fats in their diet?

SOLUTION

Individuals at risk of cardiovascular disease are advised to limit their intake of trans fats because trans fats raise LDL (bad) cholesterol levels, lower HDL (good) cholesterol levels, promote inflammation, impair blood vessel function, and increase the risk of blood clots. These factors collectively contribute to the development and progression of heart disease and make trans fats harmful to cardiovascular health.

EXAMPLE 9.11 Explain why steaming is often considered a healthier cooking method compared to boiling or frying when it comes to retaining the nutritional value of vegetables.

SOLUTION

Steaming is healthier because it minimizes nutrient loss, retains texture, uses fewer added fats, and preserves antioxidants in vegetables.

EXAMPLE 9.12 Explain the mechanism by which soap cleans dirty laundry. How does soap help remove oil and dirt from clothes during washing?

SOLUTION

Soap molecules have a hydrophilic (water-attracting) head and a hydrophobic (water-repelling) tail. When soap is added to water with dirt or oil, the hydrophobic tails of soap molecules surround and encapsulate the dirt or oil particles, forming micelles. These micelles suspend the dirt or oil in the water, preventing re-deposition on the cleaned surface. During rinsing, the micelles are carried away, leaving surfaces clean. This action enables soap to effectively remove oil and dirt from clothes during washing.

POINTS TO REMEMBER

- ✔ Ethers are a class of compounds that contain an oxygen atom bonded to two alkyl groups.
- ✔ Esters are derivatives of carboxylic acids where carboxylate group is attached to two alkyl groups.
- ✔ Compounds with the same molecular formula but different functional groups are called functional isomers and this phenomenon is called functional isomerism.
- ✔ The isomers in which there is an unequal distribution of carbon chain or atoms on either side of the functional group are called metamers and this phenomenon is termed as metamerism.
- ✔ The class of compounds where the alkyl chain is attached to –OH group is called alcohols.
- ✔ Fermentation is the process of decomposition of a complex organic compound into simpler compounds by means of microorganisms.
- ✔ The classes of compounds in which there is a > C = O group are called carbonyl compounds.
- ✔ If the carbonyl compound contains C = O group linked to hydrogen on one side and alkyl group on the other side, that class of compounds is called aldehydes.
- ✔ If the carbonyl group is linked to two same or different alkyl groups on either side, the class of compounds is called ketones.
- ✔ The organic compounds which contain — COOH (carboxyl group) as a functional group are known as carboxylic acid.
- ✔ Carbohydrates are an important class of organic molecules containing carbon, hydrogen and oxygen and defined as polyhydroxyaldehydes, polydroxyketones or compounds which produce these on hydrolysis.
- ✔ The class of carbohydrates which cannot be hydrolysed into simpler saccharide units are called monosaccharides.
- ✔ The class of carbohydrates, which on hydrolysis, gives 2–9 monosaccharide units are called oligosaccharides.
- ✔ Polysaccharides represent the class of carbohydrates which can be hydrolysed into a number of monosaccharide units.
- ✔ In contrast to monosaccharides and disaccharides, which are called sugars, polysaccharides are called non-sugars due to their bland taste.
- ✔ Ammonical silver nitrate solution so obtained is called Tollen's reagent.
- ✔ Measured proportions of sodium citrate and sodium carbonate are dissolved in water. In this solution, copper sulphate is dissolved. The resulting solution is called Benedict's reagent.
- ✔ Fehling's reagent is an alkaline solution of cupric ion complexed with sodium or potassium tartarate ions.
- ✔ Proteins are the most abundant organic molecules to be found in living cells and 50% of their total dry mass is protein.
- ✔ Amino acids are considered as the basic units of protein molecules.
- ✔ A number of amino acids can join together by means of a number of peptide bonds and the resultant molecule is called a polypeptide.
- ✔ The amount of energy released in kilocalories by the combustion of one gram of the food is called calorific value.
- ✔ Oils and fats are known as triesters of glycerol or triacylglyerol associated with long chains of fatty acids.

- ✔ The process of formation of polymers from the corresponding simple monomer molecules is called polymerization.
- ✔ Vulcanisation is the process of heating of natural rubber with sulphur which improves the elasticity as well as reduces the sticky nature of rubber.
- ✔ The substance which is used for attaching materials at their surfaces is called an adhesive.
- ✔ Cosmetics is a class of materials used for cleaning or beautification of a person
- ✔ Dyes are organic colouring materials which can impart colours to various fibres.
- ✔ The unsaturated group of the organic molecule which imparts colour to the fabric is called chromophores.
- ✔ Vitamins are the compounds which are required by animals in small quantities for their metabolic activities and for the maintenance of normal health.
- ✔ Hormones are chemical substances produced by endocrine glands inside the human or animal body.
- ✔ Soap is the sodium or potassium salt of a long chain of fatty acids.
- ✔ Detergents are sodium salts of alkyl benzene sulphonate or fatty alcohol sulphates.

DW

PRACTICE QUESTIONS CLASSROOM WING

Very Short Answer Type Questions

Directions for questions from 1 to 3:
Fill in the blanks.

1. Ethers are a class of compounds that contain an oxygen atom bonded to two ________ groups.
2. Esters are derivatives of ________ acids where the carboxylate group is attached to two alkyl groups.
3. Maltose is an example of ________.

Directions for questions from 4 to 25:
Answer the following questions.

4. How do ethers differ from esters in terms of structural bonding?
5. Define functional isomerism and provide an example.
6. What distinguishes metamers from other isomers?
7. What functional group characterizes alcohol?
8. Describe the role of microorganisms in fermentation.
9. What is the defining functional group of carbonyl compounds?
10. How do aldehydes differ structurally from ketones?
11. Why are carbohydrates called saccharides?
12. What are oligosaccharides? Give some examples.
13. What are the types of isomerism exhibited by ketones?
14. What is the general formula of polysaccharides? Give examples.
15. What is meant by vulcanization?
16. Give the reactions of ethyl alcohol with H_2SO_4.
17. What is absolute alcohol? How is it obtained from rectified spirit?
18. Write the chemical reactions involved in the manufacture of ethyl alcohol form sucrose.
19. What are essential amino acids? In what way are they different from non-essential amino acids?
20. Name some disaccharides. Give the formula.
21. What is zwitter ion? Why do amino acids form zwitter ions?
22. The secondary suffix 'al' indicates functional group in the compound.
23. What is a glycoside bond? How is it formed?
24. Give the composition of a denatured spirit.
25. Define the following:
    (a) Soap
    (b) Detergent
    (c) Fats
    (d) Oils
    (e) Unsaturated oils
    (f) Saturated oils

Short Answer Type Questions

26. Differentiate between ethers and esters in terms of their functional groups.
27. Explain the concept of functional isomerism with an example.
28. What distinguishes aldehydes from ketones in terms of structural characteristics?
29. Describe the significance of Tollen's reagent in organic chemistry.
30. How are carbohydrates classified? Explain.
31. (a) Draw the structures of glucose and fructose.
    (b) Complete the blanks by identifying A, B, C, D, E and F.

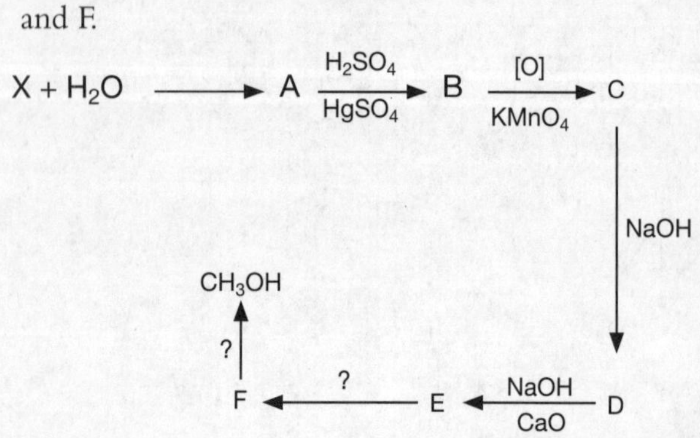

32. What are Tollen's reagent and Fehling's reagent? How do they help in identification of carbonyl compounds?

33. Give characteristics of synthetic fibres. How do they differ from other types? Give two examples.

34. What are the characteristics of a dye?

35. Define a drug. List out the characteristics of an ideal drug.

36. Explain the process of hydrogenation in detail and give its advantages.

37. What is the significance of proteins?

38. What are proteins? How are they formed?

39. What are the products of hydrolysis of sucrose, maltose, and lactose?

Essay Answer Type Questions

40. Given that both ethers and esters contain similar alkyl-oxygen bonds, why might an ester's odour be more prominent in perfumes than an ether's?

41. Considering that both Tollen's reagent and Benedict's reagent are used to detect aldehydes, how do the underlying mechanisms differ in the presence of an aldehyde?

42. Polysaccharides are not sweet, but they can be broken down into monosaccharides, which are. Why might nature design storage molecules that don't taste sweet to deter consumption?

43. The calorific value measures the energy released upon combustion. How might this differ from the energy obtained by organisms when consuming the same material, and why?

44. Explain the refining of crude oil.

45. An unsaturated hydrocarbon X is subjected to combustion. One mole of X consumed 3 moles of oxygen during combustion. The products formed are in 1 : 1 ratio. X is treated with conc. H_2SO_4 and water 75°C to give Y. Y is made to reach with PCl_5 to form Z. Identify the isomer of Y and also mention the method of preparation of this isomer from the homologue of Z. Identify X, Y and Z. Represent all the reactions involved by equations.

PRACTICE QUESTIONS COMPETITION WING

Level 1: Apply your Concepts

Direction for questions from 1 to 7:
State whether the following statements are true or false.

1. Ethyl alcohol on oxidation with acidified $K_2Cr_2O_7$ gives ethanol.
2. Propionic acid is the IUPAC name of carboxylic acid with three carbon atoms.
3. The $-\overset{\overset{\displaystyle O}{\|}}{C}-NH-$ bond is called glycoside bond.
4. Proteins are the polymers of amino acids.
5. Antiseptics are a class of chemotherapeutic drugs.
6. Lauric acid and stearic acid are unsaturated fatty acids.
7. Both glucose and sucrose give Fehling's test.
8. –CHO group is a chain terminating group.

Direction for questions from 9 to 19:
Fill in the blanks.

9. __________, Primary suffix and secondary suffix are parts of IUPAC name of organic compound.
10. The IUPAC name of $H_3C–O–C_2H_5$ is __________.
11. The common name of HCHO is __________.
12. Petrol is obtained from heavier fractions of petroleum distillation through __________.
13. The part of IUPAC name of the organic compound which denotes functional group is called ________.
14. Structural formula of methoxypropane is ________.
15. ________ is the additive used in transparent soaps.
16. Diethyl ketone and isopropyl methyl ketone are called ________.
17. The part of the dye molecule which forms bonds with fibre is called ________.
18. The addition compound obtained by treating propanone with hydrogen cyanide is _______.
19. ________ is obtained by the saponification of oils.

Direction for question 20:
Match the entries in column A with the appropriate ones in column B.

20.

Column A	Column B
A. Chloramphenicol	a. vitamin A
B. Alizarine	b. copolymer
C. Zymase	c. addition polymer
D. Alkyl benzene sulphonate	d. fermentation process
E. Nylon-6, 6	e. anti-biotic
F. Polyprene	f. mordant dyes
G. Retinol	g. detergent

Direction for questions from 21 to 45:
For each of the questions, four choices have been provided. Select the correct alternative.

21. Detergents are less or non-biodegradable when compared with soaps. For detergents to be biodegradable in nature, the non-polar part of the molecule should
    (a) consist of a hydrocarbon with more branching
    (b) consist of a hydrocarbon with more number of branches and unsaturation
    (c) have straight- or open-chain hydrocarbons
    (d) be replaced by aromatic rings substituted by alkyl groups

22. The secondary suffix, '– one' indicates the following functional group in the given compounds.
    (a) — COOH
    (b) H(—)C = O (H–C=O with one open bond)
    (c) $R_2C=O$ (R, R attached to C = O)
    (d) — OH

23. In case of oligosaccharides, the monosaccharide units are joined by
    (a) glycoside bonds
    (b) peptide bond
    (c) dative bonds
    (d) covalent bonds

24. When an amino acid solution which is slightly alkaline is subjected to electrolysis, the resulting component migrates towards
    (a) cathode due to zwitter ion formation
    (b) anode due to the conversion of zwitter ion to positive ion
    (c) migrate to cathode due to the conversion to negative ion
    (d) one component towards cathode and the other towards anode due to the zwitter ion formation

25. By treating methyl alcohol with conc. H_2SO_4 at 140°C, which of the following products is formed?
    (a) ethene (b) dimethyl ether
    (c) methyl ethylether (d) ethyne

26. The salt-like structures of amino acids are called:
    (a) zwitter ions (b) peptide bonds
    (c) essential amino acids (d) proteins

27. Which of the following enzymes is used to convert glucose into ethyl alcohol?
    (a) diastase (b) maltase
    (c) zymase (d) invertase

28. Which of the following carbohydrates is the sweetest sugar?
    (a) glucose (b) fructos
    (c) cellulose (d) maltose

29. Give the corresponding functional isomer of the product formed when ethanol is treated with ethanoic acid.
    (a) propanoic acid (b) ethyl ethanoate
    (c) butanoic acid (d) butanone

30. Which of the following is the anti-viral drug?
    (a) chloroquine (b) tetracycline
    (c) aureomycin (d) sulphadiazine

31. Tollen's reagent contains:
    (a) silver nitrate
    (b) copper nitrate
    (c) copper sulphate
    (d) ammonical silver nitrate

32. Sucrose doesn't respond to Tollen's test. But it gives a positive result after boiling with conc. HCl. It is due to the:
    (a) cleavage of glycosidic linkage
    (b) formation of glycosidic linkage
    (c) formation of a compound containing carboxylic acid group
    (d) isomerisation to glucose units

33. In deodorant soaps, the additive added in deodorant is:
    (a) glycerol
    (b) stearic acid
    (c) potassium bicarbonate
    (d) 3, 4, 5-Tribromosalicylaldehyde

34. Which of the following comes under natural adhesives?
    (a) epoxyresins
    (b) polyamides
    (c) glue
    (d) polyvinyls

35. Which among the following is a chromophore of azo dyes?
    (a) $>C=$ (b) –NO
    (c) –N≡N (d) $-NO_2$

36. Arrange the reactions given below in a proper sequence for the conversion of ethane to methane.
    (1) treatment with sodium hydroxide
    (2) treatment with aqueous KOH
    (3) treatment with NaOH + CaO
    (4) halogenation
    (5) reaction with acidified $K_2Cr_2O_7$
    (a) 5 1 4 2 3 (b) 4 2 5 1 3
    (c) 5 3 2 1 4 (d) 4 5 1 2 3

37. Identify the correct sequence of given steps for the conversion of calcium carbide to methyl alcohol.
    (1) reaction with aqueous KOH
    (2) hydrolysis
    (3) reaction with soda lime
    (4) reaction with $HgSO_4/H_2SO_4$
    (5) reaction with $HgSO_4$
    (6) reaction with PCl_5
    (a) 2 4 5 3 6 1 (b) 2 4 3 1 6 5
    (c) 2 6 4 5 1 3 (d) 4 2 3 5 6 1

38. Arrange the following carbohydrates in the order of number of monosaccharide units formed on hydrolysis.
    (1) raffinose (2) fructose
    (3) maltose (4) stachyose
    (a) 3 2 1 3 (b) 2 3 1 4
    (c) 4 1 3 2 (d) 2 1 3 4

39. The IUPAC name of CH_3COOH is:
    (a) acetic acid (b) formic acid
    (c) methanoic acid (d) ethanoic acid

40. Oxidation of ethene with cold alkaline $KMnO_4$ produces:
(a) formaldehyde (b) glyoxal
(c) ethene glycol (d) oxalic acid

41. Which of the following enzymes is required for the conversion of starch to maltose?
(a) diastase (b) maltase
(c) invertase (d) zymase

42. The chemical name of vitamin D is:
(a) retinol (b) ferridoxin
(c) calciferol (d) ergosterol

43. Arrange the following in a proper sequence for the extraction of petroleum.
(1) Processing of crude oil to remove heavy oil.
(2) Heating of the crude oil containing pure mixture of hydrocarbons over a specific range of temperature.
(3) Separation of constituents by fractional distillation.
(4) Purification of crude oil containing salt water.
(5) Drilling of the oil through the various layers under the earth's surface.
(a) 5 2 1 4 3 (b) 5 3 1 2 4
(c) 5 1 4 2 3 (d) 5 1 2 3 4

44. Four oils A, B, C, and D have the following values of melting points:
(A) 258 K (B) 273 K
(C) 295 (D) 303 K
Among these, which oil is prohibited from consumption by cardiac patients?
(a) A (b) B
(c) C (d) D

45. Which of the following statements is wrong regarding amino acids?
(a) The living systems in plants can synthesize essential amino acids.
(b) The living systems in animals can synthesize only essential amino acids.
(c) The living systems in animals can synthesize only non-essential amino acids.
(d) The living systems in plants can synthesize non-essential amino acids.

Level 2: Review Your Concepts

46. How do proteins contribute to the structure of living cells?

47. What is the relationship between amino acids and polypeptides?

48. Why is the calorific value an essential parameter for food substances?

49. Why are polysaccharides referred to as non-sugars?
(a) ethene from ethanol
(b) ethyne to acetic acid
(c) acetylene to oxalic acid

50. A compound 'X' has the molecular formula C_4H_8O. Both 'X' and its functional isomer 'Y' are treated with a solution of $AgNO_3$ dissolved in NH_4OH separately. What observations do you find in both the cases? Justify with equations.

51. Compound 'A' on treatment with copper at 300°C gives 'B' and a gas 'C.' It is possible to get back 'A' from B and C. In presence of 'D,' both B and A on treatment with certain reagent gives same compound 'E,' which on treatment with 'A,' gives compound F with a fruity smell. Identify the compounds and isomer of 'F.'

52. What is the working principle of a dye? Why does a dye generally fade?

53. Predict the products formed by the oxidation of glucose with bromine water and concentrated nitric acid respectively.

54. Ethyl alcohol obtained by the fermentation of molasses can be purified by fractional distillation to give 95% ethyl alcohol. Further purification is possible by adding a salt such as potassium acetate to ethyl alcohol and then subjecting to fractional distillation.

55. How can vulcanization improve the quality of rubber?

56. Explain the application of mordant dyes to the fabric.

57. Both sucrose and maltose contain glucose units. But sucrose is a non-reducing sugar and maltose is a reducing sugar. How do you account for this?

58. Generally, colors of clothes fade away on repeated washing or on exposure to intense sunlight gradually. Explain with a reason.

59. Supplementation with 'B' vitamin is more widely recommended than supplementation with any other vitamin. Justify.

60. Among all disaccharides, possessing one or two glucose units, sucrose is the only non-reducing sugar. How do you account for this?

Directions for questions from 61 to 70:
Application-Based Questions

61. Complete the blanks by identifying A, B, C, D and E and also specify the reagents for the given reaction.

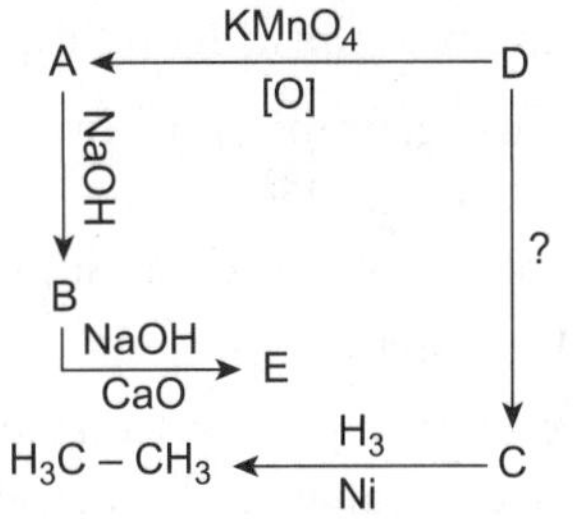

62. (a) Methanol and ethane have almost the same molecular mass. But boiling point of methanol is 65°C while that of ethane is –89°C. Justify.

(b) Acetic acid boils at higher temperature than propyl alcohol though both of them have same molecular mass. Give a reason.

63. How do you bring about the conversions of ethyl alcohol to trichloroacetic acid?

64. (a) Alcohol can act as an acid as well as a base. Justify the statement.

(b) An organic compound 'X' is found to contain 40% carbon and 6.7% hydrogen. Its succeeding homologue is treated with sodium hydroxide. The resulting compound is heated with soda lime to give compound Y. Y is made to react with iodine in the presence of sunlight to give another compound Z. Z is divided into two parts. First part is treated with alcoholic KOH. Second part is treated with aq. KOH. The compounds obtained are A and B.

(a) Identify X, Y, Z and the homologue.

(b) Figure out the series of reactions involved in the conversion of both A and B to the original compound that is 'X' by the shortest possible route.

(c) Mention the types of reactions involved in each stage.

65. Two students were performing some experiments in an organic chemistry laboratory. An unknown compound A, which was found to be a hydrocarbon was subjected to the following reactions. A on reaction with chlorine in the presence of light gave compound B, which was divided into two parts. To the 1st part aqueous KOH was added and to the second part alcoholic KOH was added. Products C and D were formed, respectively. C was subjected to oxidation to give another compound. The compound formed was same as the compound formed by the ozonolysis product of position isomer of 1-Butene. Identify A, B, C and D.

66. In a revision class in IITF, a chemistry faculty member conducted a quiz in organic chemistry. According to the rules of the quiz, each team has to prepare some questions and ask the other team. Team A asked the following question to team B. 'A hydrocarbon has two sp^3 hybrid carbons and two sp^3 hybrid carbons. The compound when subjected to controlled hydrogenation in the presence of catalyst nickel gives another hydrocarbon which decolorises bromine water forming a compound from which both the above hydrocarbons can be regenerated. But the parent hydrocarbon did not give a reddish brown precipitate when passed through ammonical cuprous chloride solution. Identify the hydrocarbon. What would be your answer for the above question and give proper justification for your answer.

67. A hydrocarbon on ozonolysis gives one mole each of compounds A and B. Both A and B on reduction with sodium borohydride gives compounds C and D belonging to same homologous series. C has no position isomer, whereas D has a position isomer. A and B do not belong to the same homologous series. However, both A and B on oxidation with acidified $KMnO_4$ give the same compound. Identify the hydrocarbon compounds A, B, C, and D and write the series of reactions.

68.

$$R-\ddot{\underset{..}{O}}-H + H^+ \longrightarrow R-OH_2^+$$

Identify X, Y, Z, P and Q. Give the significance of above series of reactions. Also predict whether the position isomer of 'X' would give a yellow precipitate or not.

69. Identify A, B, C, and D in the following conversions given and write their structural formulae.

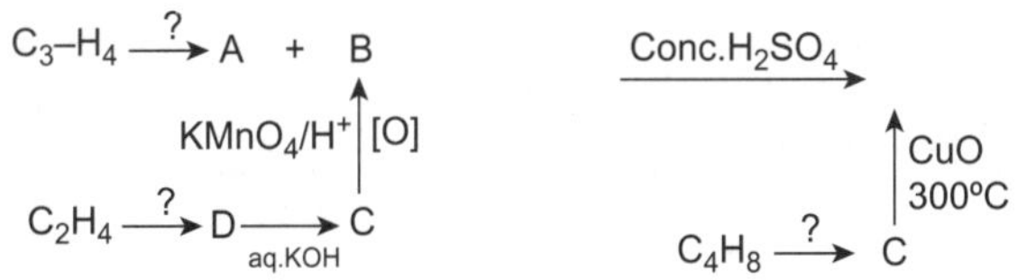

70. Paul is a student of IITF. One day, his younger brother who is one year old fell sick. Paul accompanied him to the hospital along with his mother. The doctor gave a medicine which was in the form of a powder and said that water should be added to that powder to prepare a syrup. He said that it has to be consumed within a 5-day period and any leftover syrup should be discarded as it becomes unfit for consumption. On the other hand, when Paul was suffering from high fever, the doctor administered injections. Can you give justification for both the above treatments?

Level 3: Assess Your Concepts

71. (a) Explain how proteins help to maintain pH of the body.
(b) Explain the steps involved in the following conversions.
(a) Ethane to acetic acid
(b) Acetone to methane
(c) 1, 2 – dibromoethane to ethanal

72. Detergents and soaps both serve to clean, but why might detergents be preferred in regions with hard water over soaps?

73. While both alcohols and carboxylic acids contain the –OH group, they exhibit different acidities. What structural differences account for this disparity in their acidic nature?

74. Considering that both esters and fats are derivatives of carboxylic acids, how does their structural diversity influence their respective roles in nature and industry?

75. How might the presence of chromophores in dyes contribute to their interaction with fabrics, and how can this principle be applied in textile design?

76. Proteins and polypeptides are built from amino acids. How does the structural organization and sequencing of these amino acids dictate the vast range of functionalities that proteins offer in living organisms?

77. Given that both vitamins and hormones are essential, low-concentration molecules in the body, how do their modes of action differ in supporting metabolic activities and health?

78. 'Boiling is a preferred process to frying as far as preservation of nutritive values is concerned.' Comment on this statement.

79. Three samples of amino acids A, B and C are taken in neutral, acidic and basic mediums respectively. Comment on the behaviour of these samples when subjected to an electric field and explain how amino acids in the form of proteins help in maintaining the pH of body fluids.

AT

PRACTICE QUESTIONS JEE-NEET SPECIAL WING

Multiple-Answer Type Questions

Directions for Questions number 1 to 5:

Select one or more correct alternative(s) from the given choices.

1. Correct IUPAC name of the following compound is:
   $CH_2 = CH\text{-}(CH_2)_2 - C \equiv CH$
   (a) 1-pentene-4-yne (b) 1-hexene-5 yne
   (c) 1-Pentyne-5 ene (d) Hex-1-en-5 yne
2. Large number of carbon compounds are due to :
   (a) the small size of carbon.
   (b) the presence of unique no of valence electrons in carbon.
   (c) the ability of carbon to form multiple bonds
   (d) the allotropic property of carbon.
3. Compounds containing which of the following functional groups exhibit metamerism.
   (a) Acid (b) Ether
   (c) Ester (d) Aldehyde
4. If the given compounds contain monovalent functional groups, choose the compounds with similar chemical properties.
   (a) C_2H_6O (b) C_3H_6O
   (c) CH_2O (d) C_2H_4O
5. Identify the statements that are true with respect to vitamin B_3.
   (a) Chemical name is nicotinic acid.
   (b) Deficiency causes pellagra.
   (c) Humans obtain can synthesis this vitamin.
   (d) It helps to convert nutrients into energy.

Comprehension-Based Questions

Directions for Questions 6 to 11:

Read the following passage and answer the questions given below.

In organic chemistry, ozonolysis is a reaction where ozone (O_3) selectively breaks unsaturated bonds, substituting them with carbonyl (C = O) groups like aldehydes, ketones, and carboxylic acids. While commonly employed for alkenes, this reaction extends to alkynes and azo compounds (organic chemicals featuring the azo group, —N = N—). The resulting products depend on the specific multiple bond and the conditions during the work-up process.

Following the addition of ozone, an auxiliary reagent is essential to convert the intermediate ozonide into the desired carbonyl derivative. Two techniques are commonly used for this purpose: reductive workup and oxidative workup.

- **Reductive Workup:** The ozonide is treated with a reducing agent like dimethyl sulphide or zinc dust, generating aldehydes or ketones based on the structure of the alkene.
- **Oxidative Workup:** Conducting an oxidative workup using an oxidizing agent such as hydrogen peroxide (H_2O_2) transforms any formed aldehydes into carboxylic acids.

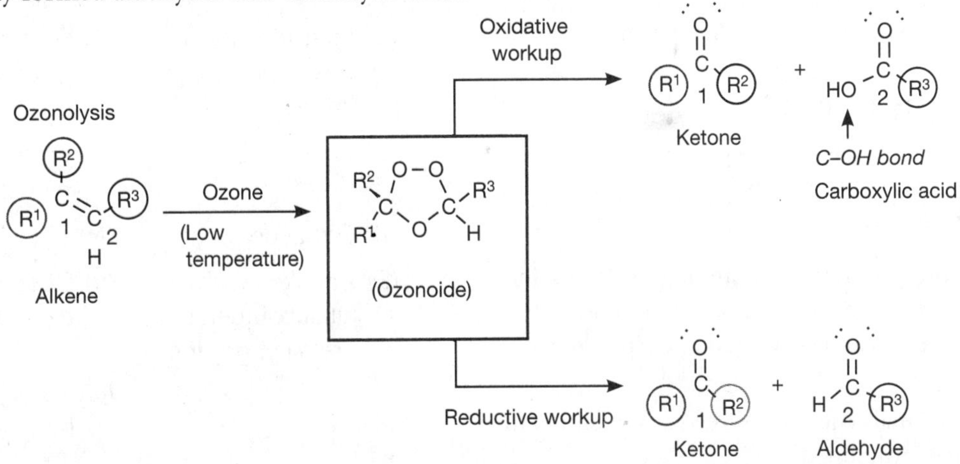

Despite being less reactive than alkenes towards ozone, alkynes typically yield acid anhydride or diketone products during oxidative cleavage. Interestingly, these reactions do not necessitate a reducing agent, and the precise mechanism remains unclear. In the presence of water, the resulting anhydride can undergo hydrolysis, producing two carboxylic acids.

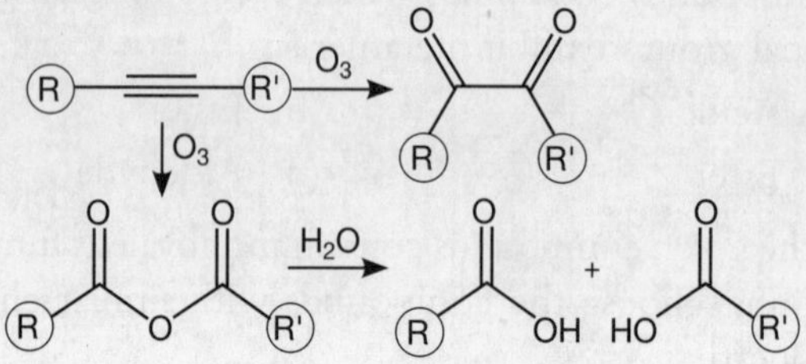

The reactivity of alkenes in ozonolysis depends on their electron density, with more electron-rich alkenes displaying faster reactions. It's important to note that cyclic alkenes undergo a shift to linear products, and molecules with multiple alkenes yield a mixture of fragments.

Ozonolysis plays a pivotal role in organic chemistry by providing a valuable tool for structural elucidation, functional group interconversion, and the synthesis of various organic compounds. Its versatility and applications contribute significantly to the understanding and manipulation of organic molecules in diverse scientific and industrial fields.

$$\text{Hydrogen (A)} \xrightarrow[\text{Ozonolysis}]{\text{Reduction}} B + C$$

Compound	Fehling's test	Treatment with I_2 and NaOH.
B	Positive	Positive
C	Positive	Negative

6. Study the following reaction

$$\underset{(X)}{\text{Hydrocarbon}} \xrightarrow[\text{(ii) Zn\HCl}]{\text{(i) } O_3} \underset{(Y)}{(CH_3)_2CH\text{–}CHO} + \underset{(Z)}{(CH_3)_2CO}$$

Which of the following given molecular formulas would be X?

(a) $(CH_3)_2C = CH\text{–}CH(CH_3)_2$
(b) $CH_3\text{–}CH_3\text{–}CH = CH\text{–}CH_3\text{–}CH_3$
(c) $CH_3\text{–}CH_3\text{–}CH = C(CH_3)_2$
(d) $(CH_3)_2\,CH = CH\text{–}CH(CH_3)_2$

7. If B and C belong to the same homologous series and C is the first member of the series, which among the following statements can be inferred as correct regarding compound A?

(a) A should be an alkyne with three carbon atoms in its molecular structure
(b) A should be a symmetrical alkene
(c) A can be any terminal unsymmetrical alkene
(d) A can only be 1-Propene.

8. **Assertion(A):** Compound B indicates the existence of a methyl ketone group in its molecular structure.

Reason(R): When treated with I_2/NaOH mixture, methyl ketones undergo oxidation, resulting in the formation of a yellow precipitate of iodoform.

(a) Both Assertion and Reason are true, and reason is the correct explanation of assertion.
(b) Both Assertion and Reason are true, and reason is not the correct explanation of assertion.
(c) A is true and R is false
(d) A is false and R is true

9. 1,3 Butadiene is treated with ozone followed by zinc dust. The products formed are

(a) Ethene and Formaldehyde
(b) Ethane and Glyoxal
(c) Two moles of methanal and Glyoxal
(d) Formaldehyde, Glyoxal and Acetaldehyde.

10. During the reductive ozonolysis of alkenes, what is the role of zinc dust?

(a) To inhibit further oxidation of the carbonyl compounds formed by hydrolysis.
(b) Acting as a catalyst.
(c) Serving as a promotor.
(d) All of the above.

11. Match the following:

List – I Compound	List – II Ozonolysis Products
(A) 2,3-Pentadiene	(i) Forms both aldehydes and ketones on reductive ozonolysis
(B) First member of alkyne homologous series	(ii) Forms 3moles of glyoxal on reductive ozonolysis
(C) Isobutane	(iii) Forms only ketones on reductive ozonolysis
(D) Benzene	(iv) Only Formic acid.
(E) An alkene where all substituents are alkyl groups	(v) Does not form an ozonide
	(vi) Carbon dioxide as one of the products

Directions for Questions 13 to 17:

Read the following passage and answer the questions given below.

A, B, C, D are compounds of carbon and X is ethanol.

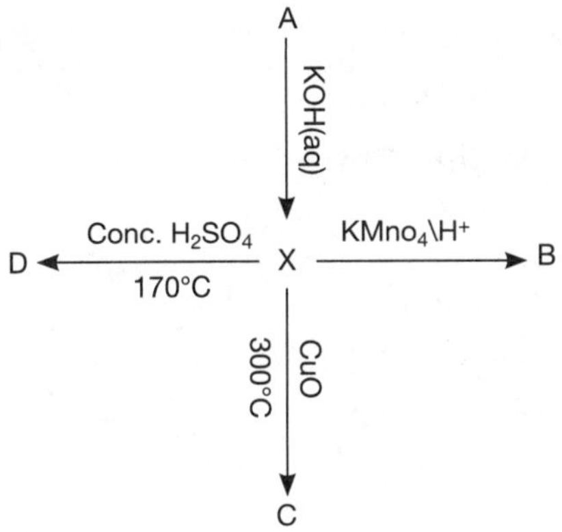

Study the given flowchart and answer the questions that follow. Choose all the options that matches.

12. Which among the following compounds is not a hydrocarbon derivative.

(a) A (b) D

(c) C (d) B

13. Choose the compound that shows position isomerism.

(a) X

(b) C

(c) B

(d) None of the given compounds

14. **Assertion(A):** Boiling point of compound X is much greater than that of the compound C .

Reason(R): Boiling point increases with the increase in the strength of Intermolecular hydrogen bonding.

(a) Both Assertion and Reason are true, and reason is the correct explanation of assertion.

(b) Both Assertion and Reason are true, and reason is not the correct explanation of assertion.

(c) A is true and R is false

(d) A is false and R is true

15. Which of the given compounds is the first member of its homologous series.

(a) B (b) C

(c) D (d) A

16. Isopropyl alcohol is heated with CuO at 300°C. Identify the correct statement with respect to its product .

(a) It shows the same characteristic reactions of compound C

(b) It contains number of carbon atoms more by one number compared to compound C

(c) It is a symmetrical compound

(d) All the above

17. Match the entries of list-I with that of list-II. Choose all the options that match.

List – I Conversion of compounds	List – II Type of the reaction
(a) A to X	(i) Dehydrogenation
(b) X to B	(ii) Addition
(c) X to C	(iii) Dehydration
(d) X to D	(iv) Hydrolysis
	(v) Reduction
	(vi) Substitution
	(vii) Oxidation

ANSWER KEYS

Crossword

Across

1. Olefins 3. Auxochrome 6. Ascorbic acid 11. Ozonolysis
13. Halogenation 17. Tollen's reagent 19. Alkanal 20. Invertase
21. Hydroxylation 22. Chromophore 23. Bakelite

Down

1. Oic acid 2. Retinol 4. Hydrogenation 5. Zymase
7. Alkanol 8. Wash 9. Root word 10. Alkanone
12. Absolute alcohol 14. Acetylenes 15. Monomer 16. Formalin
18. Pyrolysis

Classroom Wing

Very Short Answer Type Questions

1. alkyl 2. carboxylic 3. oligosaccharides

Competition Wing

Level 1: Apply Your Concepts

1. False 2. False 3. False 4. True 5. False
6. True 7. False 8. True 9. Root Word 10. Methoxy ethane
11. Formaldehyde 12. Cracking 13. Secondary suffix 14. $CH_3–O–CH_2–CH_2–CH_3$
15. Glycerol 16. Metamers 17. Auxochrome

18. Propane cyanohydrin

$$\left(H_3C-\underset{\underset{CN}{|}}{\overset{\overset{OH}{|}}{C}}-CH_3\right)$$

19. Soap

20. A : e, B : f, C : d, D : g, E : b, F : c, G : a

21. (c) 22. (c) 23. (a) 24. (b) 25. (b)
26. (a) 27. (c) 28. (b) 29. (c) 30. (c)
31. (d) 32. (a) 33. (d) 34. (c) 35. (c)
36. (b) 37. (a) 38. (b) 39. (d) 40. (c)
41. (a) 42. (c) 43. (c) 44. (d) 45. (a), (b), (d)

JEE-NEET Special Wing

Multiple-Answer Type Questions

1. (b, d)
2. (a, c)
3. (b, c)
4. (b ,c ,d)
5. (a, b, c, d)

Comprehension-Based Questions

6. (a)
7. (d)
8. (b)
9. (c)
10. (a)
11. (A)-(vi); (B)-(iv); (C)-(v); (D)-(ii); (E)-(iii)
12. (b)
13. (d)
14. (b)
15. (c)
16. (b, c)
17. (a)-(vi), (b)-(ii), (vii), (c)-(i), (vii), (d)-(iii)

Hints and Explanations

Classroom Wing

Very Short Answer Type Questions

1. alkyl
2. carboxylic
3. oligosaccharides
4. Ethers have an oxygen atom bonded to two alkyl groups, while esters are derivatives of carboxylic acids with a carboxylate group attached to two alkyl groups.
5. Functional isomerism is when compounds have the same molecular formula but different functional groups. An example would be alcohol and ethers.
6. Metamers have an unequal distribution of the carbon chain or atoms on either side of the functional group.
7. The –OH group.
8. Microorganisms decompose complex organic compounds into simpler compounds during fermentation.
9. The >C=O group.
10. Aldehydes have a C=O group linked to hydrogen on one side and an alkyl group on the other, while ketones have a carbonyl group linked to two alkyl groups.
11. Due to similarity in taste to sugar.
12. The class of carbohydrates which on hydrolysis gives 2-9 monosaccharide units
13. Chain, position, functional isomerism
14. $(C_6H_{10}O_5)n$
15. Vulcanization is the process of heating of natural rubber with sulphur.
16. $2C_2H_5OH \xrightarrow[140°C]{conH_2SO_4} C_2H_5OC_2H_5 + H_2O$

    $C_2H_5OH \xrightarrow[140°C]{conH_2SO_4} H_2C = CH_2 + H_2O$
17. 100% ethyl alcohol. By adding anhydrous CaO to the rectified spirit.
18. $\underset{\text{Sucrose}}{C_{12}H_{22}O_{11}} + H_2O \xrightarrow[30°C]{invertase} \underset{\text{Glucose}}{C_6H_{12}O} + \underset{\text{Fructose}}{C_6H_{12} + O_6}$

    $C_6H_{12}O_6 \xrightarrow[30°C]{zymase} \underset{\text{Ethyl alcohol}}{2C_2H_5OH} + 2CO_2$
19. Essential amino acids cannot be synthesized by the body. Whereas non-essential amino acids can be synthesized by the body
20. Sucrose $(C_{12}H_{22}O_{11})$, Maltose $(C_{12}H_{22}O_{11})$
21. Dipolar ions, due to the presence of acidic and basic groups in the same molecule.
22. aldehyde
23. A glycoside bond is a bond formed by the loss of one water molecule between the carbon group and hydroxyl group of monosaccharide.
24. 95% ethyl alcohol + 5% methyl alcohol
25. (a) Sodium or potassium salt of long chain fatty acids
    (b) Sodium slats of alkyl benzene sulphonate.
    (c) Triglycerides which are solids at room temperature
    (d) Triglycarides which are liquids at room temperature
    (e) Glyceriaes of unsaturated fatty acids
    (f) Glycerides of saturated fatty acids.

Short Answer Type Questions

26. Ethers have an oxygen atom bonded between two alkyl groups (R-O-R'), while esters have a carbonyl group adjacent to an ether linkage (R-COO-R').
27. Functional isomerism occurs when compounds have the same molecular formula but different functional groups. For example, alcohols and ethers might share the same molecular formula but possess different functional groups (-OH vs -O-).
28. Aldehydes contain a carbonyl group (C=O) bonded to a hydrogen atom and an alkyl or aryl group, whereas ketones have a carbonyl group bonded between two alkyl or aryl groups.
29. Tollen's reagent, an ammoniacal silver nitrate solution, is significant as it is used to test for the presence of aldehydes. Aldehydes reduce the silver ion in the reagent to metallic silver, leading to a mirror-like coating in the test tube.
30. Based on the number of monosaccharide units produced upon hydrolysis.

31. (b) NaOH + CaO is soda lime which is a reagent for the decarboxylation. C should be a carboxylic acid and D should be its alkali salt. E should be an alkanes with one carbon less than the parent acid (C). B should be an aldehyde with same number of carbon atoms. As the final product is CH_3OH, F should also posses one carbon atom. E should be methane and F should be chloromethane which is obtained by the chlorination of methane in presence of sunlight. Chloromethane on the treatment with aq. KOH gives methyl alcohol. E (methane) can be obtained from the ethanoic acid (C). B should be ethanal and A should be ethyne as ethyne on treatment with $H_2SO_4|HgSO_4$ gives ethanol (x). Ethyne (A) is obtained by the hydrolysis of calcium carbide.

$$\underset{(X)}{CaC_2} + H_2O \rightarrow \underset{(A)}{C_2H_2} \xrightarrow[H_2SO_4]{HgSO_4} \underset{(B)}{CH_3CHO}$$

$$\downarrow \xrightarrow[KMnO_4]{[O]}$$

$$\underset{(C)}{CH_3COOH}$$

$$\downarrow$$

$$\underset{(D)}{CH_3\ COONa}$$

$$CH_3OH \xleftarrow[KOH]{aq} \underset{(F)}{CH_3Cl} \xleftarrow[hv]{Cl_2} \underset{(E)}{CH_4} \xleftarrow[CaO]{NaOH}$$

32. Aldehydes undergo oxidation with Tollen's reagent and Fehling's reagent which is a distinguishing test from ketones.

33. (i) Higher tensile strength.
(ii) High resistance to aerial oxidation
(iii) High resistance to chemical reaction with alkalis.

34. (i) Resistance to sunlight, soaps, detergents, water, heat.
(ii) Ability to spread uniformly and easy drying.

35. (i) Site specificity and efficiency of action.
(ii) Negligible side effects which doesn't cause any damage to host tissues.

36. (i) Addition of 'H_2' on unsaturated oil in presence of catalyst.
(ii) Temperature and pressure at which hydrogenation is carried out.
(iii) Chemical reaction
(iv) Uses: in cooking, cosmetics, and for medicinal purpose.

37. (i) Form basic structural material of living cells.
(ii) As enzymes, they catalyse biochemical reactions.
(iii) As hormones, they regulate metabolic processes.

38. (i) Definition
(ii) Different amino acid units join together by peptide linkage to form protein molecules.

39. The products obtained by the breakdown of given oligosaccharides upon addition of water. (Hydrolysis)

Essay Answer Type Questions

40. Ethers and esters, while both containing alkyl-oxygen bonds exhibit fundamentally distinct chemical structures. Esters possess a carbonyl group (C=O) adjacent to the oxygen atom, resulting in the characteristic structure RCOOR', where R and R' represent alkyl groups. This arrangement confers esters with distinct resonance and electronic effects, which are known to contribute to their often pleasant and fruity odours. Such aromas are coveted in the realm of perfumery, where recognizable and delightful fragrances are paramount. Conversely, ethers, denoted by the structure ROR', lack this carbonyl group. As a result, their odour profile can range from being nearly odourless to exhibiting a more muted or even at times an unpleasant odour. Therefore, in the context of perfumery, esters, with their pleasant aromatic profiles, are naturally preferred over ethers.

41. Both Tollen's reagent and Benedict's reagent play pivotal roles in the domain of organic chemistry as indicators for the presence of aldehydes. Their mechanisms of action, while rooted in oxidation reactions, manifest distinct visual outcomes. In the presence of Tollen's reagent, aldehydes facilitate the reduction of silver ions (Ag+) to elemental silver (Ag0). This reduction process results in the deposition of a silver layer, which often presents as a mirror-like coating on the inner surface of the test tube, a characteristic indicator of aldehyde presence. Conversely, when aldehydes are subjected to Benedict's reagent, they engage in reducing copper (II) ions, culminating in the formation of a red-brown copper (I) oxide precipitate. While both reagents hinge on oxidation reactions, the discerning chemist appreciates the unique visual cues each provides.

42. Polysaccharides, complex carbohydrates composed of extended chains of monosaccharide units, are ingeniously designed by nature as storage molecules. Contrary to monosaccharides and certain disaccharides, which are inherently sweet to the human palate, polysaccharides exhibit a notably bland taste. This characteristic can be postulated as an evolutionary adaptation. By ensuring these storage molecules lack an appealing sweetness, plants potentially deter herbivores or other organisms from excessive consumption. Moreover, the intricate structural complexity of polysaccharides necessitates more intricate digestive processes, further safeguarding the plant's energy reserves. The delayed gratification provided by these storage molecules, in contrast to the immediate energy signal a sweet taste would indicate, serves to protect and sustain the plant's longevity.

43. The calorific value represents the total energy released when a substance undergoes complete combustion in the presence of oxygen. It provides a maximal theoretical energy value. In biological systems, however, energy extraction from consumed materials is a more intricate process. Organisms rely on a series of regulated metabolic pathways to degrade and assimilate nutrients. As these biochemical reactions progress, not all potential energy is harnessed as usable energy. A significant portion is inevitably lost, primarily as heat. Furthermore, the efficiency of these metabolic processes and the energy spent in digestion can result in the actual energy obtained by the organism being notably less than the calorific value. Hence, while combustion offers a holistic view of potential energy, the biological reality is invariably more complex and nuanced.

44. The purification of crude oil involves two major steps

1st step: Removal of impurities: Since crude oil is present with a layer of salt beneath earth's surface, it contains salt water as the major impurity. This water can be removed by passing the crude oil sample between two highly charged electrodes. Water droplets are attracted towards the electrodes and separated out. The oil so obtained is devoid of water and is subjected to treatment with copper oxide. The sulphur compounds present in the oil react with copper oxide forming copper sulphide which is removed by filtration.

2nd step: Fractional distillation: After the removal of impurities, the crude oil obtained is a pure mixture of hydrocarbons. This method involves heating of the mixture over a specific range of temperature in a fractionating column with a long tube. This allows separation of various components of the mixture according to their boiling points.

45. $C_xH_y + 3O_2 \rightarrow 2CO_2 + 2H_2O$

$C_xH_y \rightarrow C_2H_4$

X is ethene (C_2H_4)

$$\underset{(X)}{CH_2 = CH_2} + H_2SO_4\,(\text{conc.}) \rightarrow CH_3 - CH_2 - OSO_3H$$

$$\xrightarrow{75\text{–}89°C} \underset{Y}{CH_3 - CH_2 - OH} + H_2SO_4$$

$$\underset{Y}{C_2H_5OH} + PCl_5 \longrightarrow \underset{Z}{C_2H_5Cl} + POCl_3 + HCl$$

Ethyl alcohol (Y) has one functional isomer, dimethyl ether.

$$CH_3 - O - Na + Cl - CH_3 \rightarrow \underset{\text{Dimethyl ether}}{CH_3 - O - CH_3}$$

Dimethyl ether can be prepared by treating chloromethane (homologue of Z) with sodium methoxide.

Competition Wing

Level 1: Apply your Concepts

36. 4 Halogenation
2 Treatment with aqueous KOH
5 Reaction with acidified $K_2Cr_2O_7$
1 Treatment with sodium hydroxide
3 Treatment with NaOH + CaO
Hence, the correct answer is (b).

37. 2 Hydrolysis
4 Reaction with $HgSO_4/H_2SO_4$
5 Reaction with $HgSO_4$
3 Reaction with soda lime
6 Reaction with PCl_5
1 Reaction with aqueous KOH
Hence, the correct answer is (a).

38. 2 Fructose
3 Maltose
1 Raffinose
4 Stachyose
Hence, the correct answer is (b).

39. CH_3COOH is the given IUPAC name of ethanoic acid.
Hence, the correct answer is (d).

40. Ethene on oxidation with cold alkaline $KMnO_4$ gives ethene glycol.
Hence, the correct answer is (c).

41. Diastase enzyme is required for the conversion of starch to maltose.
Hence, the correct answer is (a).

42. Calciferol is the chemical name of vitamin D.
Hence, the correct answer is (c).

43. 5 Drilling of the oil through the various layers under the earth's surface.
1 Processing of crude oil to remove heavy oil
4 Purification of crude oil containing salt water
2 Heating of the crude oil containing pure mixture of hydrocarbons over a specific range of temperature
3 Separation of constituents by fractional distillation
Hence, the correct answer is (c).

44. The oils having higher unsaturation in the fatty acid component have very low melting points. Hence, on the consumption of these oils there is less chance of blockage of blood vessels. The saturated oils have higher melting points and they get solidified easily. Therefore they block the blood vessels and so are prohibited from consumption by cardiac patients. Hence oil D is prohibited from consumption by cardiac patients.
Hence, the correct answer is (d).

45. Plants can synthesize all amino acids. The living systems in animals can synthesize only non-essential amino acids.
Hence, the correct answer is ((a), (b), (d)).

Level 2: Review Your Concepts

46. Proteins are vital for cell structure and function. They make up about 50% of the cell's dry mass, playing roles in structural support, enzyme catalysis, transport, and other cellular activities.

47. Amino acids are the building blocks or monomers that link together via peptide bonds to form polypeptide chains. These chains, when folded and structured, can constitute protein molecules.

48. The calorific value represents the amount of energy a food can provide when metabolized. It's crucial for determining the energy contribution of that food to the body, aiding in dietary and nutritional planning.

49. Polysaccharides are termed non-sugars because, unlike monosaccharides and disaccharides which have a sweet taste, they are generally tasteless or have a bland taste.

50. (i) Identification of the functional group having one oxygen atom in it
(ii) Identification of isomer of organic compound namely X and Y from given molecular formula
(iii) Prediction of functional groups in X and Y on the basis of isomerism
(iv) Nature of the reagent given
(v) Requisite of an organic compound to respond to the reagent given
(vi) Comparison of type of products formed

51. (i) Nature/property of the reagent namely copper at 300°C
(ii) Property exploited by the specific reagent used namely Cu at 300°C
(iii) Prediction of functional groups of A and B from the nature of reagent used

(iv) Identification of 'D' based on 'B' and 'A.'
(v) Identification of functional groups of 'E' from B and A based on the usage of common specific reagents
(vi) Identification of F from the reaction between E and B
(vii) Prediction of functional isomer of 'F' based on nature of functional group and its molecular formula

52. (i) Composition of the dye
(ii) Group responsible for electronic transition
(iii) Type and nature of the dye used for fabric
(iv) Comparison of structure of the dye and detergent
(v) Comparison of affinity of dye to the fabric and detergent

53. (i) Strength of given oxidizing agents
(ii) Conversion of carbonyl group to corresponding acid (by suitable oxidizing agent)
(iii) Conversion of both carbonyl group and hydroxyl group to corresponding acid (by suitable oxidizing agent)

54. (i) Significance of 95% ethyl alcohol wrt fractional distillation
(ii) Nature of ethyl alcohol obtained by fermentation of molasses
(iii) Purpose of fractional distillation
(iv) Physical property of ethyl alcohol exploited for the purpose
(v) Change in physical property when 95% ethyl alcohol is obtained
(vi) Effect of the above change on the state of ethyl alcohol when the process to continued
(vii) Effect of addition of potassium acetate on the above physical property
(viii) Relation between the effect and the process carried out

55. (i) Vulcanization is the process of heating of natural rubber with sulphur which improves the elasticity as well as reduces the sticky nature of rubber. During this process, different isoprene units are joined together by C–S–S–C bonds. Synthetic rubbers are also addition polymers.
(ii) Type of bonding between the added element and major constituent of rubber
(iii) Effect of these bonds on physical properties of rubber

56. These dyes cannot dye the fabric directly. When some substances called mordants are added to these dyes, they can produce wash-fast colors. The mordants include salts of some metals like aluminium, iron, and chromium. Acidic dyes require basic mordants and basic dyes require acidic mordants.

57.

Examples	Formulae	Functional groups or types of bond	Sources	Characteristic properties	Relative sweetness
Sucrose (table sugar or cane sugar)	$C_{12}H_{22}O_{11}$	Glycoside bond between one glucose unit and one fructose unit	Sugar cane and beet root	Soluble in water, non-reducing sugars	100
Maltose	$C_{12}H_{22}O_{11}$	Glycoside bonds between two glucose units	Germinating cereals	Soluble in water, reducing sugars	32

58. (i) The parts of the dye molecule
(ii) Components of a dye molecule
(iii) Requisite for an organic compound to exhibit color
(iv) Components of dye which impart color and intensifies color
(v) Type of attractions between the component of dye molecule and fabric
(vi) Changes that take place in the dye when fabric is washed successively
(vii) Effect of solar radiation on the color of fabric

59. (i) Nature and relative requirement of vitamin 'B.'
(ii) Comparison of solubilities of vitamin B with other vitamins.
(iii) Comparison of functions of vitamin B with other vitamins

60. (i) Requisite for reducing sugar
(ii) Composition of monosaccharide units present in sucrose
(iii) Type of glycosidic linkage in sucrose
(iv) Requisite of a disaccharide to be a reducing sugar
(v) Comparison of different groups present in other disaccharides
(vi) Comparison of position of glycoside linkage in sucrose and other disaccharides

61. 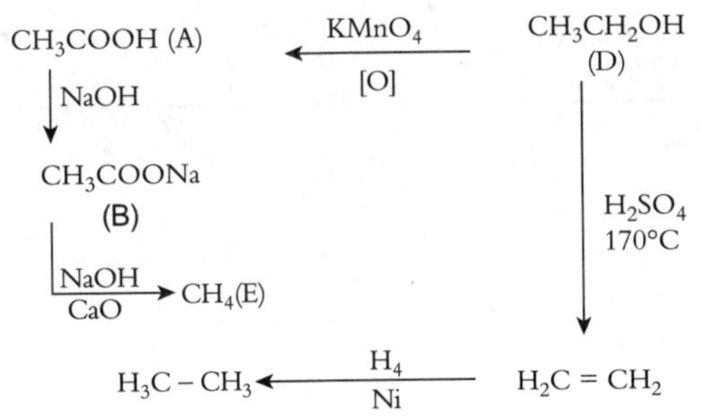

62. (a) In methanol, intermolecular forces of attraction are more due to the presence of H-bonding, whereas ethane does not have H-bonding. Therefore, the boiling point of ethanol is much higher than that of ethane though the molecular weights are almost same.

(b) A carboxylic acid contains –COOH group. Since there are two highly electronegative oxygen's attached to the carbon, they can form two hydrogen bonds with the –COOH group of adjacent molecule.

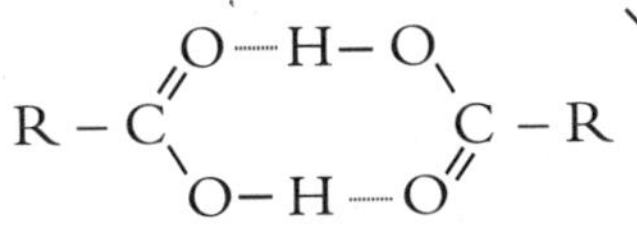

Due to the presence of high intensity of hydrogen bonding between carboxylic acids they boil relatively at high temperatures when compared to alcohols with almost same molecular weight. In between acetic acid molecules two hydrogen bonds are present while between two propyl alcohol molecules only one hydrogen bond is present. Hence more energy is required to break two hydrogen bonds in acetic acid when compared to the same molecular weight containing propyl alcohol.

	B. P.
Acetic acid	118°C
Propyl alcohol	97°C

63. $CH_3-CH_3-OH \xrightarrow{\text{alk } KMnO_4} CH_3-COOH \xrightarrow{Cl_2,\ P} CCl_3-COOH$

64. (a) The polarity of the O–H bond facilitates the removal of positively charged hydrogen thereby forming alkoxide ion. Thus, alcohol acts as an acid in presence of a base.

$$R-O-H \longrightarrow \underset{\text{alkoxide}}{RO^-} + H^+$$

Due to the presence of a lone pair of electrons on oxygen atom, the alcohol molecule can accept a proton (H+ ion) and form protonated alcohol. Thus, alcohol can act as a base in presence of an acid.

$$R-\ddot{O}-H + H^+ \longrightarrow R-OH_2^+$$

(b) (a) 'X' should be a carboxylic acid as its sodium salt undergoes decarboxylation with soda lime. The given organic compound should be its preceding homologue.

% of carbon = 40%

% of hydrogen = 6.7%

% of oxygen = 53.3%

The organic compound X should be ethanoic acid. Succeeding homologue of X is propanoic acid. Y is ethane. And Z is iodoethane.

(i) $CH_3CH_2COOH + NaOH \rightarrow$

propanoic acid X $\quad CH_3CH_2COONa + H_2O$

CaO

CH_3-CH_3 Ethane Y

(ii) $H_3C-CH_3 + I_2 \xrightarrow{hv} H_3C-CH_2I + HI$

(iii) $H_3C-CH_2I \xrightarrow{(a)\ alc.KOH} H_2C=CH_2$; $H_3C-CH_2I \xrightarrow{(b)\ aq.KOH} H_3C-CH_2-OH$

(b) (iv) $\underset{(B)}{H_3C-CH_2-OH} \xrightarrow{alk.KMnO_4} CH_3COOH$

(v) $\underset{(A)}{H_2C=CH_2} + H_2SO_4 \xrightarrow{\Delta} CH_3CH_2OH \xrightarrow{alk.KMnO_4} CH_3COOH$

(c) i. → Elimination reaction (decarboxylation)

ii. → Substitution reaction (halogenation)

iii. (a) → Elimination

(b) → Substitution

iv. Oxidation

v. Addition reaction followed by oxidation reaction

65. $\underset{1-\text{butene}}{H_2C=CH-CH-CH_3}$

$\underset{2-\text{butene}}{H_3C-HC=CH_3} + O_3 \xrightarrow[Zn]{H_2O} 2CH_3-CHO$

$\underset{C}{CH_3CH_2OH} + [O] \xrightarrow{CuO} CH_3CHO$

$$CH_3-CH_2-Cl \ (B) \xrightarrow{\text{alc. KOH}} H_2C=CH_3 \ (D)$$

$$CH_3-CH_2-Cl \ (B) \xrightarrow{\text{aq.KOH}} CH_3CH_2OH \ (C)$$

$$H_3C-CH_3 + Cl_2 \xrightarrow{h\nu} CH_3CH_2Cl \ (B)$$

66. $H_3C-C=C-CH_3 + [H] \xrightarrow{Ni} H_3C-CH=CH-CH_3$

$$\overset{sp^3}{H_3C}-\overset{sp}{CH}=\overset{sp}{CH}-\overset{sp^3}{CH_3} + Br_2 \longrightarrow H_3C-\underset{Br}{\underset{|}{CH}}-\underset{Br}{\underset{|}{CH}}-CH_3$$

$$\longrightarrow H_3C-C=C-CH_3 + 2KBr + 2H_3O$$

$$\longrightarrow H_3C-\overset{H}{\overset{|}{C}}=\overset{H}{\overset{|}{C}}-CH_3 + ZnBr_3$$

67. A and B should be carbonyl compounds since they are ozonolysis products. One should be aldehyde and the other one should be ketone.

$$H_3C-CH=\overset{CH_3}{\overset{|}{C}}-CH_3 + O_3 \xrightarrow[Zn]{H_2O} \underset{A}{CH_3CHO} + \underset{B}{CH_3\ COCH_3}$$

$$A \xrightarrow{NaBH_4\ [H]} CH_3CH_2OH \ \text{(Ethanol)} \ C$$

$$B \xrightarrow{NaBH_4\ [H]} CH_3-\underset{OH}{\underset{|}{CH}}-CH_3 \ \text{(2–propanol)} \ D$$

Position isomer of D $\longrightarrow CH_3CH_2CH_2OH$

1 propanol

$$\left.\begin{array}{c} CH_3COH \\ \text{Ethanal} \\ CH_3COCH_3 \\ \text{Propanone} \end{array}\right\rangle \xrightarrow{KMnO_4/H^+} \begin{array}{c} CH_3COOH \\ \text{Ethanoic acid} \end{array}$$

68.

$$\underset{(Q)}{R-CH_2-CH_3} \xrightarrow[Cl_2]{h\nu} R-\overset{Cl}{\overset{|}{\underset{H}{\underset{|}{C}}}}-CH_3 \xrightarrow{\text{aq.NaOH}} \underset{(X)}{R-\overset{OH}{\overset{|}{\underset{H}{\underset{|}{C}}}}-CH_3} \xrightarrow{NaOI} \underset{(Y)}{R-\overset{O}{\overset{||}{C}}-CH_3}$$

$$(Y) \xrightarrow{I_2/NaOH} \underset{(Z)}{R-\overset{O}{\overset{||}{C}}-ONa + CHI_3}$$

Yellow precipitate

The above reaction helps to identify the particular set of organic compounds with $R-\underset{H}{\overset{X}{C}}-CH_3$ structure.

(where X = halogen or –OH or $-\overset{O}{\overset{\|}{C}}-$) group and thus it helps to identify methyl ketones, 2° and 3° alcohols, alkyl-halides, etc., Among 1° alcohols and 1° alkyl halides, only ethyl alcohol and ethyl chloride will respond but not others. This is halo form or iodoform test. The position isomer of 1-Propanol doesn't give a yellow precipitate.

69. (a)

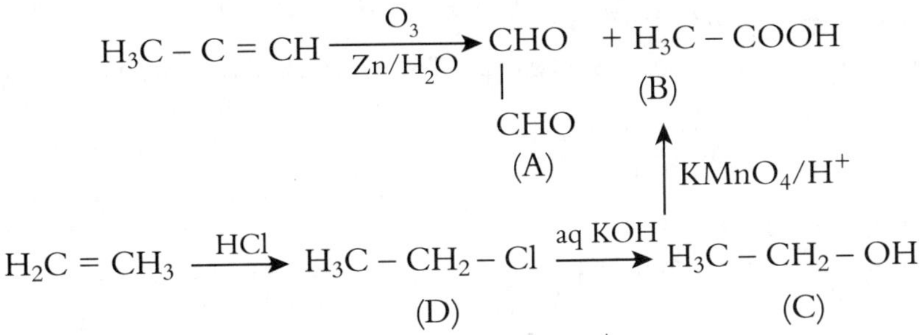

(b)

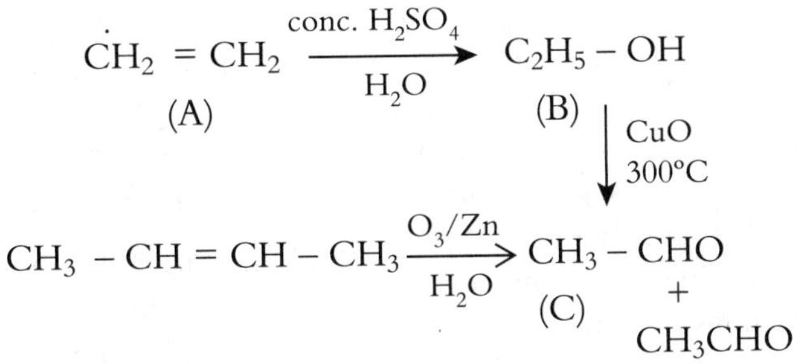

70. There are some solid forms of medicines which are insoluble in water. At the same time, they cannot be given with organic solvents. Though they cannot form a true solution, they can give suspensions when dissolved in water. Suspensions are the solutions where the particle size is much larger. But suspensions being very less stable cannot be prepared and stored. Hence, the powders have to be made into suspensions with water and then administered. They should be consumed within the stipulated time. Usually, the pediatric medicines are given in such formulations since infants cannot consume tablets. Medicines can be given in different formulations like tablets, capsules, syrups, and injections. Tablets, capsules and syrups are taken orally. They contain the drug and drug carrier so that the drug will be released only at the site of action. Before the drug reaches the site of action and gets released there, it has to pass through the system. After it is released, it has to be assimilated into the blood. Hence, the entire process requires some time before it starts its action on the particular organ system. But injections are directly given into the veins where the drug is absorbed by the blood. Being in liquid form, they start action much earlier than the solid form. Therefore, medicines in the form of injections are faster in action than the other formulations.

Level 3: Assess Your Concepts

71. (a) (i) Dipolar nature of amino acids of proteins

(ii) Functional groups present in proteins

(iii) Effect of these functional groups on the pH

(b) (a) Ethane to acetic acid

$$CH_3-CH_3 + Cl_2 \rightarrow C_2H_5Cl + HCl$$

$$CH_3-CH_2Cl + aq.KOH \rightarrow CH_3-CH_2OH + KCl$$

$$CH_3-CH_2OH + [O] \xrightarrow{KMnO_4} CH_3-COOH$$

(b) Acetone to methane

$$CH_3-\overset{\overset{O}{||}}{C}-CH_3 + [O] \xrightarrow{KMnO_4/H^+} CH_3COOH$$

$$CH_3COOH + NaOH \rightarrow CH_3COONa + H_2O$$

$$CH_3COONa + NaOH \xrightarrow{CaO} CH_4 + Na_2CO_3$$

(c) 1, 2 – dibromoethane to ethanal

$$\begin{array}{c} H_2C-Br \\ | \\ H_2C-Br \end{array} + Zn \rightarrow \begin{array}{c} CH_2 \\ || \\ CH_2 \end{array}$$

$$CH_2 = CH_2 + H_2SO_4 \text{ (conc.)} \rightarrow$$

$$CH_3-CH_2-OSO_3H \xrightarrow{75\text{-}89°C} CH_3-CH_2-OH + H_2SO_4$$

$$CH_3-CH_2-OH \xrightarrow[300°C]{Cu} \underset{\text{Ethanal}}{CH_3-CHO}$$

72. Both detergents and soaps operate as surfactants, reducing the surface tension of water and facilitating the removal of dirt and oils. However, their efficacy can vary significantly in the context of water quality. Hard water, characterized by elevated concentrations of metal ions, particularly calcium and magnesium, presents challenges for soaps. Upon interaction, soaps tend to form insoluble salts with these ions, commonly referred to as "soap scum." This not only diminishes the soap's cleaning capability but also results in undesirable residues. Detergents, particularly those of synthetic origin, are designed to circumvent this limitation. Their molecular structures are less predisposed to interact with the metal ions present in hard water, ensuring consistent solubility and unhindered cleaning efficiency. Consequently, in regions grappling with hard water challenges, the inherent advantages of detergents position them as the preferred cleaning agents.

73. The acidity of a molecule is largely influenced by how stable its conjugate base is after losing a proton. In carboxylic acids, the carboxylate anion formed after deprotonation is resonance-stabilized; the negative charge is delocalized over the two oxygen atoms, thus dispersing the charge and leading to enhanced stability. Conversely, alcohols form alkoxide ions upon deprotonation, which lack such resonance stabilization. This makes them less stable than carboxylate ions. This fundamental difference in the stability of the conjugate bases is what primarily drives the greater acidity of carboxylic acids in comparison to alcohols.

74. Esters typically consist of a single carboxylic acid moiety combined with an alcohol. Their relatively smaller size, compared to fats, often lends them volatility that makes them apt for fragrant roles in nature, such as producing the aromatic scents of fruits and flowers. In industry, this same characteristic is harnessed for use in perfumes and flavourings. Fats, on the other hand, are bulkier and involve three ester linkages with a glycerol backbone. This non-volatile and hydrophobic nature makes fats excellent for energy storage in biological systems. Additionally, in the cosmetics industry, the structural attributes of fats make them superb moisturizing agents, providing a barrier and retaining moisture in the skin.

75. Chromophores are regions within molecules that can absorb certain wavelengths of light due to transitions between molecular energy levels. The specific nature of the chromophore dictates which wavelengths (and thus, colours) are absorbed. When dyes interact with fabrics, the chromophores play a pivotal role in ensuring that the fabric reflects the desired colour. Beyond just colour, the structural nature of the chromophore and associated chemical groups can determine the dye's adherence to specific fabric types. In textile design, understanding these interactions enables designers to choose and even chemically modify dyes for desired effects, ensuring not only the desired colour but also longevity, resistance to fading, and vibrancy.

76. Proteins and polypeptides are essentially sequences of amino acids. It's not just the presence of these amino acids, but their specific order, that's critical. This order determines the way these long chains fold into unique three-dimensional structures. The nature of this folding, in turn, is governed by various forces—hydrogen bonds, van der Waals forces, disulphide bridges, ionic interactions, and more. These folded structures allow proteins to engage in precise interactions with other molecules, making them perfect for diverse tasks, from catalysing chemical reactions as enzymes to playing roles in cellular structure, transport, signalling, and many other biological processes.

77. Vitamins and hormones play distinct yet critical roles. Vitamins, often derived from dietary sources, serve primarily as precursors to coenzymes or as co-factors. These coenzymes and co-factors are molecules that assist enzymes, enhancing their efficiency and ensuring that biochemical reactions occur smoothly. For instance, Vitamin C is essential for collagen synthesis, while Vitamin K plays a role in blood clotting. Hormones, in contrast, function as messengers. Produced in one part of the body, they travel to tar-

get cells or organs to induce specific responses. They can affect growth (like growth hormone), metabolism (like insulin), mood (like serotonin), and various other physiological processes. Their action is often tied to intricate feedback loops that ensure homeostasis and adaptability in changing conditions.

78. Cooking involves loss of water-soluble vitamins, whereas frying involves loss of both water-soluble and fat-soluble vitamins.

79. (a) Amino acid with $-NH_2$ and $-COOH$ group in neutral solution. No change in the molecule and no migration to any electrode due to the formation of $NH_3^+ - R - COO^-$ (zwitter ions)

(b) Amino acid in acidic solution exists as $NH_3^+–R–COOH$. Hence migrates towards negative electrode.

(c) Amino acid in basic solution contains $NH_3^+ R - COO^-$ ions and show migration towards cathode in an electric field.

Proteins hydrolyse to give amino acids. In the presence of excess of acidic solution, the $-NH_2$ groups of amino acids form $- NH_3^+ - R - COOH$ ions and in presence of basic solution, $- COOH$ groups lose H^+ ions forming $H_2N - R - COO^-$ ions. Therefore, the excess H^+ or OH^- ions are consumed. The zwitter ion formation thus results in maintenance of pH value of body fluids.

JEE-NEET Special wing

Multiple-Answer Type Questions

1. As double bond gets higher priority over triple bond, carbon atom near to double bond has to be numbered '1'. As there are 6 carbons, root word is 'hex'. So, both the names given under option b and d are correct.

$$\overset{1}{CH_2} = \overset{2}{CH} - \overset{3}{CH_2} - \overset{4}{CH_2} - \overset{5}{C} \equiv \overset{6}{CH}$$

2. Due to its small size, carbon exhibits catenation property, enabling it to form strong C-C bonds with long-chain compounds. Its tetravalency allows carbon to form multiple bonds with other carbon atoms, permitting carbon atoms to share not only a single electron with another atom to form a single bond but also two or three electrons, resulting in double or triple bonds. This results in a multitude of potential bond combinations at various positions, leading to a wide array of possible molecules. Even a minor difference in one atom or bond position distinguishes one compound from another.

3. The isomers in which there is an unequal distribution of carbon chain or atoms on either side of the functional group are called metamers and this phenomenon is termed as 'metamerism.' Thus, metamers differ in the size of an alkyl group or chain on either side of the functional group. Hence, only the compounds with divalent functional groups (with valency two) exhibits metamerism. Acid and aldehyde functional groups are monovalent while ester and ether are divalent.

4. Compounds with same functional group show similar chemical properties. As it is given that these compounds are containing monovalent functional groups,
   (a) C_2H_6O-Is of general formula $C_{2n}H_{2n+2}O \Rightarrow$ It is an alcohol, C_2H_5OH.
   (b) C_3H_6O- Is of general formula $C_{2n}H_{2n}O \Rightarrow$ It is an aldehyde, C_2H_5CHO.
   (c) CH_2O- Is of general formula $C_{2n}H_{2n}O \Rightarrow$ It is an aldehyde, HCHO.
   (d) C_2H_4O- Is of general formula $C_{2n}H_{2n}O \Rightarrow$ It is an aldehyde, CH_3CHO.

5. Nicotinic acid, also known as vitamin B_3, plays a vital role in converting nutrients into energy within the body. Its deficiency can lead to pellagra. Unlike hormones, which the body can produce internally, vitamins (except a few), need to be sourced externally through food or supplements . However, human body can also internally synthesize niacin (vitamin B_3) through the tryptophan(an amino acid obtained from protein containing foods)-to-niacin pathway. But this conversion may not always meet the body's optimal niacin requirements.

Comprehension-Based Questions

6. Hydrocarbon X is giving an aldehyde and a ketone on reductive ozonolysis. This indicates that it should be an alkene. Also, during ozonolysis, given that ozone (O_3) selectively breaks unsaturated bonds, substituting them with carbonyl (C = O) groups, structure of X should be 2, 4-dimethylpent-2-ene

$$\underset{\substack{\text{2,4 dimethylpent–2–ene} \\ (X)}}{(CH_3)_2C–CH=C(CH_3)_2} \xrightarrow[\text{(ii) Zn\textbackslash HCl}]{\text{(i) } O_3} \underset{(Y)}{(CH_3)_2CH–CHO} + \underset{(Z)}{(CH_3)_2CO}$$

7.

Compound	Fehling's test/ inference	Treatment with I_2 and NaOH/Inference
B	Positive $\Rightarrow$ It contains aldehyde (-CHO) group	Positive $\Rightarrow$ It contains Methyl ketone ($-CH_3C = O$) group
C	Positive $\Rightarrow$ It contains aldehyde (-CHO) group	Negative $\Rightarrow$ Absence of Methyl ketone ($-CH_3C = O$) group

Given that compound B and C belong to the same homologous series and C is the first member of the series. From this we can infer B as acetaldehyde and C as formaldehyde and compound A is an unsymmetrical terminal alkene with three carbon atoms. Hence, the correct answer should be 1-Propene.

8. If compound B tests positive with an I_2/NaOH mixture, it implies the presence of a methyl ketone group ($CH_3C = O$). This is because only compounds containing the methyl ketone group can yield a positive test I_2/NaOH mixture, leading to the formation of CH_3I (iodoform), which appears as a yellow precipitate.

9. $$\underset{\text{1,3 Butadience}}{CH_2{=}CH\text{-}CH{=}CH_2} \xrightarrow[\text{(ii) Zn\textbackslash HCl}]{\text{(i) } O_3} \underset{\substack{\text{(Formaldehyde} \\ \text{or Methanal)}}}{2CH_2{=}O} \text{ or } HCHO + \underset{\text{(Glyoxal)}}{\begin{matrix} CHO \\ | \\ CHO \end{matrix}}$$

10. During the reductive ozonolysis of alkenes, role of zinc dust is to inhibit further oxidation of the carbonyl compounds formed by hydrolysis.

11.

List – I Compound	List – II Ozonolysis Products
(A) 2,3-Pentadiene	(vi) Carbon dioxide as one of the products
(B) First member of alkyne homologous series	(iv) Only Formic acid.
(C) Isobutane	(v) Does not form an ozonide
(D) Benzene	(ii) Forms 3 mol of glyoxal on reductive ozonolysis
(E) An alkene where all substituents are alkyl groups	(iii) Forms only ketones on reductive ozonolysis

So the correct match is: (A)-(vi); (B)-(iv); (C)-(v); (D)-(ii); (E)-(iii)

12. Ethanol on heating with Conc. H_2SO_4 at about 170°C undergoes dehydration to form Ethene which is a hydrocarbon as it contains only carbon and hydrogen as its constituent elements. All other given compounds contain other atoms or group of atoms or functional groups (formed by replacing one or more hydrogen atoms of the corresponding hydrocarbon with another atom or a group of atoms) besides carbon and hydrogen as their constituents.

13. Positional isomerism, an example of structural isomerism, occurs due to the difference in the position of functional group in the carbon chain. Compounds B and C contain terminal functional groups that neither show positional isomerism nor possess the necessary minimum number of carbon atoms for such isomerism. While the alcohol functional group can exhibit positional isomerism, compound X, with only two carbon atoms, results in the same compound when altering the position of the –OH group on the other carbon. Therefore, none of the provided compounds display positional isomerism.

14. Hydrogen bonding occurs when hydrogen atoms covalently bonded to highly electronegative atoms (such as nitrogen, oxygen, or fluorine) interact with another electronegative atom's lone pair in a neighbouring molecule. Unlike compounds like alcohols or carboxylic acids, where the hydrogen atom directly attached to the electronegative atom (oxygen or nitrogen) participates in hydrogen bonding, aldehydes lack hydrogen atoms bonded directly to the oxygen atom of the carbonyl group. Hence although there is a negligible difference in the molecular weight of ethyl alcohol(X) and acetaldehyde (C), boiling point of X is much greater than that of the compound C due to the presence of stronger intermolecular hydrogen bonding compared to the weak Vander Waal's forces in compound C. Additionally, greater the strength of the hydrogen bond higher will be the boiling point. Hence, both the assertion and reason are correct, but reason is not the correct explanation of the given assertion.

15. Compound D is ethene. Which is the first member of its homologous series.

16. Isopropyl alcohol is heated with CuO at 300°C undergoes dehydrogenation to give acetone.

$$CH_3\text{-}\underset{\underset{OH}{|}}{CH}-CH_3 \xrightarrow[300°C]{Cu} CH_3-\underset{\underset{O}{\|}}{C}-CH_3 + H_2$$

Acetone, a symmetrical compound, contains three carbon atoms. In contrast, compound C is acetaldehyde, which contains two carbon atoms. Thus, acetone has one more carbon atom than compound C. As the functional groups differ, acetone does not exhibit the characteristic reactions of compound C.

17.

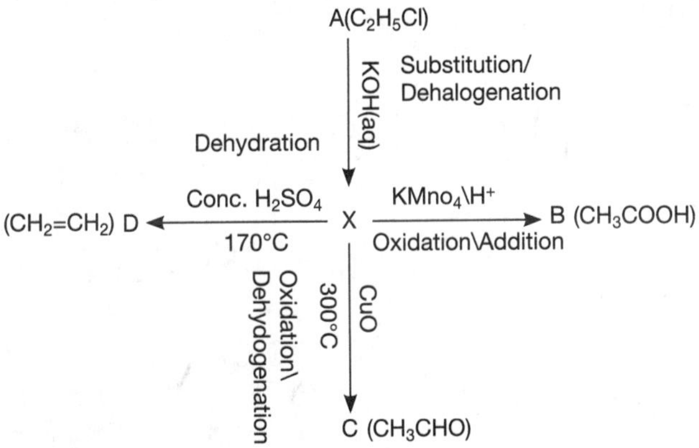

List – I Conversion of compounds	List – II Type of the reaction
(a) A to X	(vi) Substitution
(b) X to B	(ii) Addition or (vii) Oxidation
(c) X to C	(i) Dehydrogenation or (vii) Oxidation
(d) X to D	(iii) Dehydration

[illegible] hydrogen atom is bonded directly to the oxygen atom of the carbonyl group. Hence, [illegible] highly difference [illegible] the boiling point of [illegible] and [illegible] [illegible] higher than that of the [illegible]. [illegible] product, [illegible] hydrogen bonding [illegible] Additionally, [illegible] the boiling point [illegible] the correct [illegible]

15. Compound [illegible] [illegible] number of [illegible]

16. [illegible] and [illegible]

[illegible]

Answer: [illegible] compound C contains [illegible] [illegible] two [illegible] atoms. Thus, [illegible] one more carbon atom in a compound [illegible] functional group [illegible] of compound C.

[illegible]

Conversion of [illegible] compounds

[illegible]

11. [illegible] Compound [illegible] Ozonolysis product

(A) [illegible] (iii) Carbon dioxide [illegible] of [illegible] molecule

[illegible]

(D) [illegible] (IV) [illegible]

[illegible] (a) [illegible] (b) [illegible] (c) [illegible]

(d) [illegible]

12. [illegible] definition [illegible] All organic compounds contain [illegible] group of atoms [illegible] groups [illegible] by replacing one or more hydrogen atoms of the corresponding hydrocarbon [illegible] group [illegible] their constituents.

13. Functional isomerism [illegible] occurs due to the difference in the position of [illegible] group in the carbon chain [illegible] positional isomerism [illegible] number of carbon atoms [illegible] [illegible] carbon atoms [illegible] compound [illegible] position of the [illegible] group [illegible] Therefore, [illegible] positional isomerism.

14. [illegible] bonding [illegible] hydrogen atoms [illegible] bonded to highly electronegative atoms [illegible] nitrogen, oxygen, or fluorine [illegible] [illegible] carboxylic acids [illegible] [illegible] in hydrogen bonding [illegible]

CHAPTER

10

General Organic Chemistry–III

Remember

Before beginning this chapter, you should be able to:

- explain the unique features of carbon.
- classify organic compounds based on characteristics.
- name organic compounds.
- describe isomerism of organic compounds.
- understand the preparation and properties of simple alkanes, alkenes, and alkynes.

Key Ideas

After completing this chapter, you should be able to:

- recall the basic features of carbon.
- remember some terms like nomenclature of organic compounds and concepts related to it.

Scientific Crypt

A Tribute to Adolf von Baeyer (1835–1917)

Johann Friedrich Wilhelm Adolf von Baeyer (1835 - 1917) was born in Berlin and set out on a journey of discovery that would not only cement his legacy but also change the very fabric of organic chemistry. Baeyer had an insatiable curiosity from a young age. He is said to have started his experiments at his parents' house, building a makeshift laboratory in the family laundry room. His chemistry passion led him to the University of Berlin, where he studied under renowned chemist August Wilhelm von Hofmann. Later, he continued his studies under Robert Bunsen at the University of Heidelberg. By 1858, Baeyer had already received his doctorate, laying the groundwork for a distinguished career.

Adolf von Baeyer made numerous contributions to organic chemistry. He is most well-known for synthesising indigo, a naturally occurring dye. This groundbreaking achievement not only had industrial implications, affecting the dye industry significantly, but it also demonstrated the potential of organic synthesis in replicating complex natural compounds in the laboratory.

Another seminal contribution of Baeyer's is the strain theory of carbon rings. He proposed that strain occurs in cyclic compounds when bond angles deviate from the ideal tetrahedral angle. This theory has been used since to explain the stability of cyclic molecules.

In 1905, Baeyer was awarded the Nobel Prize in Chemistry in recognition of his unparalleled contributions. His legacy, however, is not only in the awards he received but also in the generations of chemists he inspired as a researcher and professor. Consider the historical significance of Adolf von Baeyer's work. It is remarkable. In an era when organic chemistry was only beginning to realise its full potential, Baeyer was at the forefront, pushing boundaries, challenging conventions, and laying the groundwork for future discoveries.

FUN TIME

CROSSWORD

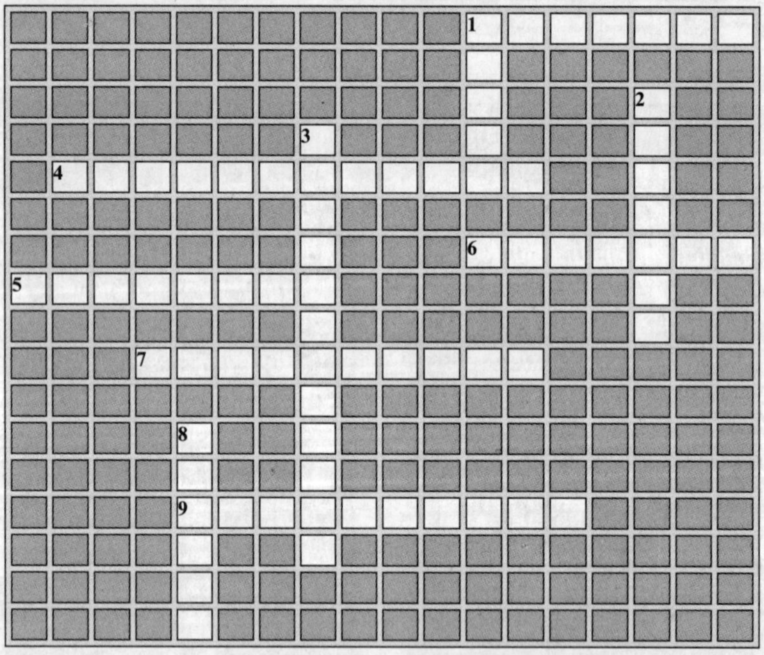

Across

1. Unsaturated hydrocarbons containing at least one carbon–carbon triple bond.
4. Organic compounds, which contain only carbon and hydrogen.
5. Heating to a very high temperature in the absence of air.
6. Unsaturated hydrocarbons containing at least one carbon–carbon double bond.
7. The ability of an atom to join with the other atoms of the same element and form long chains.
9. A series of organic compounds in which each member differs from the next member by a constant amount.

Down

1. Hydrogen obtained by the pyrolysis of methane is used in its manufacturing.
2. It can be prepared by heating a mixture of sodium acetate and soda lime in a hard glass test tube.
3. The name of reaction where the substitution is carried out by halogen.
8. Converted from 95% of alcohol when 1, 2-Dibromoethane when heated with Zn dust.

INTRODUCTION

Among 118 elements present in the periodic table, carbon is an element which acquires special status due to its characteristic properties. The chemistry of carbon compounds is studied as a separate branch called organic chemistry in contrast to the inorganic chemistry of the rest of the elements. However, elemental carbon and a few compounds of the carbon like oxides, carbonates, sulphides, and carbides are considered as inorganic substances.

Initially, the basic distinction between inorganic and organic compounds was considered to be the source of origin of these compounds. Inorganic compounds were believed to have mineral origin, whereas organic compounds were believed to have plant and animal origin.

This kind of distinction stemmed from a vital force theory. According to this theory, a vital force is responsible for the synthesis of organic compounds and this is provided by living beings like plants and animals. The name 'organic,' meaning living system, also originated from the above concept.

The idea of vital force theory was dispelled when the German scientist, Friedrich Wöhler, prepared urea by heating ammonium cyanate. Urea, being a component part of urine, is an organic compound. Synthesis of this compound from an inorganic salt paved the way for further research in this field and organic chemistry received a boost in the later years. The special status given to carbon compounds is now attributed to certain characteristic features of carbon and not to the source of origin of the compounds.

The basic characteristic which distinguishes carbon from other elements is its ability to form millions of compounds. Formation of such innumerable number of compounds by carbon can be further attributed to certain unique features possessed by carbon.

Carbon

Carbon is the chemical element with the symbol C and atomic number 6 (contains 6 protons in its nucleus). As a member of group 14 on the periodic table, it is non-metallic and tetravalent—making four electrons available to form covalent chemical bonds. The most common isotope of carbon has 6 protons and 6 neutrons, and has an atomic mass of 12.0107 amu. Its ground state electron configuration is $1s^2 2s^2 2p^2$. Its oxidation state ranges from 4 to -4, and it has an electronegativity value of 2.55 on the Pauling scale. It is a solid, and sublimes at 3,642 °C (it has the highest sublimation point of all the elements).

Info Bytes!

Historical Roots: The study of organic chemistry, which revolves around carbon-containing compounds, started with the study of substances derived from plants and animals. It wasn't until later that scientist realized that these organic compounds, including aliphatic hydrocarbons, could also be synthesized from inorganic sources.

Unique features of carbon

1. **Catenation Property:** The ability of an atom to join with the other atoms of the same element and form long chains is called **catenation**. Carbon is an element which shows maximum catenation.

   The ability to catenate can be explained on the basis of the electronic configuration of carbon.

Electronic configuration→	$1s^2$	$2s^2$	$2p_x^1$	$2p_y^1$	$2p_z^1$
Ground State→	↑↓	↑↓	↑	↑	
	$1s^2$	$2s^1$	$2p_x^1$	$2p_y^1$	$2p_z^1$
Excited State→	↑↓	↑	↑	↑	↑

There are four unpaired electrons in the excited state of a carbon atom and this gives tetravalency for carbon. As a result of this, carbon can form strong carbon–carbon covalent bonds. This gives the scope for formation of long chains of carbon.

Carbon atom can form long chains of thousands of atoms or rings of various sizes and chains and rings can have branches and cross-links.

2. **Multiple Bond Formation:** Due to the presence of four unpaired electrons in the valence shell of a carbon atom in its excited state, there is a possibility of formation of double bonds or triple bonds between carbon atoms. This ability to form multiple bonds also gives rise to various types of carbon chains.

   All the organic molecules are generally represented by the 'molecular formulae' (which give the number of atoms of the constituent elements) and the structural arrangement of atoms is represented by 'structural formulae' (which give the exact arrangement of atoms of different elements).

3. **Isomerism:** Isomerism is the phenomenon in which two or more organic molecules have the same molecular formula but differ in the structural arrangement of atoms. Those compounds are called **isomers**. Due to the difference in structure, the various organic compounds differ in their physical properties and to some extent in their chemical properties. Hence, isomerism is another feature which contributes to the existence of a large number of compounds of carbon.

Classification of Organic Compounds

Although carbon forms millions of compounds, it combines only with a few elements, chiefly with hydrogen. The others are oxygen, nitrogen, halogens, sulphur, magnesium, etc. On this basis, organic compounds, which contain only carbon and hydrogen are called hydrocarbons and those, which contain other elements in addition to carbon and hydrogen are called **organic compounds** with heteroatoms.

On the basis of structure, bonding and chemical behavior, the hydrocarbons are classified into two main categories, namely aliphatic and aromatic hydrocarbons.

Aliphatic Hydrocarbons

These include open-chain compounds and cyclic compounds based on the skeleton of carbon chain present, aliphatic hydrocarbons are categorized into two classes.

Info Bytes!

"Aliphatic" related to term "aleiphar," that means 'oil' in Greek. These hydrocarbons are so named because they are found in fats and oils. In India, oils like mustard and coconut oil contain fatty acids, which are essentially long chains of aliphatic hydrocarbons.

Acyclic Hydrocarbons (or) Open-chain Hydrocarbons

These hydrocarbons contain straight chain or branched chain of carbons with or without multiple bonds. On this basis, they are further classified into saturated and unsaturated hydrocarbons.

(a) **Saturated Hydrocarbons:** In this type of acyclic hydrocarbon molecules, there are no multiple bonds present in the carbon skeleton. Such type of hydrocarbons is referred to as saturated hydrocarbons called **alkanes**. In saturated hydrocarbons, valencies of all carbon atoms are satisfied by single covalent bonds. General formula of saturated hydrocarbons is C_nH_{2n+2}.

Examples:

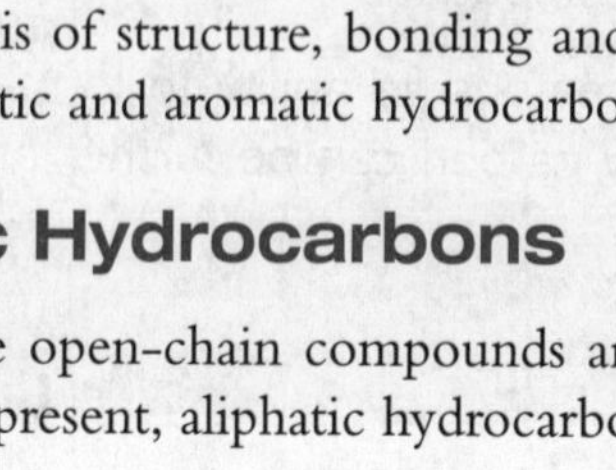

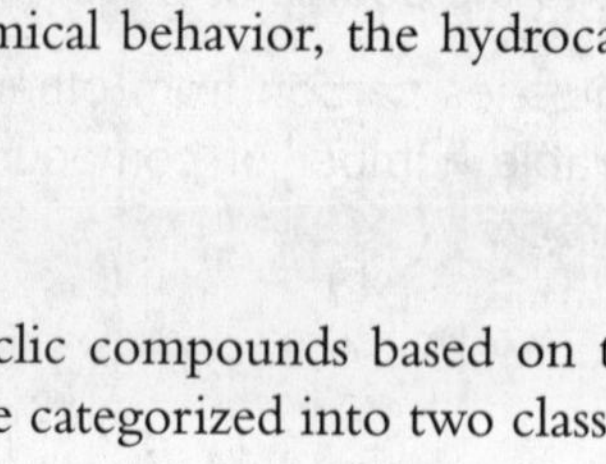

Info Bytes!

Gas Giants: The giant planets in our solar system, like Jupiter and Saturn, have atmospheres rich in aliphatic hydrocarbons. These compounds are believed to rain down, forming clouds and possibly even liquid lakes on some of these planets' moons.

(b) **Unsaturated Hydrocarbons:** If in the carbon skeleton of the acyclic hydrocarbon molecules there are one or more multiple bonds present between carbon atoms, they are called unsaturated hydrocarbons. Based on the type of multiple bond they are further classified as alkenes and alkynes.

Alkenes: Unsaturated hydrocarbons containing at least one carbon–carbon double bond are called **alkenes**. General formula of alkenes is C_nH_{2n} (assuming only one double bond).

Examples:

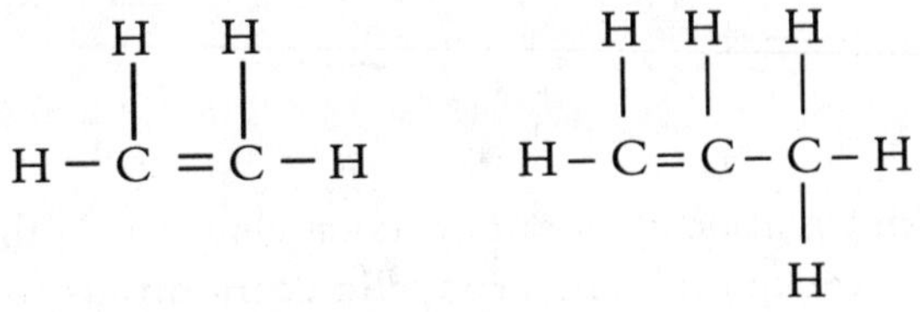

Alkynes: Unsaturated hydrocarbons containing at least one carbon–carbon triple bond are called **alkynes**. General formula of alkynes is C_nH_{2n-2} (assuming only one triple bond).

> **Info Bytes!**
> Alkynes are commonly called 'acetylenes.'

Examples:

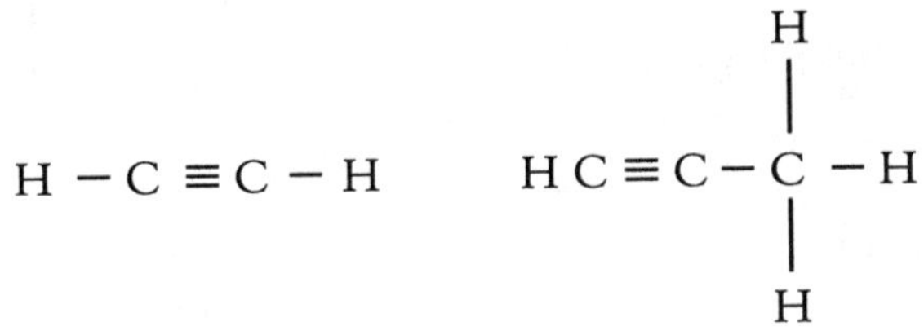

Alicyclic Hydrocarbons (or) Cycloalkanes

The aliphatic saturated hydrocarbons in which the carbon atoms are joined together to form a cyclic ring are called **alicyclic hydrocarbons**. They are represented by the general formula C_nH_{2n}.

Examples:

(a) C_3H_6: Cyclopropane

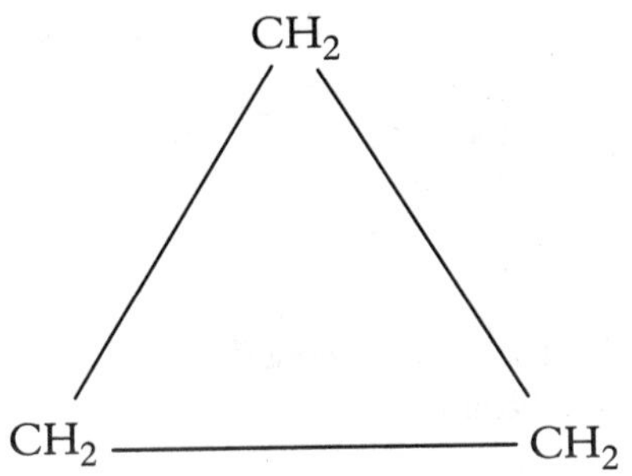

(b) C_4H_8: Cyclobutane

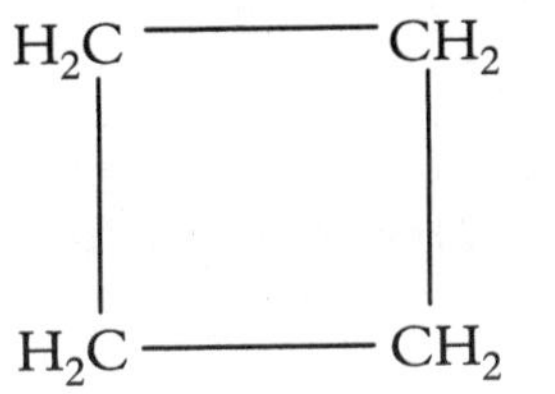

(c) C_5H_{10}: Cyclopentane

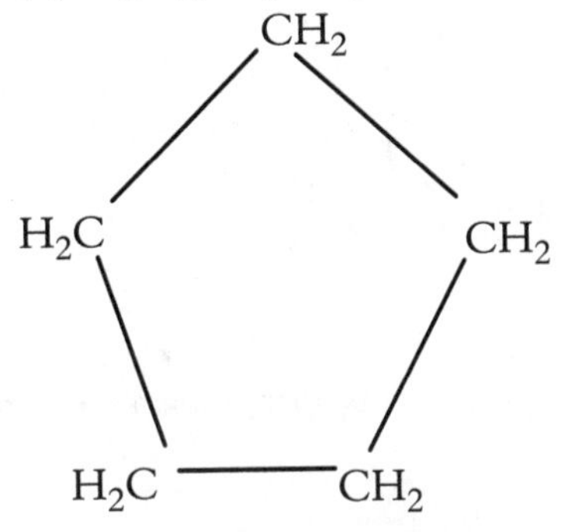

Aromatic Compounds

Aromatic compounds are benzene and the compounds that resemble benzene in chemical behavior.

> **Konnect**
> Nature's Perfumery: Some aromatic compounds aren't just structurally aromatic but are literally aromatic in the sense of having a pleasant smell. Many essential oils and fragrances extracted from plants owe their aroma to such compounds. For instance, the fragrance of roses, loved globally, comes from an aromatic compound called geraniol.

Examples:

(a) C_6H_6: Benzene

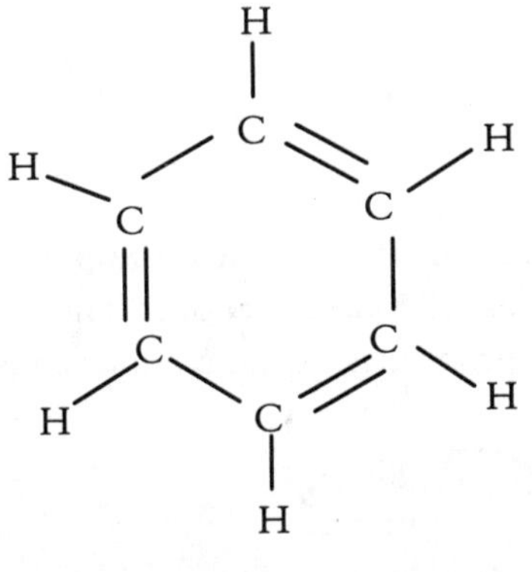

(b) $C_{10}H_8$: Naphthalene

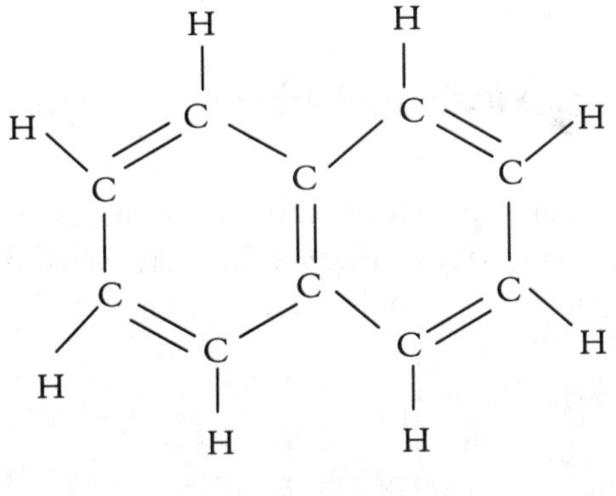

However, there are certain other cyclic compounds in which the ring has atoms other than carbon atoms. Such compounds are called heterocyclic compounds.

Heterocyclic Compounds

The cyclic compounds in which the ring is made up of carbon atoms chiefly and other heteroatoms like O, N and S (ring made of more than one kind of atoms) are known as **heterocyclic compounds**.

Examples:

(a) Pyrrole: C_4H_5N

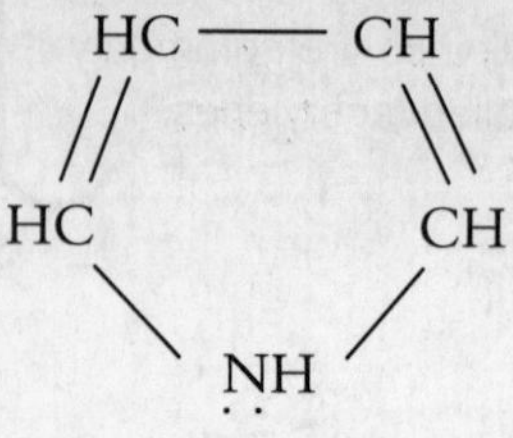

(b) Furan: C_4H_4O

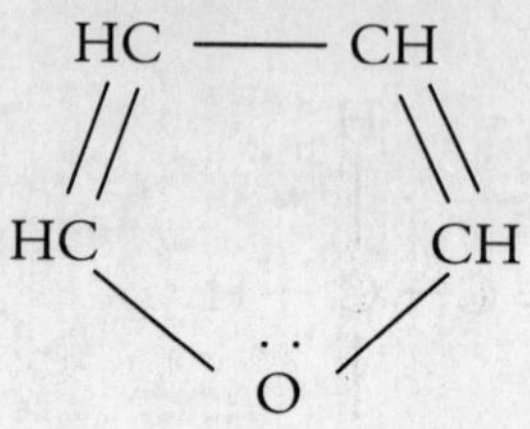

(c) Pyridine: C_5H_5N

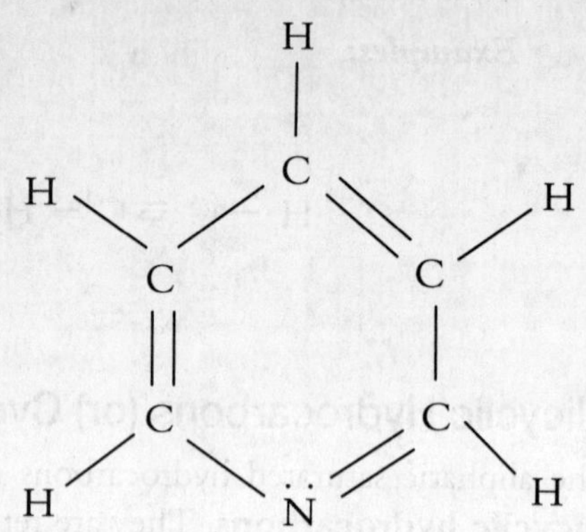

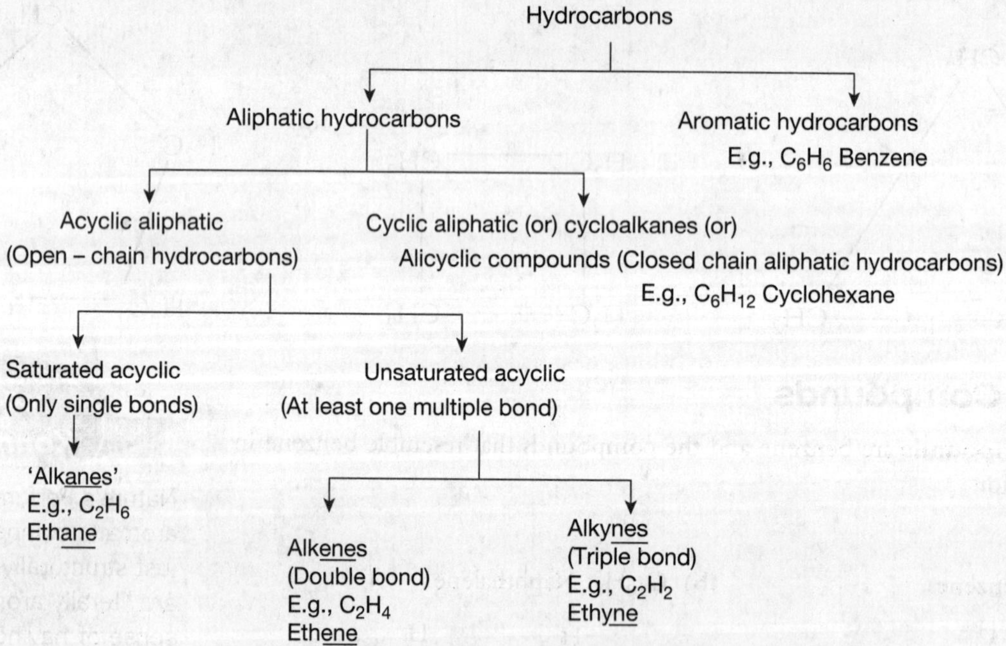

Figure 10.1 Classification of hydrocarbons

The organic compounds with heteroatoms can be formed by replacing one or more carbon atoms of the corresponding hydrocarbon with another atom or a group of atoms. Hence, these are called **derivatives of hydrocarbons**. The atom or group attached to the hydrocarbon part is responsible for the physical and chemical properties of the compound and hence, is called a **functional group**. Therefore, based on the nature of the functional group attached to the carbon skeleton, they are further classified into various classes.

Table 10.1 General classification of functional groups

Functional groups	General formulae	Classes of compound	Example of formulae	Common names
$-OH$	$R-OH$	Alcohol	CH_3OH C_2H_5OH	Methyl alcohol Ethyl alcohol
$\text{H}{>}C=O$	$R-CHO$	Aldehyde	$HCHO$ CH_3CHO	Formaldehyde Acetaldehyde
$-\overset{O}{\overset{\|}{C}}-$	$R-\overset{O}{\overset{\|}{C}}-R$	Ketone	$CH_3-\overset{O}{\overset{\|}{C}}-CH_3$	Acetone
$-\overset{O}{\overset{\|}{C}}-OH$	$R-\overset{O}{\overset{\|}{C}}-OH$	Carboxylic acid	$\begin{matrix}H\\OH\end{matrix}{>}C=O$	Formic acid
$-X$	$R-X$	Alkyl halide	CH_3Cl C_2H_5Cl	Methyl chloride Ethyl chloride

Nomenclature of Organic Compounds

Prior to the end of the nineteenth century, the names of the various organic compounds were based on either the source of origin of the compound or on some specific property of the compound. For example, methane gas is found to get released in marshy places. Hence, it is called marsh gas. Since it easily catches fire, it is called fire damp. In fact, the name methane also originated on the basis of the same concept.

Methane is the parent hydrocarbon of methyl alcohol, CH_3OH. Methyl alcohol was originally obtained by the destructive distillation of wood and was named as 'wood alcohol.' From this arose the word methyl, which is a combination of two Greek words methu (wine) and hule (wood). Another example of this way of naming compounds is acetic acid, which is the chief constituent of vinegar (Latin: acetum, i.e., vinegar).

Konnect

The names which were in use till then are retained and are now called trivial names or common names.

This method of naming the organic compounds at random could be justified as long as vital force theory could hold good. In the later period, the synthesis of many organic compounds in the laboratory opened new vistas to the branch of organic chemistry. In order to give names for the huge number of organic compounds used all over the world, a more systematic method of nomenclature was required.

The International Union of Pure and Applied Chemistry (IUPAC) developed a systematic approach to the nomenclature of organic compounds, which is purely based on its structure and reflects the physical and chemical properties.

IUPAC Nomenclature of Hydrocarbons

The IUPAC name of a hydrocarbon basically contains two parts:

1. **Root Word:** It indicates the number of carbon atoms in the chain. For naming the root word, the trivial names of the first four members of alkanes are taken as the basis. Beyond that, Greek numerals are used for indicating the number of carbon atoms.

Table 10.2 Root words

Number of carbon atoms present in the longest chain	Root words
1	Meth
2	Eth
3	Prop
4	But
5	Pent
6	Hex
7	Hept
8	Oct
9	Non
10	Dec

2. **Primary Suffix:** Primary suffix indicates saturation or unsaturation of a hydrocarbon. This is attached to the root word.
   Saturated hydrocarbon → ane
   Double bonded unsaturated hydrocarbon → ene
   Triple bonded unsaturated hydrocarbon → yne

   Examples: $H_3C - CH_2 - CH_3 \rightarrow$ propane
   $H_3C - CH = CH_2 \rightarrow$ propene
   $H_3C - C \equiv CH \rightarrow$ propyne

Rules for Naming of a Hydrocarbon

1. The longest possible continuous chain of carbon atoms is selected as the parent hydrocarbon. The root word corresponding to the number of carbon atoms in the longest chain is noted.
   Example:

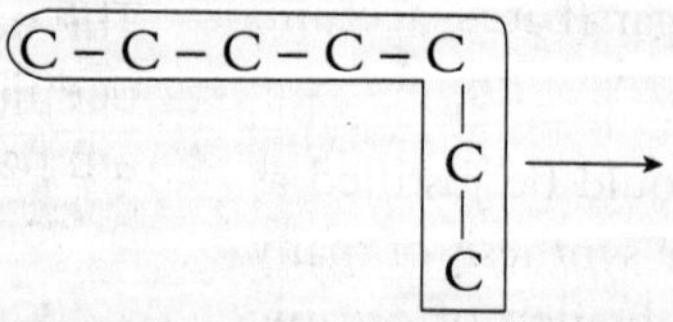

Longest chain with six carbon atoms. The root word corresponding to this is 'hex'.

2. The selected longest chain should possess double bond or triple bond in case of unsaturation in the chain.
   Example:

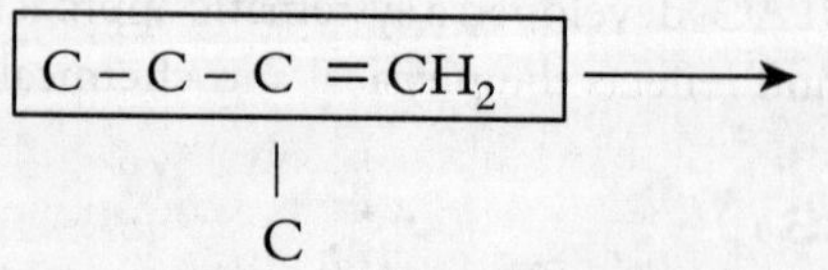

Longest chain with four carbon atoms. The root word corresponding to this is 'but'.

3. The longest carbon chain selected is numbered in such a way that the multiple bonded carbon or the carbon having alkyl substituent gets the least number.

Univalent group formed after the removal of one hydrogen atom from alkane is called **alkyl group**. The position number is added before the root word to indicate the position of multiple bond or substituent (alkyl or functional group).

Table 10.3 Parent hydrocarbons and their names

Parent hydrocarbons	Alkyl groups (formula)	Alkyl groups (name)
CH_4 (methane)	$-CH_3$	methyl
C_2H_6 (ethane)	$-C_2H_5$	ethyl
C_3H_8 (propane)	$-C_3H_7$	propyl
C_4H_{10} (butane)	$-C_4H_9$	butyl

Examples:

$$\underset{5}{CH_3}-\underset{4}{CH_2}-\underset{3}{CH}=\underset{2}{CH}-\underset{1}{CH_3}$$

2 – Pentene

$\longrightarrow$ Double bonded carbon is given 2nd position by numbering the carbon atoms in the chain.

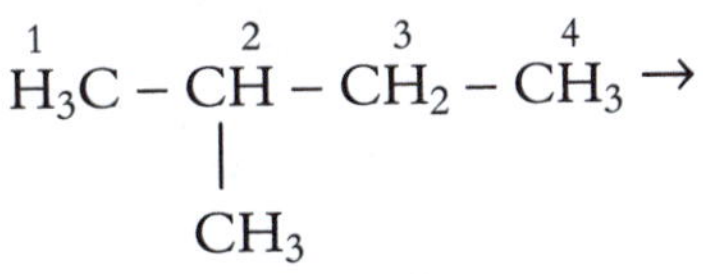

2 – Methylbutane

$\rightarrow$ The carbon chain containing four carbon atoms is numbered in such a way that the carbon having constituent methyl group gets the least position.

Isomerism in Hydrocarbons

The existence of an organic compound with the same molecular formula and different structural formulae is called **isomerism**.

The isomerism can be of various types depending on the type of variation in the structures of the molecules.

1. **Chain Isomerism:** The phenomenon in which two or more organic compounds have the same molecular formula but differ in the arrangement of carbon atoms in the longest chain.

   All types of hydrocarbons (alkanes, alkenes and alkynes), with more than three carbon atoms exhibit this type of isomerism.

   The molecule in which all carbon atoms are arranged in a straight chain is called **n-isomer**. The molecule in which there is a branched chain arrangement in the molecule, a prefix iso or neo is used depending on the type of branching.

   Examples:

   (a) Chain isomers of Pentane

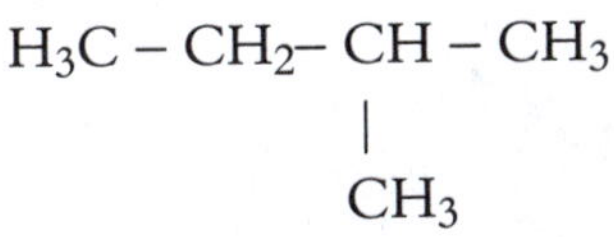

Isopentane

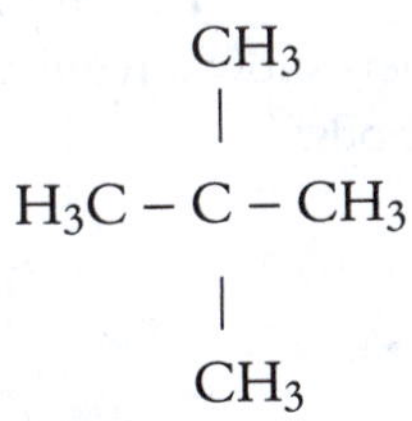

Neopentane

(b) Chain isomers of Pentene

$$H_2C = CH - CH_2 - CH_2 - CH_3$$
n-Pentene

$$\begin{array}{c} \qquad\quad CH_3 \\ \qquad\quad | \\ H_2C = CH - CH - CH_3 \end{array}$$
Isopentene

(c) Chain isomers of Pentyne

$$HC = C - CH_2 - CH_2 - CH_3$$
n-Pentene

$$\begin{array}{c} HC \equiv C - CH - CH_3 \\ \qquad\quad | \\ \qquad\quad CH_2 \end{array}$$
Isopentyne

2. **Position isomerism:** The phenomenon in which the hydrocarbon has the same chain but differs in the position of multiple bonds or constituents on the parent chain is called **position isomerism.**

   This is exhibited by unsaturated hydrocarbons (alkenes and alkynes) with more than three carbon atoms or saturated hydrocarbons with substituents as side chain.

   Examples:

   (a) Butene

   Molecular formula – C_4H_8

$$H_3C - CH_2 - CH = CH_2$$
1-Butene

$$H_3C - CH = CH - CH_3$$
2-Butene

   (b) Pentyne

   Molecular formula – C_5H_8

$$CH_3 - CH_2 - CH_2 - C \equiv CH$$
1-Pentyne

$$CH_3 - CH_2 - C \equiv C - CH_3$$
2-Pentyne

   (c) 5-carbon chain with methyl substituent

$$\begin{array}{c} \overset{1}{H_3C} - \overset{2}{CH_2} - \overset{3}{CH} - \overset{4}{CH_2} - \overset{5}{CH_3} \\ | \\ CH_3 \end{array}$$
3 – Methylpentane

$$\begin{array}{c} \overset{1}{H_3C} - \overset{2}{CH} - \overset{3}{CH_2} - \overset{4}{CH_2} - \overset{5}{CH_3} \\ | \qquad\qquad\qquad\qquad \\ CH_3 \qquad\qquad\qquad\qquad \end{array}$$
2 –Methylpentane

Homologous Series

A series of organic compounds in which each member differs from the next member by a constant amount when arranged in an increasing order of their molecular weights is called a **homologous series.**

The adjacent members of this series differ by 14 in their molecular weights or $-CH_2$ group and can be represented by the same general formula. The members show a regular gradation in physical properties, similar chemical properties and hence can be prepared by similar methods.

Table 10.4 Homologous series of alkanes (general formula C_nH_{2n+2})

IUPAC name of the alkanes	Molecular formulae	Structural formulae
Methane	CH_4	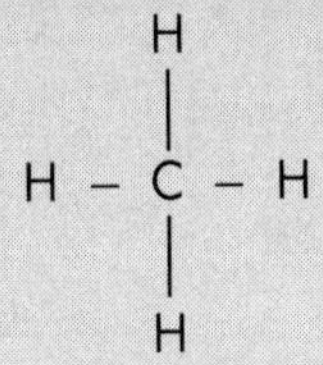
Ethane	C_2H_6	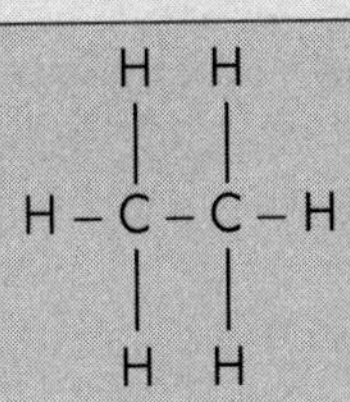
Propane	C_3H_8	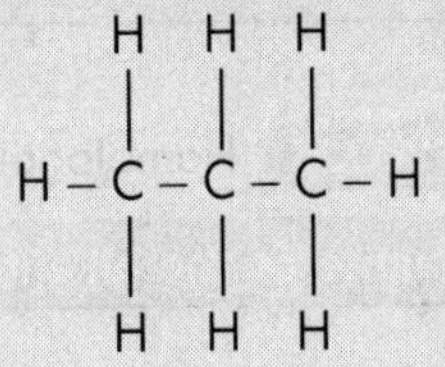
Butane	C_4H_{10}	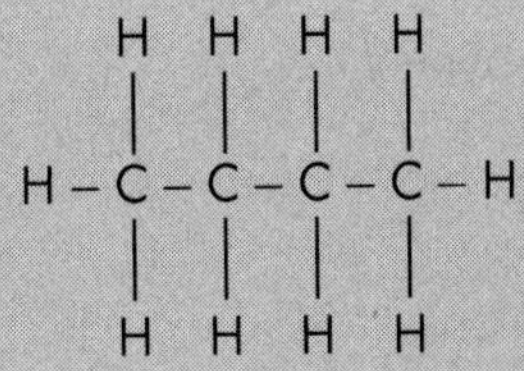
Pentane	C_5H_{12}	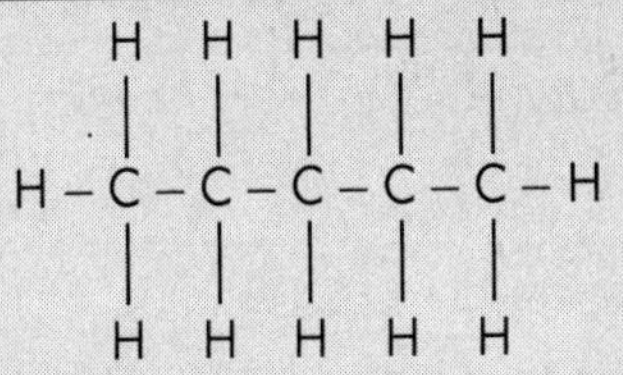

Table 10.5 Homologous series of alkenes (general formula C_nH_{2n})

IUPAC name of the alkenes	Molecular formulae	Structural formulae
Ethene	C_2H_4	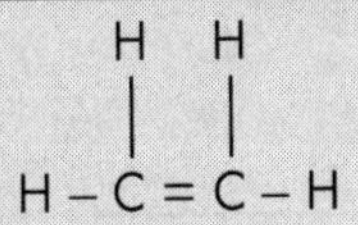
1-Propene	C_3H_6	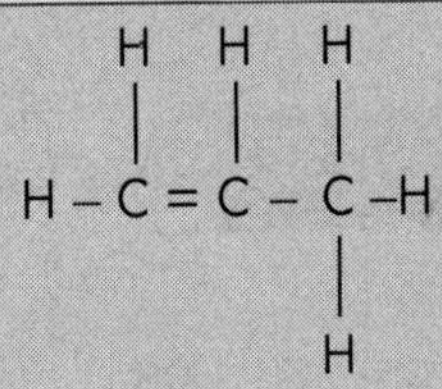

(continued)

Table 10.5 Continued

IUPAC name of the alkenes	Molecular formulae	Structural formulae
1-Butene	C_4H_8	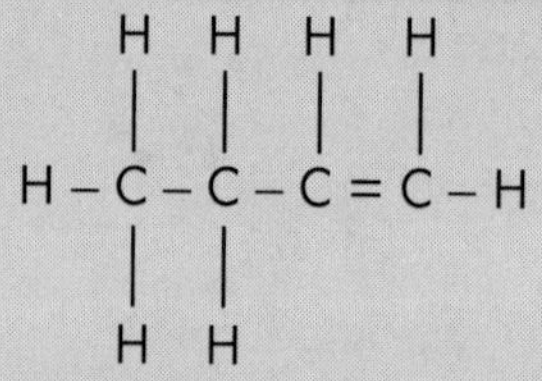
1-Pentene	C_5H_{10}	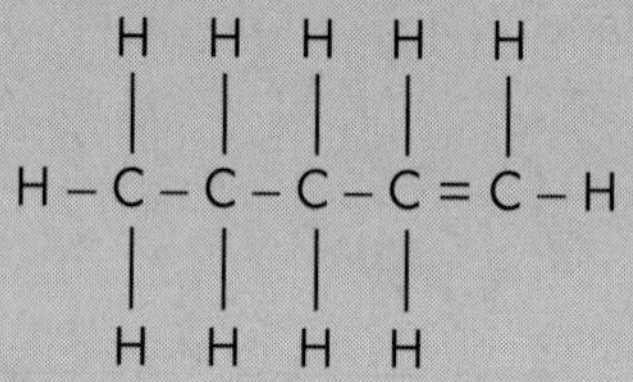

Table 10.6 Homologous series of alkynes (general formula C_nH_{2n-2})

IUPAC name of the alkenes	Molecular formulae	Structural formulae
Ethyne	C_2H_2	H – C ≡ C – H
1-Propyne	C_3H_4	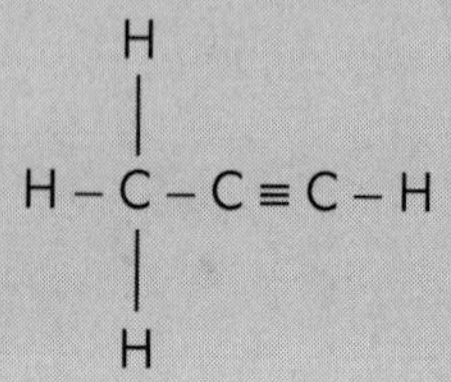
1-Butyne	C_4H_6	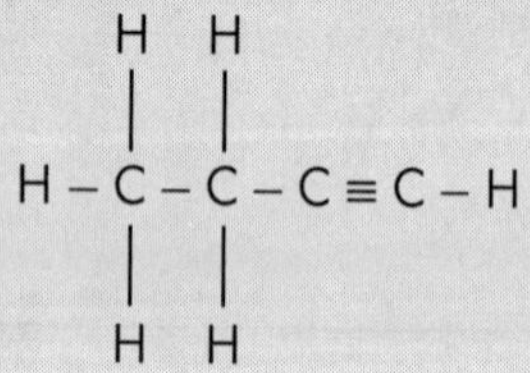
l-Pentyne	C_5H_8	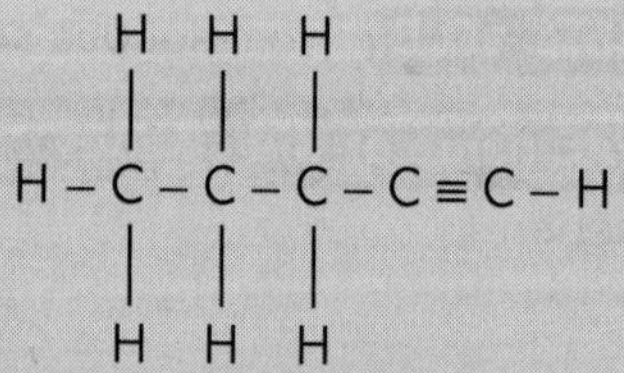

EXAMPLE 10.1

Write the IUPAC names of the following compounds.

(i) 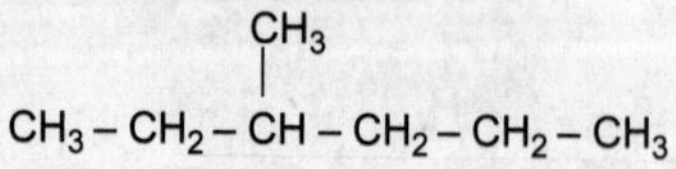

(ii) 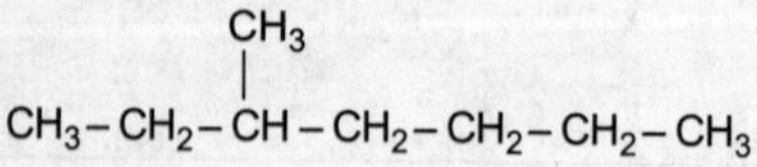

(iii) 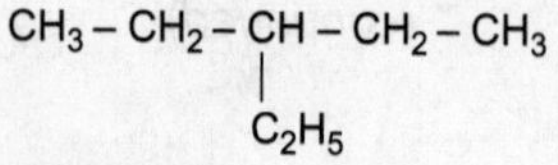

(iv) 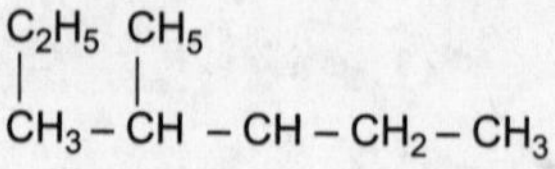

SOLUTION

(i) 3 – Methyl hexane

(ii) 3 – Methyl heptane

(iii) 3 – Ethyl pentane

(iv) 3, 4 – Dimethyl hexane

EXAMPLE 10.2 **(i)** Draw the structural formula of butane and its structural isomers. Mention their IUPAC names.

(ii) Draw the structural formula of a compound with three carbon atoms in each of the following cases.

(a) An alkane with carbon-carbon single bond.

(b) An unsaturated hydrocarbon with carbon-carbon double bond.

SOLUTION

(i) n-butane and 2-Methyl propane are structural isomers.

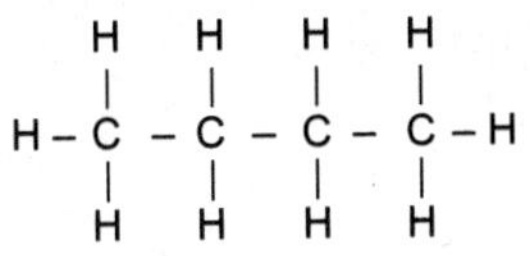

n-butane

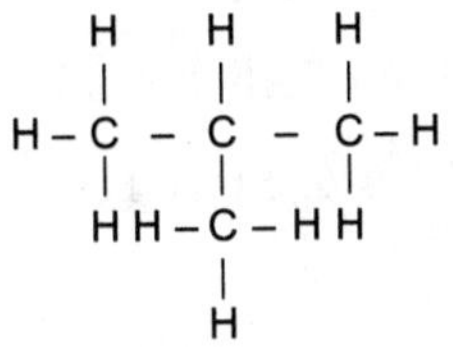

2-Methyl propane

(ii) (a) Propane

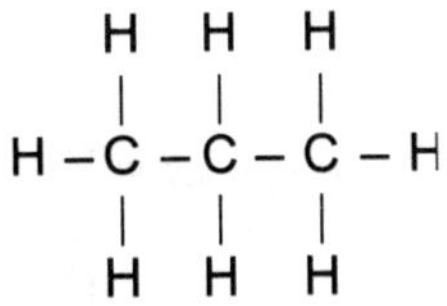

(b) Propene

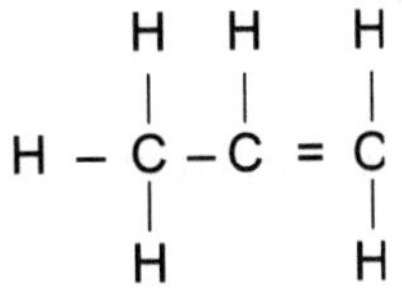

EXAMPLE 10.3 Complete the structures of following hydrocarbons by placing only hydrogens.

(i) C − C = C − C

(ii) 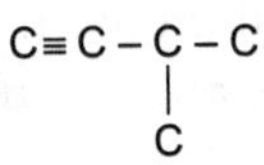

(iii) 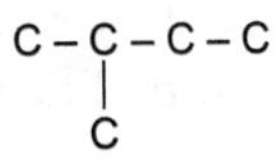

(iv) C = C − C

(v) C − C − C − C − C

SOLUTION

(i) 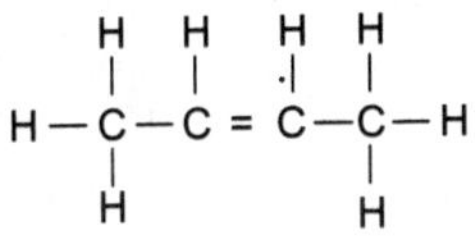

(ii) 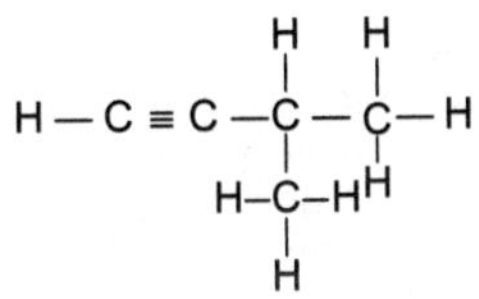

(iii) 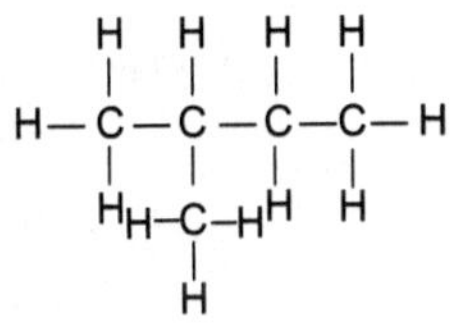

(iv) 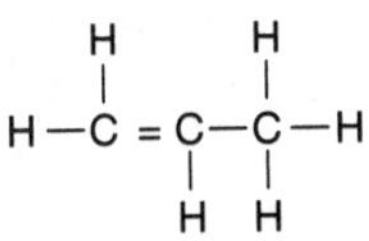

(v) 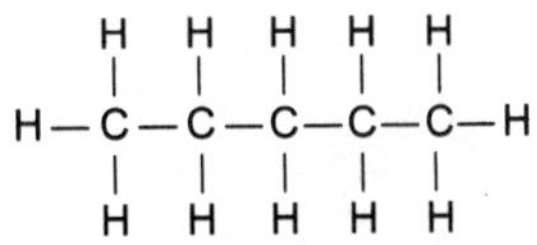

Aliphatic Hydrocarbons—Alkanes

Methane gas is found in marsh gas, natural gas, coal gas, gobar gas, sewage gas, bio gas, etc. Ethane is available in a smaller percentage in natural gas.

Preparation of Methane and Ethane

1. **Decarboxylation of sodium salt of carboxylic acids**

   Methane can be prepared by heating a mixture of sodium acetate and soda lime in a hard glass test tube:

$$CH_3COONa + NaOH \xrightarrow[\Delta]{CaO} CH_4 + Na_2CO_3$$

Ethane can be prepared in the similar fashion by taking sodium propanoate instead of sodium acetate:

$$C_2H_5COONa + NaOH \xrightarrow[\Delta]{CaO} C_2H_6 + Na_2CO_3$$

2. **Preparation by reduction of alkyl halides**

Methyl iodide is reduced to methane by nascent hydrogen produced by the action of Zn/Cu couple on ethyl alcohol:

$$CH_3I + 2[H] \rightarrow CH_4 + HI$$

Ethane on the other hand can be prepared by reduction of ethyl iodide by nascent hydrogen:

$$C_2H_5I + 2[H] \rightarrow C_2H_6 + HI$$

3. **Preparation by hydrolysis of carbides**

Pure methane can also be prepared by the action of water on aluminium carbide (Al_4C_3):

$$Al_4C_3 + 12H_2O \rightarrow 4Al(OH)_3 + 3CH_4$$

Physical Properties

These are colorless, odorless, tasteless gases which are insoluble in water, but soluble in non-polar solvents like alcohol, carbon tetrachloride, etc.

Chemical Properties

1. **Substitution Reaction:** Substitution reaction is a characteristic reaction of alkanes. Here one or more hydrogen atoms of methane or ethane are substituted by some other functional group. If the substitution is carried out by halogen, the reaction is called **halogenation**. The products depend upon the amount of chlorine.

(a) $CH_4 + Cl_2 \xrightarrow{\text{sunlight}} CH_3Cl + HCl$
(chloromethane)

In excess chlorine, the reactions are

$CH_4 + 2Cl_2 \rightarrow CH_2Cl_2 + 2HCl$
(dichloromethane)

$CH_4 + 3Cl_2 \rightarrow CHCl_3 + 3HCl$
(trichloromethane)

$CH_4 + 4Cl_2 \rightarrow CCl_4 + 4HCl$
(tetrachloromethane)

(b) $C_2H_6 + Cl_2 \rightarrow C_2H_5Cl + HCl$
(chloroethane)

$C_2H_6 + 2Cl_2 \rightarrow C_2H_4Cl_2 + 2HCl$
(dichloroethane)

$C_2H_6 + 3Cl_2 \rightarrow C_2H_3Cl_3 + 2HCl$
(trichloroethane)

$C_2H_6 + 4Cl_2 \rightarrow C_2H_2Cl_4 + 4HCl$
(tetrachloroethane)

$C_2H_6 + 5Cl_2 \rightarrow C_2HCl_5 + 5HCl$
(pentachloroethane)

$C_2H_6 + 6Cl_2 \rightarrow C_2Cl_6 + 6HCl$
(hexachloroethane)

2. Combustion

In excess of O_2, these burn with a pale blue flame to form CO_2 and H_2O:

$$CH_4 + 2O_2 \xrightarrow{\text{Excess air}} CO_2 + 2H_2O + \text{heat}$$

$$2C_2H_6 + 7O_2 \xrightarrow{\text{Excess air}} 4CO_2 + 6H_2O + \text{heat}$$

In an inadequate supply of air, CO gas and water vapors are formed:

$$2CH_4 + 3O_2 \rightarrow 2CO + 4H_2O$$

$$2C_2H_6 + 5O_2 \rightarrow 4CO + 6H_2O$$

3. Pyrolysis or Cracking

Heating to a very high temperature in the absence of air is called **cracking** or **pyrolysis**. Methane decomposes to carbon and hydrogen when heated to 1000°C in the absence of air.

$$CH_4 \xrightarrow{1000°C} C + 2H_2$$

Ethane when heated to 450°C in absence of air, decompose to give ethylene, methane and hydrogen:

$$3C_2H_6 \xrightarrow{450°C} 2C_2H_4 + 2CH_4 + H_2$$

Conversions of Methane/Ethane into Useful Organic Compounds

1. Alkane to Alcohol

Formation of ethyl/methyl alcohol from their respective alkanes is also a two-step reaction.

1st step: When equal volumes of alkane and chlorine gas are made to react they form their respective alkyl chlorides on exposure to sunlight:

$$CH_4 + Cl_2 \xrightarrow{\text{sunlight}} CH_3Cl + HCl$$

$$C_2H_6 + Cl_2 \xrightarrow{\text{sunlight}} C_2H_5Cl + HCl$$

2nd step: Alkyl chloride so formed when treated with aqueous KOH solution, and gets hydrolysed to the corresponding alcohol:

$$CH_3Cl + KOH\ (aq) \rightarrow CH_3OH + KCl$$

$$C_2H_5Cl + KOH\ (aq) \rightarrow C_2H_5OH + KCl$$

2. Alkane to Aldehyde

Formation of formaldehyde from alkane is a 3-step reaction.

1st step: Conversion of alkane to alkyl chloride

2nd step: Conversion of alkyl chloride to alcohol

3rd step: When alcohol vapor is passed over heated cupric oxide, it gets oxidized to aldehyde:

$$CH_3OH + CuO \xrightarrow{300°C} \underset{\text{(formaldehyde)}}{HCHO} + Cu + H_2O$$

$$C_2H_5OH + CuO \xrightarrow{300°C} \underset{\text{(acetaldehyde)}}{CH_3CHO} + Cu + H_2O$$

> ***Info Bytes!***
>
> Methane, a major component of natural gas, can be converted into synthesis gas, a mixture of carbon monoxide and hydrogen, which serves as a precursor for many organic compounds. Ethane, on the other hand, can be cracked to produce ethene, a compound used extensively in the petrochemical industry.

3. Alkane to Carboxylic Acid

Formation of carboxylic acid from alkane involves a 3-step reaction.

1st step: Conversion of alkane to alkyl chloride

2nd step: Conversion of alkyl chloride to alcohol

3rd step: Alcohol so obtained when treated with acidified $KMnO_4$ gets oxidized to carboxylic acid:

$$CH_3OH + KMnO_4 \xrightarrow{H^+} HCOOH + MnO_2 + KOH$$

$$C_2H_5OH + KMnO_4 \xrightarrow{H^+} CH_3COOH + MnO_2 + KOH$$

Uses

1. **As a Fuel:** Methane and liquefied ethane are used as non-polluting fuels in automobile industries and other industries also.
2. **As a Source of Important Organic Compounds:** These are used for the manufacture of important organic compounds like alcohol, aldehyde and carboxylic acid, which are widely used in the paint industry and other different industries for the manufacture of adhesives, plastics, artificial fibre, etc.
3. **In Fertilizer Industry:** Hydrogen obtained by the pyrolysis of methane is used in the manufacture of ammonia, which is further used in the manufacture of nitrogenous fertilizers.

Aliphatic Hydrocarbons—Alkenes

The smallest alkene is an **ethene**. It is an unsaturated hydrocarbon having a carbon–carbon double bond. Out of those, one is a strong sigma bond and another one is a weak pi bond. Its common name is ethylene.

Molecular formula: C_2H_4

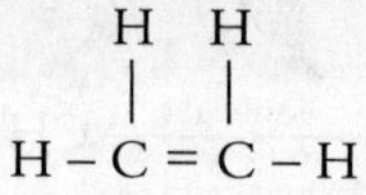

Structural formula

Laboratory Preparation of Ethene

1. **Dehydration of Ethyl Alcohol**

   Ethyl alcohol on heating with conc. H_2SO_4 at 170°C produces ethene. Aluminium sulphate is added to this mixture to avoid frothing during the heating of the mixture:

   $$C_2H_5OH \xrightarrow[170°C]{95\% H_2SO_4} H_2C = CH_2 + H_2O$$

   The above reaction can also be carried out by using Al_2O_3 at 350°C:

   $$C_2H_5OH \xrightarrow[350°C]{Al_2O_3} H_2C = CH_2 + H_2O$$

2. **Dehalogenation of 1, 2-Dibromoethane**

   1, 2-Dibromoethane when heated with Zn dust along with 95% alcohol converts to ethene.

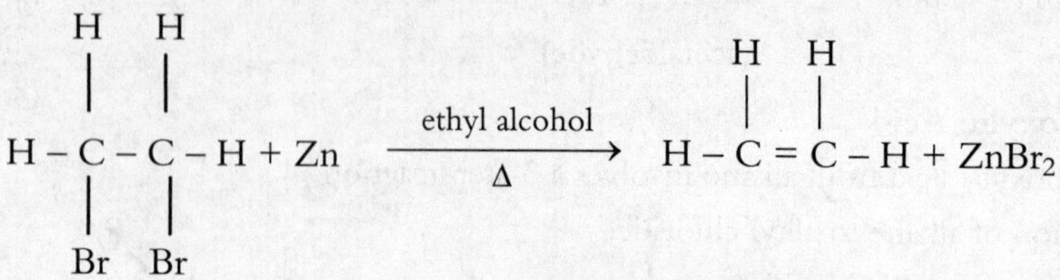

Physical Properties

Ethene is a colorless, tasteless gas with a peculiar odor. It is insoluble in water, but soluble in non-polar organic compounds like ether, alcohol, benzene, etc.

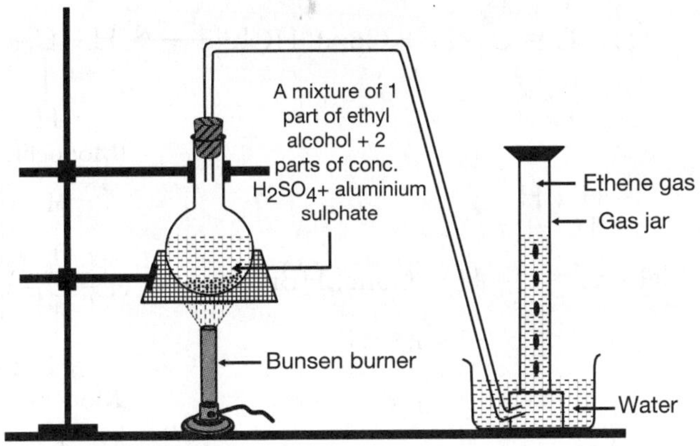

Figure 10.2 Laboratory preparation of ethene

Chemical Properties

1. Addition Reaction

Ethene is an unsaturated hydrocarbon with a single π bond between the carbon atoms. Addition of a molecule of hydrogen, halogen, hydrogen halide or ozone to ethene under specific conditions results in breakage of π bond, forming corresponding addition compounds.

(a) Catalytic Hydrogenation: Equal volumes of ethene gas and hydrogen when passed over heated nickel or platinum at 300°C form ethane.

$$\begin{array}{c} \quad H \quad H \\ \quad | \quad\; | \\ H-C=C-H \end{array} + H_2 \xrightarrow[300\ °C]{\text{Ni catalyst}} \begin{array}{c} \quad H \quad H \\ \quad | \quad\; | \\ H-C-C-H \\ \quad | \quad\; | \\ \quad H \quad H \end{array}$$

(b) Halogenation (addition of halogen): Alkenes are readily converted to corresponding saturated dihalide upon addition of halogen.

Ethene is readily converted to dichloroethane, (ethylene dichloride) when it is made to react with chlorine, in the presence of inert solvent CCl_4:

$$H_2C=CH_2 + Cl_2 \xrightarrow{CCl_4} \begin{array}{c} H_2C-CH_2 \\ |\qquad | \\ Cl\quad Cl \end{array}$$

1, 2 – Dichloroethane

$$H_2C=CH_2 + Br_2 \xrightarrow{CCl_4} \begin{array}{c} H_2C-CH_2 \\ |\qquad | \\ Br\quad Br \end{array}$$

1, 2 – Dibromoethane

Konnect

Decolorization of bromine is the test for identification of carbon–carbon multiple bond or unsaturation.

(c) Addition of Halogen Acid: When ethene gas is passed through concentrated halogen acids like HCl, HBr or HI, formation of respective addition compounds takes place.

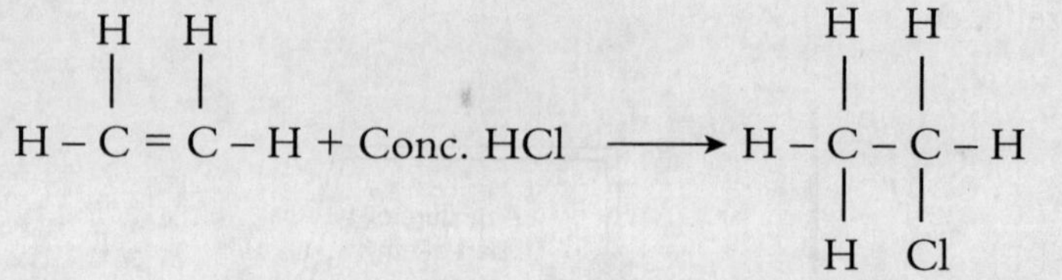

(Monochloroethane)

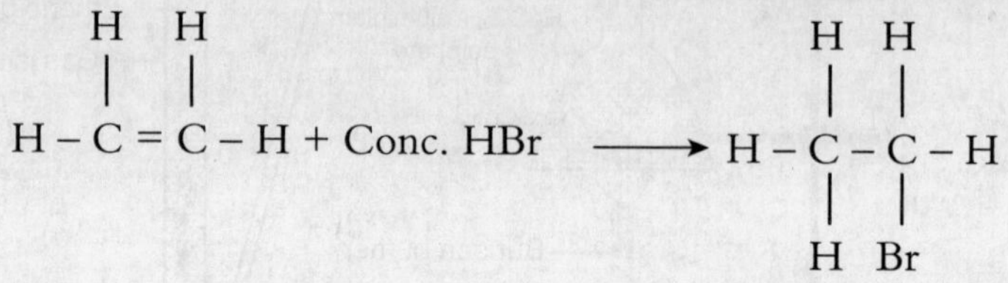

(Monobromoethane)

(d) Ozonolysis: On the addition of ozone to an unsaturated hydrocarbon, it forms an intermediate ozonide, which on further hydrolysis, in the presence of zinc dust gives corresponding carbonyl compound (aldehydes and ketones). This reaction is used to identify and locate the multiple bonds in an unsaturated hydrocarbon.

When a molecule of ozone is added to ethene at room temperature, it forms a compound called ethene ozonide, which on hydrolysis, in the presence of zinc dust gives two molecules of formaldehyde.

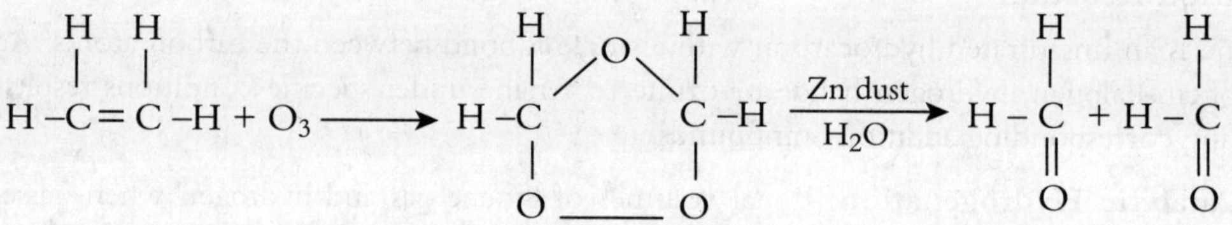

Ethylene ozonide

(e) Addition of Sulphuric Acid: An additive compound, ethyl hydrogen sulphate is formed when ethene gas is passed through cold conc. H_2SO_4 at room temperature. This on further hydrolysis with water gives ethyl alcohol.

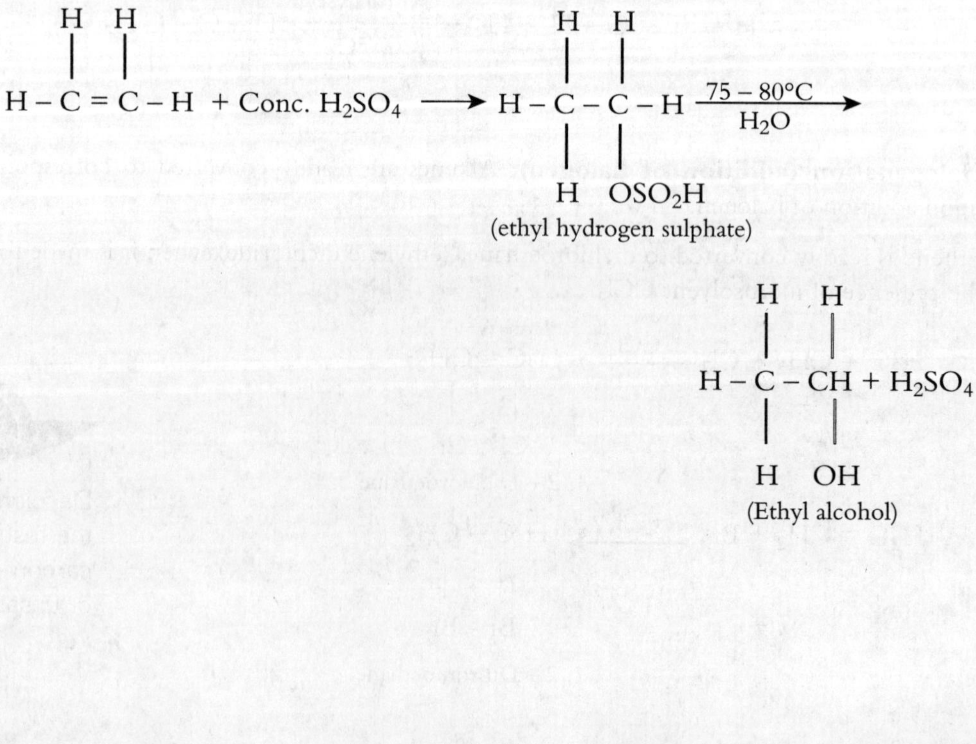

(ethyl hydrogen sulphate)

(Ethyl alcohol)

(f) Hydroxylation (introduction of –'OH' groups): Hydroxylation is a reaction which involves oxidation followed by subsequent hydrolysis in the presence of suitable oxidizing agents.

Ethylene when subjected to hydroxylation in the presence of cold, dilute, alkaline potassium permanganate (Baeyer's reagent) gets oxidized to ethylene glycol.(a dihydroxy alcohol containing two –'OH' groups on adjacent carbons).

In this reaction, $KMnO_4$ gets decolorized, which is a test for unsaturation.

$$\underset{\text{ethylene}}{3H_2C = CH_2} + 2KMnO_4 + 4H_2O \xrightarrow[\text{alk. } KMnO_4]{\text{cold dil.}} \underset{\text{ethylene glycol}}{3\underset{OH}{\underset{|}{CH_2}} - \underset{OH}{\underset{|}{CH_2}}} + 2MnO_4 + 2KOH$$

2. Combustion

Ethene gas completely burns with a pale blue, sooty flame in excess of air forming CO_2 gas and water vapor:

$$C_2H_4 + 3O_2 \xrightarrow[\text{air}]{\text{excess}} 2CO_2 + 2H_2O$$

Info Bytes!

The combustion of ethene is highly exothermic.

3. Polymerization

Polymerization is a process in which a large chain like molecule of higher molecular mass is formed due to combination of smaller molecules of similar structure with low molecular mass. The large molecule is called **polymer** and the constituent smaller molecules are called **monomers**. Ethene gas when passed through catalysts like HF and H_2SO_4 at a high temperature (2000°C) and under high pressure (1500–2000 atm), polymerizes to form polyethene:

$$\underset{\text{Ethene or ethylene}}{nH_2C = CH_2} \xrightarrow[\text{High temp and pressure}]{\text{Catalyst}} \underset{\text{Polyethene or polyethylene}}{(H_2C - CH_2)_n}$$

Conversion of Ethene into Useful Organic Compounds

Conversion of ethene into ethyl alcohol, acetaldehyde, and acetic acid.

When ethene is treated with concentrated HCl, monochloroethane or ethyl chloride is produced:

$$C_2H_4 + HCl \rightarrow \underset{\text{Ethyl chloride}}{C_2H_5Cl}$$

Ethyl chloride on hydrolysis with aqueous KOH solution forms ethyl alcohol:

$$C_2H_5Cl + KOH\ (aq.) \rightarrow KCl + \underset{\text{(Ethyl alcohol)}}{C_2H_5OH}$$

When ethyl alcohol vapors are passed over heated cupric oxide at 300°C, they oxidize to form acetaldehyde, whereas when ethyl alcohol is treated with acidified potassium dichromate, it gets oxidized to acetic acid:

$$C_2H_5OH + CuO \xrightarrow{300°C} \underset{\text{(Acetaldehyde)}}{CH_3CHO} + Cu + H_2O$$

$$C_2H_5OH + 2[O] \xrightarrow[K_2Cr_2O_7]{\text{acidified}} \underset{\text{(Acetic acid)}}{CH_3COOH} + H_2O$$

Konnect

Magic of Plants: The conversion of ethene to ethane might seem like an industrial topic, but nature has been doing this for ages. Plants produce ethene as a hormone to regulate growth and fruit ripening. However, in some cases, plants have enzymes that can convert this ethene back into ethane to prevent over-ripening.

Uses

1. Ethylene is used in the manufacture of the above mentioned organic compounds, which have a wide application in organic chemical industries.
2. It is used in the manufacture of polythene, which has an extensive use for different purposes like bags, bucket and various other things.
3. Ethylene is used for the manufacture of ethylene glycol, which is used as an anti-freeze.
4. It is also used for artificial ripening of fruits like bananas and mangoes.

Aliphatic Hydrocarbons—Alkynes

The simplest alkyne possible is ethyne. The trivial or common name of ethyne gas is acetylene. It is an unsaturated hydrocarbon where carbon–carbon triple bond is present. Among these, one is a strong sigma bond and other two are weak pi-bonds.

Info Bytes!

Alkynes act as starting materials in the synthesis of numerous chemicals and pharmaceuticals. Acetylene, the simplest alkyne, is frequently employed in welding due to its high-temperature flame when combusted with oxygen.

Molecular formula: C_2H_2

Structural formula: $H-C\equiv C-H$

Laboratory Preparation of Ethyne Gas

1. **Hydrolysis of Calcium Carbide:** Calcium carbide on reaction with distilled water evolves acetylene gas:

$$CaC_2 + 2H_2O \rightarrow Ca(OH)_2 + C_2H_2$$

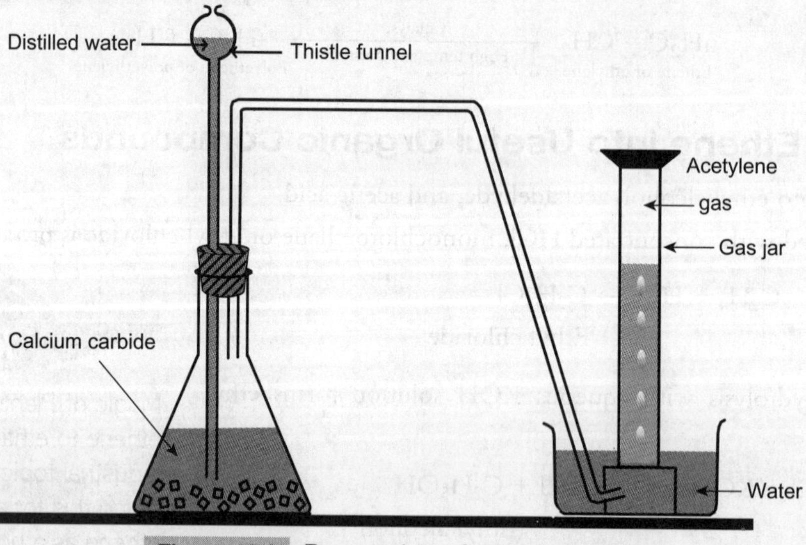

Figure 10.3 Preparation of acetylene gas

2. **Dehalogenation of Tetrahaloethane:** A mixture of 95% ethyl alcohol and 1,1,2,2-Tetrabromoethane along with zinc dust when heated gently evolves acetylene gas:

$$\underset{\text{Br}\ \ \text{Br}}{\overset{\text{Br}\ \ \text{Br}}{H-C-C-H}} + 2Zn \xrightarrow[\text{alcohol}]{\text{ethyl}} HC\equiv CH + 2ZnBr_2$$

Physical Properties

Ethyne is a colorless, tasteless gas with a characteristic garlic odor. It is insoluble in water, but dissolves in organic solvents like CCl_4, benzene, ether, etc. It is slightly lighter than air as its vapor density is 13.

Chemical Properties

1. **Addition Reaction:** Due to the presence of two weak pi bonds, ethyne molecule is highly reactive. Since two π bonds are present in a molecule of ethyne, addition of two molecules of halogen, hydrogen, hydrogen halide, etc., is possible.

   (a) Catalytic Hydrogenation: A mixture of one volume of ethyne gas and two volumes of hydrogen gas when passed over heated nickel at 300°C ethane gas is produced.

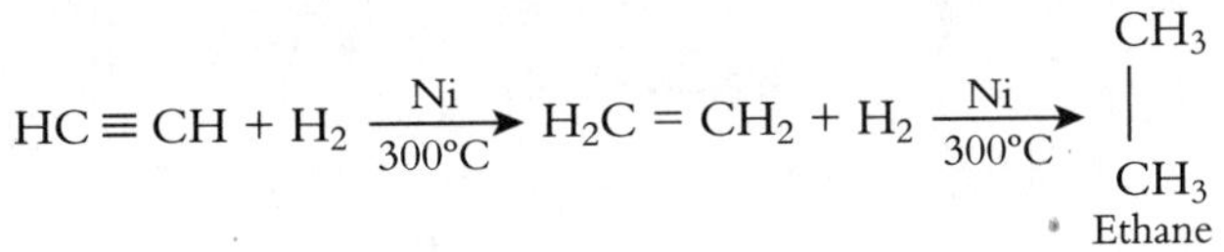

   (b) Halogenation: Addition of a molecule of halogen to ethyne molecule in the presence of CCl_4 gives 1,2-Dihaloethene which undergoes further addition of another halogen molecule to give 1,1,2,2-Tetrahaloethane. When this reaction takes place with bromine, bromine water gets decolorized:

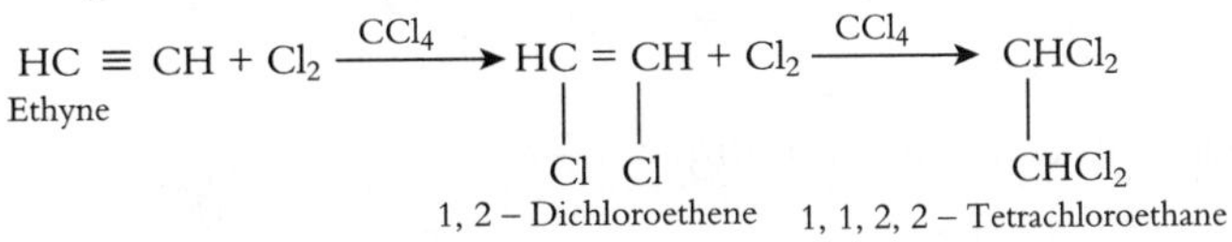

   (c) Addition of Halogen Acids: Halogen acids like HCl and HBr form addition compounds with ethyne when the gas is passed through them. This reaction takes place in two stages:

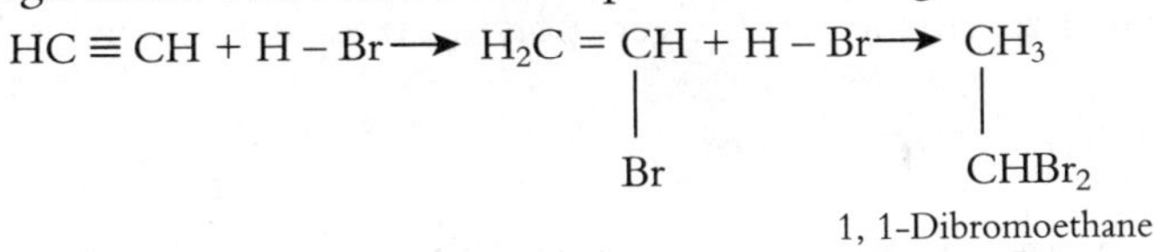

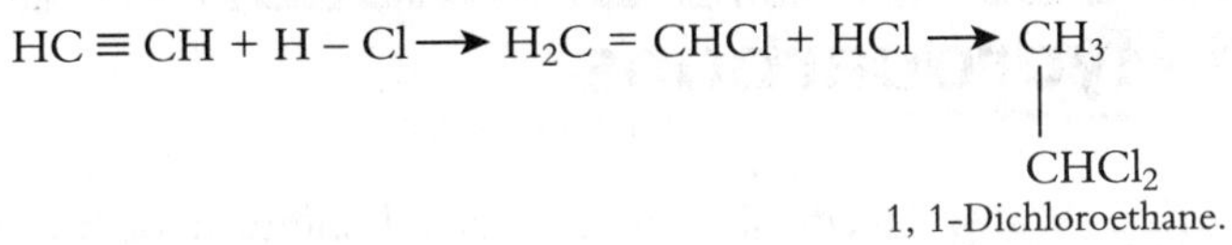

   (d) Ozonolysis: Addition of a molecule of ozone to a molecule of ethyne at room temperature gives an addition compound, ethyne ozonide, which on further hydrolysis with zinc dust gives glyoxal:

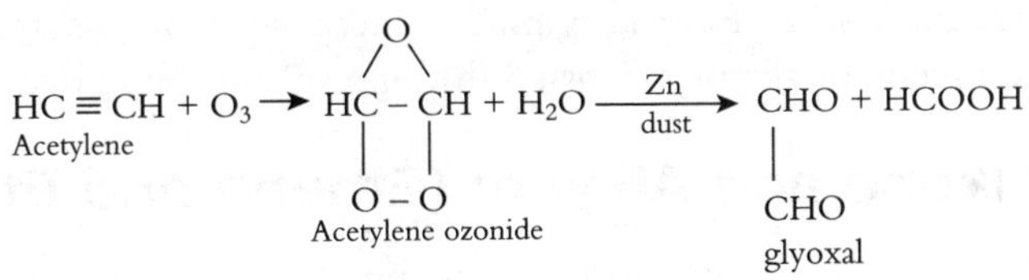

2. **Combustion:** It burns in air with the evolution of a large amount of heat. CO_2 and water vapor are the products if it burns in excess supply of air:

$$2C_2H_2 + 5O_2 \xrightarrow[\text{air}]{\text{excess}} 4CO_2\,2H_2O$$

3. **Action with Ammonical Cuprous Chloride:** A reddish brown precipitate of cuprous acetylide is obtained when acetylene gas is passed through ammonical cuprous chloride solution:

$$HC \equiv CH + 2CuCl + 2NH_4OH \rightarrow \underset{\text{(Cuprous acetylide)}}{CuC \equiv CCu} + 2NH_4Cl + 2H_2O$$

4. **Action with Ammonical Silver Nitrate:** White precipitate of silver acetylide is formed when acetylene gas is passed through ammonical silver nitrate solution:

$$HC \equiv CH + 2AgNO_3 + 2NH_4OH \rightarrow \underset{\text{(Silver acetylide)}}{AgC \equiv CAg} + 2NH_4NO_3 + 2H_2O$$

5. **Polymerization:** Ethyne gas when passed through red hot Cu tube gives benzene:

$$\underset{\text{Ethyne}}{3\,HC \equiv CH} \xrightarrow[\text{copper tube}]{300\ ^\circ C\ \text{Red hot}}$$

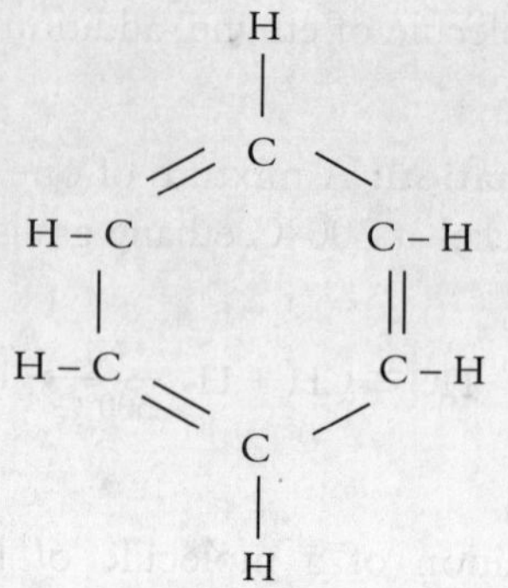

Benzene

Uses

1. Oxyacetylene flame is used for cutting and welding metals.
2. Acetylene lamps are used for illumination purpose.
3. Ripening of fruits like apples and mangoes takes place in the atmosphere of acetylene.
4. Acetylene gas is hydrogenated to ethene, which gets polymerized to form polyethylene which is very useful in packaging industry.

Tests Carried Out for the Distinction of Saturated and Unsaturated Hydrocarbons

1. **Decolorization of Bromine Water:** Reddish brown colored solution of bromine in CCl_4 disappears when unsaturated hydrocarbons (alkenes or alkynes) are passed through it. Saturated hydrocarbons do not respond to this test.
2. **Decolorization of Alkaline Potassium Permanganate:** Pink color of potassium permanganate fades away when an unsaturated hydrocarbon (alkene or alkyne) is passed through the alkaline potassium permanganate solution.

Test to Distinguish Alkene and Alkyne: (Ethene and Ethyne)

Formation of Metal Acetylides: Acetylene can form red precipitate of copper acetylide when it is passed through ammonical cuprous chloride solution. Alkenes do not respond to this test.

EXAMPLE 10.4 Explain why shorter-chain hydrocarbons, such as methane (CH_4) and ethane (C_2H_6), are not suitable as lubricant oils in comparison to longer-chain hydrocarbons like octadecane ($C_{18}H_{38}$). Provide reasons based on their physical properties and molecular structures.

SOLUTION

Shorter-chain hydrocarbons like methane (CH_4) and ethane (C_2H_6) are not suitable as lubricant oils in comparison to longer-chain hydrocarbons like octadecane ($C_{18}H_{38}$) because shorter-chain hydrocarbons have lower molecular masses, higher volatility, and are typically in the gaseous state at room temperature and pressure. Lubricant oils need to have higher molecular masses, lower volatility and remain in the liquid state over a wide range of temperatures and pressures to effectively lubricate and protect machinery. Additionally, longer-chain hydrocarbons have more complex molecular structures, allowing them to form stable and durable lubricating layers on metal surfaces, further enhancing their suitability as lubricants.

EXAMPLE 10.5

Why is methane often preferred as a fuel for residential heating systems, such as natural gas furnaces, over other hydrocarbon fuels like propane or butane? Provide reasons for its suitability.

SOLUTION

Methane is preferred for residential heating systems over other hydrocarbon fuels like propane or butane due to its cost-effectiveness, clean-burning properties, higher heating efficiency, safety, and infrastructure compatibility. It produces fewer pollutants, is widely available, and aligns with environmental goals by emitting fewer carbon emissions per unit of heat generated.

EXAMPLE 10.6

(i) Explain any two methods of preparation of ethene.

(ii) Write any two methods of preparation of ethyne.

(iii) How does acetylene react with ozone? Write the names of all reactants and products.

SOLUTION

(i) Ethene can be prepared by the following processes.

(a) From ethyl alcohol: Dehydration of ethyl alcohol in presence of Conc.sulphuric acid produces ethene.

$$C_2H_5OH \rightarrow C_2H_4 + H_2O$$

(b) From 1, 2 – Dibromoethane: When 1, 2 – Dibromoethane is warmed with zinc in presence of ethyl alcohol it forms ethene.

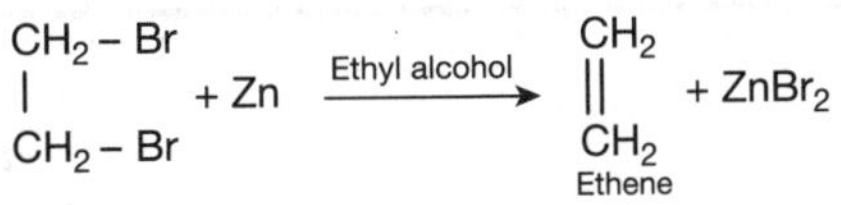

(ii) Ethyne can be prepared by the following processes.

(a) From calcium carbide: Calcium carbide on hydrolysis forms acteylene or ethyne.

$$CaC_2 + 2H_2O \rightarrow C_2H_2 + Ca(OH)_2$$

Ethyne

(b) From 1, 1, 2, 2 – Tetrabromoethane: Zinc dust when added to a mixture of 1, 1, 2, 2 – Tetrabromoethane and 95% ethyl alcohol produces acetylene gas (ethyne) and zinc bromide.

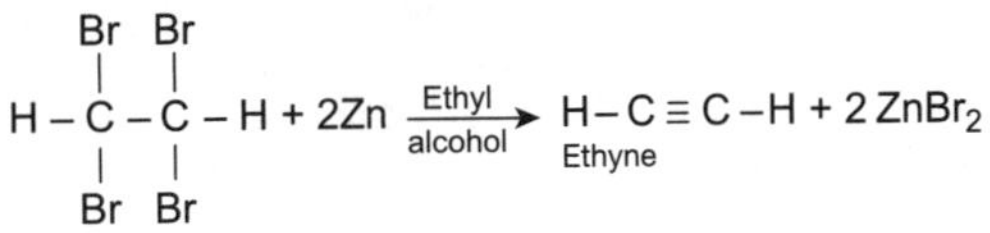

(iii) Reaction of acetylene with ozone: Acetylene or ethyne on reaction with ozone at room temperature, forms acetylene ozonide which on further hydrolysis with zinc dust gives glyoxal and formic acid.

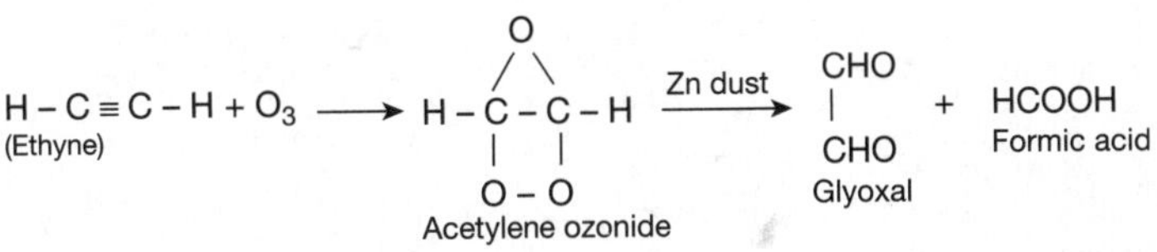

EXAMPLE 10.7

How does ethene react with the following compounds? Write the names of all reactants and products.

(i) H_2SO_4 **(ii)** HCl **(iii)** H_2 **(iv)** O_3 **(v)** Cl_2

SOLUTION

(i) Ethene on reaction with H_2SO_4 at room temperature forms ethyl hydrogen sulphate.

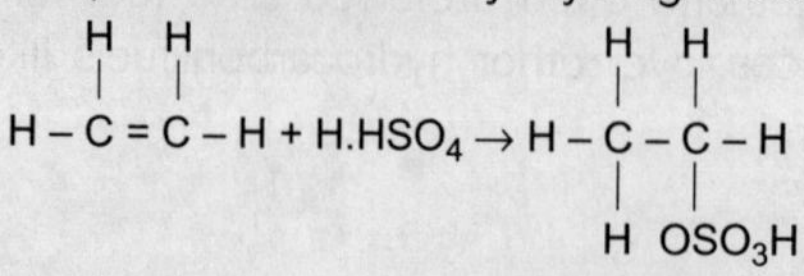

Ethyl hydrogen sulphate

(ii) Ethene reacts with hydrochloric acid to form additive compound that is 1, 1 – Dichloroethane.

$$H_2C = CHCl + HCl \rightarrow H_3C - CHCl_2$$

1, 1 – Dichloroethane

(iii) Ethene on reaction with hydrogen forms ethane. $C_2H_4 + H_2 \rightarrow C_2H_6$

Ethane

(iv) Ethene gas reacts with ozone at room temperature to form ethene ozonide which on hydrolysis in the presence of zinc dust gives two molecules of formaldehyde.

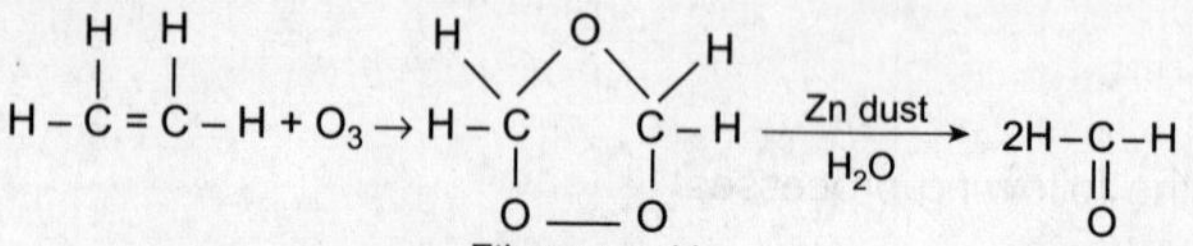

Ethene ozonide Formaldehyde

(v) Ethene on reaction with chlorine gives 1, 2-Dichloroethane.

$$C_2H_4 + Cl_2 \rightarrow C_2H_4Cl_2$$

1, 2–Dichloroethane

POINTS TO REMEMBER

- ✔ The ability of an atom to join with the other atoms of the same element and form long chains is called catenation.
- ✔ Isomerism is the phenomenon in which two or more organic molecules have the same molecular formula but differ in the structural arrangement of atoms. Those compounds are called isomers.
- ✔ organic compounds, which contain only carbon and hydrogen are called hydrocarbons and those, which contain other elements in addition to carbon and hydrogen are called organic compounds with heteroatoms.
- ✔ In this type of acyclic hydrocarbon molecules, there are no multiple bonds present in the carbon skeleton. Such type of hydrocarbons is referred to as saturated hydrocarbons called alkanes.
- ✔ Unsaturated hydrocarbons containing at least one carbon–carbon double bond are called alkenes.
- ✔ Unsaturated hydrocarbons containing at least one carbon–carbon triple bond are called alkynes.
- ✔ The aliphatic saturated hydrocarbons in which the carbon atoms are joined together to form a cyclic ring are called alicyclic hydrocarbons.
- ✔ Aromatic compounds are benzene and the compounds that resemble benzene in chemical behaviour.
- ✔ The cyclic compounds in which the ring is made up of carbon atoms chiefly and other heteroatoms like O, N and S (ring made of more than one kind of atoms) are known as heterocyclic compounds.
- ✔ The organic compounds with heteroatoms can be formed by replacing one or more carbon atoms of the corresponding hydrocarbon with another atom or a group of atoms. Hence, these are called derivatives of hydrocarbons.
- ✔ The atom or group attached to the hydrocarbon part is responsible for the physical and chemical properties of the compound and hence, is called a functional group.
- ✔ Univalent group formed after the removal of one hydrogen atom from alkane is called alkyl group.
- ✔ The phenomenon in which two or more organic compounds have the same molecular formula but differ in the arrangement of carbon atoms in the longest chain is called chain isomerism.
- ✔ The phenomenon in which the hydrocarbon has the same chain but differs in the position of multiple bonds or constituents on the parent chain is called position isomerism.
- ✔ A series of organic compounds in which each member differs from the next member by a constant amount when arranged in an increasing order of their molecular weights is called a homologous series.
- ✔ If the substitution is carried out by halogen, the reaction is called halogenation.
- ✔ Heating to a very high temperature in the absence of air is called cracking or pyrolysis.
- ✔ Polymerisation is a process in which a large chain like molecule of higher molecular mass is formed due to combination of smaller molecules of similar structure with low molecular mass.

PRACTICE QUESTIONS CLASSROOM WING

Very Short Answer Type Questions

Directions for questions from 1 to 8:
Fill in the blanks.

1. The unique ability of an atom to join with other atoms of the same element and create long chains is termed as ________.
2. In the realm of organic chemistry, molecules that possess identical molecular formulas but exhibit different structural arrangements are recognized as ________.
3. Compounds that exclusively comprise carbon and hydrogen atoms are termed ________, whereas those incorporating other elements in their structures are often referred to as organic compounds with ________.
4. Acyclic hydrocarbon molecules with no multiple bonds within their carbon skeleton are classified as saturated hydrocarbons or ________.
5. Hydrocarbons containing at least one carbon-carbon double bond are termed ________, while those with at least one carbon-carbon triple bond are labelled ________.
6. The hydrocarbon obtained by treating sodium ethanoate with soda lime is ________.
7. Polymerization of ethylene gives ______.
8. Saturated compound obtained by the addition of halogen to acetylene is ________.

Directions for questions from 9 to 25:
Answer the following questions.

9. Which category of compounds demonstrates resonance or delocalization of electrons?
10. What entity primarily defines the reactivity and properties of an organic molecule?
11. When two molecules have the same longest carbon chain but differ in bond location, what isomerism do they exhibit?
12. Which term describes a sequence of compounds where each member differs by a CH_2 unit?
13. What is the term for hydrocarbons that, when subjected to high heat in an oxygen-deprived environment, undergo a breaking of bonds?
14. Which reaction involves the introduction of halogens into hydrocarbons?
15. If a compound contains a C≡C bond, it is termed as?
16. Observe the molecular formulae and classify the following hydrocarbons into alkanes, alkenes and alkynes.
    (i) C_2H_4 (ii) C_2H_6 (iii) C_4H_{10}
    (iv) CH_4 (v) C_3H_6 (vi) C_3H_8
    (vii) C_4H_8 (viii) C_5H_{10} (ix) C_7H_{14}
    (x) C_6H_{14}
17. n-propane does not exhibit chain isomerism. Why?
18. What is pyrolysis of methane? What is the use of this reaction?
19. Name the following compounds:
    (i) 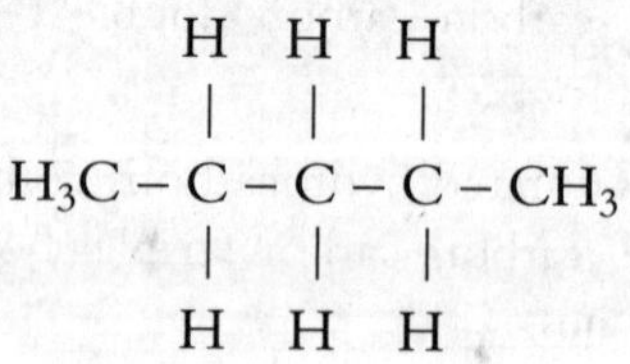
    (ii) 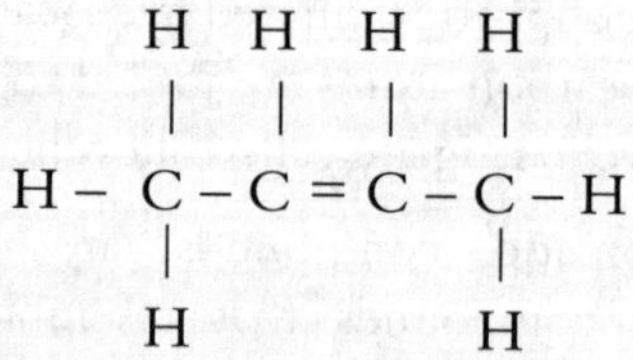
    (iii) $H_3C - C \equiv CH$
    (iv) 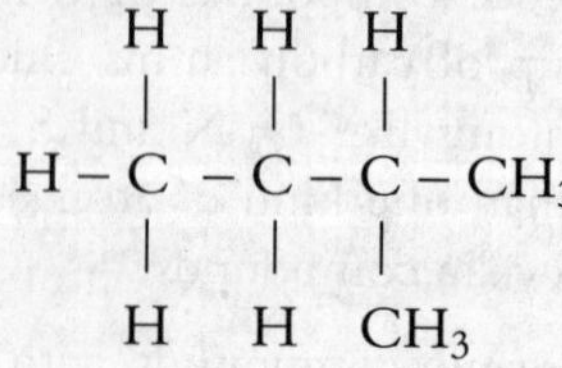
    (v) $H_3C - C \equiv C - CH_3$
20. Write the structural formula of the third compound of homologous series of alkane.

21. Complete the structures of following hydrocarbons by placing hydrogens only

(i) C – C = C – C

(ii) 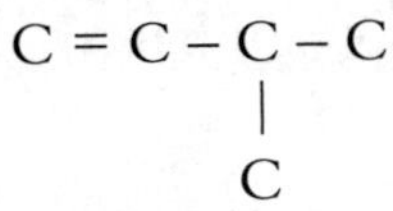

(iii) 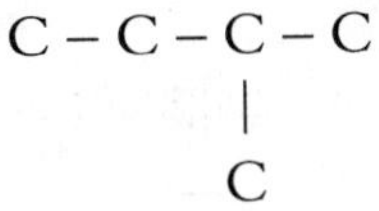

(iv) C = C – C

(v) C – C – C – C – C

22. How is the position of alkyl group determined from the IUPAC name of the hydrocarbon?

23. Draw the structural formulae of n-Pentane and isopentane.

24. How can we understand the position of a double bond or triple bond from the name of the hydrocarbon?

25. Draw the structural formula of the second compound of the homologous series of alkene.

Short Answer Type Questions

26. Write the structural reactions for the laboratory preparation of methane and ethane with a brief description.

27. Give the structural formulae of first four homologues of alkanes and alkenes.

28. Explain hydroxylation of ethene.

29. Describe the formation of ethyl alcohol from ethane.

30. Write the different products obtained by the chlorination of ethane.

31. What is chain isomerism? How many structural isomers are possible for the compound with molecular formula C_4H_{10}?

32. Give the two reactions of acetylene which are used to distinguish it from alkenes.

33. Which reagents oxidize ethyl alcohol to acetaldehyde and acetic acid? Why are two different reagents required for these conversions?

34. Describe the process by which methane converts to formaldehyde.

35. Write the laboratory preparation of ethyne gas in brief.

36. Describe the halogenation of acetylene gas.

37. How is acetylene gas produced from 1, 1, 2, 2-Tetrabromoethane?

38. Give the reactions representing the combustion of methane, ethane and ethyne.

39. Why do alkenes and alkynes undergo addition reaction while alkanes do not?

40. Describe the catalytic hydrogenation of ethene gas.

Essay Answer Type Questions

41. Discuss the implications of isomerism on the physical and chemical properties of organic molecules.

42. Elaborate on how the presence of functional groups in organic molecules can dictate their behaviour and reactivity.

43. Delve into the importance of aromatic compounds in both industrial applications and natural systems.

44. (i) Describe in detail one test to distinguish saturated hydrocarbon from unsaturated hydrocarbon.
 (ii) Describe in detail one test to distinguish ethene and acetylene.

45. Describe the following conversions:
 (i) ethene to acetic acid
 (ii) acetylene to acetaldehyde
 (iii) methane to formic acid

PRACTICE QUESTIONS COMPETITION WING

Level 1: Apply your Concepts

Directions for questions from 1 to 8:
State whether the following statements are true or false.

1. Both alkenes and cycloalkanes both can be represented by the same general formula.
2. The general formula C_nH_{2n} is valid for any alkene with any number of multiple bonds.
3. Acetone is the common name of propanone.
4. The number of carbons present in isopentane and 2-Methylpentane are same.
5. 1, 2-Dibromoethane gives corresponding alkyne by treating with Zn dust under suitable conditions.
6. Isomers always show same chemical properties.
7. Ethylene when subjected to hydroxylation in the presence of Baeyer's reagent gets oxidized to glyoxal.
8. Catenation and multiple bond formation result in structural isomerism,

Directions for questions from 9 to 19:
Fill in the blanks.

9. Organic compounds that share an identical molecular formula but differ based on the positioning of multiple bonds or constituents on their primary chain display ________ isomerism.
10. A consistent series of organic entities where each successive member has a molecular weight incrementally greater than the previous one is identified as a ________ series.
11. The process of heating substances to elevated temperatures in the absence of air, leading to their breakdown, is called ________.
12. When smaller molecules of analogous structures combine to yield a larger molecule with an enhanced molecular mass, the process is recognized as ________.
13. When methane is mixed with excess chlorine and the mixture is exposed to sunlight, the final product is ____.
14. The compound formed when ethyl alcohol is treated with conc. H_2SO_4 at 170°C is ____.
15. By treating alkylchloride with aq. KOH ______ is produced along with KCl.
16. Pyrolysis of methane takes place in ____ of air and the products are ____ and ____.
17. Decolorization of $KMnO_4$ solution takes place when it reacts with ethene. The final product of this reaction which is used as an anti-freeze is ____.
18. Difference in molecular weight between two successive compounds in alkane homologous series is ________.
19. C_6H_{12} and C_6H_6 are the examples of ______ and ______ hydrocarbons, respectively.

Directions for question 20:
Match the entries in Column A with the appropriate ones in Column B.

20.

Column A	Column B
A. Unsaturated hydrocarbon	a. C_6H_6
B. Aromatic hydrocarbon	b. CH_4
C. Saturated hydrocarbon derivative	c. $CHCl_3$
D. Sugar in water	d. C_4H_8
E. Action of water on aluminium carbide	e. $(CH_3)_2CHCH_2CH_3$

Directions for questions from 21 to 50:
For each of the questions, four choices have been provided. Select the correct alternative.

21. What differentiates an alkene from an alkyne?
    a) Presence of a carbon-oxygen bond
    b) Presence of a single carbon-carbon bond
    c) Presence of a double carbon-carbon bond
    d) Presence of a triple carbon-carbon bond

22. The functional group in an organic compound is mainly responsible for its:
a) Molecular weight
b) Isomerism pattern
c) Catenation ability
d) Physical and chemical properties

23. Which process leads to the formation of high molecular mass compounds by combining smaller molecules?
a) Cracking
b) Halogenation
c) Polymerization
d) Catenation

24. Which property allows carbon to form complex structures like fullerenes, nanotubes, and graphene?
a) Polymerization
b) Catenation
c) Halogenation
d) Resonance

25. In the realm of isomerism, two hydrocarbons that possess the same chain length but differ in the placement of a double bond exhibit:
a) Chain isomerism
b) Functional isomerism
c) Position isomerism
d) Tautomeric isomerism

26. Which of the following groups consists of triple bond?
(a) $-C_3H_7$ (b) $-C_4H_7$
(c) $-C_5H_7$ (d) $-C_5H_{11}$

27. What is the correct structural formula of 3-Methyl-1-Pentyne?

(a)

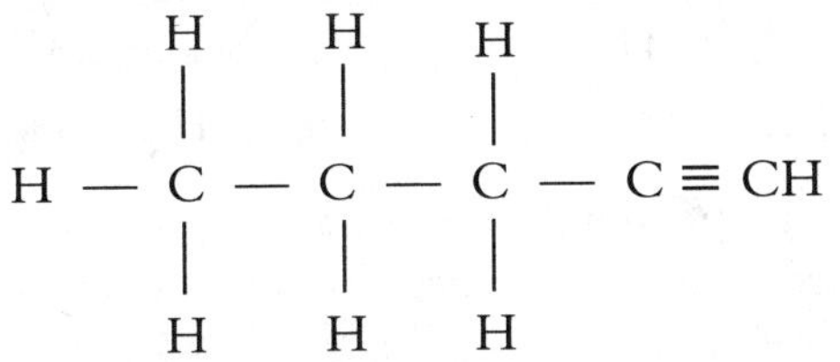

(b)

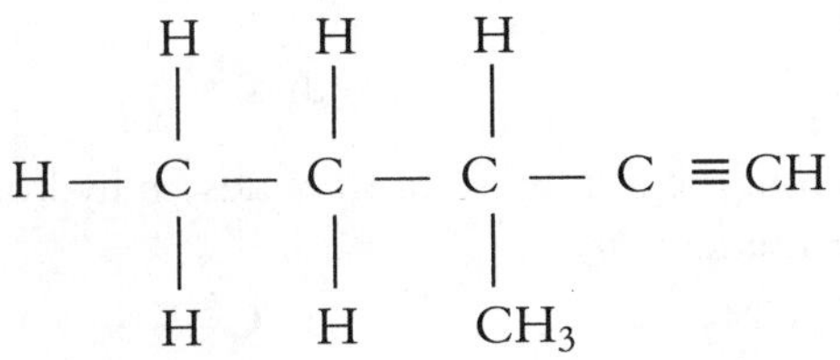

(c)

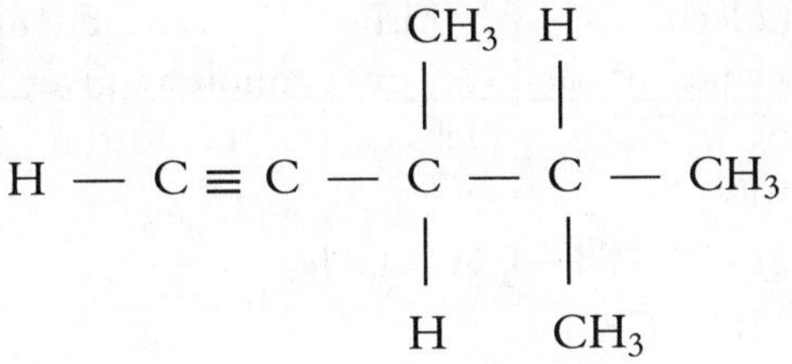

(d)

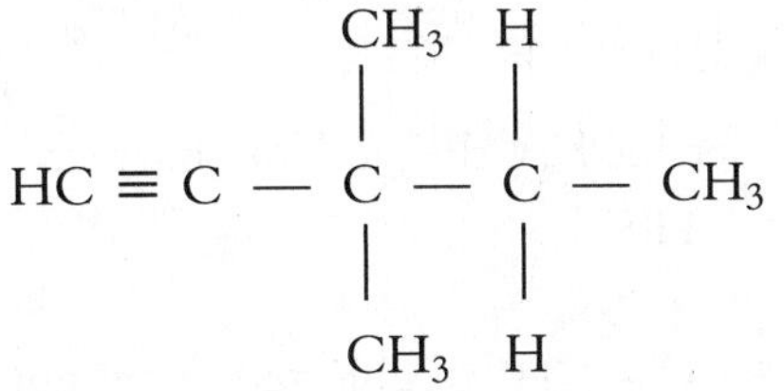

28. Which of the following compounds cannot exhibit chain isomerism?
(a) propane (b) butane
(c) pentane (d) hexane

29. Polymerization of acetylene gives rise to ______.
(a) polyethylene
(b) polyacetylene
(c) benzene
(d) polypropene

30. Which of the following hydrocarbons can decolorize the alkaline potassium permanganate solution?
(a) C_2H_6 (b) C_3H_8
(c) C_5H_{12} (d) C_3H_6

31. Identify the organic compound which can react with only one mole of sodium metal in the presence of strong base.
(a) propyne (b) ethyne
(c) 2-Butyne (d) ethene

32. Ethylene glycol is used as
(a) an anti-freezer
(b) a fuel
(c) a refrigerant
(d) an agent for ripening of fruits

33. Which of the following components is present in major proportions in LPG and why?
(a) Methane because it is easily liquefiable.
(b) n-butane because it is easily liquefiable.
(c) Isooctane because it reduces knocking property.
(d) n-propane because it has high calorific value.

34. A molecule of hydrocarbon 'X' can add upon two molecules of Br_2. 'X' on ozonolysis gives two different products which cannot be further oxidized. Identify 'X.'

(a) $H_2C = CH - CH = CH_2$
(b) $HC \equiv CH$
(c) $H_3C - C \equiv CH$
(d) $H_3C - CH = CH - CH_3$

35. Products obtained at the end of the reaction when

$$H_3C - \underset{\displaystyle CH_3}{\overset{\displaystyle H}{C}} = C - CH_3$$

is subjected to ozonolysis are

(a) acetaldehyde
(b) propanaldehyde
(c) acetone, acetaldehyde
(d) acetone, formaldehyde

36. The various steps for writing IUPAC name of an organic compound are given below. Arrange the steps in the correct order.

(1) numbering of carbon chain
(2) identification of primary suffix
(3) selection of the longest chain
(4) identification of secondary suffix
(5) identification of number and nature of alkyl groups attached to carbon chain

(a) 3 1 2 4 5 (b) 3 1 5 2 4
(c) 3 2 4 1 5 (d) 1 3 2 4 5

37. Hexane exhibits chain isomerism. One of its isomers possesses two tertiary carbon atoms. Arrange the following steps in a proper sequence to write IUPAC name for the respective isomer.

(1) Identification of number of carbon atoms in the main chain.
(2) Writing the structure of respective isomer of hexane.
(3) Numbering of carbon chain.
(4) Giving position numbers for the alkyl groups attached to main chain.
(5) Identification of nature of tertiary carbon atom.

(a) 2 1 3 5 4 (b) 5 1 2 3 4
(c) 2 5 3 1 4 (d) 5 2 1 3 4

38. Arrange the following hydrocarbons in the increasing order of volume of oxygen required for complete combustion per mole under the same conditions.

(1) ethane (2) propyne
(3) ethyne (4) propene
(5) propane (6) ethene

(a) 3 6 1 2 4 5 (b) 5 4 2 1 6 3
(c) 3 2 6 4 1 5 (d) 5 2 4 6 1 3

39. Preceding and succeeding homologues of $C_{10}H_{22}$ respectively are

(a) C_9H_{20}, $C_{11}H_{22}$
(b) C_9H_{20}, $C_{11}H_{24}$
(c) $C_{11}H_{24}$, C_9H_{20}
(d) C_8H_{18}, C_9H_{20}

40. Which of the following compounds contains a triple bond?

(a) C_2H_6 (b) C_4H_8
(c) C_5H_8 (d) C_5H_{12}

41. The part of IUPAC name which indicates saturation or unsaturation is

(a) root word (b) primary suffix
(c) secondary suffix (d) prefix

42. Which of the hydrocarbons cannot decolorize the red-colored solution of bromine in CCl_4?

(a) CH_4 (b) C_2H_4
(c) C_2H_2 (d) C_3H_6

43. Complete hydrogenation of ethyne gives ______.

(a) ethane (b) ethane
(c) methane (d) none of these

44. The hydrocarbons obtained by pyrolysis of ethane are ______ and ______.

(a) C_2H_4, C_2H_2 (b) CH_4, C_2H_2
(c) C_2H_4, CH_4 (d) C_2H_2, C_6H_6

45. What is the number of hydrogen atoms present in the hydrocarbon formed by the hydrogenation of ethylene?

(a) 4 (b) 6
(c) 8 (d) 2

46. Which of the following compounds on hydrolysis produces methane?

(a) $CaCN_2$ (b) CaC_2
(c) Al_4C_3 (d) SiC

47. How many grams of hydrogen is required to saturate one mole of acetylene?

(a) 3 g (b) 6 g
(c) 10 g (d) 4 g

48. Which of the following molecular formulae corresponds to an unsaturated hydrocarbon with triple bond?

(a) C_4H_8 (b) C_4H_6
(c) C_4H_{10} (d) C_6H_{12}

49. **Assertion (A):** Unsaturated hydrocarbons decolorize the red colored bromine water.

Reason (R): Unsaturated hydrocarbon undergoes substitution reaction with bromine water.

(a) Both A and R are correct and R is the correct explanation of A.
(b) Both A and R are correct but R is not the correct explanation of A.
(c) A is correct and R is wrong.
(d) A is wrong and R is correct.

50. Arrange the following in a proper sequence for writing the structural formula from the given IUPAC name 4-Methyl-4-Nonene.

(1) Locate the primary suffix and insert at the given position.
(2) Identify the substituent and insert at the given position.
(3) Add suitable number of hydrogen atoms to satisfy the valencies of each carbon atom.
(4) Identify the root word and write down the parent carbon chain.

(a) 4 1 3 2 (b) 2 4 1 3
(c) 4 1 2 3 (d) 4 2 3 1

Level 2: Review Your Concepts

51. Explain how carbon's atomic structure contributes to its unparalleled ability for catenation.

52. How do heteroatoms in organic compounds influence their chemical behaviour compared to their hydrocarbon counterparts?

53. Why might alkanes be generally less reactive than alkenes or alkynes, even though they all belong to the hydrocarbon family?

54. (i) $A + Br_2 \xrightarrow[Zn]{CCl_4} \begin{array}{c} HC-Br \\ \| \\ HC-Br \end{array} + Br_2 \longrightarrow C$

(ii) $CH_3I \xrightarrow[\text{ethyl alcohol}]{Zn/Cu} A + Cl_2 \xrightarrow{bv} C \xrightarrow[\text{water}]{KOH} D$

Give IUPAC names of A, C and D in both (i) and (ii) set of reactions.

55. How does the concept of aromaticity go beyond just the presence of a benzene ring in a molecule?

56. Why might two structural isomers have different boiling points despite having the same molecular formula?

57. How does the concept of a homologous series reflect the systematic nature of organic chemistry?

58. Why is the dipole moment of all alkanes zero?

59. Both methane and ethane can be used as fuels. By giving the balanced equations corresponding to the reactions responsible for the above use, justify which is a better fuel.

60. $CH_4 + Cl_2 \xrightarrow{?} CH_3Cl + HCl$. Is it possible to carry out the reaction under incandescent bulb? Justify.

61. How is polyvinyl chloride obtained from acetylene?

62. The first homologue of the series with general formula C_nH_{2n} on oxidation with alkaline $KMnO_4$ gives a compound is added to water which is used as a coolant in automobiles. Identify the compound and explain the purpose of its addition to water.

63. Methanol and ethane have almost the same molecular weight. But boiling point of methanol is 65°C and ethane is –89°C. Explain why.

64. Write the possible structural isomers for the compound with molecular formula C_5H_{10} and explain how these isomers can be identified with ozonolysis.

65. What is the role of sunlight in the halogenation of a hydrocarbon?

66. In an examination, structures for four organic compounds are given. A student, Jujo, has written the names corresponding to the structures. Identify whether the name is appropriate for the given structure. If not, give a reason and suggest the correct name for the structure.

(a) 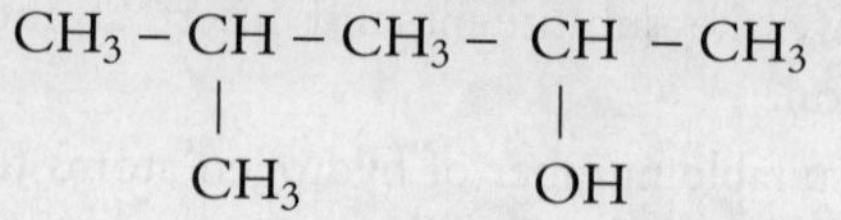

2 – Methyl–4–pentanol

(b) 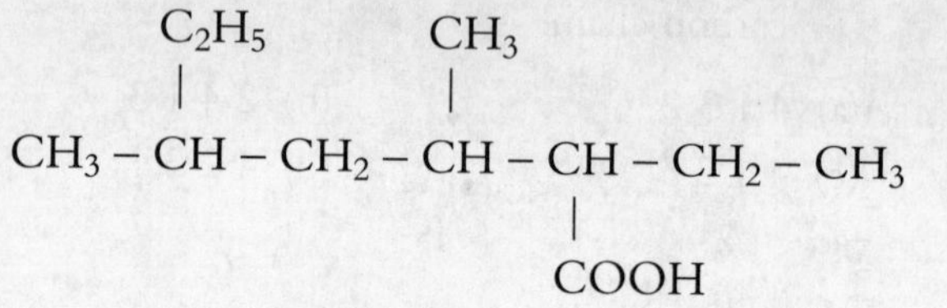

4, 6–Dimethyl–3–octanoic acid

(c) 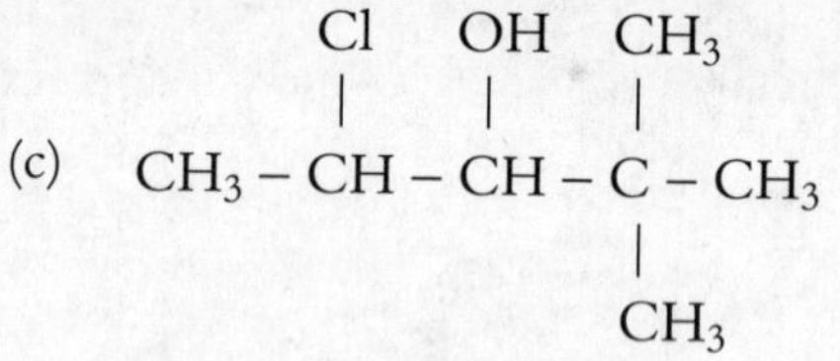

4 – Chloro –2, 2 – dimethyl–3–pentanol

(d) 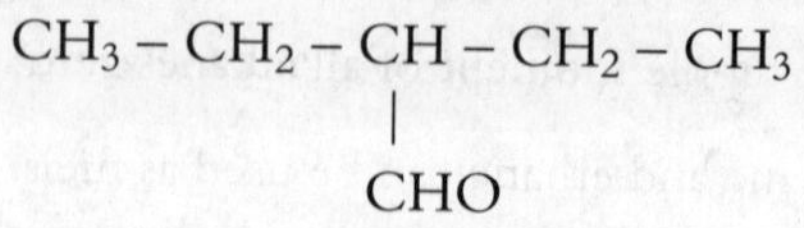

3 – Hexanal

67. How many structural isomers can pentene have? Give their structures and IUPAC names.

68. Two metals X and Y have 3 and 2 electrons in their valence shells 'M' and 'N,' respectively. These metals can form binary compounds A and B with the same non-metal carbon. Both A and B can undergo hydrolysis forming hydrocarbons C and D. Identify C and D and write the steps required for the conversion of D to second member of alkanes.

69. How is ozonolysis of unsaturated hydrocarbon used to find out the position of unsaturation? Explain the role of zinc dust used in the reaction.

70. Based on the products of ozonolysis, is it possible to distinguish branched chain and straight chain alkenes? Explain by taking the homologue with vapor density 35.

71. Propane does not exhibit chain isomerism. Why?

72. A hydrocarbon Y decolorizes bromine water. The saturated compound resulted in this reaction, on treatment with Zn dust gives back hydrocarbon Y. Y when passed through a solution of $AgNO_3$ dissolved in NH_4OH gives a white precipitate. The next higher homologue of Y that is X gives ketone as the product upon addition of water. Identify X and Y and give equations.

73. Explain the similarities and dissimilarities between C_2H_4 and C_2H_2 by using the following reagents.

(a) bromine (Br_2) in presence of CCl_4

(b) alkaline $KMnO_4$

(c) ammonical silver nitrate

(d) ammonical cuprous chloride

74. Write the structural formulae for the following compounds:

(a) 2-Butanol

(b) 3, 4, 5-Trimethyl heptane

(c) 4-Ethyl-2-Methyl heptane

(d) 2-Ethyl-1-Pentene

(e) 4-Chloro-5-Methyl 2-Octene

75. The molar ratio of CO_2 and H_2O produced by the combustion of one mole of hydrocarbon X is 5 : 4. Write the balanced equation for the combustion of X, succeeding and preceding homologues of X. Mention the chain isomers of X and their names.

Level 3: Assess Your Concepts

76. Given that silicon, a member of the same group as carbon in the periodic table, also has a capacity for catenation, why is it that silicon-based life forms aren't as prevalent or complex as carbon-based ones?

77. Considering that isomers have the same molecular formula but different structural arrangements, how might isomerism impact the therapeutic potential and side effects of certain drugs?

78. If organic compounds with heteroatoms are derivatives of hydrocarbons, what could be the implications on their reactivity, stability, and biological activity compared to their hydrocarbon counterparts?

79. Methane is made to react with chlorine and iodine in closed containers in two separate reactions in presence of sunlight. The yield of CH_3I was much less when compared to the yield of CH_3Cl. Give a rea-

son. However, if the reaction is carried out in presence of HNO_3 or HIO_3, the yield of CH_3I is found to increase. How do you account for this?

80. Saturated hydrocarbons or alkanes are perceived as less reactive than their unsaturated counterparts. What might be the underlying molecular reason for this and how does this impact their potential uses?

Directions for questions from 81 to 84:
Application-Based Questions

81. Aromatic compounds, like benzene, exhibit resonance. How does this phenomenon contribute to the stability of aromatic compounds, and how might it affect their reactivity compared to non-aromatic compounds?
82. Why are alkanes hydrophobic in nature?
83. Identify the molecular formula of an alkane which has only three chain isomers. Suggest a suitable method of separation of these isomers and draw a comparison of their dipole moments.
84. Three hydrocarbons X, Y and Z have carbon which combine with hydrogen in the ratio of 3 : 2 : 1, respectively. Comment on their characteristic reactions.l

AT

PRACTICE QUESTIONS JEE-NEET SPECIAL WING

Multiple-Answer Type Questions

Directions for Questions number 1 to 5:

Select one or more correct alternative(s) from the given choices.

1. The correct statement regarding the IUPAC name of the following compound is:

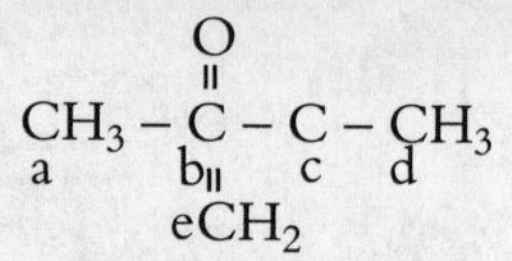

(a) The Root word is 'But'

(b) The parent chain is dcba

(c) The Primary suffix is 'one'

(d) The group numbered 'e' is the substituent attached to the carbon numbered 'b'

2. A hydrocarbon 'X' with no substituents, gives a positive test with ammonical cuprous chloride solution. 'X' is

(a) A saturated compound

(b) An unsaturated compound.

(c) Contains the functional group on its terminal carbon

(d) a symmetric compound.

3. Examine the given reaction.

$$RCOONa + NaOH \xrightarrow[\Delta]{CaO} X + Y \text{ (Salt)}$$

In this reaction, X:

(a) Is a carboxylic acid

(b) Is insoluble in water

(c) Is an unsaturated compound with one carbon atom less than the corresponding carboxylic acid of RCOONa

(d) Is a saturated compound with the same number of carbon atoms as in R

4. Select the correctly matched pairs.

	Metal carbide	Product formed on Hydrolysis
(a)	Beryllium carbide	CH_4
(b)	Calcium carbide	C_2H_2
(c)	Magnesium carbide	C_3H_4
(d)	Aluminium carbide	CH_4

5. Examine the table showing reactions of hydrocarbons C_2H_4 and C_2H_2 with specific reagents:

Hydrocarbon	Test with	
	Br_2/CCl_4	$AgNO_3$ / NH_4OH
C_2H_4	P	Q
C_2H_2	R	S

Identify the options that correctly describe the products (P, Q, R, and S) formed from the reactions of these hydrocarbons with the respective reagents.

(a) P- Substitution product-Dibromoethane

(b) Q- Nil product (no reaction)

(c) R- Addition product-Tetrabromoethyne.

(d) S- Silver acetylide.

Comprehension-Based Questions

Directions for Questions 6 to 11:

Read the following passage and answer the questions given below.

Proteins, vital macromolecules in the human body, play a pivotal role in its structure and function. Consisting of amino acids, proteins act as the foundational elements for tissues, muscles, enzymes, and hormones. Amino acids are categorized as essential or non-essential based on the organism's ability to synthesize them internally. Non-essential amino acids are derived from essential ones.

The general formula for amino acids is R — $CH(NH_2)$ — COOH. The distinctiveness of each amino acid is attributed to the nature of the attached alkyl group. Two amino acids on condensation polymerization forms a peptide bond (OH from -COOH of one amino acid and H from $-NH_2$ of another amino acid gets removed as water molecule). The amino acid has the tendency to transfer the H^+ ion from the —COOH group to the —NH_2 group. As a result of this, the molecule carries a negative charge on one end and positive charge on the other end.

$$H_3C-\underset{NH_2}{\overset{H}{C}}-COOH \longleftrightarrow H_3C-\underset{NH_3^+}{\overset{H}{C}}-COO^-$$

Amino acid Zwitter ion

It is this charge separation which makes the molecule dipolar, and the dipolar ions thus formed are called zwitter ions. Amino acids in this form are amphoteric in nature. A notable characteristic of zwitterions is their isoelectric point, the pH at which the molecule's charge is neutral. The overall charge of a molecule is typically influenced by the pH of its surroundings.

6. Identify the compound that is not made up of amino acids?
   (a) Triglyceride (b) DNA
   (c) Hemoglobin (d) Glycogen

7. Two amino acids on condensation polymerization forms a peptide bond. Identify a peptide linkage.
   (a) $-\overset{H}{N}-$ (b) $-\overset{O}{\overset{||}{C}}-\overset{H}{N}-$
   (c) $-\overset{O}{\overset{||}{C}}-O-\overset{O}{\overset{||}{C}}-$ (d) $-\overset{O}{\overset{||}{C}}-O-$

8. Molecular formula of an amino acid 'X' is $C_3H_7NO_2$. The alkyl group present in X is ________.
   (a) CH_3 (b) C_2H_5
   (c) H (d) C_3H_7

9. 'The overall charge of a molecule is typically influenced by the pH of its surroundings'. Predict the species formed If pH of the solution containing Zwitter ions is increased.
   (a) $\overset{+}{H_3N}-\overset{R}{\overset{|}{CH}}-COOH$
   (b) $\overset{+}{H_3N}-\overset{R}{\overset{|}{CH}}-COO^-$
   (c) $H_2N-\overset{R}{\overset{|}{CH}}-COO^-$
   (d) $H_2N-\underset{+}{\overset{R}{\overset{|}{CH}}}-COOH$

10. Amino acids are polar covalent compounds. Consequently,
    (a) they can dissolve in water,
    (b) they have elevated melting points
    (c) their solutions can conduct electricity
    (d) All the above

11. 'Amino acids in this form are amphoteric in nature'. What definition most accurately characterizes the term 'amphoteric'?
    (a) Amino acids are soluble in both polar and non-polar solvents.
    (b) Amino acids contain acidic and basic functional groups
    (c) Amino acid solutions can conduct electricity at any dilution
    (d) Amino acids exist as dipolar ions called zwitterions in their solid state.

Directions for Questions 12:

Study the given reaction conversions and find the correct match for P, Q, R and S.

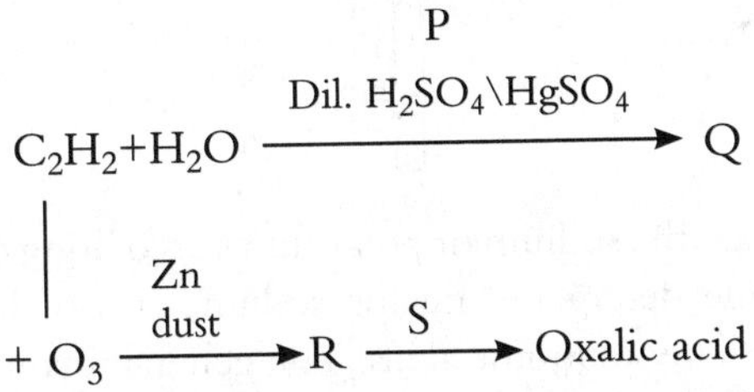

12. Match the following:

List – I	List – II
(A) P	(i) $C_2H_2O_2$
(B) Q	(ii) Strong reducing agent
(C) R	(iii) Acetaldehyde
(D) S	(iv) Strong Oxidizing agent
	(v) Glycol
	(vi) Hydrating agent
	(vii) Alkaline $KMnO_4$
	(viii) Acetone

Find the correct match.

	(A)	(B)	(C)	(D)
(a)	(vi)	(iii)	(i)	(vii)
(b)	(ii)	(viii)	(v)	(iv)
(c)	(ii)	(i)	(iii)	(vi)
(d)	(vi)	(i)	(vi)	(ii)

Directions for Questions 13 to 17:

Read the following passage and answer the questions given below.

The hydrolysis of ester takes place in an acidic or basic medium. In an acidic medium, ester interacts with the water molecule to give a carboxylic acid and alcohol. In contrast, ester interacts with the water molecule to give a carboxylate salt and alcohol in a basic medium. Generally, soaps are prepared by heating animal fat or oil(chemically, fats and oils are also called triglycerides) with alkalies like sodium hydroxide or potassium hydroxide. This is saponification reaction. Following figures shows the manufacturing of soap using a vegetable oil

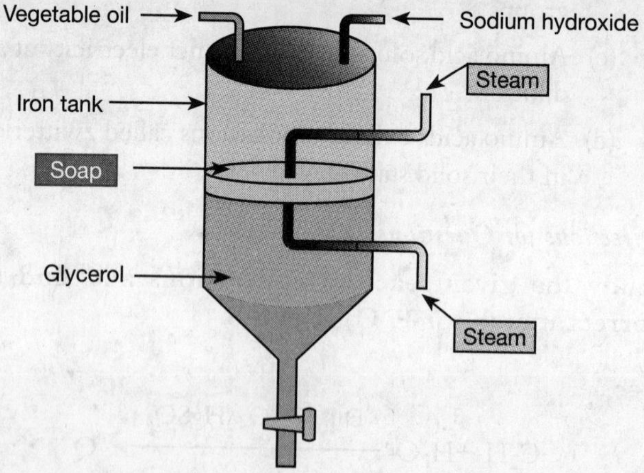

Soaps are the sodium or potassium salts of long chain fatty acids while detergents are the sodium salts of long-chain alkyl benzene sulphonic acids. The general formula of soap is $RCOO^-M^+$ where R is a long chain of hydrocarbon made up of 12–18 carbon atoms and M^+ is a metal cation that is usually sodium or potassium ion. pH testing is crucial when making handmade soap to determine its skin suitability. Handmade soaps typically fall within an alkaline pH range of 8 to 10, considered safe for skin use. However, a pH exceeding 11 becomes excessively harsh and may cause skin irritations. Conversely, soaps with a pH below 8 lack effective cleaning power.

Study the given passage and answer the questions that follow. Choose all the options that matches.

13. Vegetable oils or animal fats are composed of________
    (a) Glyceryl esters of fatty acids
    (b) Sodium esters of fatty acids
    (c) Alcoholic esters of fatty acids
    (d) None of the above statements.

14. Formation of soap is an example of.
    (a) Neutralization reaction
    (b) Esterification reaction
    (c) Hydroxylation reaction
    (d) Hydrolysis reaction

15. **Assertion(A):** Detergents are generally more effective at removing dirt and stains than soaps.
    Reason(R): Generally, pH value of detergents will be greater than that of soaps.
    (a) Both Assertion and Reason are true, and reason is the correct explanation of assertion.
    (b) Both Assertion and Reason are true, and reason is not the correct explanation of assertion.
    (c) A is true and R is false
    (d) A is false and R is true

16. Predict which formula among the given options represents the correct formula of a soap.
    (a) $C_{12}H_{25}OSNa$ (b) $C_{17}H_{33}COONa$
    (c) $C_{16}H_{31}O_2K$ (d) $C_{17}H_{35}O_2Na$

17. The effectiveness of soap for cleansing is commonly observed to diminish in hard water compared to soft water. Which of the following reasons can be attributed to this phenomenon?
    (a) Hard water contains dissolved sodium salts
    (b) Soaps form insoluble precipitates with hard water
    (c) Drastic pH changes of soap in hard water
    (d) All the above

ANSWER KEYS

Crossword

Across

1. Alkyne 4. Hydrocarbon 5. Cracking 6. Alkene 7. Catenation
9. Homologous

Down

1. Ammonia 2. Methane 3. Halogenation 8. Ethene

Classroom Wing

Very Short Answer Type Questions

1. catenation 2. isomers 3. hydrocarbons, heteroatoms 4. alkanes
5. alkenes, alkynes 6. methane 7. Polythene 8. 1, 1, 2, 2 - tetrahaloethane

Competition Wing

Level 1: Apply your Concepts

1. True 2. False 3. True 4. False 5. False
6. False 7. False 8. True 9. position 10. homologous
11. cracking or pyrolysis 12. polymerization 13. CCl_4 14. Ethene
15. Alcohol 16. Absence of C, H_2 17. Ethylene glycol 18. 14
19. alkane, aromatic compound 20. A : d, B : a, : e, D : c, E : b
21. (c) 22. (d) 23. (c) 24. (b) 25. (c)
26. (c) 27. (b) 28. (a) 29. (c) 30. (d)
31. (a) 32. (b) 33. (b) 34. (c) 35. (c)
36. (a) 37. (a) 38. (a) 39. (b) 40. (c)
41. (b) 42. (a) 43. (a) 44. (c) 45. (b)
46. (c) 47. (d) 48. (b) 49. (c) 50. (c)

JEE-NEET Special Wing

Multiple-Answer Type Questions

1. (a, c) 2. (b, c) 3. (c, d) 4. (a, b, c, d) 5. (b, d)

Comprehension-Based Questions

6. (d) 7. (b) 8. (a) 9. (c) 10. (d)
11. (b) 12. (a) 13. (a) 14. (d) 15. (b)
16. (c) 17. (b)

Hints and Explanations

Classroom Wing

Very Short Answer Type Questions

1. catenation
2. isomers
3. hydrocarbons, heteroatoms
4. alkanes
5. alkenes, alkynes
6. methane
7. Polythene
8. 1, 1, 2, 2 - tetrahaloethane
9. Aromatic
10. Functional group
11. Position
12. Homologous
13. Cracking
14. Halogenation
15. Alkyne
16. C_2H_6, C_4H_{10}, CH_4, C_3H_8, C_6H_{14} are alkanes

    C_2H_4, C_3H_6, C_4H_8, C_5H_{10}, C_7H_{14} are alkenes
17. Structure of n-propane and isopropane both are same.
18. (i) Cracking

    (ii) Utility of product produced on pyrolysis
19. (i) Pentane

    (ii) 2-butene

    (iii) Propyne

    (iv) 2-methyl butane

    (v) 2-butyne

20. 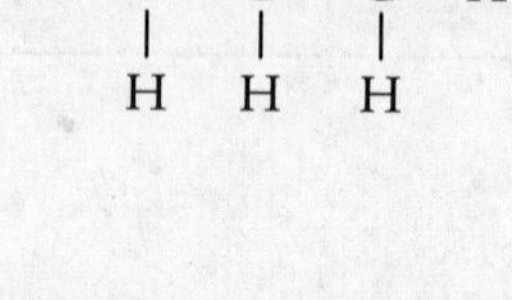

21. (i) $H_3C - HC = HC - CH_3$

    (ii) 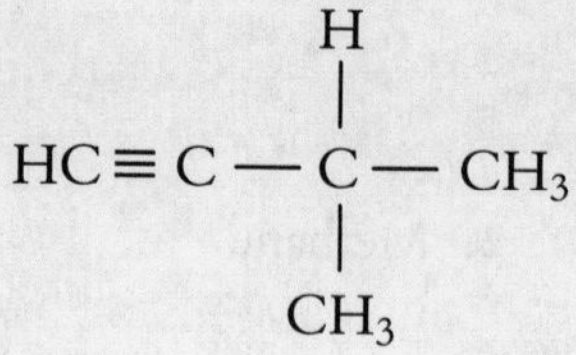

    (iii) 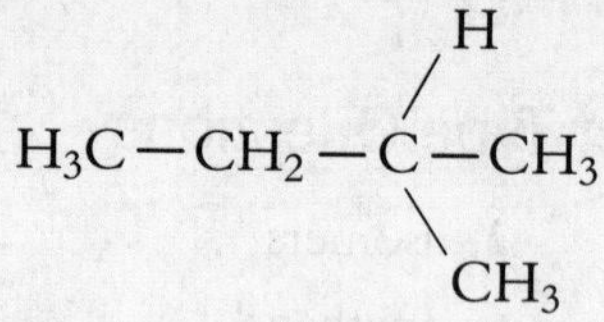

    (iv) $H_2C = CH - CH_2$

    (v) $H_3C - CH_2 - CH_2 - CH_2 - CH_3$

22. The carbon atom present in long chain which consists of alkyl group should get least number.

23. $CH_3 - CH_2 - CH_2 - CH_2 - CH_3$

    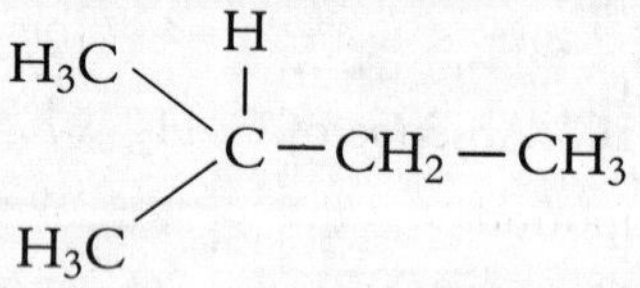

24. The selected longest chain should possess the double bond or triple bond in case of unsaturation in the chain. When both double and triple bonds are present, numbers as low as possible are given to double and triple bonds even though this may at times give "-yne" a lower number than "-ene".

25. 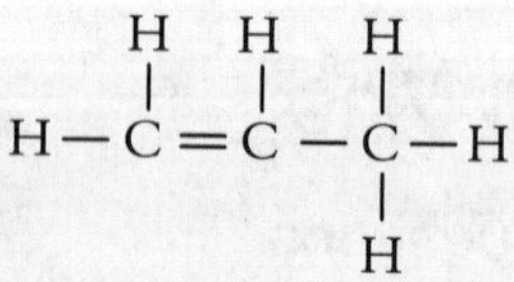

Short Answer Type Questions

26. 1. Decarboxylation of sodium salt of carboxylic acids

    Methane can be prepared by heating a mixture of sodium acetate and soda lime in a hard glass test tube:

    $$CH_3COONa + NaOH \xrightarrow[\Delta]{CaO} CH_4 + Na_2CO_3$$

Ethane can be prepared in the similar fashion by taking sodium propanoate instead of sodium acetate:

$$C_2H_5COONa + NaOH \xrightarrow[\Delta]{CaO} C_2H_6 + Na_2CO_3$$

2. Preparation by reduction of alkyl halides

Methyl iodide is reduced to methane by nascent hydrogen produced by the action of Zn/Cu couple on ethyl alcohol:

$CH_3I + 2[H] \rightarrow CH_4 + HI$

Ethane on the other hand can be prepared by reduction of ethyl iodide by nascent hydrogen:

$C_2H_5I + 2[H] \rightarrow C_2H_6 + HI$

3. Preparation by hydrolysis of carbides

Pure methane can also be prepared by the action of water on aluminium carbide (Al_4C_3):

$Al_4C_3 + 12H_2O \rightarrow 4Al(OH)_3 + 3CH_4$

28. Hydroxylation of ethene (ethylene), $CH_2{=}CH_2$, using cold, alkaline potassium permanganate solution produces ethane-1,2-diol (1,2-ethanediol or ethylene glycol).

29. (i) Halogenation (chlorination)
(ii) Reaction with aqueous KOH solution
(iii) Reaction involved

30. $C_2H_6 + Cl_2 \rightarrow C_2H_5Cl + HCl$
(monochloroethane)

$C_2H_6 + 2Cl_2 \rightarrow C_2H_4Cl_2 + 2HCl$
(dichloroethane)

$C_2H_6 + 3Cl_2 \rightarrow C_2H_3Cl_3 + 2HCl$
(trichloroethane)

$C_2H_6 + 4Cl_2 \rightarrow C_2H_2Cl_4 + 4HCl$
(tetrachloroethane)

$C_2H_6 + 5Cl_2 \rightarrow C_2HCl_5 + 5HCl$
(pentachloroethane)

$C_2H_6 + 6Cl_2 \rightarrow C_2Cl_6 + 6HCl$
(hexachloroethane)

31. Chain isomers have the same molecular formula, but the way their carbon atoms are joined together differs from isomer to isomer. The two possible structures are butane, which is $CH_3CH_2CH_2CH_3$, or isobutane, which is $HC(CH_3)_3$.

32. Acetylene can form red precipitate of copper acetylide when it is passed through ammonical cuprous chloride solution. Alkenes do not respond to this test.

33. (i) CuO and $KMnO_4$
(ii) CuO – mild oxidizing agent and $KMnO_4$ – strong oxidising agent

34. Formation of formaldehyde from alkane is a 3-step reaction.

1st step
Conversion of alkane to alkyl chloride

2nd step
Conversion of alkyl chloride to alcohol

3rd step
When alcohol vapor is passed over heated cupric oxide, it gets oxidized to aldehyde:

$$CH_3OH + CuO \xrightarrow{300°C} HCHO + Cu + H_2O$$
(formaldehyde)

$$C_2H_5OH + CuO \xrightarrow{300°C} CH_3CHO + Cu + H_2O$$
(acetaldehyde)

35. Laboratory Preparation of Ethyne Gas

1. **Hydrolysis of calcium carbide:** Calcium carbide on reaction with distilled water evolves acetylene gas:

$CaC_2 + 2H_2O \rightarrow Ca(OH)_2 + C_2H_2$

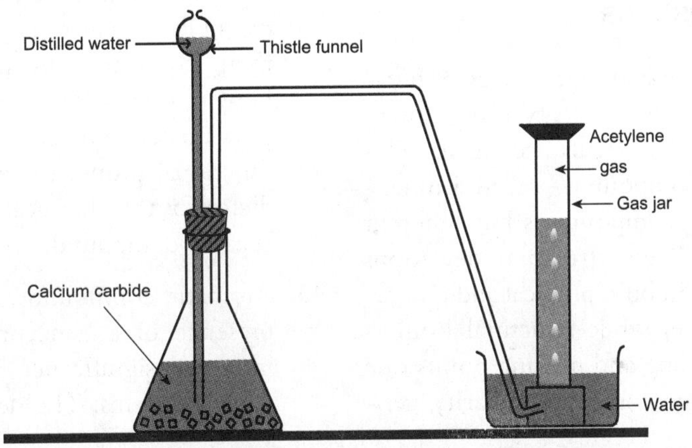

Preparation of acetylene gas

2. **Dehalogenation of tetrahaloethane:** A mixture of 95% ethyl alcohol and 1,1,2,2-Tetrabromoethane along with zinc dust when heated gently evolves acetylene gas:

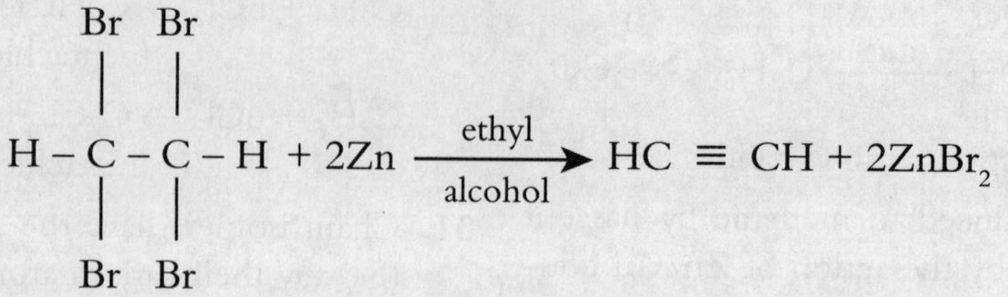

36. Addition of a molecule of halogen to ethyne molecule in the presence of CCl_4 gives 1,2-Dihaloethene which undergoes further addition of another halogen molecule to give 1,1, 2, 2-Tetrahaloethane.

When this reaction takes place with bromine, bromine water gets decolorized:

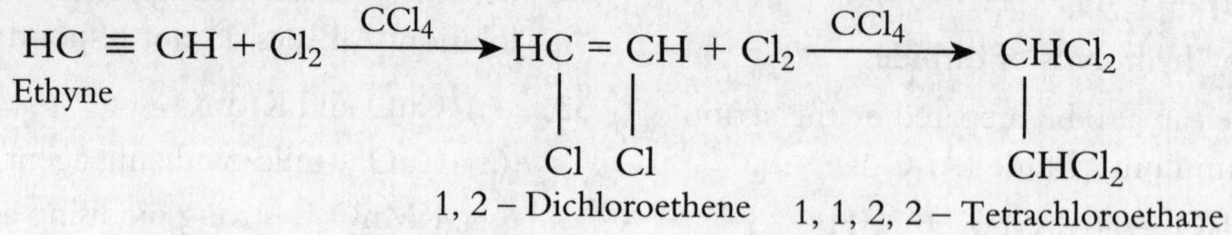

37. A mixture of 95% ethyl alcohol and 1,1,2,2-Tetrabromoethane along with zinc dust when heated gently evolves acetylene gas.

39. (i) Types of bonds in alkenes and alkynes
(ii) Changes in bonds during addition reactions

40. **Catalytic hydrogenation:** Equal volumes of ethene gas and hydrogen when passed over heated nickel or platinum at 300°C form ethane.

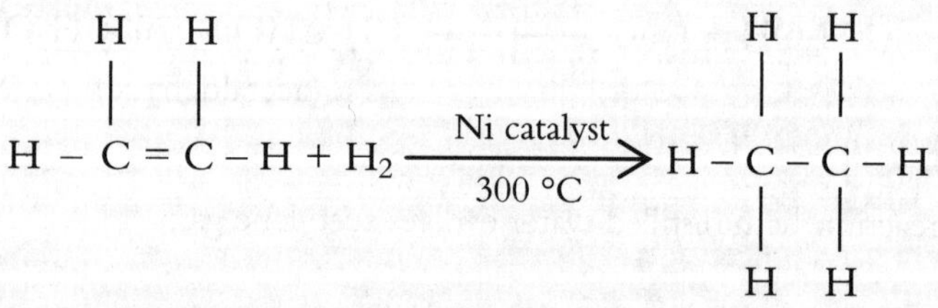

Essay Answer Type Questions

41. Isomerism in organic chemistry introduces a fascinating dimension of structural diversity even among molecules with the same molecular formula. This phenomenon results in compounds, called isomers, that have identical atomic compositions but different structural arrangements. These structural deviations can lead to vast differences in both physical and chemical properties. For instance, while structural isomers might possess different boiling and melting points due to variations in molecular geometry and polarity, geometric isomers (like cis-trans isomers) can display differences in stability and reactivity. Optical isomers can even interact differently with plane-polarized light. Such diversity in properties has profound implications, from industrial applications to biological systems. For example, the different isomers of a drug molecule can exhibit varying levels of therapeutic activity or side effects.

42. Functional groups in organic molecules act as centres of reactivity and play pivotal roles in determining the behaviour of the compound. Composed of specific atoms or atom clusters, these groups introduce characteristics that are often distinct from the hydrocarbon skeleton they are attached to. The electronegativity differences between atoms in the functional group can create polar regions, influencing intermolecular forces, solubility, and boiling or melting points. Moreover, functional groups provide reactive sites, making the molecule susceptible to specific types of reactions. For example, a hydroxyl group (-OH) in alcohols makes them prone to dehydration reactions, while the carbonyl group (>C=O) in aldehydes and ketones undergoes nucleophilic addition. The presence and type of functional group, therefore, serve as an essential predictor for the chemical behaviour and properties of an organic compound.

43. Aromatic compounds, characterized primarily by the presence of a benzene ring or its derivatives, hold immense significance in both industrial realms and natural systems. The delocalization of electrons in the

aromatic ring grants these compounds unique stability, which is reflected in their distinct reactivity patterns. In industry, aromatic compounds serve as the backbone for a myriad of chemical products, ranging from polymers to dyes. Their derivatives, such as toluene, are vital solvents in chemical processes. In natural systems, the aromatic motif is ubiquitous. From the bases in DNA, which store genetic information, to the chlorophyll molecule that drives photosynthesis, the aromatic structure plays a crucial role. Furthermore, many drugs and bioactive molecules, like aspirin, possess an aromatic core. The convergence of stability, reactivity, and versatility makes aromatic compounds indispensable in both synthetic and natural domains.

44. (i) Bromine water.

(ii) Formation of metal acetylides

Competition Wing

Level 1: Apply your Concepts

9. position

10. homologous

11. cracking or pyrolysis

12. polymerization

21. Presence of a double carbon-carbon bond and d) Presence of a triple carbon-carbon bond

Explanation: Alkenes contain at least one carbon-carbon double bond, whereas alkynes contain at least one carbon-carbon triple bond.

Hence, the correct option is (c).

22 Physical and chemical properties

Explanation: A functional group in an organic molecule imparts specific chemical and physical properties, determining its reactivity and interactions with other molecules.

Hence the correct option is (d).

23 Polymerization

Explanation: Polymerization is the process where small molecules, often called monomers, combine to form a large chain-like molecule called a polymer, exhibiting a higher molecular mass.

Hence the correct option is (c).

24 Catenation

Explanation: The property of catenation allows carbon atoms to bond with each other in various ways, forming chains, rings, and more intricate structures, thereby giving rise to fullerenes, nanotubes, and graphene.

Hence the correct option is (b).

25. Position isomerism

Explanation: Position isomerism occurs when compounds with the same molecular formula differ due to the different positions of functional groups or multiple bonds on the parent chain.

Hence the correct option is (c).

36. 3 Selection of the longest chain
1 Numbering of carbon chain
2 Identification of primary suffix
4 Identification of secondary suffix
5 Identification of number and nature of alkyl groups attached to carbon chain

Hence, the correct answer is (a).

37. 2 Writing the structure of respective isomer of hexane
1 Identification of nature of tertiary carbon atom
3 Numbering of carbon chain
5 Identification of number of carbon atoms in the main chain
4 Giving position numbers for the alkyl groups attached to main chain

Hence, the correct answer is (a).

38. 3 Ethyne
6 Ethene
1 Ethane
2 Propyne
4 Propene
5 Propane

Hence, the correct answer is (a).

39. Preceding homologue of $C_{10}H_{22}$ is C_9H_{20} and succeeding homologue of $C_{10}H_{22}$ is $C_{11}H_{24}$

Hence, the correct answer is (b).

40. Formula C_5H_8 corresponds to C_nH_{2n-2} and is an alkyne. It contains a triple bond.

Hence, the correct answer is (c).

41. Primary suffix indicates saturation or unsaturation

Hence, the correct answer is (b).

42. Saturated hydrocarbons (methane) cannot decolorize red-colored solution of bromine in CCl_4.

Hence, the correct answer is (a).

43. $HC \equiv CH + 2H_2 \xrightarrow{Ni} H_3C - CH_3.$

Ethane is formed.

Hence, the correct answer is (a).

44. $3C_2H_6 \xrightarrow{450°C} 2C_2H_4 + CH_4 + H_2$

Hence, the correct answer is (c).

45. Ethylene on hydrogenation gives ethane. Ethane has six hydrogen atoms.

Hence, the correct answer is (b).

46. Aluminium carbide on hydrolysis produces methane.

Hence, the correct answer is (c).

47. One mole of acetylene requires 2 moles of hydrogen to give ethane. Two moles of hydrogen corresponds to 4 g.

Hence, the correct answer is (d).

48. C_4H_6 corresponds to general molecular formula C_nH_{2n-2} which possesses one triple bond.

Hence, the correct answer is (b).

49. Since unsaturated hydrocarbons are reactive they decolorize reddish brown bromine water by forming additions compound by addition reaction and not by substitution reaction.

Hence, the correct answer is (c).

50. 4 Identify the root word and write down the parent carbon chain.
   1 Locate the primary suffix and insert.
   2 Identify the substituent and insert.
   3 Add suitable number of hydrogen atoms to satisfy the valencies of each carbon atom.

Hence, the correct answer is (c).

Level 2: Review Your Concepts

51. Carbon is distinct due to its tetravalent nature, which means it has four valence electrons. This enables the formation of four covalent bonds. Furthermore, because of its small atomic size, it can form strong and stable covalent bonds with a wide range of atoms, including itself. Catenation is the ability to link oneself. Carbon can form extended chains, branched structures, and cyclic compounds as a result of catenation, giving rise to a wide range of organic molecules.

52. Heteroatoms, such as oxygen, nitrogen, sulphur, etc., introduce unique properties to organic compounds. Their difference in electronegativity compared to carbon creates polar bonds. This can lead to the overall molecule having a polarity, which influences its solubility, boiling point, and melting point. Additionally, these heteroatoms can act as reactive sites for various chemical reactions. For instance, a hydroxyl group (OH) in alcohols can participate in acid-base reactions, something a pure hydrocarbon wouldn't do.

53. Alkanes consist solely of single C-C and C-H bonds. These bonds are strong and have no significant electron density that can easily initiate a reaction. Alkenes and alkynes, on the other hand, contain pi bonds (double or triple bonds), which are regions of high electron density. These pi bonds are more exposed and can be targeted by various reactants, making alkenes and alkynes more chemically reactive. For instance, they can readily participate in addition reactions, a feature not seen in alkanes.

54. (i) Identification of nature of the compounds A, C and D
   (ii) Identification of A based on type of product formed and reagents used
   (iii) Identification of C
   (iv) Identification of from D with the given specific reagent.

55. Aromaticity is a concept rooted in electron delocalization over a cyclic system. While benzene, with its six pi electrons in a cyclic arrangement, is the most recognized aromatic compound, the idea of aromaticity is broader. According to Huckel's rule, for a molecule to be aromatic, it should be cyclic, planar, and have a count of (4n+2) pi electrons, where n is a non-negative integer. This rule allows various compounds, even those without a benzene ring, to exhibit aromatic characteristics, provided they meet these criteria.

56. Structural isomers may differ in the arrangement of atoms or functional groups, which can lead to differences in molecular shape, size, and polarity. These variations directly influence the intermolecular forces between the molecules. A molecule with a longer chain may have stronger London dispersion forces compared to a branched isomer, leading to higher boiling points. Additionally, differences in polarity can cause variations in dipole-dipole interactions, further affecting the boiling points.

57. A homologous series is a group of compounds with a recurring structural pattern and a consistent incremental difference, usually a CH_2 unit. Each member of the series shares similar chemical properties but exhibits a gradual change in physical properties, like boiling point or melting point. This systematic progression makes it easier for chemists to predict and understand the behaviour of unfamiliar compounds within the series. It exemplifies how organic chemistry, despite its vastness, possesses inherent patterns and rules.

58. Dipole moment is always exist whenever there is difference in electron density between two atoms forming bond. Whereas in alkanes the electron density is equal due to bond formation b/w two similar atoms. Hence, dipole moment is zero.

59. (i) Comparison of ΔH values of the two equations
   (ii) Comparison of percentage composition of hydrogen in methane and ethane
   (iii) Relation between percentage of hydrogen and calorific value
   (iv) Balanced chemical equations for combustion of methane and ethane
   (v) Comparison of ΔH values
   (vi) Calculation of amount of energy released per gram of methane and ethane from ΔH values
   (vii) Relation between amount of energy released and the efficiency of the fuel

(viii) Comparison of amount of harmful product formed per unit weight of hydrocarbon

60. (i) Conditions required to carry out the reaction

(ii) Relation between the conditions and the process taking place in the reaction

(iii) Heat produced by incandescent bulb

(iv) Comparison of heat produced by incandescent bulb and the actual conditions required for reaction

61. PVC Formula: $(C_2H_3Cl)_n$

Acetylene reacts with anhydrous hydrogen chloride gas over a mercuric chloride catalyst to give vinyl chloride:

$C_2H_2 + HCl \rightarrow CH_2{=}CHCl$

62. (i) Identification of first homologue

(ii) Identification of the product of the first homologue upon oxidation with alk. $KMnO_4$

(iii) Prerequisite of a substance to act as coolant

(iv) Changes that take place in physical properties of water upon addition of the product obtained in (i)

(v) Effect of change in physical property of water on efficiency of its action as coolant

63. (i) Comparison of forces existing among methanol and ethane molecules

(ii) Effect of the extent of intermolecular forces of attraction on boiling points

64. (i) Comparison of the products obtained on ozonolysis

(ii) Identification of nature of hydrocarbon (saturated/unsaturated) from given molecular formula

(iii) Number of possible isomers based on number of carbon atoms, nature of hydrocarbon and arrangement of carbon atoms

(iv) Reactive centres required for addition of O_3

(v) Identification of nature of products obtained by ozonolysis

(vi) Comparison of products of ozonolysis of different isomers

65. The function of ultraviolet light is to provide energy for the homolytic cleavage of halogen (Cl-Cl or Br-Br). The products are haloalkanes (RX) and hydrogen halides (HX).

66. (a) 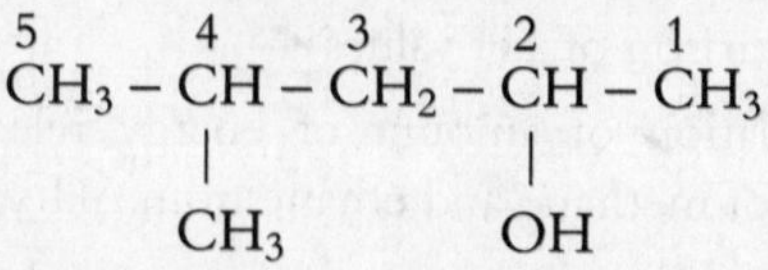

correct name 4-Methyl-2-Pentanol

2-Methyl-4-Pentanol is a wrong name. This is because the carbon attached to functional group should get the least position. Between subsistent and functional groups, the functional group gets priority.

(b) 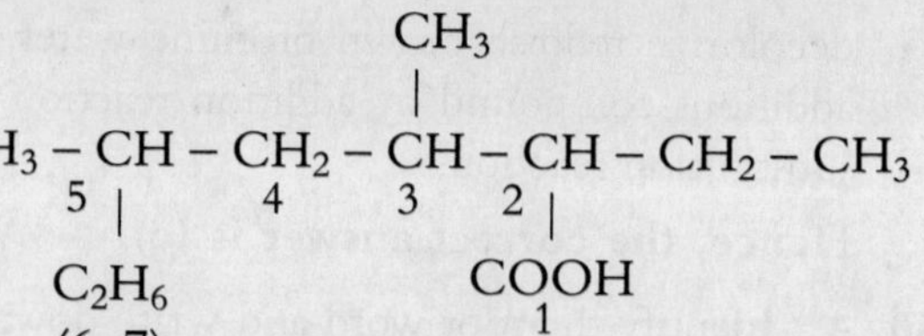

(6, 7)

Correct name is 2-Ethyl 3, 5-Dimethyl heptanoic acid

(c) 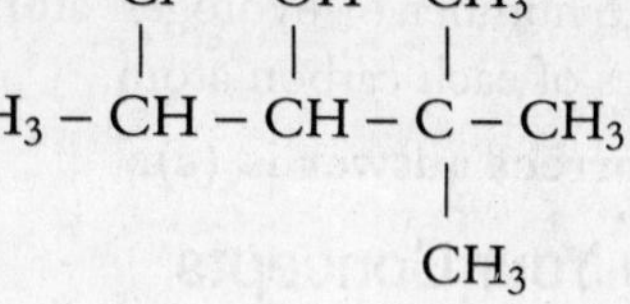

2-Chloro 4, 4-Dimethyl-3-Pentanol is the correct name. Among alkyl and halo groups, halo group should have the least number.

(d) 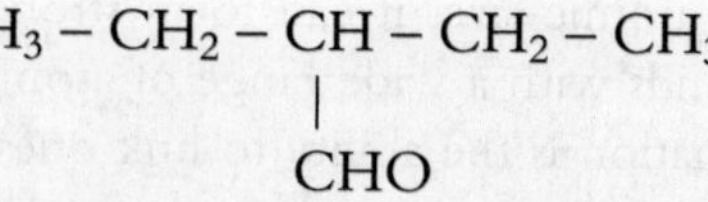

Correct name is 2-Ethyl butanal

3-Hexanal is the wrong name since the –CHO group is a terminal functional group and should always be taken as a first carbon.

67. Structural isomers for pentene

(i) $H_3C - CH_2 - CH_2 - CH = CH_2$

1–pentene

(ii) $H_3C - CH_2 - CH = CH - CH_3$

2–pentene

(iii) 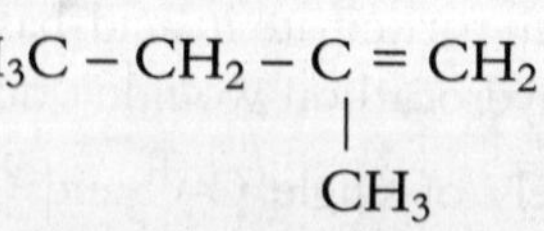

2 – methyl – 1– butene

(iv) 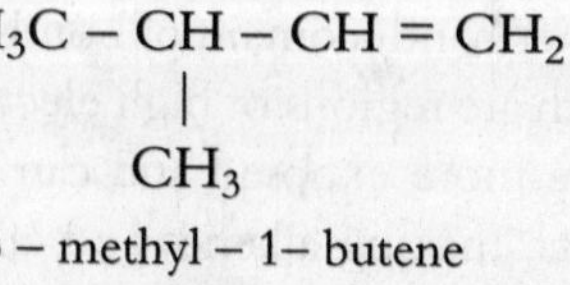

3 – methyl – 1– butene

(v) 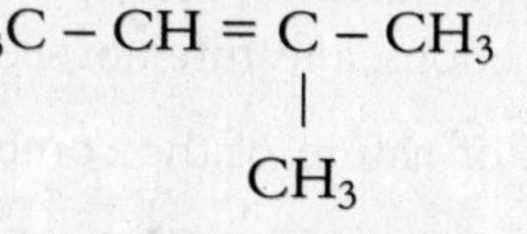

2 – methyl – 2– butene

68. The binary inorganic compounds which undergo hydrolysis to form hydrocarbons are aluminium carbide and calcium carbide.

$X \rightarrow 2, 8, 3, Al \rightarrow Al_4C_3$ (A)

$Y \rightarrow 2, 8, 8, 2, Ca \rightarrow CaC_2$ (B)

$$\underset{(A)}{Al_4C_3} + H_2O \rightarrow Al(OH)_3 + \underset{(C)}{CH_4}$$

$$\underset{(B)}{CaC_2} + H_2O \rightarrow Ca(OH)_2 + \underset{(D)}{C_2H_2}$$

$$\underset{\text{Ethyne}}{CH \equiv CH} \xrightarrow{H_2/Ni} \underset{\text{Ethene}}{H-\overset{H}{\overset{|}{C}}=\overset{H}{\overset{|}{C}}-H} \xrightarrow{H_2/Ni} \underset{\text{Ethane}}{H-\underset{H}{\underset{|}{\overset{H}{\overset{|}{C}}}}-\underset{H}{\underset{|}{\overset{H}{\overset{|}{C}}}}-H}$$

69. When ozone reacts with unsaturated hydrocarbon, the pi bond breaks and ozonide formation takes place at the point of unsaturation and hydrolysis of ozonide gives respective hydrocarbon derivatives. Depending on the structure of the hydrocarbon derivative the position of unsaturation can be determined. If Zn dust is not used H_2O_2 would be formed which oxidizes the aldehydes and ketones further to acids. Hence, Zn dust prevents oxidation.

70. Alkene with vapor density 35 is C_5H_{10} (M. Wt. = 70). Chain isomers of pentene are

$$H_3C-CH_2-CH_2-CH=CH_2 \xrightarrow[H_2O]{O_3} H_3C-CH_2-CH_2-CHO + CH_2O$$

$$H_3C-CH_2-\underset{CH_3}{\underset{|}{C}}=CH_2 \xrightarrow[H_2O]{O_3} H_3C-CH_2-CO-CH_3 + CH_2O$$

$$H_3C-\underset{CH_3}{\underset{|}{CH}}-CH=CH_2 \xrightarrow[H_2O]{O_3} H_3C-\underset{CH_3}{\underset{|}{CH}}-CHO + CH_2O$$

n-alkenes on ozonolysis give straight chain aldehydes only. Among branched chain alkenes, if the alkyl chain is attached to double-bonded carbon, one of the ozonolysis products should be ketone. If the branched chain alkene contains alkyl chain on a single-bonded carbon, on ozonolysis, it gives branched chain aldehyde.

71. Propane has only three carbon atoms and hence cannot have a branched chain.

72.

$$\underset{\text{White ppt}}{Ag-C\equiv C-Ag} \xleftarrow{AgNO_3/NH_4OH} \underset{(Y)}{HC\equiv CH} \xrightarrow{Br_2}$$

$$2ZnBr_2 + \underset{(Y)}{HC\equiv CH} \longleftarrow 2Zn + H-\underset{Br}{\overset{Br}{C}}-\underset{Br}{\overset{Br}{C}}-H$$

$$\underset{(X)}{H_3C-C\equiv CH} \xrightarrow[HgSO_4]{H_2O} \underset{\text{Acetone}}{H_3C-\overset{O}{\overset{\|}{C}}-CH_3}$$

73. (a) Both C_2H_4 and C_2H_2 decolorize bromine (Br_2) in presence of CCl_4 and form dibromo ethane and tetrabromoethane, respectively as the final products:

$$C_2H_4 + Br_2 \xrightarrow{CCl_4} C_2H_4Br_2$$

$$C_2H_2 + Br_2 \xrightarrow{CCl_4} C_2H_2Br_2 \xrightarrow{CCl_4} C_2H_2Br_4 + Br_2$$

(b) Both C_2H_4 and C_2H_2 decolorize the pink color of alkaline $KMnO_4$ to colorless and undergo oxidation to form ethylene gylcol and glyoxal, respectively.

$$\underset{(Y)}{C_2H_4 + H_2O + 2[O]} \xrightarrow[KMnO_4]{\text{alkaline}} \underset{\text{Ethylene glycol}}{H-\underset{H}{\overset{OH}{C}}-\underset{H}{\overset{OH}{C}}-H}$$

$$HC\quad CH + 2H_2O + 2[O] \xrightarrow[KMnO_4]{\text{alkaline}} \underset{\text{(unstable)}}{H-\underset{OH}{\overset{OH}{C}}-\underset{OH}{\overset{OH}{C}}-H} \xrightarrow{-2H_2O} \underset{\text{Glyoxal}}{\begin{matrix}CHO\\|\\CHO\end{matrix}}$$

(c) C_2H_4 does not react with ammonical silver nitrate, whereas C_2H_2 reacts with ammonical silver nitrate to form a white precipitate of silver acetylide:

$C_2H_4 + AgNO_3 + NH_4OH \rightarrow$ No reaction

$C_2H_2 + 2AgNO_3 + 2NH_4OH$
$\rightarrow Ag\text{–}C\equiv C-Ag + 2NH_4NO_3 + 2H_2O$

(d) C_2H_4 does not react with ammonical cuprous chloride, whereas C_2H_2 reacts with it and forms a reddish precipitate of cuprous acetylide:

$H_2C=CH_2 + CuCl + NH_4OH \rightarrow$ No reaction

$HC\equiv CH + 2CuCl + 2NH_4OH \rightarrow$
$Cu\text{-}C\equiv C-Cu + 2NH_4Cl + 2H_2O$

74. (a) $H_3C-\overset{CH_3}{\overset{|}{HC}}-CH-OH$

(b) $H_3C-H_2C-\underset{CH_3}{\underset{|}{CH}}-\underset{CH_3}{\underset{|}{CH}}-\underset{CH_3}{\underset{|}{CH}}-CH_2-CH_3$

(c) $CH_3-\underset{CH_3}{\underset{|}{CH}}-CH_2-\underset{CH_2-CH_3}{\underset{|}{CH}}-CH_2-CH_2-CH_3$

(d) $CH_3 - CH_2 - CH_2 - C = CH_2$

$$\begin{array}{l} CH_3 - CH_2 - CH_2 - \underset{\underset{\displaystyle CH_3}{|}}{\underset{\displaystyle CH_2}{\underset{|}{C}}} = CH_2 \end{array}$$

(e)

$$H_3C - H_2C - CH_2 - \underset{\displaystyle CH_3}{\underset{|}{CH}} - \underset{\displaystyle Cl}{\underset{|}{CH}} - CH = CH - CH_3$$

75. Balanced equation for the combustion of hydrocarbon is

$$C_xH_y + \left(x + \frac{y}{4}\right)O_2 \rightarrow xCO_2 + \frac{y}{2}HO_2$$

$$\text{The molar ratio of } CO_2 \text{ and } H_2O = \frac{x}{\frac{y}{2}} = \frac{5}{4}$$

$$\Rightarrow \frac{2x}{y} = \frac{5}{4} \Rightarrow \frac{x}{y} = \frac{5}{8}$$

$\rightarrow$ X is C_5H_8

Succeeding homologue of X is C_6H_{10}

Preceding homologue of X is C_4H_6

$2C_5H_8 + 14O_2 \rightarrow 10CO_2 + 8H_2O$

$2C_6H_{10} + 17O_2 \rightarrow 13CO_2 + 10H_2O$

$2C_4H_6 + 11O_2 \rightarrow 8CO_2 + 6H_2O$

Chain isomers of X (C_5H_8) are

$CH \equiv C - CH_2 - CH_2 - CH_3 \rightarrow$ 1-Pentyne

$$CH \equiv C - \underset{\displaystyle CH_3}{\underset{|}{CH}} - CH_3 \rightarrow 3 - \text{methyl} - 1 - \text{butyne}$$

Level 3: Assess Your Concepts

76. While both carbon and silicon can form chains through catenation, carbon has a unique ability to form stable and varied bonds with other carbon atoms and different elements. Carbon-carbon bonds are strong and can create a plethora of organic structures. Silicon, on the other hand, forms larger molecules that are less stable, making it less suitable for the diverse molecules essential for life. Additionally, the silicon-silicon bond is weaker than the carbon-carbon bond, limiting the extent and stability of catenation in silicon compounds. This fundamental difference is a pivotal reason carbon forms the basis of life on Earth while silicon-based life forms remain a topic of speculation.

77. Isomers, having different structural arrangements, can have varied physical, chemical, and biological properties. In the pharmaceutical world, this is crucial. Some isomers of a drug might be therapeutic, while others could be inactive or even harmful. For instance, thalidomide, a drug once used for morning sickness, had two isomers: one relieved nausea and the other caused severe birth defects. Hence, understanding and controlling isomerism in drug design is paramount to ensuring therapeutic efficacy and safety.

78. Organic compounds with heteroatoms often exhibit enhanced reactivity and diversity in function. The introduction of heteroatoms, like nitrogen or oxygen, introduces new sites of reactivity and can alter electronic distribution, making the compound more reactive than its hydrocarbon counterpart. For instance, the presence of a hydroxyl group in alcohols allows for hydrogen bonding and increased reactivity. Additionally, heteroatoms can significantly influence biological activity, allowing molecules to partake in specific biochemical interactions or pathways.

79. (i) Comparison of reactions of methane with Cl_2 and I_2.

(ii) Comparison of products obtained from chlorination and iodination

(iii) Comparison of reactivities of by-products produced in above two reactions

(iv) Effect of the by-product produced in iodination on nature and yield of the reaction

(v) Conditions or suitable reagents required to increase the yield

80. Alkanes, having only single bonds, are saturated and possess no areas of high electron density. This makes them less reactive than unsaturated hydrocarbons like alkenes and alkynes, which contain double and triple bonds respectively. These unsaturated bonds have areas of high electron density, making them more prone to electrophilic attacks. The reactivity of alkanes is limited to conditions of high energy or in the presence of specific reactive species, making them less versatile in synthetic reactions but more stable for storage and use as fuels.

81. Aromatic compounds, particularly benzene, are characterized by a ring of pi electrons delocalized over the entire molecule, a phenomenon called resonance. This electron delocalization imparts a unique stability to aromatic compounds, making them less reactive than simple alkenes. However, when they do react, they typically undergo substitution rather than addition reactions, preserving the aromatic core. The inherent stability from resonance influences the compound's reactivity patterns, often making them resistant to reactions that would break the aromatic system.

82. Alkane molecules do not have any resultant dipole moment due to the presence of symmetrical bond that is symmetrical structure. Hence, they neither ionize in water nor form H-bonding. Since no attractive force acts between water and methane molecules, they try to maintain minimum area of contact. Therefore, alkanes are hydrophobic.

83. C_5H_{12} (pentane) is the molecular formula of alkane which can give three chain isomers. When n-pentane, isopentane and neopentane are compared, the increase in branching decreases the surface area of the molecule. Therefore, the intermolecular forces of attraction decrease with increase in branching. As a result, the boiling points decrease. Further, n-alkanes have the highest boiling points, isoalkanes have low boiling points and neoalkanes have least boiling points. Therefore, they can be separated by fractional distillation.

$H_3C - CH_2 - CH_2 - CH_2 - CH_3$

n-pentane

$H_3C - CH(CH_3) - CH_2 - CH_3$

isopentane

$H_3C - C(CH_3)_2 - CH_3$

neopentane

Alkanes have regular tetrahedral structure at each carbon because of sp^3 hybridization and hence the vectorial sum of the dipole moments of the bonds add up to zero even though the hydrogens are replaced by alkyl groups.

84. The hydrocarbons X, Y and Z respectively as per given data are C_2H_6, C_2H_4 and C_2H_2. Alkanes do not undergo addition reactions because of no double bond. They undergo substitution reactions. In alkenes and alkynes, one or more π bonds are present between carbons which are susceptible to addition reactions.

JEE-NEET Special wing

Multiple-Answer Type Questions

1. The compound contains two functional groups, a ketone (-C = O) and a double bond (= ene). The parent chain should include carbons of both functional groups. Since the carbon of the ketone group is preferred over the double-bonded carbon, the parent chain is dcbe, where 'c' has a lower number than 'b.' With four carbons, the root word is 'but' and the substituent attached to the third carbon is the methyl group labelled as 'a.' Therefore, the correct IUPAC name for the compound is 3-Methylbut-3-en-2-one.

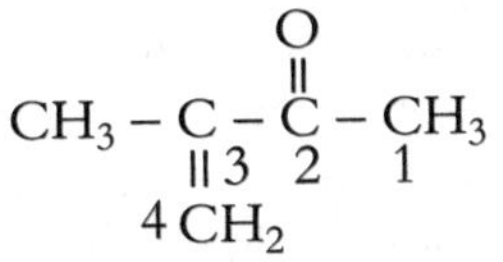

2. Terminal alkynes (with triple bond on its first carbon) gives positive test with ammonical cuprous chloride solution.

3. Sodium salts of carboxylic acids on heating with soda lime give alkanes containing one carbon atom less than the carboxylic acid. This reaction is known as decarboxylation.

$$RCCONa + NaOH \xrightarrow[\Delta]{CaO} RH + Na_2CO_3\ (salt)$$

4. Generally metal carbides on hydrolysis gives alkynes. But beryllium and Aluminium carbide on hydrolysis gives methane. So, all the given options are correctly matched.

5. Unsaturated compounds like ethene (C_2H_4) and Ethyne (C_2H_2) reacts with Br_2/CCl_4, undergoing addition reaction to form a dibromoethane and tetrabromoethane respectively. Alkenes (C_2H_4) does not react with $AgNO_3/NH_4OH$ but C_2H_2 being a terminal alkyne, forms a white precipitate of silver acetylide.

Comprehension-Based Questions

6. Except glycogen, which is a carbohydrate, all other compounds are made of amino acids.

7. -CO-NH- bond is known as peptide bond.

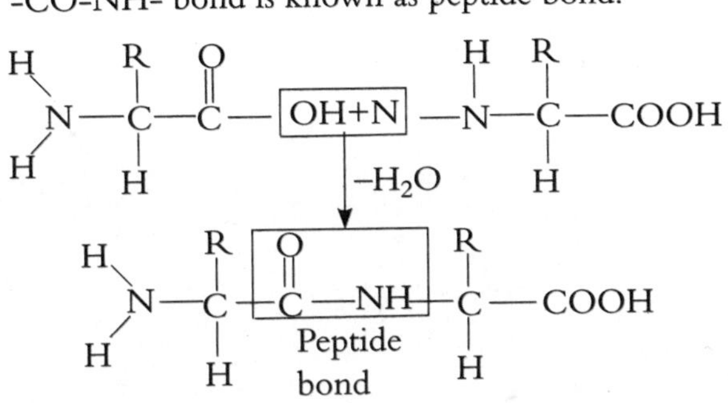

8. General molecular formula of amino acid is R — CH(NH_2) — COOH. Means, R– $C_2H_4NO_2$. As the given molecular formula contains one 'C' and 3 'H' extra, the alkyl group R should be CH_3 i.e., methyl group.

9. Addition of a base to the solution increases its pH .

So 'H' atom from NH_3^+ of the zwitter ion combines with the OH^- ions of the base to form a water molecule. So zwitter ion changes to anion.

Additon of Base:

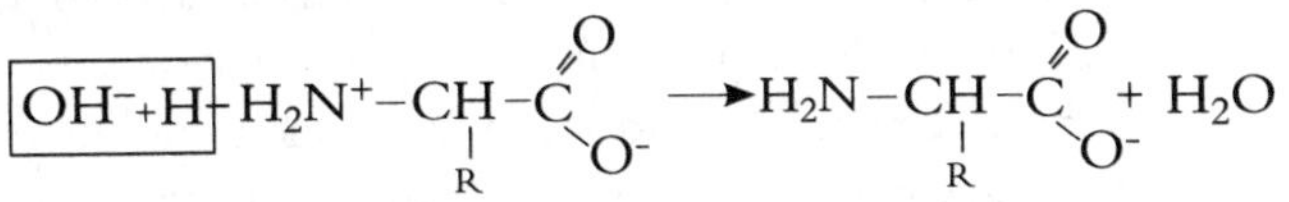

10. Like dissolves in like. Water is a polar solvent. Hence, amino acids are soluble in water. Polar molecules have strong intermolecular forces of attraction (dipole-dipole in case of amino acids) between them. It takes more energy to separate the molecules from each other, so polar substances have relatively high melting points and boiling points. Polar compounds can conduct electricity as they can form ions.

11. Amphoteric means having both acidic and basic characteristics. As Amino acid contains both acidic (carboxyl) group and basic (amino) group in the same molecule, it shows both acidic and basic characteristics. Hence is considered as amphoteric in nature.

12. Reaction occur as follows:

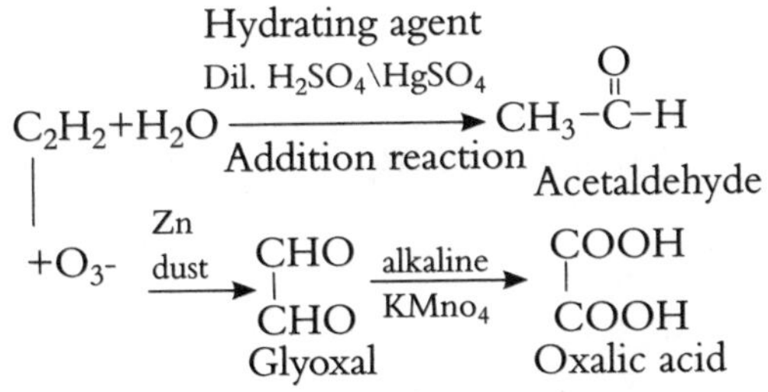

Alkaline $KMnO_4$ is a strong oxidising agent

List – I	List – II
(A) P	(vi) Hydrating agent
(B) Q	(iii) Acetaldehyde
(C) R	(i) $C_2H_2O_2$ or Glyoxal
(D) S	(vii) Alkaline $KMnO_4$ or (iv) Strong Oxidizing agent

So, the correct match.

	(A)	(B)	(C)	(D)
(a)	(vi)	(iii)	(i)	(vii)

13. Chemically, fats and oils are also called triglycerides. They are esters of glycerol, with a varying blend of fatty acids.

14. Formation of soap involves the basic hydrolysis of triglycerides(esters of long chain fatty acids).

15. The effectiveness of detergents in removing dirt and stains compared to soap primarily arises from their chemical composition rather than solely due to pH differences. While pH differences between detergents and soap can exist, they are not the sole reason for the difference in cleaning efficiency. Detergents are formulated to work well in a wide range of pH levels, which allows them to perform effectively in various water conditions, including both acidic and alkaline environments. Their molecular structure and ability to emulsify oils and dirt into smaller particles, which can be easily rinsed away, contribute significantly to their superior cleaning effectiveness compared to soap. The statement given under reason is often true. Generally, the pH value of detergents tends to be higher (more alkaline) compared to that of soaps. Hence, Both A and R are true, but R is not the correct explanation of A.

16. 'Given that the general formula of a soap is $RCOO^-M^+$ where R is a long chain of hydrocarbon made up of 12–18 carbon atoms and M^+ is a metal cation that is usually sodium or potassium ion'.
As the general formula of alkyl group is C_nH_{2n-1}, from the given options, $C_{16}H_{31}O_2K$ or $C_{15}H_{31}COOK$ will be the correct formula of a soap.

17. The ability of soaps to emulsify oils and suspend dirt diminishes in hard water due to the presence of dissolved calcium and magnesium ions. In hard water, these ions react with soap, forming insoluble salts called soap scum or soap curd. This reaction reduces the soap's capacity to create a lather and form effective cleaning micelles, leading to a decrease in its ability to emulsify oils and suspend dirt. Consequently, this results in reduced cleansing effectiveness when using soap in hard water compared to using it in soft water. However, the decrease in soap effectiveness isn't due to the pH change of the soap or the dissolved salts of sodium in hard water.

Photo Credits

CHAPTER 2

Page 2.34— Zern Liew/Shutterstock

CHAPTER 3

Page 3.26—HL Studios/Pearson Education Ltd